INTERNATIONAL SERIES IN PURE AND APPLIED PHYSICS

LEONARD I. SCHIFF, *Consulting Editor*

NUCLEAR PHYSICS

INTERNATIONAL SERIES IN PURE AND APPLIED PHYSICS

LEONARD I. SCHIFF, *Consulting Editor*

Becker Introduction to Theoretical Mechanics
Clark Applied X-rays
Edwards Analytic and Vector Mechanics
Evans The Atomic Nucleus
Finkelnburg Atomic Physics
Green Nuclear Physics
Gurney Introduction to Statistical Mechanics
Hall Introduction to Electron Microscopy
Hardy and Perrin The Principles of Optics
Harnwell Electricity and Electromagnetism
Harnwell and Livingood Experimental Atomic Physics
Harnwell and Stephens Atomic Physics
Houston Principles of Mathematical Physics
Houston Principles of Quantum Mechanics
Hughes and DuBridge Photoelectric Phenomena
Hund High-frequency Measurements
Kemble The Fundamental Principles of Quantum Mechanics
Kennard Kinetic Theory of Gases
Marshak Meson Physics
Morse Vibration and Sound
Morse and Feshbach Methods of Theoretical Physics
Muskat Physical Principles of Oil Production
Read Dislocations in Crystals
Richtmyer, Kennard, and Lauritsen Introduction to Modern Physics
Schiff Quantum Mechanics
Seitz The Modern Theory of Solids
Slater Introduction to Chemical Physics
Slater Microwave Transmission
Slater Quantum Theory of Matter
Slater and Frank Electromagnetism
Slater and Frank Introduction to Theoretical Physics
Slater and Frank Mechanics
Smythe Static and Dynamic Electricity
Squire Low Temperature Physics
Stratton Electromagnetic Theory
Thorndike Mesons: A Summary of Experimental Facts
Townes and Schawlow Microwave Spectroscopy
White Introduction to Atomic Spectra

The late F. K. Richtmyer was Consulting Editor of the series from its inception in 1929 to his death in 1939. Lee A. DuBridge was Consulting Editor from 1939 to 1946; and G. P. Harnwell from 1947 to 1954.

Nuclear Physics

ALEX E. S. GREEN

Associate Professor of Physics
The Florida State University
Tallahassee, Florida

McGRAW-HILL BOOK COMPANY, INC.

New York   Toronto   London

1955

NUCLEAR PHYSICS

Library of Congress Catalog Card Number 54-6215

II

THE MAPLE PRESS COMPANY, YORK, PA.

PREFACE

Nuclear physics may be fittingly introduced with a clear delineation of its subject matter because considerable confusion now exists as to whether certain classes of phenomena belong to molecular physics, atomic physics, nuclear physics, or fundamental-particle physics. For this reason we shall describe briefly the domains of these fields of inquiry, recognizing at the outset that it is impossible to draw perfectly sharp boundaries around any natural science.

The physics of microscopic systems, which is sometimes loosely referred to as "atomic physics," may be subdivided into more definitive realms on the basis of the entities whose characteristics, behavior, and internal structure are the subject of inquiry.

Accordingly, we may define molecular physics as the domain of microscopic physics which is concerned with the characteristics, behavior, and internal structure of molecules. To a great extent, it is possible to interpret molecular phenomena in terms of a model in which atoms are the basic units. These atoms are characterized by a few simple properties such as mass, charge number, electrovalence, etc. In most aspects of molecular physics a detailed consideration of the internal structure of atoms is not required.

On the other hand, atomic physics, in the meaning of the phrase which is now gaining acceptance, is concerned with the characteristics, behavior, and internal structure of atoms. The units in terms of which the structure and behavior of atoms are now described are electrons and nuclei, and the model of the atom universally accepted is the electron-nuclear model of Rutherford. In atomic physics one simply identifies with electrons and nuclei a few simple properties such as mass, charge, spin, magnetic moment, etc., and assumes certain laws of behavior which are expressed in terms of these properties. The internal structures of nuclei and electrons are not important in atomic physics.

Nuclear physics may be defined as the field of inquiry which is concerned with the characteristics, behavior, and internal structure of nuclei. There is very substantial evidence to indicate that the nucleus is made of types of two particles called protons and neutrons. It is further believed by physicists today that by ascribing a few properties to protons and neutrons, the structure and behavior of nuclei will finally be given in terms of a proton-neutron model of the nucleus in conjunction with laws of nuclear physics which are not yet fully understood.

Fundamental-particle physics, or elementary-particle physics, the most recently recognized microscopic field of inquiry, embraces the experimental and theoretical efforts to find explanations for the existence and properties of the electron, proton, and neutron, the building blocks of matter, as well as of such transitory particles as photons, positrons, and mesons.

Since this is a book devoted to nuclear physics, we shall confine our attention primarily to theories and experiments which are directly concerned with the detailed characteristics, behavior, and internal structure of nuclei. Of course, in doing so we cannot completely disregard the atom and the molecule, since in many respects these larger entities are the laboratories within which we investigate the nucleus. We also cannot completely ignore questions which belong to fundamental-particle physics, since the properties of the neutron and the proton are studied in both fields. In nuclear physics, however, the interest centers on the nature of the interactions between neutrons and protons rather than on properties of the isolated particles themselves.

This book follows a pattern of development which we believe is appropriate for a field in an active state of flux and development. In general our chapters fall into the major topical groups (1) background, (2) instruments and methods, (3) experimental results and their interpretation, (4) systematics and semiempirical theory, and (5) theory. Although, of course, the actual historical pattern is erratic, we believe this sequence represents the over-all trend of growth of nuclear physics.

In Chap. 1 we discuss relativistic dynamics and present a review of atomic physics, giving particular emphasis to the topics and concepts which are needed in nuclear physics. We describe in Chap. 2 the static properties of nuclei, mostly as revealed in studies of atomic and molecular physics. In Chaps. 3 to 5 we present the basic principles of the instruments and techniques which have been developed primarily for nuclear physics. Since it would be inappropriate in a work of this nature, we do not give the specialized design details of these nuclear instruments or describe the standard electrical and electronic instruments which are used in nuclear measurements. In most instances, however, we refer the reader to sources of such information. We devote Chaps. 6 and 7 to a discussion of important experimental results and the concepts needed for their interpretation, and Chaps. 8 and 9 to a discussion of the systematics of nuclei, to a semiempirical theory of the nucleus, and to the subject of fission.

To follow Chaps. 1 to 9 of this book, the reader needs only a sound background of intermediate courses in physics and mathematics, including a course in atomic physics, the term being used either in a general sense or in the specific sense defined above. Unfortunately, the subject of the remainder of the book, nuclear theory, as it is now evolving, seems to require the use of modern quantum mechanics, a methodology which is notorious as one of the most difficult in physics. The omission of nuclear theory, even in an introductory work, would completely distort the actual picture of nuclear physics today, but as an unavoidable consequence of its inclusion, the difficulty level rises appreciably in the last part of the book. It will be best if the reader, when he reaches the last part of this book, has already been introduced to the principles of quantum mechanics in an earlier or collateral course. However, in the event that this is not the case, we include a chapter (Chap. 10) which presents the principles of quantum mechanics which are most necessary in the remainder of our discussions.

We devote Chap. 11 to a description of several theoretical models of nuclei, with particular emphasis given to the independent-particle model, and Chaps. 12 and 13 to the theory of nuclear decay and nuclear reactions. The book is concluded with a chapter (Chap. 14) devoted to a description of attempts to infer the basic nature of nuclear forces, mainly from studies of the two-body problems of nuclear physics.

At the end of each chapter problems are included, which, in the main, fall into the following catagories: (1) simple problems which are intended to illustrate certain important concepts and relationships, as well as to familiarize the reader with the orders of magnitudes of the physical quantities involved in nuclear physics; (2) problems (denoted by an asterisk) whose resolution will require that the reader devote a substantial amount of effort and ingenuity; (3) problems (denoted by a dagger) which are intended to compel the reader to refer to the periodic literature for information so that he may begin to familiarize himself with the current work in this rapidly growing subject. For this same purpose we include at the end of each chapter a list of references, consisting of general references (indicated by superior numbers in section titles), which refer to books, monographs, review articles, or major research articles, and specific references (indicated by superior numbers in the body of the text), which refer to the sources of detailed information or data. Because of limitations of space the vast majority of detailed contributions to nuclear physics have been noted, indirectly, through the reference lists contained in works to which we refer.

The experience of the author with a mimeographed version of this book indicates that it contains more material than can normally be covered in a one-semester course meeting three hours per week. Accordingly, if the book is used as a text for such a course, a selection of topics is essential. With the use of some supplementary material from the current literature the book may serve as a text for a two-semester course.

The author would like to express his thanks for the kind permissions to use illustrations and to quote data which have been given to him by many editors and scientists and to acknowledge his indebtedness to Profs. L. Katz, H. J. Kersten, M. A. Melvin, B. Podolsky, G. L. Rogosa, G. Schwarz, R. K. Sheline, C. W. Snyder, B. F. Wissler, I. D. Wollerman, and Dr. W. F. Stubbins for their helpful criticisms and suggestions. The author would also like to express deep gratitude to the many other persons—colleagues, students, friends, and relatives—who in one way or another have helped in the preparation of this book and its earlier mimeographed and hectographed versions, to Mrs. Mildred DeWitt for her painstaking efforts in typing the final manuscript, and to his wife, Freda K. Green, for her encouragement and tireless assistance.

ALEX E. S. GREEN

CONTENTS

Preface v

List of Symbols xi

1. Relativistic Dynamics and Review of Atomic Physics . . . 1
2. Static Properties of Nuclei 35
3. Accelerators 59
4. Precision Instruments and Methods 91
5. Detectors and Nuclear Techniques 124
6. Radioactivity 175
7. Nuclear Reactions 205
8. Systematics and Tendencies of Nuclei 244
9. Liquid-drop Model and Fission 281
10. Quantum Mechanics and the Nucleus 317
11. Nuclear Periodic Table 356
12. Nuclear Decay 390
13. Theory of Nuclear Reactions 433
14. Nuclear Forces 474

Appendix I 519

Appendix II 520

Index 529

LIST OF SYMBOLS

The following list contains the important symbols used in this text. A brief definition and a reference to the page on which a symbol is defined or first used are also given. In general, standard mathematical symbols or specialized symbols which do not recur at a later point in the text are not listed. Ordinary vectors, which appear boldface in the text, are here indicated by the italicized symbols representing their scalar magnitudes. On the other hand, angular-momentum vectors are given in boldface, and it is understood that the corresponding italicized symbols represent the quantum numbers which characterize the magnitudes of these vectors. [See Eq. (1-71).] Boldface symbols are sometimes used for other specialized purposes, such as to denote a quantity in a specific unit or to indicate a time-dependent function.

English Letters

A mass number, p. 36
A mass number in units of hundreds, p. 194
A activity, p. 194
A transition probability per unit time, p. 396
a_B the Bohr radius, p. 9
a mass number of a small nuclear particle, p. 54
a range of force, p. 322
B nuclear binding energy, p. 55
B_x binding energy of last x particle, p. 57
B magnetic induction, p. 6
B_e electronic stopping power, p. 164
b, b_0 nuclear-radius constants, p. 37
b impact parameter, p. 163
C capacitance, p. 127
c velocity of light, p. 1
D neutron excess $D = N - Z$, p. 54
D average level spacing, p. 277
d, D denote $l = 2$ state, p. 20
d deuteron, p. 4
d neutron excess of a small nuclear particle, p. 54
d Fermi scattering length, p. 480
E total energy of a particle, p. 1
E_0 intrinsic rest energy, p. 1
E_0 natural energy unit, p. 334
E nuclear energy, p. 55
$E_{a,nucl}$ total atomic and nuclear energy, p. 54
E_a atomic (electronic) energy, p. 55
E_γ gamma-ray energy, p. 105
e the magnitude of the electronic charge, p. 5
F total nuclear and electronic angular momentum, p. 41
f force, p. 2
f oscillator or cyclotron frequency, pp. 62, 65
f packing fraction, p. 55
f, F denote $l = 3$ state, p. 20

G radial wave function, p. 330
g g factor, or gyromagnetic ratio, p. 28
H magnetic field, p. 6
H pairing function, p. 249
H Hamiltonian, p. 321
h Planck's constant, p. 7
I beam intensity, p. 222
I total nuclear angular momentum, p. 39
i total angular momentum of a nucleon, p. 374
J parabolic-breadth function, p. 246
J Bessel function, p. 339
J total electronic angular momentum, p. 19
j total angular momentum of an electron, p. 19
K the angular-momentum quantum number, p. 18
K angular-momentum vector, p. 18
K_z z component of angular momentum, p. 18
k propagation constant, p. 12
k characteristic spring constant, p. 44
L total orbital angular momentum, p. 19
l orbital angular momentum, p. 18
M atomic mass, p. 36
M_c chemical atomic weight, p. 36
M_K magnetic quantum number for **K** vector, p. 18
m mass of a particle, p. 1
m_e mass of the electron, p. 8
m_r reduced mass of a two-body system, p. 9
m_l magnetic quantum number for orbital angular momentum, p. 18
m_s magnetic quantum number for spin, p. 18
N neutron number, p. 52
N_A Avogadro's number, p. 36
N_s number of scatterers in beam, p. 221
n neutron, p. 4
n neutron number of a small nuclear particle, p. 57
n magnetic field parameter, p. 74
n integral quantum number, p. 8
n integral isobar parameter, p. 186
P probability distribution function, p. 320
P_n nth Legendre function, p. 299
p momentum, p. 1
p, P denote $l = 1$ state, p. 20
Q quadrupole moment, p. 51
Q reaction energy, p. 180
Q_l matrix element associated with 2^l multipole moment, p. 398
q charge, p. 46
R, R_∞ the Rydberg constant, p. 10
R radius of nucleus, p. 37
R residual, p. 262
R radial wave function, p. 326
R range of a charged particle in matter, p. 152
$\bar{R}$ mean range, p. 160
R_c classical distance of closest approach, p. 192
r radial distance, p. 21
r_0', r_0'' range constants, p. 363
r_0 effective range, p. 480
S total spin, p. 19
S shell correction, p. 266
S area of source, p. 92
$S_{1,2}$ tensor-force operator, p. 498
s displacement, p. 2
s spin angular momentum, p. 18
s, S denote $l = 0$ state, p. 20
T period, p. 12
T kinetic energy, p. 2
T total isobaric spin, p. 491
t triton, p. 4
t time, p. 5
t half-life, p. 424
t isobaric spin of a nucleon, p. 491
U, U' velocity of target and residual nuclei in center-of-mass coordinate system, p. 212

U magnitude of bond energy, p. 281
u phase velocity, p. 12
u, u' velocity of incident and ejected particles in center-of-mass system, p. 212
V volume of nucleus, p. 38
V potential energy, p. 5
V voltage, p. 60
V_h height of coulomb barrier, p. 191
V_0 well depth, p. 322
v the radial quantum number, p. 15
v velocity, p. 1
v, v' velocities of incident and ejected particles in laboratory coordinate system, p. 213
W the total energy, p. 7
W_K, W_L critical X-ray energies, p. 30
W^a activation energy for fission, p. 297
w probability per unit time, p. 230
X a nuclide, p. 176
$X(x)$ function of x, p. 324
x small nuclide, p. 57
x a small radial displacement, p. 95
x distance of penetration, p. 160
x fissionability parameter, p. 301
Z atomic number, p. 8
$\mathbf{Z}$ atomic number in units of 100, p. 415
z a small integer, p. 5
z proton number of a small nuclear particle, p. 57

Greek Letters

α alpha particle, p. 4
α fine-structure constant, p. 238
α_K, α_L internal-conversion coefficients, p. 179
$\alpha_1, \alpha_2, \ldots$ nuclear distortion parameters, p. 299
α reciprocal of deuteron radius, p. 477
β beta particle, p. 4
Γ energy width (transition probability multiplied by $\hbar$), p. 310
γ dynamical parameter $= \left(1 - \frac{v^2}{c^2}\right)^{-\frac{1}{2}}$, p. 2
γ gamma ray, p. 4
γ the ratio U/u', p. 235
Δ mass decrement $= M - A$, p. 54
Δ increment of, p. 68
Δ uncertainty in, p. 91
Δ Laplacian operator, p. 318
δ nuclear phase shift, p. 438
ϵ nuclear distortion parameter, p. 51
ϵ average nuclear energy, p. 55
ϵ dimensionless energy parameter, p. 334
ζ gamma-ray energy in units of m_ec^2, p. 238
η neutrino, p. 4
η number of atoms per unit volume, p. 163
η probability for decay, p. 309
η dimensionless multipole parameter, p. 398
Θ angular wave function, p. 326
θ polar angle, p. 43
θ deviation of neutron excess from line of beta stability, p. 250
κ reciprocal length $= mc/\hbar$, p. 13
λ wavelength, p. 8
λ decay constant, p. 175
μ magnetic permeability, p. 6
$\boldsymbol{\mu}$ magnetic-moment vector, p. 28
μ_B Bohr magnetron $= 0.92732 \times 10^{-20}$ erg-gauss^{-1}, p. 28
μ_N nuclear magneton, p. 39

μ_e electrostatic dipole moment, p. 46
μ linear absorption coefficient, p. 222
ν frequency, p. 7
ν additional energy associated with unpaired neutron, p. 264
Ξ Wigner symmetry number, p. 363
π additional energy associated with unpaired proton, p. 264
ρ dimensionless distance parameter, p. 334
ρ density, p. 39
ρ_c nuclear charge density, p. 283
σ cross section, p. 222
σ_i partial cross section, p. 223
$\sigma(\theta,\varphi)$ differential cross section per unit solid angle, p. 230
$\sigma(\theta)$ an integrated cross section, p. 230
σ_e classical cross section of an electron, p. 238
σ_x capture cross section, p. 309
$\sigma_{x,x'}$ reaction cross section, p. 309
σ^l cross section of lth partial wave, p. 439
$\boldsymbol{\sigma}$ unit spin vector, p. 492
τ time of passage, p. 62
τ resolution time, p. 125
$\bar{\tau}, \tau$ average lifetime, pp. 176, 349
$\tau_{\frac{1}{2}}$ half lifetime, p. 175
τ volume of charge distribution, p. 391
Φ dimensionless fissionability function, p. 301
Φ azimuthal wave function, p. 326
ϕ electrostatic potential, p. 37
ϕ_η neutrino wave function, p. 419
φ azimuth angle, p. 43
φ_β beta-particle wave function, p. 418
χ symbol for He^3, p. 4
$\boldsymbol{\Psi}$ time-dependent wave function, p. 320
Ψ time-independent wave function, p. 319
Ω solid angle, p. 92
Ω power radiated, p. 395
ω angular frequency, p. 12

Script Letters

$\mathcal{E}$ electric field strength, p. 5
$\mathcal{G}$ penetrability parameter, p. 414
$\mathcal{I}$ incident probability per unit area per unit time, p. 230
$\mathcal{I}$ moment of inertia, p. 44
$\mathcal{I}_\pi(\mathcal{I}_\nu)$ total proton (neutron) angular momentum, p. 374
$\mathcal{J}$ Bessel function, p. 437
$\mathcal{N}$ number of states per unit volume, p. 361
$\mathcal{O}$ surface tension, p. 155
$\mathcal{P}$ penetrability, p. 451
$\mathcal{R}$ reflection coefficient, p. 465
$\mathcal{T}$ torque on a magnetic dipole, p. 40
$\mathcal{T}$ transmission coefficient, p. 465

Subscripts

c classical, p. 7
c critical, p. 179
c Compton, p. 237
c Coulombic, p. 190
cl classical, p. 140
cm center of mass, p. 346
E electric multipole, p. 395
e electrostatic, p. 46
e electronic, p. 54
e exterior, p. 339
f final state, p. 9
f fission, p. 295
f photoelectric, p. 237
H hydrogen, p. 56
i interior, p. 340
i initial state, p. 9

I nuclear spin, p. 40
K K shell, p. 30
L L shell, p. 30
L rotational, p. 356
l orbital, p. 18
l laboratory system, p. 213
l lth partial wave, p. 437
M M shell, p. 31
M magnetic multipole, p. 399
m magnetic, p. 28
m minimum, p. 42
max maximum, p. 180
n neutron, p. 54
op operator, p. 320
p proton, p. 54
p pair production, p. 237
p pairing, p. 249
p peak, p. 78
q quadratic, p. 246
r radial, p. 94
r resonance, p. 454
s spin, p. 18
so spin orbit, p. 370
th threshold, p. 214
W total energy, p. 334
x x particle, p. 57
∞ in asymptotic limit, p. 410
ν neutron, p. 374
π proton, p. 374

Superscripts

e empirical, p. 250
l lth partial wave, p. 439
m gamma-emitting isomer, p. 178
w Weiszäcker, p. 286
x experimental, p. 255
1 on left denotes singlet state ($S = 0$), p. 481
3 on left denotes triplet state ($S = 1$), p. 481
$'$ residual or product, p. 206
$*$ excited or radioactive, p. 176
$*$ compound nucleus, p. 206
$*$ magic, p. 268
$+$ positron, p. 4
$-$ electron, p. 4

Special Symbols

𝔡 pairing parameter, p. 249
ƛ reduced wavelength $= \lambda/2\pi$, p. 433
$\hbar$ Planck's constant divided by $2\pi = 1.0544 \times 10^{-27}$ erg-sec, p. 8
$\doteq$ "can only take on the values of," p. 7
$\langle\ \rangle$ expectation or average value, p. 41
$\overline{}$ denotes average, p. 62
$\rightarrow$ in asymptotic limit, p. 332
$|\ |$ absolute magnitude of, p. 18
𝔷 charge number, p. 85

CHAPTER 1

RELATIVISTIC DYNAMICS AND REVIEW OF ATOMIC PHYSICS

1-1. Relativistic Dynamics. The underlying law governing energy transformations in nuclear physics is Einstein's mass-energy equation

$$E_0 = mc^2 \tag{1-1}$$

where c is the velocity of light, m is the mass of an object, and E_0 is its intrinsic energy content. This equation is a consequence of relativistic dynamics, which like Newtonian dynamics is based upon the well-known Newtonian laws of motion. The reader will recall that in Newtonian dynamics we accept as the definition of the momentum of a particle

$$\mathbf{p} = m\mathbf{v} \tag{1-2}$$

or

$$p_x = mv_x \qquad p_y = mv_y \qquad p_z = mv_z$$

where m is the mass of the particle and $\mathbf{v}$ is a vector whose components v_x, v_y, and v_z characterize the velocity of a particle relative to an inertial frame of reference. The magnitude of this velocity vector is

$$v = |\mathbf{v}| = (\mathbf{v} \cdot \mathbf{v})^{\frac{1}{2}} = (v_x^2 + v_y^2 + v_z^2)^{\frac{1}{2}} \tag{1-3}$$

In relativistic dynamics, instead of Eq. (1-2) we accept as the definition of the momentum of a particle

$$\mathbf{p} = \frac{m\mathbf{v}}{(1 - v^2/c^2)^{\frac{1}{2}}} \tag{1-4}$$

or

$$p_x = \frac{mv_x}{(1 - v^2/c^2)^{\frac{1}{2}}} \qquad p_y = \frac{mv_y}{(1 - v^2/c^2)^{\frac{1}{2}}} \qquad p_z = \frac{mv_z}{(1 - v^2/c^2)^{\frac{1}{2}}}$$

In addition, in relativistic dynamics we define the total energy content of a moving particle as

$$E = \frac{mc^2}{(1 - v^2/c^2)^{\frac{1}{2}}} \tag{1-5}$$

Einstein's mass-energy equation for a particle at rest follows from this equation. [Throughout this book the symbol m will denote the rest mass of a particle. We shall make no use of the concept of variable mass, $m/(1 - v^2/c^2)^{\frac{1}{2}}$, which was introduced in many early discussions of relativity.]

It would be inappropriate here to go into the details of the origins of these definitions. It is necessary only to say that both the Newtonian and the Einstein definitions are consistent with the principle of relativity: *The physical laws are the same in all coordinate systems which are moving relative to each other in uniform translational motion.*

The Newtonian definition of momentum is consistent with the additional postulate: *The law of addition of velocities governs the transformations of velocities relative to coordinate systems moving in relative translatory motion,* whereas the definition of momentum given by Einstein is consistent with the postulate: *The velocity of light in a vacuum is the same in all coordinate systems moving in relative translatory motion.* Experiments indicate that reality is more closely described by the Einstein velocity-of-light postulate. We refer the reader to works on relativity[1-3] for the verification of these statements.

Accepting Eqs. (1-1) and (1-5) for the energy content of a particle, at rest and moving, we find that the kinetic energy T of an object, *i.e.*, the energy an object possesses by virtue of its motion alone, is

$$T = E - E_0 = mc^2\left[\frac{1}{(1 - v^2/c^2)^{\frac{1}{2}}} - 1\right] \tag{1-6}$$

This equation may be verified directly by using the defining equations for momentum and the second law of motion ($\mathbf{f} = d\mathbf{p}/dt$). Recall that, using Newtonian mechanics, we may calculate the kinetic energy of a particle by computing the work done in accelerating it along a line from rest to its final velocity. Thus

$$T = \int_0^v f\,ds = \int_0^v \frac{dp}{dt}\,ds = \int_0^v \frac{ds}{dt}\,dp = \int_0^v vm\,dv = \frac{1}{2}mv^2$$

In relativistic dynamics we use for *linear* motion

$$p = \frac{mv}{(1 - v^2/c^2)^{\frac{1}{2}}} \tag{1-7}$$

Hence the dp in the expression under the third integral sign above is $m(1 - v^2/c^2)^{-\frac{3}{2}}\,dv$. The integration, which may be carried out without difficulty, gives Eq. (1-6) as the result.

In calculations in which relativistic dynamics must be used, it is usually convenient to regard

$$\gamma = \gamma(v) = \left(1 - \frac{v^2}{c^2}\right)^{-\frac{1}{2}} \tag{1-8}$$

as a distinct dimensionless dynamical parameter which characterizes the motion. Using Eqs. (1-6) to (1-8), it is simple to show that

$$\gamma = \gamma(p) = \left(1 + \frac{p^2}{m^2c^2}\right)^{\frac{1}{2}} \tag{1-9}$$

and

$$\gamma = \gamma(T) = 1 + \frac{T}{E_0} \tag{1-10}$$

The inverse equations are

$$v = c\left(1 - \frac{1}{\gamma^2}\right)^{\frac{1}{2}} \tag{1-11}$$

$$p = mc(\gamma^2 - 1)^{\frac{1}{2}} \tag{1-12}$$

and

$$T = mc^2(\gamma - 1) \tag{1-13}$$

In terms of γ the relativistic momentum and energy expressions corresponding to Eqs. (1-4) and (1-5) are

$$\mathbf{p} = m\mathbf{v}\gamma \tag{1-14}$$

$$E = mc^2\gamma \tag{1-15}$$

A useful form of Eq. (1-15) which follows from Eq. (1-9) is

$$E = (m^2c^4 + p^2c^2)^{\frac{1}{2}} \tag{1-16}$$

Using this for a particle with vanishing mass, we find

$$E = pc \tag{1-17}$$

According to Eq. (1-7) such a particle may exist and possess momentum only if it moves with the velocity c.

The expansions of γ as a power series in v/c or in p/mc are frequently useful in nuclear physics. These expansions are

$$\gamma = 1 + \tfrac{1}{2}\left(\frac{v}{c}\right)^2 + \tfrac{3}{8}\left(\frac{v}{c}\right)^4 + \tfrac{5}{16}\left(\frac{v}{c}\right)^6 + \cdots \tag{1-18}$$

$$\gamma = 1 + \tfrac{1}{2}\left(\frac{p}{mc}\right)^2 - \tfrac{1}{8}\left(\frac{p}{mc}\right)^4 + \tfrac{1}{16}\left(\frac{p}{mc}\right)^6 - \cdots \tag{1-19}$$

For the fastest macroscopic objects on earth, $v/c \approx 10^{-5}$ and the successive terms in Eq. (1-18) decrease by factors of the order of 10^{-10}. Thus we see that the departures from Newtonian expressions for momentum and kinetic energy could not be detected unless experimental measurements could be carried out giving results accurate to about 10 significant figures. On the other hand, the motions of microscopic particles in atomic, nuclear, and fundamental-particle physics often depart significantly from those predicted by Newtonian dynamics.

The magnitude of $\gamma - 1$ associated with a moving particle is a useful parameter, which may be employed to determine whether nonrelativistic dynamics is adequate or whether relativistic dynamics is required. If $\gamma - 1 \ll 1$, a nonrelativistic treatment is adequate, and the percentage error made by neglecting relativistic effects is of the order of $100(\gamma - 1)$. On the other hand when $\gamma - 1 \gtrsim 1$, a strictly relativistic treatment is needed. The simplest way of estimating $\gamma - 1$ is to find the ratio of the kinetic energy to the rest energy of the particle [see Eq. (1-10)].

In Table 1-1 we indicate the rest energies of various particles involved in nuclear physics, the ranges of kinetic energies which are usually encountered, and the corresponding ranges for $\gamma - 1$. We see that the motions of the massless and very light particles listed in this table

TABLE 1-1. ENERGIES OF PARTICLES IN NUCLEAR PHYSICS

Particle	Symbol	Rest energy, Mev†	Kinetic energy, Mev	$\gamma - 1$	Dynamics
Massless:					
Photon	γ	0	0.1–25	∞	R.
Neutrino	η	0	0.1–5	∞	R.
Very light:					
Electron	β^-	0.511	0.1–10	0.2–20	R.
Positron	β^+	0.511	0.1–10	0.2–20	R.
Light nuclear particles:					
Neutron	n	939.5	10^{-8}–25	10^{-11}–0.025	N.R.-I.
Proton	p	938.2	0.1–25	10^{-4}–0.025	N.R.-I.
Deuteron	d	1875.4	0.1–25	10^{-4}–0.01	N.R.-I.
Tritium	t	2808.7	0.1–25	10^{-4}–0.01	N.R.-I.
He^3	χ	2808.2	0.1–25	10^{-4}–0.01	N.R.-I.
Alpha particle	α	3727.1	0.1–25	10^{-4}–0.006	N.R.-I.
Massive atoms	X	10^4–2×10^5	0.001–1	10^{-7}–10^{-4}	N.R.

† Mev stands for million electron volts.

always require a strictly relativistic dynamics (R.) for their description. On the other hand the usual nonrelativistic dynamics (N.R.) is almost always adequate for treating the motion of massive atoms. For light nuclear particles, when the kinetic energies are about 1 Mev or less, nonrelativistic dynamics is usually adequate. However, when kinetic energies are of the order of 10 to 25 Mev, relativistic effects are within the range of measurement. Since most of nuclear physics (the so-called classical nuclear physics) is concerned with the energy range less than 25 Mev, we need not resort to a strictly relativistic treatment for fast light nuclear particles. Instead, we may correct the nonrelativistic treatment by including in all energy calculations the third term in the expansion of γ in the power series in v/c [Eq. (1-18)] or p/mc [Eq. (1-19)]. The percentage error made by neglecting still higher terms is of the order of $100(\gamma - 1)^2$. We wish to caution the reader that, in using this intermediate dynamics (I.), he must always be cognizant that only in a limited range of energies is such a modification of Newtonian dynamics adequate.

1-2. Motion of Charged Particles. It will be helpful later on to have available the equations governing the motion of charged particles in certain simple arrangements of electric and magnetic fields. We shall assume that these particles have a charge ze, where e is the magnitude of the electronic charge and z is a small positive or negative integer.

If a particle having a charge ze and mass m is accelerated from rest through an electrostatic potential V, the kinetic energy acquired by the particle is equal to the work done on it; *i.e.*,

$$T = zeV \tag{1-20}$$

The velocity or momentum may therefore be computed using either the nonrelativistic equations

$$zeV = \tfrac{1}{2}mv^2 \tag{1-21}$$

and

$$zeV = \frac{p^2}{2m} \tag{1-22}$$

or the relativistic equations

$$zeV = mc^2[\gamma(v) - 1] \tag{1-23}$$

and

$$zeV = mc^2[\gamma(p) - 1] \tag{1-24}$$

where $\gamma(v)$ and $\gamma(p)$ are given by Eqs. (1-8) and (1-9).

Since the force acting on a particle in an electric field of strength $\boldsymbol{\mathcal{E}}$ is $\mathbf{f} = ze\boldsymbol{\mathcal{E}}$, the motion conforms to the differential equation

$$ze\boldsymbol{\mathcal{E}} = \frac{d\mathbf{p}}{dt} \tag{1-25}$$

If the field is uniform and constant in time, the integration of each component yields three component equations, which may be represented by

$$\mathbf{p} = ze\boldsymbol{\mathcal{E}}t + \mathbf{p}_0 \tag{1-26}$$

where $\mathbf{p}_0$ is the initial momentum. Using $\mathbf{p} = m\mathbf{v} = m(d\mathbf{r}/dt)$, the second integration in the nonrelativistic case leads to the familiar equation of motion in a uniform field of force

$$\mathbf{r} = \frac{ze\boldsymbol{\mathcal{E}}}{2m}t^2 + \frac{\mathbf{p}_0}{m}t + \mathbf{r}_0 \tag{1-27}$$

where $\mathbf{r}_0$ is the initial-position vector. The second integration in the relativistic case is complicated by the more elaborate connection between the velocity and momentum and by the interdependence of the various degrees of freedom. It may be solved by using Eqs. (1-14) and (1-9) to express each component of the velocity as a function of time. We may then integrate to obtain the equations of motion.

If a charged particle moves in a magnetic field of constant intensity **H**, a force acts upon it which is given by

$$\mathbf{f} = ze\mu \, \mathbf{v} \times \mathbf{H} \tag{1-28}$$

where μ is the permeability of the medium (unity in a vacuum when the emu system of units is employed). Since no work is done on the charged particle, the numerical value of the velocity remains constant. When the field is uniform and the velocity is perpendicular to the field, the first integration may be carried out very simply. Since the acceleration, which is perpendicular to the velocity, is constant, the particle moves in a circle of constant radius R. Considering only magnitudes of the vectors, we have (see Fig. 1-1)

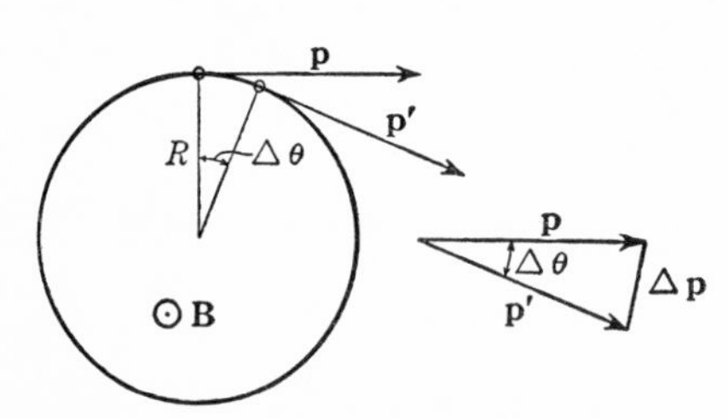

FIG. 1-1. The motion of a positive charge ze in a uniform perpendicular magnetic field. (B is directed out of the paper.)

$$|\mathbf{f}| = \mu H z e v = \left| \frac{\Delta \mathbf{p}}{\Delta t} \right| = p \frac{\Delta \theta}{\Delta t} = \frac{pv}{R} \tag{1-29}$$

Therefore

$$p = \mu H z e R = B z e R \tag{1-30}$$

where $B = \mu H$ is the magnetic induction. This equation is valid in both relativistic and nonrelativistic dynamics.

An arrangement of uniform electric and magnetic fields perpendicular to each other and to the direction of a beam of charged particles is frequently used to measure the velocity of the particles in the beam or to select particles of a particular velocity. If the fields are adjusted so that the net force acting on the particles is zero, as indicated by a null deviation of the beam, we have

$$f = Bzev = ze\mathcal{E} \tag{1-31}$$

The velocity of the undeviated particles is thus

$$v = \frac{\mathcal{E}}{B} \tag{1-32}$$

1-3. Structure of the Atom.(4–8) In the first decade of the twentieth century, several important facts about the structure of an atom were already established. It was clear that it contained light negative electrons and heavy positive charges. Approximate estimates of the volume of the atom could be made, based on the density of a liquid or solid and Avogadro's number, on an equation from kinetic theory relating atomic volume to the mean free path of gas molecules, or on the empirical atomic volume constant in van der Waals' equation of state. These and other methods led to the conclusion that the atom is an entity with a radius of the order of magnitude of 10^{-8} cm. The detailed arrangement of the electrons and the positive charges within an atom was the subject of considerable speculation and study. Lenard[7] in 1903, on the basis of experiments in which electrons of different velocities were scattered by thin metallic foils, suggested that most of the mass of the atom was concentrated in a region very small compared with the atomic radius. Rutherford[9] in 1911, on the basis of experiments in which alpha particles were scattered by various substances, arrived at a more explicit model resembling in many respects our solar system. According to this model, almost all the mass of the atom is contained in a small nucleus which has a radius slightly less than 10^{-12} cm. The nucleus also bears a positive charge, which is an integer Z times the basic unit of charge, e. To make the atom neutral, Rutherford assumed that Z electrons rotate about the nucleus at distances of the order of 10^{-8} cm, where they are held in dynamical equilibrium against the electrostatic force by centrifugal force. Rutherford's model was highly successful in accounting for the observed scattering of alpha particles. Barkla[(10)] (1911) and Moseley[(11)] (1913) confirmed the general features of the Rutherford nuclear atom by measurements of the scattering of X rays. This electron-nucleus model of the atom has been assumed in practically all theoretical studies since the work of Rutherford and has become one of the main pillars upon which atomic physics is based.

1-4. Early Quantum Theory.[(4–7)] Quantum theory originated in a successful effort by Planck[(12)] in 1900 to obtain a theoretical expression which fits the experimental distribution of energy in the spectrum emitted from a small hole in a heated enclosure (black-body radiation). Although this study is extremely complicated, the substance of Planck's new contribution is quite simple. Essentially Planck postulated that a microscopic harmonic oscillator such as those which may be identified with a radiation field can only take on or exist with the energies

$$W = nh\nu_c \tag{1-33}$$

where ν_c is the classical frequency of the harmonic oscillator, h is a basic constant of nature, and

$$n \doteq 0, 1, 2, 3, \ldots \tag{1-34}$$

We use the symbol $\doteq$ in connection with natural quantum numbers which arise in physics to mean "can only take on the values."

Einstein[13] in 1905 made the next major contribution to the development of quantum theory by his explanation of the photoelectric effect. The essentially new idea in this work is the suggestion that light impinging upon a metallic surface may be treated as a beam of massless particles called photons, each of which has the energy

$$E = h\nu \tag{1-35}$$

where ν is the frequency of the light wave.

Compton[14] in 1923 used Einstein's energy-frequency relation to explain the particlelike behavior of X rays which he had observed in scattering experiments. In explaining this phenomenon Compton made use of Eq. (1-35) and the relation

$$p = \frac{h}{\lambda} \tag{1-36}$$

where λ is the wavelength of the radiation. Equation (1-36) for photons follows immediately from Eqs. (1-35) and (1-17) and the well-known relation for light

$$\nu\lambda = c \tag{1-37}$$

In 1913 Bohr,[15] in formulating the first successful theory of atomic spectra, suggested that the orbital angular momentum $\mathbf{l}$ of the electron in the hydrogen atom is quantized according to

$$|\mathbf{l}| = \frac{nh}{2\pi} = n\hbar \tag{1-38}$$

where

$$n \doteq 1, 2, 3, \ldots \tag{1-39}$$

Adopting Rutherford's planetary model and the usual laws of dynamics and electrostatics, Bohr showed that, as a consequence of this quantization of angular momentum, the hydrogen atom can exist only in certain states having certain discrete orbital radii and energies. For a hydrogenic system (*i.e.*, a system consisting of a single electron with mass m_e and charge $-e$ surrounding a nucleus of charge Ze with mass M) these radii and energies are (see Fig. 1-2)

$$r = \frac{n^2 a}{Z} \tag{1-40}$$

and

$$W = -\frac{Z^2 e^2}{2an^2} \tag{1-41}$$

where

$$a = \frac{\hbar^2}{m_r e^2} = \left(\frac{\hbar^2}{m_e e^2}\right)\left(1 + \frac{m_e}{M}\right) = a_B\left(1 + \frac{m_e}{M}\right) \tag{1-42}$$

and

$$m_r = \frac{m_e M}{m_e + M} \tag{1-43}$$

The quantities a_B and m_r are known as the Bohr radius and the reduced mass of the system, respectively. Bohr further assumed that radiation

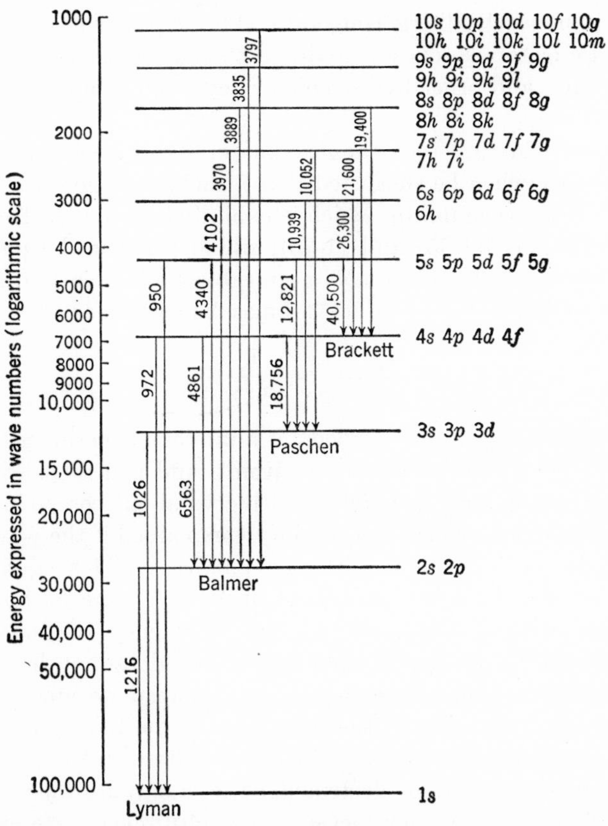

FIG. 1-2. Hydrogen energy levels. The ordinates are the wave numbers $|W|/ch$, plotted on a logarithmic scale for convenience. The zero is taken at the ion. Transitions are indicated by vertical lines; the corresponding wavelengths in angstrom units are given beside them. Electron orbitals are shown on the right (see Sec. 1-9 for significance of notation). (*From Harnwell and Livingood, Ref.* 6.)

is not emitted when an atom is *in* an energy state but is emitted when an atom spontaneously jumps from a state of higher energy (W_i) to a state of lower energy (W_f). Since the energy emitted is $W_i - W_f$, according to Eq. (1-35) the frequency of the photon is

$$W_i - W_f = h\nu_{if} \tag{1-44}$$

From Eqs. (1-41) and (1-37) it follows immediately that

$$\frac{1}{\lambda_{if}} = Z^2\left(\frac{1}{n_f^2} - \frac{1}{n_i^2}\right)\frac{e^2}{2ach} = \frac{RZ^2}{(1 + m_e/M)}\left(\frac{1}{n_f^2} - \frac{1}{n_i^2}\right) \tag{1-45}$$

where

$$R = \frac{e^2}{2a_Bch} = \frac{2\pi^2e^4m_e}{ch^3} \tag{1-46}$$

is the well-known Rydberg constant. The experimental wavelengths characteristic of the isotopes of hydrogen, singly ionized helium, doubly ionized lithium, and other hydrogenic systems conform quite accurately to Eq. (1-45).

De Broglie[16] in 1924 took the next major step in the development of quantum theory when he suggested that atomic particles also may show the dual wave-particle nature which is exhibited by light. He proposed that the equations [(1-35) and (1-36)] which connect the particle and wave parameters of light are also applicable to atomic particles. For application to matter waves Eq. (1-36) may be written as

$$\lambda = \frac{h}{p} = \frac{h}{mv\gamma} \tag{1-47}$$

This relation has now been verified by numerous experiments in which beams of particles such as electrons, atoms, and neutrons, with known momenta, give rise, upon interaction with crystal lattices, to interference and diffraction effects which can be simply explained if the wavelength λ is assumed to be associated with the particles. This equation thus represents a very basic law of atomic physics. There is, however, no experimental method for measuring the frequency of matter waves directly; hence the energy-frequency relation does not have a basic physical significance for matter waves, and instead we must regard the energy-frequency equation as the definition of the frequency of matter waves. Indeed, to a certain extent it is necessary to take the same point of view for the frequencies of electromagnetic radiation which are beyond direct experimental frequency measurement (10^{11} cycles/sec or greater).

1-5. Wave Functions and Wave Parameters. Practically all recent systems and theories proposed to explain the behavior and characteristics of nuclei are within the theoretical framework known as quantum mechanics, or wave mechanics. Since in many respects quantum mechanics employs the mathematical methods used in theories of dynamical continua, we shall give here some of the elementary concepts of wave theory.

In ordinary dynamics we are concerned with the motions of particles and rigid bodies. These motions may be specified by expressing each one of a discrete set of coordinates associated with the particles or rigid bodies as a function of the single parameter time [for example, $q_1 = q_1(t)$, $q_2 = q_2(t)$, . . .].

Very often in nature we encounter the disturbance of a space continuum such as a string, a membrane, or an air enclosure. Motion in a continuum is specified by expressing the functional dependence of some physical parameter or parameters, such as tension, surface tension, or pressure, on the space coordinates and on time [for example, $T = T(x,t)$, $p = p(x,y,z,t)$, . . .]. We shall call such functions "wave functions," and we shall refer to motion in a continuum as wave motion, although we must recognize at the outset that all motions in continuous media do not resemble what we commonly picture as the motion of waves.

In ordinary dynamics the laws of motion may be expressed as ordinary differential equations. A problem is solved when the solutions of these equations which satisfy given initial or final conditions are found. In the dynamics of the continuum, the laws of motion may be expressed as partial differential equations. To find the solutions of such equations which satisfy given initial or boundary conditions generally requires much more mathematical knowledge and skill than is needed for problems in ordinary dynamics. The tremendous increase in complexity in going from particle problems to continuum problems is perhaps indicated if the reader considers what is needed to specify one-dimensional motion in a continuum in contrast with the one-dimensional motion of a particle. For example, in the case of a plucked string, the description of the motion must contain the values of a physical parameter, such as tension or displacement, at a continuous infinity of points, each such point value being a function of time. In contrast, only one function of time suffices to describe the one-dimensional motion of a particle. Accordingly the description of wave motion must contain infinitely more information than a description of particle motion. Special examples of wave motion, in our broader sense, have many properties which are considered to be characteristic of particle motion. For example, the average position of a pulse propagated on a long string may be a function of time which corresponds to a possible motion of a particle. Thus special functions $Q(x,t)$ of the form $Q = Q[x - f(t)]$ are inferentially connected with a particle moving according to the equation $x = f(t)$.

The apparent contradiction between wave and particle descriptions of a motion exists only if wave functions are restricted to those which correspond to infinite monochromatic wave trains. If wave functions describing more general types of wave motions are admitted, the functions of t which describe particle motion are simply special cases. We shall now consider some simple examples of wave functions in order to become acquainted with the parameters and concepts needed to describe motion in a continuum.

The wave function which characterizes a monochromatic wave train is of particular interest in physics because it represents the simplest idealization of a motion which arises frequently and because more complicated wave functions can be expressed as superpositions of monochromatic waves. Such a wave function may be expressed in the form

$$Q(x,t) = A \sin 2\pi \left(\frac{x}{\lambda} - \frac{t}{T} + \frac{\delta}{2\pi}\right) \tag{1-48}$$

where A is the amplitude, λ is the wavelength, T is the period, and δ is the phase constant.

By studying the development of $Q(x,t)$ as a function of x with t fixed, as a function of t with x fixed, and as a function of both x and t, which are related such that the value of Q is fixed, we can readily establish:

1. For fixed t the wave function is a periodic function of distance with the amplitude A and with the repeat distance, or wavelength, λ.

2. For a fixed x the wave function is a periodic function of time with amplitude A and with the period T or frequency $\nu = 1/T$.

3. The entire configuration represented by the wave function at a single instant advances along the x axis at a constant rate given by

$$u = \frac{\lambda}{T} = \lambda\nu \tag{1-49}$$

In discussions of wave motion, a monochromatic wave is often characterized by the angular frequency ω and the propagation constant k, parameters which are defined respectively by

$$\omega = \frac{2\pi}{T} = 2\pi\nu \tag{1-50}$$

and

$$k = \frac{2\pi}{\lambda} \tag{1-51}$$

In terms of these wave parameters Eq. (1-48) becomes

$$Q(x,t) = A \sin (kx - \omega t + \delta) \tag{1-52}$$

For matter waves Einstein's and de Broglie's relations become

$$E = \hbar\omega \tag{1-53}$$

and

$$p = \hbar k \tag{1-54}$$

In view of these last two equations a relation $E = E(p)$ between particle parameters may be transformed into a relation $\omega = \omega(k)$ between wave parameters. This wave relationship is known as the dispersion relation. For light

$$E = cp \tag{1-55}$$

becomes

$$\omega = ck \tag{1-56}$$

which is equivalent to Eq. (1-37). If we take the kinetic energy for the definition of the frequency of matter waves, we have in the nonrelativistic dynamics

$$\omega = \frac{\hbar k^2}{2m} \tag{1-57}$$

In the relativistic dynamics we find

$$\omega = c(k^2 + \kappa^2)^{\frac{1}{2}} - c\kappa \tag{1-58}$$

where

$$\kappa = \frac{mc}{\hbar} \tag{1-59}$$

is a basic reciprocal length which we may identify with the particle associated with the waves.

1-6. Standing Waves. It is well known that a string having fixed end points at $x = 0$ and $x = a$ may be excited into a type of wave motion, called standing wave motion, which is characterized by the wave function

$$Q(x,t) = 2A \sin kx \sin \omega t \tag{1-60}$$

In this case the fixed boundaries restrict the allowed vibrations such that the propagation constants must satisfy

$$|k|a = n\pi \qquad \text{or} \qquad n\lambda = 2a \tag{1-61}$$

where n is the integer which characterizes the mode of vibration. The number of intermediate nodes in the standing wave pattern is $n - 1$.

The restriction of the propagation constant to discrete values in standing-wave phenomena has the immediate consequence that quantities connected to it, such as wavelength or angular frequency (through the dispersion relation), are also restricted to discrete values. The relations $E = \hbar\omega$ and $p = \hbar k$, which are fruitful equations in connection with electromagnetic and matter waves, then immediately imply that the energies and momenta of the system are restricted to discrete values. These natural results are in marked contrast with the *ad hoc* restrictions of dynamical quantities to discrete values in the work of Planck and Bohr.

To illustrate this conclusion, we call attention to the provocative connection between de Broglie's hypothesis and the assumption of Bohr.

Let us allow the electron in a hydrogen atom to have only de Broglie wavelengths satisfying the condition $n\lambda = C$, where C is the circumference of a circular orbit. This is the appropriate modification of Eq. (1-61) for standing waves on a circle. Then using $C = 2\pi r$ and $p = h/\lambda$, it follows that $l = pr = n\hbar$, which is Bohr's quantization rule.

As an illustration of the manner in which boundary conditions restrict the energies of a particle to discrete values, let us consider the hypothetical problem of a particle which is confined inside a potential barrier given by

$$\begin{aligned} V &= 0 \qquad 0 \leq x \leq a \\ V &= \infty \qquad \text{elsewhere} \end{aligned} \tag{1-62}$$

This is known as the problem of a particle in a one-dimensional box. Without going into physical interpretations we may, in view of our previous discussion of standing waves, identify with the particle in a box the wave functions

$$\begin{aligned} \Psi &= C \sin \frac{n\pi x}{a} \sin \omega t \qquad 0 \leq x \leq a \\ \Psi &= 0 \qquad \text{elsewhere} \end{aligned} \tag{1-63}$$

where n conforms to Eq. (1-39).

The propagation constants associated with the allowed modes are given by

$$k = n \frac{\pi}{a} \tag{1-64}$$

Consequently, the allowed energies (all kinetic in this case) corresponding to these states are

$$W = \frac{\hbar^2 k^2}{2m} = n^2\pi^2 \frac{\hbar^2}{2ma^2} \tag{1-65}$$

For the case of the three-dimensional box with sides a, the wave function

$$\Psi = C \sin \frac{n_x \pi x}{a} \sin \frac{n_y \pi y}{a} \sin \frac{n_z \pi z}{a} \sin \omega t \tag{1-66}$$

has the desired property of vanishing at the boundaries (the six planes defined by x, y, and z in turns taking the values 0 and a). The energies corresponding to these standing waves are

$$W = (n_x^2 + n_y^2 + n_z^2)\pi^2 \left(\frac{\hbar^2}{2ma^2}\right) \tag{1-67}$$

where n_x, n_y, and n_z are restricted like the n in Eq. (1-39).

1-7. Stationary States of Hydrogenic Systems. Unfortunately we cannot infer the standing wave patterns for an electron in a hydrogenic system by such simple considerations as are applicable to the particle in a box. Instead, it is necessary to go rather deeply into the substance and mathematical formalism of wave mechanics. To avoid undue involvement in the complexities of wave mechanics at this point, we shall here simply present some of the important results of this study. The details are given in many books[17–23] on wave mechanics or quantum mechanics (see also Chap. 10).

When applied to the hydrogenic system, wave mechanics yields a set of wave functions which characterize the stationary states of the electron just as Eq. (1-66) characterizes the stationary states, or standing waves, of a harmonic wave disturbance which is confined inside a cubic box. Three quantum numbers v, l, and m_l, known as the radial, azimuthal, and magnetic quantum numbers, respectively, are required to label and order the stationary states of the hydrogenic system. The quantum numbers v and l are restricted to the values 0, 1, 2, . . . , whereas m_l may take on positive or negative integral values, such that $|m_l| \leq l$. The wave-mechanical determination of the allowed energy values of a hydrogenic system leads to the result

$$W = -\frac{Z^2 e^4 m_e}{2\hbar^2(v + l + 1)^2[1 + (m_e/M)]} \tag{1-68}$$

Since the energy depends upon the combination $v + l + 1$, it is customary to define the "principal" quantum number n by

$$n = v + l + 1 \tag{1-69}$$

Inserting this into Eq. (1-68), we obtain exactly Eq. (1-41), the result of the Bohr theory, which is in excellent agreement with experiment.

A basic assumption of wave mechanics is that the square of the magnitude of the wave function representing a state is proportional to the probability of finding an electron in a given element of volume surrounding the nucleus. Although not directly implied by this probability assumption, it is a useful pictorial and computational device in many problems to regard the electron as a cloud of electricity which is smeared out over the probability distribution pattern. In Fig. 1-3 we show radial distributions corresponding to some of the lower energy states of hydrogen. Meaning is given to these radial distribution functions $D_{vl}(r)$ by defining

$$dq = -eD_{vl}(r)\, dr \tag{1-70}$$

as the effective quantity of charge in a spherical shell of thickness dr surrounding the nucleus. Consider for a moment the distributions corresponding to the fixed value $l = 0$. We observe that the first distribution, $v = 0$, has no intermediate nodes; the second, $v = 1$, has one intermediate node; and the third, $v = 2$, two; etc. This correspondence between the order of levels for a given value of l and the number of nodes in the radial function is a general one which serves to give physical mean-

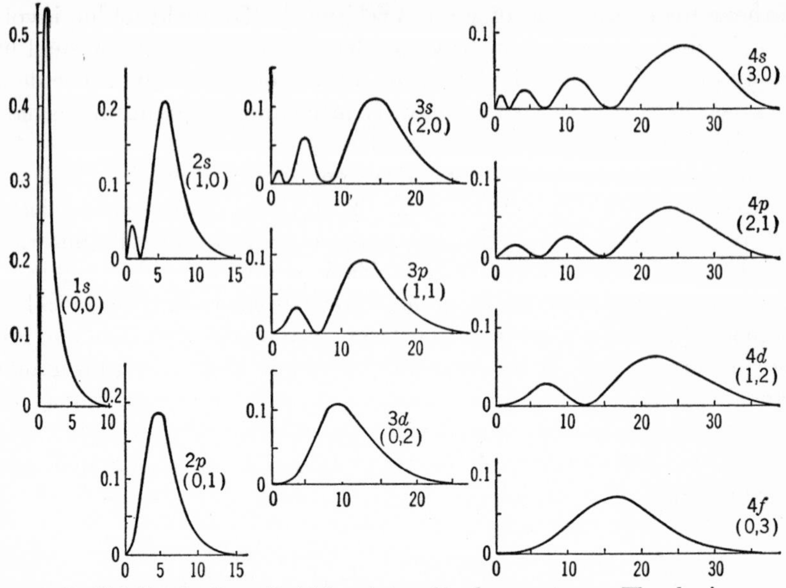

FIG. 1-3. Radial distributions $D_{vl}(r)$ for states of hydrogen atom. The abscissas are in units of a_B, whereas the ordinates are in units of a_B^{-1}. Designations of states are given according to spectroscopic notation (Sec. 1-9) and according to values of v and l (v,l).

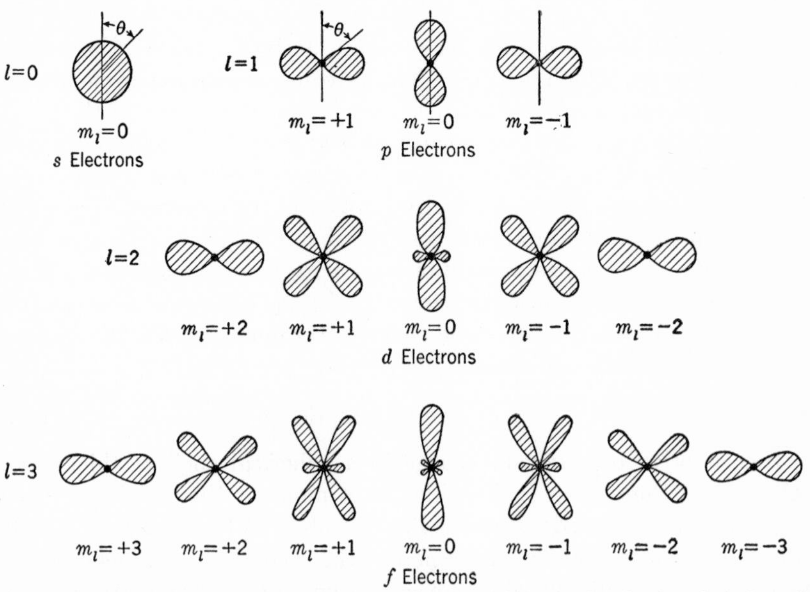

FIG. 1-4. Angular distributions plotted as a function of the angle θ for $l = 0, 1, 2,$ and 3 states. For $m_l = 0$ the scale is approximately $1/(l + 1)$ times that of the other states. (*From White, Ref.* 17.)

ing to v, the radial quantum number. In addition to the dependence upon r, the probability distributions depend upon the angle of the electron position vector $\mathbf{r}$ relative to a direction in space established by an external field. The characteristic angular distributions for various quantum numbers l and m_l are shown in Fig. 1-4. The physical significance of the quantum numbers l and m_l will be discussed in the next section.

When applied to the hydrogenic-system problem, wave mechanics, as proposed by Schroedinger,[(24)] to a large extent merely duplicates the successes of the Bohr theory. However, wave mechanics, in conjunction with certain generalizations introduced by Heisenberg,[(25)] Dirac,[(26)] Pauli,[(27)] Born and Jordan,[(28)] and others (the entire theoretical structure is known as quantum mechanics), has proved adequate for the treatment of a tremendous range of atomic, molecular, and nuclear phenomena, whereas the Bohr theory met with success in only a few special problems and has definitely been found inadequate for the treatment of most. For example, helium, next to hydrogen in simplicity of structure, has not been successfully analyzed using a Bohr type of theory, whereas quantum mechanics has proved quite successful in correlating the experimental observations dealing with helium, as well as all other elements. Before indicating the manner in which quantum mechanics is applied to the explanation of the periodic table, it will be necessary to consider the fundamental quantized characteristics of the angular momenta which arise in microscopic physics.

1-8. Angular Momenta. The quantization of angular momenta is an attribute of microscopic dynamics which has very widespread ramifications. Theoretical spectroscopists, during the years 1922 to 1925, in attempting to explain atomic fine structure, proposed several general quantization rules for angular momentum to supplant the rule of Bohr [Eq. (1-38)], which was found to have a restricted range of application. Several rather successful empirical rules were proposed; however, the development of advanced forms of quantum mechanics has led to general quantization rules, which have a firm theoretical basis and which have proved applicable to molecular, atomic, nuclear, and fundamental-particle physics.

These advanced forms of quantum mechanics start out with a few simple algebraic relations (suggested by properties of classical Poisson brackets) between entities which represent the components of an angular momentum. The quantization rules then follow as a direct consequence of these algebraic relations and of such theoretical methods as the matrix methods of Born and Jordan,[(28)] the symbolic methods of Dirac,[(26)] and the group-theoretic methods of Weyl[(29)] and Wigner.[(30)] In expressing these quantization rules, we shall, to avoid confusion with the specific angular momenta which arise in atomic and nuclear physics, use the symbol **K** to represent an arbitrary angular-momentum vector.

According to quantum mechanics an independent angular-momentum vector **K** may have only magnitudes given by

$$|\mathbf{K}| = [K(K+1)]^{\frac{1}{2}}\hbar \tag{1-71}$$

where the quantum number

$$K \doteq 0, \tfrac{1}{2}, 1, \tfrac{3}{2}, 2, \tfrac{5}{2}, \ldots \tag{1-72}$$

Which one of these allowed integral or half-integral values K will actually take on must be determined by other considerations. However, for any value of K, it follows from the advanced treatments that K_z, the component of **K** in the z direction (the direction of an external magnetic or electric field), is restricted to

$$K_z = M_K\hbar \tag{1-73}$$

where

$$M_K \doteq K, K-1, \ldots, -K \tag{1-74}$$

It can be shown that the quantum number l which arises in the study of hydrogenic systems characterizes the electronic orbital angular momentum **l**, and consequently the magnitude of **l** is given by

$$|\mathbf{l}| = [l(l+1)]^{\frac{1}{2}}\hbar \tag{1-75}$$

The orbital angular-momentum quantum number is restricted by the analysis of Schroedinger to the values

$$l \doteq 0, 1, 2, 3, \ldots, n-1 \tag{1-76}$$

The quantum number m_l associated with l fixes the z component of orbital angular momentum by the equation

$$l_z = m_l\hbar \tag{1-77}$$

where

$$m_l \doteq l, l-1, \ldots, -l \tag{1-78}$$

The spin angular momentum of an electron is another quantity which is basic to the explanation of the periodic table and atomic fine structure. Its magnitude is given by

$$|\mathbf{s}| = [s(s+1)]^{\frac{1}{2}}\hbar \tag{1-79}$$

where

$$s \doteq \tfrac{1}{2} \tag{1-80}$$

is a requirement imposed on the basis of experiment. It follows therefore that

$$s_z = m_s\hbar \tag{1-81}$$

where

$$m_s \doteq \tfrac{1}{2}, -\tfrac{1}{2} \tag{1-82}$$

This is precisely the result used by Uhlenbeck and Goudsmit[31] to account for the fine structure of certain spectral lines.

In addition to the basic electronic angular momenta **l** and **s**, we encounter in atomic physics certain derived angular momenta such as

$$\mathbf{j} = \mathbf{l} + \mathbf{s} \qquad \mathbf{L} = \mathbf{l}_1 + \mathbf{l}_2 \quad \mathbf{S} = \mathbf{s}_1 + \mathbf{s}_2$$
$$\mathbf{J} = \mathbf{L} + \mathbf{S} \qquad \mathbf{J} = \mathbf{j}_1 + \mathbf{j}_2$$

where **j** is the total angular momentum of an electron, **L** is the net orbital angular momentum of two electrons, **S** is the net spin angular momentum of two electrons, and **J** is the grand-total angular momentum of two electrons. Under most of the circumstances which arise in atomic physics the derived angular momenta have the same properties as basic angular momenta. When dealing with a derived angular momentum defined by

$$\mathbf{K} = \mathbf{K}_1 + \mathbf{K}_2 \tag{1-83}$$

where $\mathbf{K}_1$ and $\mathbf{K}_2$ are given, the general quantum-mechanical theory gives, as the additional consideration which fixes the possible values of the quantum number K,

$$K \doteq K_1 + K_2, K_1 + K_2 - 1, \ldots, |K_1 - K_2| \tag{1-84}$$

The number of allowed values of K accordingly is $2K_2 + 1$ or $2K_1 + 1$, whichever is the smaller number. A rule of combination which is both a specialization and generalization of Eq. (1-84) states that an odd (even) number of spin $\frac{1}{2}$ particles can combine to form only odd half-integral (integral) total angular-momentum quantum numbers not exceeding $n/2$, where n is the number of particles.

All of these properties apply to the angular momenta which are involved in nuclear physics.

1-9. Periodic Table. Using the results of the study of hydrogenic systems along with the known results for the quantization of electronic orbital and spin angular momenta, we can now give a reasonable interpretation of the observed periodicities in the chemical and physical characteristics of the elements.

We have indicated that a hydrogenic system, which may be regarded as an electron in a potential field given by

$$V = -\frac{Ze^2}{r} \tag{1-85}$$

may have the energies

$$W = -\frac{Z^2e^2}{2an^2} \qquad \text{where } n \doteq 1, 2, 3, \ldots \tag{1-86}$$

the orbital angular momentum

$$|\mathbf{l}| = [l(l+1)]^{\frac{1}{2}}\hbar \qquad \text{where } l \doteq 0, 1, 2, \ldots, n-1 \tag{1-87}$$

the z component of orbital momentum

$$l_z = m_l\hbar \qquad \text{where } m_l \doteq l, l-1, \ldots, -l \tag{1-88}$$

the spin angular momentum

$$|\mathbf{s}| = [s(s+1)]^{\frac{1}{2}}\hbar \qquad \text{where } s \doteq \tfrac{1}{2} \tag{1-89}$$

and the z component of spin angular momentum

$$s_z = m_s\hbar \qquad \text{where } m_s \doteq \tfrac{1}{2}, -\tfrac{1}{2} \tag{1-90}$$

The complete set of quantum numbers n, l, s, m_l, and m_s not only fixes the magnitudes of the corresponding dynamical variables but also serves to label the electronic states. The quantum number s is generally suppressed, since it has only one allowed value.

In spectroscopic work it is customary to employ the following notation to indicate the value of the quantum number l:

l	0	1	2	3	4	5	6 . . .
Notation	s	p	d	f	g	h	i . . .

The reader will find it necessary to take great pains to minimize the confusion caused by use of the letter s as a quantum number characterizing spin angular momentum and the use of the same letter to designate the state $l = 0$. The n and l labels associated with an electronic state are said to specify the *orbital* occupied by the electron. In the table below we list several of the lowest permissible orbitals for an electron in a hydrogenic structure, and below each is given the degeneracy number of these orbitals (*i.e.*, the number of substates with the same energy).

1s	2s	2p	3s	3p	3d	4s	4p	4d	4f	5s	5p	5d	5f	5g
2	2	6	2	6	10	2	6	10	14	2	6	10	14	18

These degeneracy numbers readily follow if one counts the number of different combinations of m_l and m_s values which are allowed for any l. For example, in a p state the six substates correspond to (m_l,m_s) values

$$(1,\tfrac{1}{2}) \quad (1,-\tfrac{1}{2}) \quad (0,\tfrac{1}{2}) \quad (0,-\tfrac{1}{2}) \quad (-1,\tfrac{1}{2}) \quad (-1,-\tfrac{1}{2})$$

To explain the periodic table, we now must make two major assumptions, which are thoroughly justified in view of the success of the results based upon them. Those two assumptions are known as the independent-particle model and the Pauli exclusion principle, respectively.

In a complex neutral atom we may, as a good approximation, assume that each electron moves independently in an effective central field which is due to the attractive coulomb field of the nucleus and the average repulsive coulomb field due to all the other electrons. The effective central field for each electron in a neutral atom is therefore a function which, on the basis of simple electrostatic considerations, can be shown to have the following limiting forms:

$$V = -\frac{Ze^2}{r} + c \qquad \text{as } r \to 0 \tag{1-91}$$

$$= -\frac{e^2}{r} \qquad \text{as } r \to \infty \tag{1-92}$$

The limit for large r is simply due to the coulomb field of the nuclear charge screened by the charge of the remaining $Z - 1$ electrons. The limit for small r is primarily due to the coulomb field of the nuclear charge with a small constant due to the screening effect of the external electrons. To determine the effective potential function between these extremes is a major computational task which has been completed only for the lighter elements. However, the most important conclusion which we need for our further discussion is simply the fact that the energy states associated with a modified coulomb field differ somewhat from the energy states of a strict coulomb field given by Eq. (1-85). In a modified coulomb field, for a given principal quantum number n the energies are always such that the s state is the most stable, the p state the next, the d state somewhat higher, etc. This separation of the substates of a given principal quantum state sometimes becomes large so that the s substate of a given shell may be more stable than the d or f substate of the shell whose n value is lower. A simple physical explanation for this separation of the substates of a shell can be given if we assume that the radial distributions for each electron in a complex atom are somewhat similar to the hydrogenic distributions (Fig. 1-3). For example, if we compare the $3s$, $3p$, and $3d$ radial distributions, we observe that the $3s$ electron distribution has two penetrating antinodes, and the $3p$ electron distribution has a single penetrating antinode. Because of the strong attractive field in the neighborhood of the nucleus the very penetrating $3s$ orbital is more stable than the penetrating $3p$ orbital, which is more stable than the nonpenetrating $3d$ orbital. Reasoning qualitatively in this fashion, we may conclude that the effect of the electronic repulsions is to separate the energy eigenvalues for the orbitals associated with a given n so that the orbitals with larger l values correspond to the higher energy states. Equation (1-86) for the electronic energies in terms of n alone is no longer valid. In Fig. 1-5 we indicate schematically the energy levels of an electron in a modified coulomb field, showing the separation of the orbitals which occurs as compared with the orbitals in Fig. 1-3.

The second major assumption needed to account for the periodic table is the exclusion principle for electrons put forth by Pauli[32] in 1925. A brief statement of this principle is:

No two electrons can occupy the same electronic quantum state, or alternatively, *the complete set of quantum numbers assigned to each electron must be unique.*

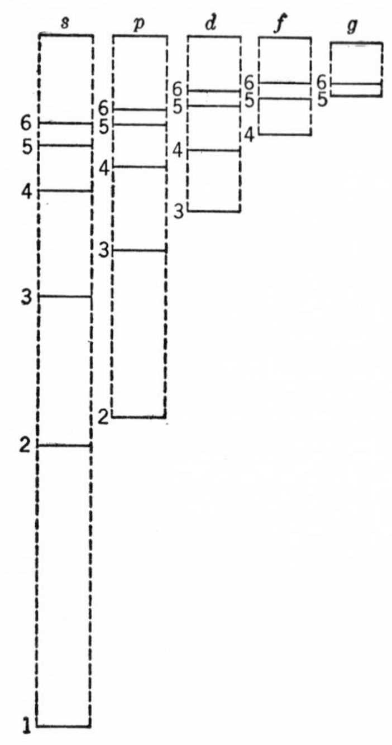

Fig. 1-5. Schematic energy-level diagram for an electron in a modified coulomb field.

Accordingly, to arrive at the ground state of an atom, we must consider only configurations which fulfill this requirement. Appealing to our discussion of the order of the orbitals for a modified coulomb field and the degeneracy numbers of orbitals, we may now assign all the electrons of any neutral atom in its ground state to the lowest available orbitals. The totality of orbitals occupied by the electrons is called the configuration of the atom. In Fig. 1-6 we indicate the order of filling in the various electronic orbitals which was arrived at on the basis of the quantum-mechanical considerations indicated above with the assistance of experimental information (mostly from spectroscopic data). Since the $s, p, d, f, \ldots$ subshells are (2,6,10,14, . . .)-fold degenerate, they can accommodate 2, 6, 10, 14, . . . electrons. The reader must be careful not to interpret this diagram as an energy-level diagram. For a fixed Z

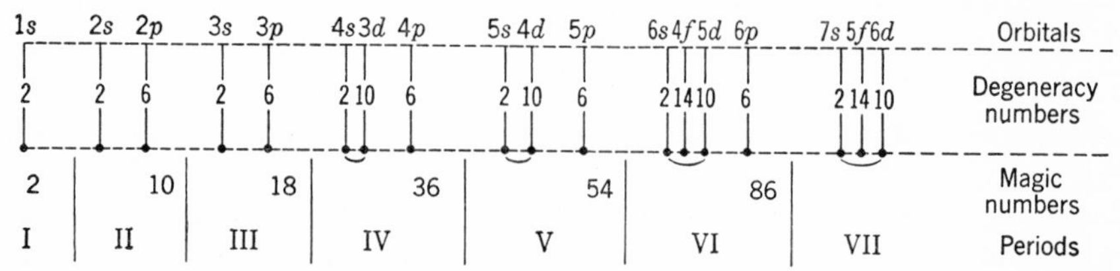

Fig. 1-6. Filling order of orbitals, the degeneracy numbers, and the "magic" numbers of the atomic periodic table.

the diagram showing the unfilled electronic energy levels will not differ very greatly from Fig. 1-6. However, the energy levels shift somewhat as Z is varied, particularly as we come to the region of closed shells. The closing of a shell generally enhances the stability of that configuration as a consequence of small exchange effects and magnetic effects, which we have not discussed. Thus we may expect the actual energy levels to shift relative to the positions indicated in Fig. 1-6 as we go from element to element. We may now write down the electronic configuration of any element with almost complete confidence. Thus, given the atomic number, we follow the sequence of orbitals indicated in Fig. 1-6 until the exponents add up to Z. For example, if $Z = 37$, we have the configuration

$$1s^2 2s^2 2p^6 3s^2 3p^6 4s^2 3d^{10} 4p^6 5s^1$$

For convenience we shall use an abbreviated notation based upon the configurations of the rare gases given below, in which only the orbitals assigned to the outer electrons are specified. In this notation the configuration given above is simply (Kr)$5s^1$.

Element	Z	Configuration
He	2	$1s^2$
Ne	10	(He)$2s^2 2p^6$
A	18	(Ne)$3s^2 3p^6$
Kr	36	(A)$4s^2 3d^{10} 4p^6$
Xe	54	(Kr)$5s^2 4d^{10} 5p^6$
Rn	86	(Xe)$6s^2 4f^{14} 5d^{10} 6p^6$

Surveying the results to be expected from Fig. 1-6, we see that the elements may be grouped into seven periods which close at $Z = 2, 10, 18, 36, 54, 86$, and presumably 118. On the whole the observed configurations, which are given in Table 1-2, follow closely the sequence indicated in Fig. 1-6. However, the close proximity of the $4s$ and $3d$ levels, the $5s$ and $4d$, and the $6s$, $4f$, and $5d$ gives rise to a few anomalies, which may be noted. The first anomaly occurs in the fourth period at Cu ($Z = 29$), which has the ground-state configuration (A)$4s^1 3d^{10}$ instead of (A)$4s^2 3d^9$, as might be expected. The expected configuration (A)$4s^2 3d^{10}$, however, is realized by Zn ($Z = 30$). The following configurations progress in orderly fashion with the filling up of the $4p$ subshell to complete the fourth period.

The next irregularities occur from $Z = 40$ to $Z = 48$. The krypton core ($Z = 36$) being filled, the additional electrons first fill the $5s$ subshell and proceed with the $4d$ subshell until $Z = 40$ is reached. Experiment then indicates that the closely competing $5s$ and $4d$ orbitals are filled in an irregular fashion. At Pd ($Z = 46$) the completed $4d$ subshell is so stable as to yield the configuration Kr($4d^{10}$), with no $5s$ electrons at all. The $5s$ orbitals are then filled successively in Ag ($Z = 47$) and

Cd (Z = 48). The build-up then proceeds in an orderly fashion toward the completion of the fifth period with the filling of the $5p$ subshell.

The next irregularity occurs in the sixth period at La (Z = 57). This has the configuration (Xe)$6s^2 5d^1$. The 14 rare earths following add

TABLE 1-2. CONFIGURATIONS OF THE OUTER ELECTRONS OF THE ELEMENTS

I

Z	Sym	$1s$
1	H	1
2	He	2

II

Z	Sym	$2s$	$2p$
3	Li	1	
4	Be	2	
5	B	2	1
6	C	2	2
7	N	2	3
8	O	2	4
9	F	2	5
10	Ne	2	6

III

Z	Sym	$3s$	$3p$
11	Na	1	
12	Mg	2	
13	Al	2	1
14	Si	2	2
15	P	2	3
16	S	2	4
17	Cl	2	5
18	Ar	2	6

IV

Z	Sym	$4s$	$3d$	$4p$
19	K	1		
20	Ca	2		
21	Sc	2	1	
22	Ti	2	2	
23	V	2	3	
24	Cr	2	4	
25	Mn	2	5	
26	Fe	2	6	
27	Co	2	7	
28	Ni	2	8	
29	Cu	1	10	
30	Zn	2	10	
31	Ga	2	10	1
32	Ge	2	10	2
33	As	2	10	3
34	Se	2	10	4
35	Br	2	10	5
36	Kr	2	10	6

V

Z	Sym	$5s$	$4d$	$5p$
37	Rb	1		
38	Sr	2		
39	Y	2	1	
40	Zr	2	2	
41	Cb	1	4	
42	Mo	1	5	
43	Tc	2	5	
44	Ru	1	7	
45	Rh	1	8	
46	Pd		10	
47	Ag	1	10	
48	Cd	2	10	
49	In	2	10	1
50	Sn	2	10	2
51	Sb	2	10	3
52	Te	2	10	4
53	I	2	10	5
54	Xe	2	10	6

VI

Z	Sym	$6s$	$4f$	$5d$	$6p$
55	Cs	1			
56	Ba	2			
57	La	2		1	
58	Ce	2	2		
59	Pr	2	3		
60	Nd	2	4		
61	Pm	2	5		
62	Sm	2	6		
63	Eu	2	7		
64	Gd	2	7	1	
65	Tb	2	8	1	
66	Dy	2	9	1	
67	Ho	2	10	1	
68	Er	2	11	1	
69	Tm	2	13		
70	Yb	2	14		
71	Lu	2	14	1	
72	Hf	2	14	2	
73	Ta	2	14	3	
74	W	2	14	4	
75	Re	2	14	5	
76	Os	2	14	6	
77	Ir	2	14	7	
78	Pt	1	14	9	
79	Au	1	14	10	
80	Hg	2	14	10	
81	Tl	2	14	10	1
82	Pb	2	14	10	2
83	Bi	2	14	10	3
84	Po	2	14	10	4
85	At	2	14	10	5
86	Rn	2	14	10	6

VII

Z	Sym	$7s$	$5f$	$6d$
87	Fr	1		
88	Ra	2		
89	Ac	2		1
90	Th	2		2
91	Pa	2	2	1
92	U	2	3	1
93	Np	2	4	1
94	Pu	2	5	1
95	Am	2	7	
96	Cm	2	7	1
97	Bk	2	8	1
98	Cf	2	9	1
99	...	2	10	1
100	...	2	11	1

electrons to the $4f$ subshell. The $5d$ orbitals then start to fill uniformly until Pt (Z = 78), which prefers the configuration (Xe)$6s^1 4f^{14} 5d^9$. After a few irregularities the competing orbitals are all filled, and the orderly filling of the $6p$ orbitals takes place until the sixth period is completed.

Fr (Z = 87) and Ra (Z = 88) start the seventh period with the filling of the 7*s* orbitals. The subsequent order is still uncertain, although present indications are that, after slight competition from the 6*d* orbitals the 5*f* orbitals start to fill, leading to a new rare-earth group.

1-10. Atomic Energy Levels: Gross Structure.[17,33–36] The characteristic energy levels of any atom may be subdivided into various classes based upon the instruments and techniques used in the study of the spectral lines associated with transitions between these levels. The most interesting sets of atomic levels from the standpoint of nuclear physics are the excited states of a single valence electron (the optical levels) and the excited states associated with the removal of an interior electron (the

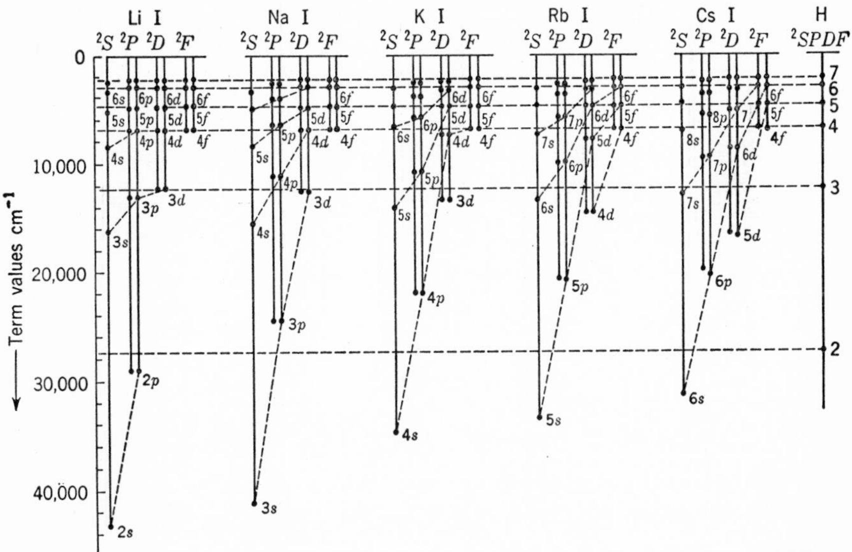

FIG. 1-7. Energy diagrams of the alkali metals, lithium, sodium, potassium, rubidium, cesium, and hydrogen. (*From White, Ref.* 17.)

X-ray levels). The optical levels are interesting because their study involves many concepts which are useful in nuclear physics. The X-ray levels are interesting because they enter into various nuclear phenomena.

The gross structure of the optical levels may be explained on the basis of the concepts introduced in our discussion of the periodic table. These levels may be viewed as the characteristic energy levels or orbitals of the valence electron in the effective central field due to the nuclear charge and the other electrons. The ground state is the lowest available orbital, the first excited state is the next orbital, etc. Since an electron in a higher orbital is effectively in a central field which approaches that given by Eq. (1-92), we may expect the energy levels to take on the characteristic spacing of the hydrogen-atom levels. In fact, if the energy values assigned to gross levels of an element on the basis of the wavelength determinations are adjusted by the addition of a constant, so that the state of single ionization is the zero energy state, then the $s, p, d, f, g, \ldots$ states for large values of n monotonically approach the nth hydrogen level. This behavior is clearly illustrated for the energy levels of the alkali metals in Fig. 1-7. While the alkali metals afford a particularly favorable case for this discussion, since they consist of a rare-gas core and a single valence electron, nevertheless this same discussion is applicable to more complicated elements.

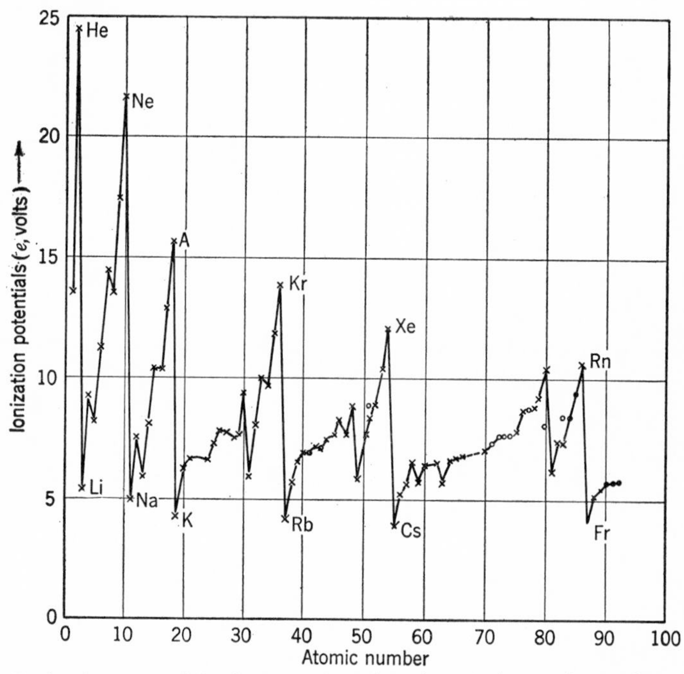

FIG. 1-8. Ionization potentials of atoms plotted against their atomic numbers. (*From Finkelnburg, Ref.* 7.)

Spectroscopists have developed empirical formulas which represent rather accurately the gross levels of various elements in terms of a principal quantum number and a secondary symbol which we today associate with the quantum number l. The fact that these formulas are successful is readily explained on the basis of quantum mechanics, since the major conclusion of the quantum-mechanical treatment based upon the independent-particle model and the central-field assumption is that the gross atomic levels are dependent upon the quantum numbers which specify the configuration. The ionization potentials of the elements are important limiting energies associated with the excited states of the outermost electron. Relative to the ground state, all of these excited states must be smaller than the ionization energy. In Fig. 1-8 we show the ionization potentials of the elements.

1-11. Fine Structure of Optical Levels. Optical spectrometers having moderate resolutions indicate quite definitely that there are far more characteristic levels associated with any atom than there are configurations. In fact, the experiments force one to the conclusion that each gross energy level in reality consists of many substates, which are generally separated by energy differences which are small compared to the differences which separate the gross energy levels.

It is a peculiar fact that the theory of fine structure has been developed to a remarkable extent, whereas calculations of the gross levels have been carried out in only a few special cases. This fact has its explanation in the large number of substates of most configurations, particularly in the presence of a magnetic field. For example, when an atom is in a very strong magnetic field, a single valence electron can be in $2(2l + 1)$ substates characterized by the various allowed values of the quantum numbers m_l and m_s. For two valence electrons the number of substates is $2(2l + 1) \times 2(2l' + 1)$. For three valence electrons the number of substates is $2(2l + 1) \times 2(2l' + 1) \times 2(2l'' + 1)$. We list below the number of substates of various configurations for systems of one, two, and three valence electrons.

One electron		Two electrons		Three electrons	
ns	2	$ns\ n's'$	4 (1)	$ns\ n's\ n''s''$	8 (2)
np	6	$ns\ n'p'$	12	$ns\ n's\ n''p''$	24 (6)
nd	10	$ns\ n'd'$	20	$ns\ n'p'\ n''p''$	72 (30)
nf	14	$np\ n'p'$	36 (15)	$ns\ n'p'\ n''d''$	120
ng	18	$np\ n'd'$	60	$np\ n'p'\ n''p''$	216 (90) (20)
		$nd\ n'd'$	100 (45)	$nd\ n'd'\ n''d''$	1000 (450) (120)

The quantities in parentheses for two-electron configurations are the number of states which are allowed by the Pauli exclusion principle when the two electrons are equivalent, *i.e.*, when they have the same values of n and l. The reader may verify these numbers by using the rules of combinations to calculate the various ways of putting two electrons in the 2, 6, 10, 14, . . . substates of an $s, p, d, f,$ . . . orbital without placing more than one in a substate. The complexity of the fine structure of atoms with a relatively large number of valence electrons is readily accounted for by the multiplicities shown in the table. Fortunately, for the elements with almost closed shells, the exclusion principle operates to bring back the relative simplicity characteristic of the level structure of elements with one or two valence electrons. Accordingly, each of the configurations s^2, p^6, d^{10}, and f^{14} has only one substate. The configurations s^1, p^5, d^9, and f^{13} have 2, 6, 10, and 14 substates, respectively. The configurations p^4, d^8, and f^{12} have 15, 45, and 91 substates, respectively.

To determine the fine structure of atomic energy levels, we must turn to the numerous small energetic effects which were ignored in the central-field approximation and consider several of the most important. For an atom with a single valence electron the most important interaction is spin-orbit interaction

$$W_{ls} = \frac{1}{2m_e^2c^2}\left(\frac{1}{r}\frac{\partial V}{\partial r}\right)\mathbf{l}\cdot\mathbf{s} \tag{1-93}$$

which was inferred from a classical model by Frankel[37] and Thomas.[38] The application of a magnetic field gives rise to the additional energy

$$W_m = (g_l\mathbf{l}\cdot\mathbf{H} + g_s\mathbf{s}\cdot\mathbf{H})\mu_B\hbar^{-1} \tag{1-94}$$

where g_l and g_s are the orbital and spin gyromagnetic ratios (or g factors) of the electron and μ_B is the Bohr magneton. According to the highly successful Dirac theory of the electron, these quantities are given by

$$g_l = 1 \tag{1-95}$$

$$g_s = 2\left(1 + \frac{\pi}{2}\frac{e^2}{\hbar c}\right) \tag{1-96}$$

and

$$\mu_B = \frac{e\hbar}{2m_ec} \tag{1-97}$$

The energy terms represented by Eqs. (1-93) and (1-94) may be attributed to orbital and spin magnetic moments of an electron, which are given by

$$\boldsymbol{\mu}_l = -g_l\mathbf{l}\mu_B\hbar^{-1} \tag{1-98}$$

and

$$\boldsymbol{\mu}_s = -g_s\mathbf{s}\mu_B\hbar^{-1} \tag{1-99}$$

The small correction to the spin g factor has only recently been pointed out by Schwinger[39] and substantiated by the experimental work of Kusch and Foley[40] and Kusch and Taub.[41]

In addition to the spin-orbit and magnetic interactions for each electron, energy terms exist, when two valence electrons are present, which are the combined effect of the residual electrostatic interaction and the phenomenon of electron exchange. The residual electrostatic interaction arises because it is not entirely possible to represent the effective electrostatic field for each electron simply as a function of the radial coordinate of that electron. Instead the field for a valence electron depends slightly upon the radial coordinate of the other electron and on the angle between the two radius vectors. If this residual effect is calculated, using methods which are consistent with certain requirements imposed by the Pauli exclusion principle, it is found that the energy has an indirect dependence upon the spin and orbital angular momonta of the two electrons. This dependence upon spin and orbital angular momenta had been noted, before the discovery of the quantum mechanics, by spectroscopists, who postulated the existence of an interaction given by

$$W_{re} = a_{ss}\mathbf{s}_1 \cdot \mathbf{s}_2 + a_{ll}\mathbf{l}_1 \cdot \mathbf{l}_2 \tag{1-100}$$

where the subscript *re* stands for residual electrostatic. That such a representation of the effect of the residual electrostatic interaction and electron exchange can be successful has been shown by Dirac(26) to be a deep-seated consequence of the equivalence of spin $\frac{1}{2}$ particles.

Using certain semiclassical methods, in which it is assumed that the energy effects given by Eqs. (1-93), (1-94), and (1-100) are associated with torques which cause the quantized angular-momentum vectors to undergo complex precessional motions, it is possible to derive simple expressions for the energy shifts of the substates of various gross levels for atoms with one or two valence electrons. The results may be expressed in terms of the quantum numbers which characterize various angular momenta and a few experimentally adjusted parameters. These expressions work rather well in many situations, agreeing with the experimental results and the results of strict quantum-mechanical methods. Their greatest usefulness, however, lies in the fact that they provide a simple basis for organizing and classifying atomic energy levels. Since these methods appear to have a similar usefulness in nuclear physics, we shall go into these methods in somewhat greater detail in Sec. 10-15.

1-12. X Rays.(42) Experiments indicate that, when the voltage applied to an X-ray tube exceeds certain critical values, which depend upon the target material, a discrete spectrum is superimposed upon the continuous spectrum. The precise wavelengths of the lines in the discrete spectrum are characteristic of the target material, although the general nature of the discrete X-ray spectrum varies quite simply from element to element. We shall consider now the explanation of the gross features of characteristic X-ray spectra.

If the incoming electrons (cathode rays) have sufficient energy to eject electrons completely from the inner shells of the target atom, the atoms will be raised to states of excitation having energy values much greater than those for optical excitation. In X-ray work it is customary to take the normal state of the atom as the zero energy state, so that all excited states correspond to positive energies. Historically, the labels $K, L, M, N, O, \ldots$ have been used to specify the characteristic X-ray levels. If an electron is removed from the K shell, the atom is said to be in a K energy state (W_K). Similarly L, M, and N states correspond to an electron missing, respectively, from the L, M, and N shells. A characteristic X-ray line is emitted when the atom jumps from a state of higher energy to a state of lower energy. The K_α, K_β, K_γ, . . . lines result from transitions in which the atom changes from the K to the L state, from the K to the M state, from the K to the N state, etc. Note that in these transitions the jumping electron goes from the L shell to the K shell, from the M shell to the K shell, and from the N shell to the K shell, respectively. One can avoid confusion in some discussions by talking about the transitions of the hole left by the missing electron, since the hole or vacancy characterizes the state of the atom. Thus, should a cathode ray eject an electron from the K shell of a target atom, thereby creating a hole, this hole can jump to the L shell with the emission of the K_α line. The hole in the L shell could then jump to the M shell, emitting an L_α line, etc., until finally the hole reaches the valence shell of the atom. It then jumps to infinity, a step which corresponds to the capture of a free electron. This electron proceeds by radiation through the optical levels to the ground state of the valence electron. However, X-ray spectroscopists are not concerned with the spectra accompanying these latter transitions, since their wavelengths are too long to be detected by X-ray techniques. The X-ray spectroscopist is primarily interested in the first few radiative transitions started when an electron is ejected from an inner shell of the atom. Since the interior conditions do not vary much from element to element, X-ray spectroscopy is a simpler subject than optical spectroscopy.

A highly desirable feature of X-ray work is the fact that there are two simple and precise methods for directly observing the energy levels. The critical voltage necessary to excite the discrete X-ray spectrum gives directly the energy of the states ($V_K e = W_K$, etc.). The critical wavelengths of the absorption coefficient for X rays also give directly the energy levels of the absorbing material. The values of the critical absorption wavelengths may be obtained by plotting the absorption coefficient of a substance as a function of X-ray wavelength, using the radiation selected from a continuous spectrum by means of an X-ray spectrometer. The sharp breaks in the curve occur at

$$\lambda_K = \frac{hc}{W_K} \qquad \lambda_{L_1} = \frac{hc}{W_{L_1}} \qquad \text{etc.} \tag{1-101}$$

For wavelengths longer than these critical values the incoming photons do not have sufficient energy to eject the electrons from the corresponding state.

The gross X-ray energy values can be explained quite simply by accepting the following correlation between the X-ray levels and the quantum numbers n and l:

Notation	K	L	M	N	O
n	1	2	3	4	5
Substates	s^{-1}	s^{-1},p^{-1}	s^{-1},p^{-1},d^{-1}	$s^{-1},p^{-1},d^{-1},f^{-1}$	$s^{-1},p^{-1},d^{-1},f^{-1},g^{-1}$
Multiplicity	1	3	5	7	9

We have indicated the orbitals by a negative exponent to denote the location of the hole. Also shown are the multiplicities of the states.

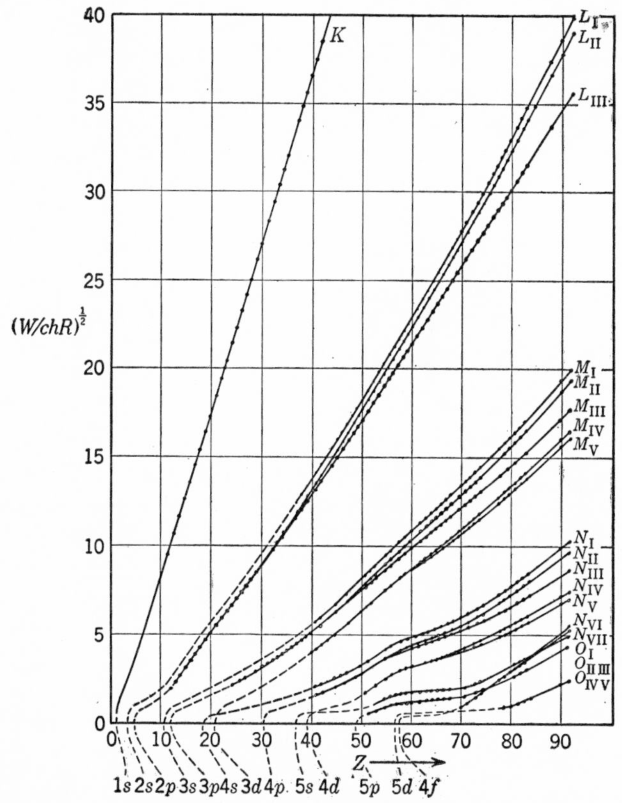

FIG. 1-9. Moseley-Sommerfeld diagram of X-ray energy levels. The ordinates give $(W/chR)^{\frac{1}{2}}$, and the abscissas the atomic number. (*From White, Ref.* 17.)

These are detected when the absorption limits of a heavy element are examined with high-resolution instruments. The observed multiplicities may readily be accounted for if we assume that all orbitals except *s* states are doublets. This doubling of states is a consequence of the spin-orbit interaction of the interior electrons.

The full experimental sweep of X-ray terms is revealed on a Moseley-Sommerfeld diagram (see Fig. 1-9), which represents the square root of the ratio of the X-ray energy term to the Rydberg constant as a function of the atomic number. The diagram bears a simple relation to Fig. 1-6 which was used to account for the periodic table. The fact that the lighter elements do not have as many X-ray terms as do the heavier elements follows from the truism that, if there are fewer electrons to start with, there are fewer ways of having one electron missing. Examining this diagram, we note that, as the subshells fill up and recede into the interior, the orbitals associated with a given n are drawn together until they do not overlap the orbitals associated with an adjacent n. Thus, in a heavy element such as uranium, the 60 interior electrons are grouped into four major shells (*i.e.*, the K, L, M, and N shells, or the $n = 1, 2, 3$, and 4 shells), and there is no overlapping in the energy levels associated with the removal of one electron from different major shells. We shall make use of the X-ray concepts discussed above in connection with such nuclear phenomena as K capture and internal conversion.

PROBLEMS

1-1. (*a*) What is the energy of an electron at rest?

(*b*) What is the total energy of an electron moving at three-fifths the velocity of light?

(*c*) What is the kinetic energy of an electron moving at three-fifths the velocity of light?

(*d*) What is the momentum of an electron moving at three-fifths the velocity of light?

(*e*) What voltage will accelerate an electron to this velocity?

1-2. (*a*) Verify Eq. (1-6) by integrating to find the work done in bringing a particle from rest to the velocity v.

(*b*) Verify Eqs. (1-9) to (1-12) by algebra.

1-3. (*a*) What are the momenta acquired by an electron, a proton, and a singly ionized silver atom which have been accelerated through 1 million volts?

(*b*) What are the radii of curvature if these particles move in a magnetic field of 10,000 oersteds perpendicular to their path?

***1-4.** Find the relativistic equation of motion of an electron in a uniform electric field when the initial velocity is perpendicular to the direction of the uniform field. What are the equations of the trajectory in the nonrelativistic and relativistic cases?

***1-5.** What are the perpendicular deflections if a 1-Mev electron, a 1-Mev proton, and a 1-Mev singly ionized silver atom are passed between two plates parallel to the initial direction of motion which are 1 cm apart, 10 cm long, and maintained at a difference of potential of 10,000 volts?

1-6. What are the de Broglie wavelengths of an electron, a proton, and a singly ionized silver atom accelerated through 1 Mev?

1-7. (*a*) What is the wavelength of the shortest possible X ray emitted if a 1-Mev electron is stopped suddenly by a target atom?

(*b*) What is the momentum possessed by such an X-ray photon?

1-8. If a 1-Mev photon strikes an electron at rest and rebounds directly backward, what is the velocity imparted to the electron? (Use conservation of energy and momentum.) What are the kinetic energies of the electron and product photon (in Mev)?

1-9. Assume a model of the atom (nucleus) in which the valence electron (proton) is confined to a cubic box with sides 10^{-8} cm (10^{-12} cm). What are the 10 lowest energy levels in ev (Mev) of this system relative to the (1,1,1) ground state?

1-10. The critical absorption wavelengths for the K and L levels of tungsten are 0.1784 A and 1.025, 1.075, and 1.216 A. What are the characteristic X-ray energy levels of tungsten in ev?

1-11. An atom with a missing K electron may decay by a double process in which one L electron jumps to the K shell and a second L electron is ejected from the atom. For the case of tungsten, what approximately is the kinetic energy of the electron (the Auger electron) ejected in this process?

1-12. What quantum numbers can characterize $\mathbf{j} = \mathbf{l} + \mathbf{s}$ when $l = 0$, $s = \frac{1}{2}$? $l = 1$, $s = \frac{1}{2}$? $l = 2$, $s = \frac{1}{2}$? What values can m_j take on in each of these cases?

1-13. What possible quantum numbers can characterize $\mathbf{S} = \mathbf{s}_1 + \mathbf{s}_2 + \cdots + \mathbf{s}_n$, where all $s = \frac{1}{2}$, when $n = 2$? $n = 3$? $n = 14$? $n = 21$?

1-14. What and how many quantum numbers can characterize $\mathbf{F} = \mathbf{I} + \mathbf{J}$ when $I = \frac{3}{2}$, $J = 1$? $I = \frac{3}{2}$, $J = 2$?

REFERENCES

1. Lorentz, H., A. Einstein, H. Minkowski, and H. Weyl: "The Principle of Relativity," Dodd, Mead & Company, Inc., New York, 1923.
2. Bergman, P.: "Introduction to the Theory of Relativity," Prentice-Hall, Inc., New York, 1942.
3. Einstein, A.: "The Meaning of Relativity," Princeton University Press, Princeton, N.J., 1950.
4. Richtmyer, F. K., and E. H. Kennard: "Introduction to Modern Physics," 4th ed., McGraw-Hill Book Company, Inc., New York, 1947.
5. A. Sommerfield: "Atomic Structure and Spectral Lines," Methuen & Co., Ltd., London, 1923.
6. Harnwell, G. P., and J. J. Livingood: "Experimental Atomic Physics," McGraw-Hill Book Company, Inc., New York, 1933.
7. Finkelnburg, W.: "Atomic Physics," McGraw-Hill Book Company, Inc., New York, 1950.
8. Semat, H.: "Introduction to Atomic Physics," Rinehart & Company, Inc., New York, 1946.
9. Rutherford, E.: *Phil. Mag.*, **21**, 669 (1911).
10. Barkla, C. G.: *Phil. Mag.*, **21**, 648 (1911).
11. Moseley, H. G.: *Phil. Mag.*, **26**, 1024 (1913).
12. Planck, M.: *Ann. Physik*, **4**, 553 (1901).
13. Einstein, A.: *Ann. Physik*, **17**, 132 (1905).
14. Compton, A. H.: *Phys. Rev.*, **21**, 715 (1923).
15. Bohr, N.: *Phil. Mag.*, **26**, 1 (1913).
16. De Broglie, L.: *Phil. Mag.*, **47**, 446 (1924).
17. White, E. H.: "Introduction to Atomic Spectra," McGraw-Hill Book Company, Inc., New York, 1934.
18. Pauling, L., and E. B. Wilson, Jr.: "Introduction to Quantum Mechanics," McGraw-Hill Book Company, Inc., New York, 1935.
19. Rojansky, V.: "Introductory Quantum Mechanics," Prentice-Hall, Inc., New York, 1938.
20. Houston, W. V.: "Principles of Quantum Mechanics," McGraw-Hill Book Company, Inc., New York, 1951.
21. Schiff, L. I.: "Quantum Mechanics," McGraw-Hill Book Company, Inc., New York, 1949.

22. Lande, A.: "Quantum Mechanics," Pitman Publishing Corporation, New York, 1951.
23. Bohm, D.: "Quantum Theory," Prentice-Hall, Inc., New York, 1951.
24. Schroedinger, E.: *Ann. Physik*, **79**, 361 (1926).
25. Heisenberg, W.: *Z. Physik*, **33**, 879 (1925).
26. Dirac, P. A. M.: "The Principles of Quantum Mechanics," 3d ed., Oxford University Press, New York, 1947.
27. Pauli, W.: *Z. Physik*, **43**, 601 (1927).
28. Born, M., and P. Jordan: "Elementare Quantenmechanik," Springer-Verlag OHG, Berlin, 1930.
29. Weyl, H.: "Gruppentheorie und Quantenmechanik," S. Hirzel Verlag, Leipzig, 1928.
30. Wigner, E.: "Gruppentheorie und Quantenmechanik," Vieweg-Verlag, Brunswick, Germany, 1931.
31. Uhlenbeck, G. E., and S. A. Goudsmit: *Naturwiss.*, **13**, 953 (1925).
32. Pauli, W.: *Z. Physik*, **31**, 765 (1925).
33. Herzberg, G.: "Atomic Spectra and Atomic Structure," Prentice-Hall, Inc., New York, 1937.
34. Pauling, L., and S. A. Goudsmit: "The Structure of Line Spectra," McGraw-Hill Book Company, Inc., New York, 1930.
35. Bacher, R. F., and S. A. Goudsmit: "Atomic Energy States," McGraw-Hill Book Company, Inc., New York, 1932.
36. Condon, E. U., and G. H. Shortley: "The Theory of Atomic Spectra," Cambridge University Press, New York, 1935.
37. Frankel, J.: *Z. Physik*, **37**, 243 (1936).
38. Thomas, L. H.: *Nature*, **107**, 514 (1926).
39. Schwinger, J.: *Phys. Rev.*, **73**, 416 (1948).
40. Kusch, P., and H. M. Foley: *Phys. Rev.*, **74**, 250 (1948).
41. Kusch, P., and H. Taub: *Phys. Rev.*, **75**, 1477 (1949).
42. Compton, A. H., and S. K. Allison: "X Rays in Theory and Experiment," D. Van Nostrand Company, Inc., New York, 1935.

CHAPTER 2

STATIC PROPERTIES OF NUCLEI

The nuclei of atoms may be characterized by certain static properties which influence in various ways the behavior of atoms and molecules. Since the subjects of atomic and molecular physics are quite highly developed and since nuclear influences upon the behavior and characteristics of atoms and molecules are well understood, we may use certain observations within the fields of atomic and molecular physics to determine these static nuclear properties. This chapter will be devoted primarily to nuclear effects in atomic and molecular physics and to the conclusions regarding static nuclear properties drawn from studies of these effects.

2-1. Charge and Mass. The early work in atomic physics of Rutherford, Barkla, Moseley, Chadwick, and others conclusively established the fact that the order number Z of an element in the periodic table is identical with the number of outer electrons of an atom of that element and also identical with the number of positive basic units of charge on its nucleus. Accordingly, the charge of the nucleus may be regarded as the fundamental attribute which characterizes an element in atomic physics. Obviously, therefore, the chemical and physical properties of an element lead to the determination of the charge or charge number of the nucleus of that element.

The mass of the nucleus influences the chemical properties of atoms much less than the charge does. However, the atomic weight of an element is mainly determined by the mass or masses of the nuclei of that element. The fact that atoms of a single element may have different masses was first discovered by Soddy[1] in 1910. His investigations showed that the forms of lead associated with uranium, thorium, and actinium ores differ in atomic mass. The existence of forms of an element which differ in atomic mass (called isotopes) was confirmed by J. J. Thomson,[2] who, using an early form of mass spectroscope (see Chap. 4), showed that natural neon consists of two isotopic forms, with masses approximately 20 and 22. We shall base all our discussions of atomic mass upon the physicist's standard, the mass unit (MU), which is defined by:

One MU is equal to one-sixteenth of the mass of an atom of the most abundant stable isotope of oxygen. Alternatively we may accept

$$1 \text{ MU} = \frac{1}{N_A} \text{ g} \tag{2-1}$$

where N_A is the physical Avogadro's number.

Chemical atomic weights refer to the average weight of the natural isotopic mixture of atoms relative to the average weight of the natural mixture of oxygen atoms. To relate the chemical atomic weights to the physical isotopic weights, we use

$$M_c = \frac{16{,}000{,}000}{16{,}004{,}482} \sum_i M_i X_i \tag{2-2}$$

where X_i is the fractional part present of the ith isotope and M_i is the atomic mass of this isotope on the physical scale.

Using a great variety of experimental techniques, nuclear scientists have found or produced approximately 1100 species of atoms. Direct mass determinations and indirect mass estimates indicate that, relative to the physical standard, all of these species of atoms have almost integral masses. Since we know today of the existence of 100 elements, clearly we must, in addition to giving the atomic number or chemical symbol, further label or specify the isotopes which make up an element in order to characterize a particular species of atoms completely. It is customary to use the integer nearest to the actual atomic mass, an integer which is called the mass number and is universally designated by the symbol A. For example, the most abundant stable isotope of oxygen is represented by O-16 or O^{16} or $_8O^{16}$, where in the last form the left subscript is the atomic number. We shall henceforth use the word "nuclide"[3] to denote an atomic species which is characterized both by its atomic number Z and the mass number A.

The earliest observations of the almost integral nature of the atomic masses when measured by physical methods came at a time when the Rutherford electron-nucleus model of the atom had just been strongly established. It was already known that the electrons represent only a minute part (~ 0.03 per cent) of the mass of an atom. Consequently the integral nature of atomic masses could be interpreted to mean that the nucleus itself is made of basic building blocks each having a mass of approximately 1 Mu. It was then natural to assume that the integral charge is contributed by Z protons, each of which weighs approximately 1 Mu. To account for the difference between the mass number A and the charge number Z, it was first assumed that the nucleus contains $A - Z$ extra protons, whose charge is canceled by $A - Z$ nuclear electrons. This proton-electron model, however, is inconsistent with certain experimental results in atomic hyperfine structure and in molecular spectra. We shall return to the question of a nuclear model after we have discussed the other static properties of nuclei.

2-2. Nuclear Size. If the nuclear charge Ze were located within an infinitesimal region, it would give rise everywhere to the electrostatic coulomb potential

$$\phi = \frac{Ze}{r} \tag{2-3}$$

where r is the distance from this point. Quantum theory enables us to predict the probability distribution of electrons for allowed states of an atom held together by such a field. The distributions corresponding to penetrating orbitals (s and p states) have appreciable values in the neighborhood of the nucleus. These distributions and the corresponding atomic energies are, therefore, affected by departures from the coulomb field due to the finite extension of the nucleus. We might expect that the electron probability density near the center of the atom with a finite-sized nucleus would be less than that which would exist if the nucleus were simply a point. Indirect evidence[4,5] does reveal this effect and suggests that to a good approximation the nucleus must be regarded as a sphere with a finite radius.

The radius of a nucleus may be defined in various ways depending upon the experimental arrangement used for its determination. The usual definition is taken as the distance at which the electrostatic field of the nucleus departs appreciably from the coulomb expression for a point charge. The earliest estimates of this nuclear radius were made by Rutherford in his famous scattering experiments which established the electron-nucleus model of the atom. In these experiments Rutherford observed deviations from the distribution of scattered alpha particles which was predicted on the basis of a pure coulomb interaction. These deviations could be attributed to the finite extension of the nucleus. Careful scattering experiments of this nature have indicated that an approximate relationship exists between the nuclear radius and the mass number A which is given by

$$R = bA^{\frac{1}{3}} + b_0 \tag{2-4}$$

where b and b_0 are natural lengths which are conveniently expressed in units of 10^{-13} cm.

Recently a careful set of experiments[18] in which 22-Mev protons were scattered from various substances clearly revealed the finite size of the nucleus by the minima and maxima which were observed in the angular distributions of the scattered particles. These variations may be interpreted as diffraction patterns of the proton waves which are scattered by a sphere with sharp boundaries. The positions of these maxima and minima for various substances indicate that nuclear radii are given by Eq. (2-4) with $b_0 = 0$. Experiments have also been performed recently[19–21] with 15- to 150-Mev electrons, and these also clearly show departures from point-charge scattering. The absence of diffraction minima and maxima in the case of electron scattering has led to the suggestion[22] that the nuclear boundaries are not sharp, but that root-mean-square radii satisfy Eq. (2-4) with $b_0 = 0$. The extent of the "tailing off" necessary to account for the observations of electron scattering is still unclear.

The recent development[23] of the X-ray spectroscopy of μ^--mesonic atoms has also provided excellent information about the finite extension of the nucleus. A μ^--mesonic atom consists of an ordinary atom which has captured a μ^- meson. This transitory particle behaves in many respects like an ordinary electron with the exception that its mass is about 207 times as great. Consequently the stationary-state distributions of a μ^--mesonic atom on the average are concentrated about 207 times closer to the nucleus than the equivalent electron distributions. In consequence μ^--mesonic charge distributions are more sensitive to departures of the nuclear charge distribution from a point than are the corresponding electronic distributions. Rather precise measurements have been made of the $2p \rightarrow 1s$ μ^--mesonic transition energies for a number of elements. An analysis of these measurements yields nuclear radii in approximate conformity with Eq. (2-4) with $b_0 = 0$ and $b = 1.2$.

The energy associated with interactions between protons in nuclei is obviously sensitive to the radius of the charge distribution. This coulomb energy, which constitutes a calculable portion of the nuclear mass, has been analyzed recently,[24] and on the basis of these analyses the radius constants $b = 1.22$ and $b_0 = 0$ have been assigned.

The determinations of nuclear radii discussed above are all based upon experiments which cause no alterations in the nuclear structure. In addition, a linear relationship between R and $A^{\frac{1}{3}}$ is confirmed in a variety of experimental and theoretical studies in which changes in nuclear structure occur. We shall discuss the details of these studies in later chapters. However, we might indicate that these studies have led to estimates of b ranging from 1.3 to 1.7, with b_0 values ranging from 0 to 1.3. The discrepancies between various estimates of the radius constant have not yet been resolved. For most discussions, unless we specify otherwise, we shall follow the older convention and let

$$b = 1.5 \times 10^{-13} \text{ cm} \qquad \text{and} \qquad b_0 = 0 \tag{2-5}$$

Accordingly, the volume of a spherical nucleus is estimated to be

$$V = \tfrac{4}{3}\pi b^3 A \tag{2-6}$$

Since the mass of a nucleus is approximately A/N_A, the density of nuclear matter is approximately a constant given by

$$\rho = \frac{M}{V} = \frac{3}{4\pi b^3 N_A} \approx 10^{14} \text{ g/cm}^3 \tag{2-7}$$

The density of water is also a constant (1 g/cm³); hence these simple calculations suggest that the nucleus has the properties of an exceedingly dense, incompressible fluid.

2-3. Mechanical and Magnetic Moments of Nuclei. A great variety and abundance of experimental evidence clearly shows that many nuclei possess a mechanical moment (*i.e.*, spin angular momentum), a magnetic dipole moment, and an electrostatic quadrupole moment. In more familiar terms, we may say that many nuclei reveal the characteristics of a spinning top, a magnet, and a charged distorted sphere.

The general types of phenomena which have indicated these characteristics of nuclei are (1) hyperfine structure and the magnetic splitting of hyperfine structure in atomic spectra, (2) the band spectra of homonuclear molecules, (3) magnetic deflection and resonance with atomic and molecular beams, (4) resonance and relaxation effects in nuclear paramagnetism, and (5) hyperfine structure in microwave spectroscopy. In addition the investigation of certain properties of special substances such as hydrogen and deuterium has revealed the presence of these nuclear moments.

The effects upon atomic energy levels of these moments were first revealed in the study of atomic spectral lines using interferometers and spectrometers with very high resolution. The small spectral splittings which are identified with effects arising from interactions of electrons with the nucleus are referred to as hyperfine structure, in contrast with the splittings associated with electron-electron interactions, which are known as fine structure. The hyperfine structure of atomic levels can be largely accounted for if we assume that certain nuclei possess an intrinsic angular momentum or mechanical moment **I** which conforms to the quantization rules given in Chap. 1. This intrinsic angular momentum is usually referred to as the nuclear spin. We must also assume that nuclei effectively possess a magnetic dipole moment which is given by

$$\boldsymbol{\mu}_I = g_I \mu_N \mathbf{I} \hbar^{-1} \tag{2-8}$$

where μ_N is a natural unit of magnetic moment and g_I is known as the gyromagnetic ratio, or g factor. In nuclear physics we take the nuclear magneton as the basic unit, a unit which is defined by

$$\mu_N = \frac{e\hbar}{2m_p c} \tag{2-9}$$

where m_p is the mass of the proton. Based on this standard, the observed g's of nuclei run of the order of unity and are both positive and negative. In the presence of a magnetic field $\mathbf{H}$, the nucleus possesses a magnetic energy

$$W_m = -\boldsymbol{\mu}_I \cdot \mathbf{H} = -\mu_I H \cos\theta \tag{2-10}$$

where θ is the angle between $\boldsymbol{\mu}_I$ and $\mathbf{H}$. To justify this expression, we note that, since work is required to change the orientation of a magnetic dipole in a magnetic field, we may identify a magnetic potential energy with such a system. From elementary magnetostatics the magnitude of the torque $\mathfrak{T}$ (see Fig. 2-1) exerted by the field on a magnet with pole strength p and length d is

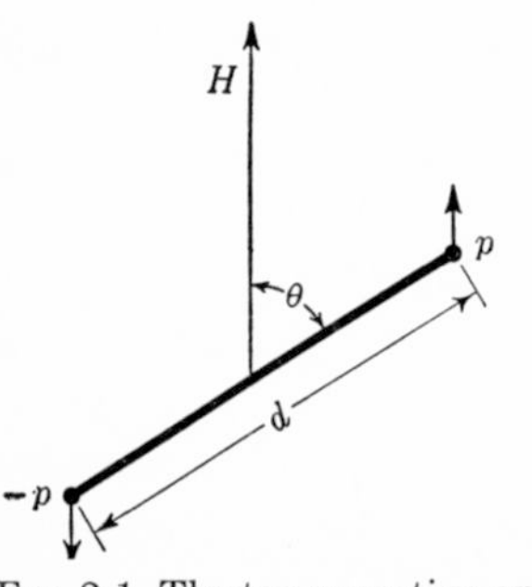

FIG. 2-1. The torque acting on a magnet in a magnetic field.

$$\mathfrak{T} = pdH \sin\theta = \mu H \sin\theta \tag{2-11}$$

where $\mu = pd$. The external work done against the field in changing the orientation of a magnet from θ_i to θ_f therefore is

$$W_m = \int_{\theta_i}^{\theta_f} \mu H \sin\theta \, d\theta = -\mu H \cos\theta \Big|_{\theta_i}^{\theta_f} \tag{2-12}$$

If we chose $\theta_i = \pi/2$, $\theta_f = \theta$, we find Eq. (2-10) for the potential energy which a magnet possesses by virtue of its orientation with respect to a magnetic field. In transitions, only differences are observable; consequently the choice of the zero-energy orientation is immaterial.

2-4. Hyperfine Structure of Atomic Levels. The magnetic fields which act upon the nuclei of atoms may be divided into (1) the field due to the spin and orbital motion of the atomic electrons and (2) the external magnetic field. For a single electron which is not in an s state (that is, $l \neq 0$), the magnetic field at the nucleus is given by

$$\mathbf{H} = -\left\{\frac{2\mathbf{l}}{r^3} + g_s\left[\frac{\mathbf{s}}{r^3} - \frac{3(\mathbf{r}\cdot\mathbf{s})\mathbf{r}}{r^5}\right]\right\}\frac{\mu_B}{\hbar} \tag{2-13}$$

Inserting $g_s = 2$, the interaction energy of a single valence electron with the nucleus becomes

$$W_m = \frac{2g_I\mu_N\mu_B}{r^3\hbar^2}\left[\mathbf{l}\cdot\mathbf{I} + \mathbf{s}\cdot\mathbf{I} - \frac{3(\mathbf{r}\cdot\mathbf{s})(\mathbf{r}\cdot\mathbf{I})}{r^2}\right] \tag{2-14}$$

The first term in this expression is just the counterpart of the classical interaction of a magnetic dipole with a current loop. The remainder is the counterpart of the interaction between two magnetic dipoles.

It can be shown, either by semiclassical methods[6,7] or by strict quantum-mechanical methods,[8] that the atomic energy shift arising from the magnetic interaction of the nucleus with the valence electron of an atom having a single valence electron is given by

$$\Delta W_m = Cg_I[F(F+1) - I(I+1) - J(J+1)] \qquad (2\text{-}15)$$

where

$$C = 2\mu_N\mu_B \left\langle \frac{1}{r^3} \right\rangle \frac{l(l+1)}{j(j+1)} \qquad (2\text{-}16)$$

$$\mathbf{J} = \mathbf{j} = \mathbf{l} + \mathbf{s} \qquad (2\text{-}17)$$

$$\mathbf{F} = \mathbf{J} + \mathbf{I} \qquad (2\text{-}18)$$

We use the symbol $\langle\ \rangle$ to denote the average value computed with respect to the probability distribution function for the electron. The vector angular momentum **F**, which is the sum of the total electronic angular momentum **J** (the total angular momenta for the electrons in closed orbits cancel out) and the nuclear angular momentum **I**, may be called the grand-total angular momentum of the atom. Now, for a given atom, I is a characteristic constant of the nucleus. The quantum numbers l and j are fixed for a given atomic energy state. Consequently, according to the quantization rule, F can take on $2I + 1$ or $2J + 1$ values given by

$$F \doteq I + J, I + J - 1, \ldots, |I - J| \qquad (2\text{-}19)$$

Therefore according to Eq. (2-19) a given level splits into $2I + 1$ sublevels if $I < J$ or into $2J + 1$ levels if $I > J$. The maximum multiplicity of all the hyperfine levels associated with a one valence atom is $2I + 1$, and consequently this maximum multiplicity gives I.

It can be shown by rather simple semiclassical considerations that Eq. (2-15) is valid even for atoms with two or more valence electrons, although the expression for C is then more complicated. Accordingly, the hyperfine multiplicity of atomic energy levels, which may be inferred from observations of the hyperfine structure of spectral lines, gives us precisely the quantum number I which characterizes the angular momentum of the nucleus.

If it were possible to evaluate the constant C for a given (l,j) state from theoretical considerations, the experimentally observed splittings might then be used to determine the value of g_I, the nuclear gyromagnetic ratio. The earliest known gyromagnetic ratios were obtained in this way. These gyromagnetic ratios, however, are not very reliable because the splittings are quite small and difficult to measure. Further, the quantum-mechanical calculation of the constant C is very difficult, and certain theoretical difficulties arise because of the r^{-3} singularity in Eq. (2-16). Fortunately there are other approaches to the determination of g_I which give results with great precision. These approaches are based primarily upon the measurement of the Larmor precession of nuclei, which we shall now discuss.

2-5. The Larmor Precession.[25] If an external magnetic field is applied, an additional energy term arises, of the type given by Eq. (2-10), which splits a hyperfine multiplet into many components. The dependence of this splitting upon the magnetic field is quite similar to the corresponding dependence in ordinary fine structure, *i.e.*, in the Zeeman and Paschen-Back effects. Let us here consider only the extreme case when the external magnetic field at the nucleus completely overwhelms the magnetic field due to the atomic electrons. This case is particularly feasible when the atoms are combined into molecules so that the net magnetic field at the nucleus due to electronic spin and orbital motion is small. Assuming, therefore, that **I** moves independently of the electronic angular momenta and accepting the direction of the magnetic field as the z axis, we obtain from the rule for the z components of angular-momentum vectors

$$W_m = -\boldsymbol{\mu}_I \cdot \mathbf{H} = -g_I \mu_N M_I H \tag{2-20}$$

where

$$M_I \doteq I, I - 1, \ldots, -I \tag{2-21}$$

Thus the quantization of the z component of angular momentum causes quantization of the magnetic energy. According to Eqs. (2-20) and (2-21) the minimum magnetic energy of a nuclear dipole is

$$W_{m,0} = -g_I I \mu_N H \tag{2-22}$$

where the subscript zero indicates the minimum value. If we compare this with the minimum energy of a classical dipole (denoting classical by the subscript c),

$$W_{m,0,c} = -\mu H \tag{2-23}$$

which occurs when the field and the moment are parallel, we may justify the colloquial identification

$$\mu = g_I I \tag{2-24}$$

as the "magnetic moment" of the nucleus in units of the nuclear magneton.

In a transition between adjacent states of a magnetic multiplet, that is, $M_f = M_i \pm 1$, the frequency emitted or absorbed is

$$\nu = \left| \frac{W_m(M_i \pm 1) - W_m(M_i)}{h} \right| = \frac{g_I \mu_N H}{h} = g_I \frac{e}{4\pi m_p c} H \tag{2-25}$$

This frequency, known as the Larmor frequency, may also be derived from certain simple classical considerations.

Let us consider from the classical point of view the effect of a homogeneous magnetic field on a magnetized gyroscope with the mechanical moment **I** and the magnetic moment $\boldsymbol{\mu}_I$. Since the field exerts a torque

$$\mathfrak{T} = \boldsymbol{\mu}_I \times \mathbf{H} = g_I \mu_N \hbar^{-1}(\mathbf{I} \times \mathbf{H}) \tag{2-26}$$

I will change to satisfy

$$\frac{d\mathbf{I}}{dt} = \frac{g_I \mu_N (\mathbf{I} \times \mathbf{H})}{\hbar} \tag{2-27}$$

In terms of magnitudes alone this becomes

$$\left| \frac{d\mathbf{I}}{dt} \right| = \frac{g_I \mu_N I H \sin \theta}{\hbar} \tag{2-28}$$

It is well known from the theory of gyroscopes that a vector with fixed magnitude which obeys a differential equation of this type undergoes a precessional motion in which the plane formed by the gyroscopic axis and the magnetic-field vector "chases" the torque. In Fig. 2-2 we show the change in **I** and the corresponding change in the azimuthal angle φ in a time interval Δt. From this figure and Eq. (2-28) it is apparent that the classical precession frequency is

$$\nu_L = \frac{1}{2\pi}\frac{d\varphi}{dt} = \frac{1}{I(2\pi \sin \theta)}\left|\frac{d\mathbf{I}}{dt}\right| = g_I \frac{e}{4\pi m_p c} H \tag{2-29}$$

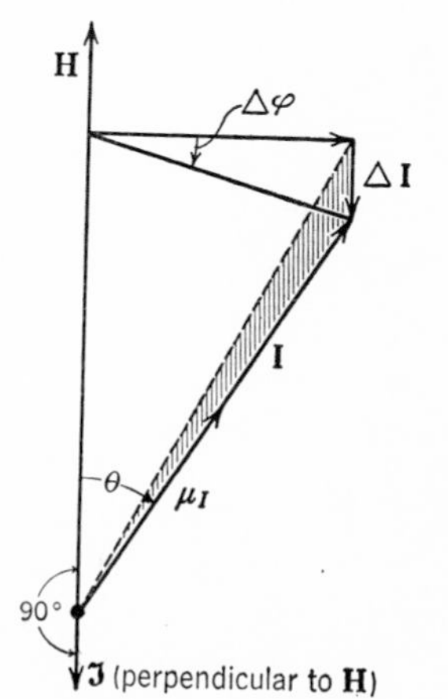

FIG. 2-2. The classical precession of a magnetized gyroscope under the influence of a magnetic field. The angular-momentum vector **I** precesses about the field **H** in such a way as to chase the torque $\boldsymbol{\mu}_I \times \mathbf{H}$.

which is just the Larmor frequency derived above. When the magnetic moment is in the same direction as the mechanical moment (that is, when g_I is positive), the vector representing the precessional frequency (using the right-hand rule) is opposite to the direction of the magnetic field.

For readily attainable magnetic fields ($H \sim 1000$ gauss) and typical nuclei ($g_I \sim 1$) the Larmor frequency is of the order of 10^6 cycles/sec, which is in the short radio-wave region of the electromagnetic spectrum.

2-6. Nuclear Effects in Molecular Spectroscopy.[9] The observations of molecular spectra may be interpreted using the Bohr combination law [Eq. (1-44)] if consideration is given to the energy levels of molecules. These energy levels may generally be subdivided into three categories, the electronic levels, the vibrational levels, and the rotational levels. The electronic levels are separated by gross energy differences corresponding to optical or ultraviolet frequencies. These levels are characterized by differences in coordinates of the valence electrons or the quantum numbers which fix these degrees of freedom. The vibrational levels, for a given electronic configuration, are usually separated by energy differences corresponding to infrared wavelengths. The vibrational levels are characterized by a quantum number v and depend primarily upon the degree of freedom associated with the relative separation of nuclei. The rotational energy levels usually are sublevels of the vibrational levels and are separated by energy differences corresponding to long infrared rays or ultra-high-frequency radio waves. These levels depend upon a quantum number l which characterizes the rotational angular momentum of the molecule.

The general subject of molecular spectroscopy including fine structure is fully as complicated as the study of atomic spectroscopy. In the brief discussion here, which is devoted primarily to nuclear effects, we shall consider only the levels which correspond to the substates of the ground electronic state of diatomic molecules.

Using quantum-mechanical considerations, it can be shown that the energies of the low-lying vibrational states of the ground electronic state are given approximately by

$$W_v = (v + \tfrac{1}{2}) \frac{h}{2\pi} \left(\frac{k}{m_r}\right)^{\frac{1}{2}} \tag{2-30}$$

where k is a characteristic constant associated with vibrational states and m_r is the reduced mass of the system. Recalling the classical formula $\nu_c = (2\pi)^{-1}(k/m_r)^{\frac{1}{2}}$, we see that the first term of (2-30), apart from the constant $\frac{1}{2}$, is the same expression assumed by Planck in his treatment of the harmonic oscillators associated with the radiation field [Eq. (1-33)].

For a given vibrational state the various rotational states possess energies given by the approximate formula

$$W_l = \frac{\hbar^2}{2m_r r_v^2} l(l + 1) \tag{2-31}$$

where r_v is a characteristic constant for the vibrational state. This term may be interpreted simply as the counterpart of the classical kinetic energy $|\mathbf{l}|^2/2\mathcal{I}$ of a rigid rotator having the moment of inertia $\mathcal{I} = m_r r_v^2$. The direct influence of the reduced mass upon the vibrational and rotational levels indicates that two molecules which differ only in that an atom in one is an isotope of the corresponding atom in the second (*e.g.*, HCl and DCl) will have appreciably different vibrational and rotational energy levels and spectra. Thus the precise measurement of these frequencies gives information relating to the mass differences.

The molecular spectra of homonuclear (*i.e.*, having identical nuclei) diatomic molecules have been an important source of information concerning nuclear spins. Historically this source of information has played an important role in the establishment of the proton-neutron model of the nucleus as well as in the general clarification of the theoretical relationship between spin and statistical weight. The theory indicates that the relative intensities of adjacent lines in the rotational spectra of homonuclear diatomic molecules with nuclear spin I are as $I/(I + 1)$. Examples of these ratios are:

I	0	$\frac{1}{2}$	1	$\frac{3}{2}$	2	$\frac{5}{2}$
$I/(I + 1)$	0	1/3	1/2	3/5	2/3	5/7

Accordingly, when I is not large, only moderate accuracy in the intensity measurements is needed to assign an I value uniquely. In Fig. 2-3 we

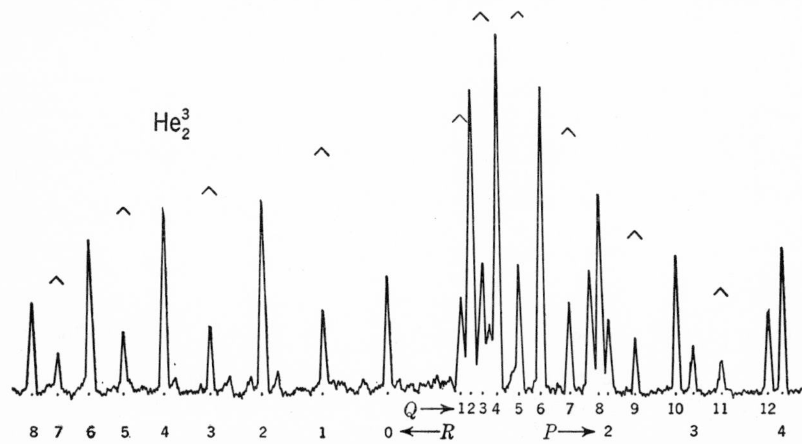

Fig. 2-3. Photoelectric trace of the He_2^3 band at 4650 A. The carets represent the length of the weak lines multiplied by 3. This proves the nuclear spin of He^3 to be $\frac{1}{2}$. (*From Dieke and Robinson, Ref.* 10.)

show a photoelectric trace of the He_2^3 band at 4650 A which clearly reveals the expected alternation in intensities corresponding to the ratio of 1/3, thus indicating that the nuclear spin of He^3 is $\frac{1}{2}$. The intensities can be corrected for the slow variation which is dependent upon the temperature of the absorber in a manner which is well understood.[9]

Another important nuclear parameter which is revealed in the molecular spectra of certain molecules is the nuclear quadrupole moment. The existence of nuclear quadrupole moments was first detected in studies of hyperfine structure in atomic spectra. However, an investigation[(11)] of the molecular spectrum of ammonia in the microwave region disclosed an easily measured effect due to the interaction of the nuclear quadrupole moment with the electrostatic field of the molecule. The quadrupole-moment concept does not arise in physical phenomena as often as the dipole concept. For this reason we shall give a simple classical discussion of the meaning of the electric quadrupole moment and its significance in regard to the shape of the nucleus. Certain modifications are necessary in the definition of quadrupole moments when quantum-mechanical concepts are used; however, for our purposes here, these modifications may be ignored.

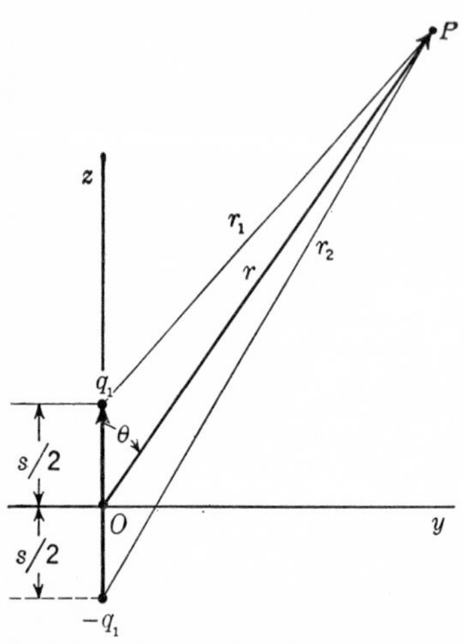

FIG. 2-4. An electric dipole and an electric pole.

2-7. Quadrupole Moments of Nuclei. Let us consider first the interaction energy between an electric pole and an electric dipole when the two entities are separated by a distance which is large compared to the dimensions of either (see Fig. 2-4). For convenience we shall assume that the dipole consists of charges $+q_1$ and $-q_1$ located along the z axis a distance $s/2$ above and below the xy plane. We shall also assume that the pole, which has the strength q, is located in the yz plane at a distance r from the origin, where $r \gg s$, and that the radius vector makes an angle θ relative to the z axis. Following the usual elementary treatment and using approximations which are justified if $s/r \ll 1$, we find that the total interaction energy is

$$W = \frac{q_1 q}{r - (s/2)\cos\theta} - \frac{q_1 q}{r + (s/2)\cos\theta} = \frac{q\mu_e \cos\theta}{r^2} \tag{2-32}$$

where $\mu_e = q_1 s$ is the magnitude of the electrostatic dipole moment. If we introduce now the intermediary of a field, we may interpret this result in two possible ways: On the one hand, we may say that the dipole sets up an electrostatic field at the point P which is characterized by the electrostatic potential ($\mathbf{r}$ is drawn from O to P)

$$\phi_D(\mathbf{r}) = \frac{\mu_e \cos\theta}{r^2} \tag{2-33}$$

and that the energy of the system is simply the usual result obtained by multiplying the charge at $\mathbf{r}$ by the local potential, *i.e.*,

$$W = q\phi_D(\mathbf{r}) \tag{2-34}$$

On the other hand we might take the point of view that the pole sets up a field at the origin and that the energy given by Eq. (2-32) represents the interaction energy of the dipole with the field in its neighborhood. The potential at O due to the charge q at P is

$$\phi_p = \frac{q}{|\mathbf{r}'|} = \frac{q}{r} \tag{2-35}$$

where $\mathbf{r}' = -\mathbf{r}$ is a vector drawn from P to O. We note that Eq. (2-32) is not the product of the dipole moment and the potential in its neighborhood. However, it follows, from a simple geometric proof similar to that used in deriving Eq. (2-32), that

$$\frac{\partial \phi_p}{\partial z} = \frac{q}{r^2} \cos \theta \tag{2-36}$$

Accordingly, we may write Eq. (2-32) as

$$W = \mu_e \frac{\partial \phi_p}{\partial z} \tag{2-37}$$

This equation no longer has explicit reference to the pole at P which sets up the field in the neighborhood of O. It is only a slight generalization to assume that the energy of an electrostatic dipole in any electrostatic field is the scalar product of the dipole moment and the space derivative of the local field along the dipole axis.

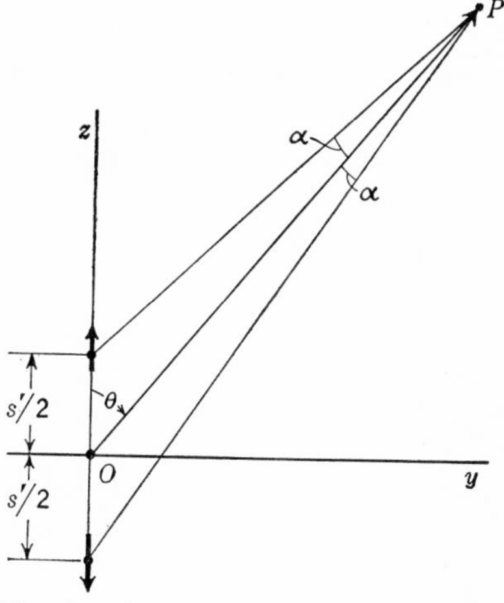

FIG. 2-5. An electric quadrupole and an electric pole.

Let us now consider the interaction energy between a linear electric quadrupole and an electric pole. We shall assume the quadrupole consists of two equal dipoles at $\pm s'/2$ which are aligned along the z axis but have opposite orientations (see Fig. 2-5). Using Eq. (2-32), the interaction energy may be written as

$$W = \frac{q\mu_e \cos(\theta + \alpha)}{[r - (s'/2) \cos \theta]^2} - \frac{q\mu_e \cos(\theta - \alpha)}{[r + (s'/2) \cos \theta]^2} \tag{2-38}$$

where $\alpha = s' (\sin \theta)/2r$. Using reasonable approximations, it readily follows that

$$W = \frac{q\mu_e s'[3 (\cos^2 \theta) - 1]}{r^3} = \frac{qQ}{4r^3} [3 (\cos^2 \theta) - 1] \tag{2-39}$$

where we define $Q = 4\mu_e s'$ in order to obtain a result in conventional form. Again we may give two field interpretations to this interaction energy: We may take the point of view that the quadrupole sets up a potential at $\mathbf{r}$ given by

$$\phi_Q = \frac{Q}{4r^3} [3 (\cos^2 \theta) - 1] \tag{2-40}$$

and that Eq. (2-39) is simply the energy of the charge q in this potential. Alternatively, we may observe that

$$\frac{\partial^2 \phi_p}{\partial z^2} = \frac{q[3 (\cos^2 \theta) - 1]}{r^3} \tag{2-41}$$

Hence the interaction energy may be written in the form

$$W = \frac{Q}{4} \frac{\partial^2 \phi_p}{\partial z^2} \tag{2-42}$$

Again we might generalize our result and conclude that the energy of a linear electric quadrupole in any field depends upon the second space derivative of the potential along the quadrupole axis multiplied by one-quarter of the quadrupole moment.

The electrostatic interactions which arise in nuclear physics, even when treated classically, are far more complicated than the two we have just discussed. In practice, we must deal with the interaction between a distribution of nuclear charge and a distribution of electronic charge. However, since nuclei are small compared to the dimensions of electronic distributions, we may treat the nucleus as an infinitesimal entity which has an equivalent electric monopole moment, dipole moment, quadrupole moment, etc. In consequence we may assign various interaction energies of the type $q\phi$, $\mu_e(\partial\phi/\partial z)$, and $(Q/4)(\partial^2\phi/\partial z^2)$, where ϕ is the electrostatic potential in the neighborhood of the nucleus due to all the charges which surround the nucleus. Using our knowledge of atomic physics to determine the electronic distributions, we can make fairly good estimates of the potential and its derivatives at the nucleus. Consequently experimental measurements of the energy effects associated with the above interactions can be used to make experimental determinations of the effective parameters q, μ_e, and Q, etc., associated with the nucleus.

The expression $W = q\phi$, when applied to this study, is just another way of writing the coulomb interaction between the electrons and the nucleus. Consequently the experiments which cast light upon the monopole electric moments of nuclei comprise almost the whole subject of atomic physics. As we know, this subject reveals simply that the nuclear monopole moment q equals Ze, where Z is the atomic number.

A great mass of spectroscopic data reveals no indication of an interaction energy associated with a nuclear dipole moment. In view of the precision of these data, this absence constitutes strong evidence in favor of the assumption that nuclei do not possess electrostatic dipole moments. However, as we mentioned earlier, energy effects have been noted which can be attributed to a nuclear electrostatic quadrupole moment, and the measurement of these effects in conjunction with detailed quantum-mechanical analysis has been used to assign quadrupole moments to many nuclei.

We come now to the question of the significance which may be attached to the observations of nuclear electric quadrupole moments and the absence of nuclear electric dipole moments. To answer this question, we must consider how the internal distribution of nuclear charge contributes to produce the effective moments. For simplicity let us first consider a hypothetical situation in which the external electric potential in the interior of the nucleus is constant so that all its derivatives vanish. Since each element of the nuclear volume contains the charge $\rho(x,y,z)\,dV$, where $\rho(x,y,z)$ is the nuclear charge distribution function, this element contributes the energy $\phi\rho\,dV$. The total interaction energy with the constant potential ϕ therefore is

$$W = \iiint \phi\rho(x,y,z)\,dV = \phi \iiint \rho(x,y,z)\,dV \tag{2-43}$$

where the integrations extend over the entire charge distribution. Comparing this with Eq. (2-34) (but ignoring the subscript), we see that the effective monopole moment associated with a nucleus is simply the total charge

$$q = \iiint \rho(x,y,z)\,dV \tag{2-44}$$

Thus in so far as a charge distribution interacts with a uniform potential, it is the total charge that is important.

Let us now consider a hypothetical situation in which $\partial\phi/\partial z$ is a constant C, all the other derivatives vanish identically, and ϕ itself vanishes at x, y, $z = 0$. An explicit potential which satisfies these conditions obviously is

$$\phi = Cz = \frac{\partial\phi}{\partial z}\,z \tag{2-45}$$

Following the methods of the preceding discussion, we see that the interaction energy in this case is

$$W = \iiint Cz\rho(x,y,z)\,dV = \frac{\partial\phi}{\partial z} \iiint z\rho(x,y,z)\,dV \tag{2-46}$$

Comparing this with Eq. (2-37), we see that the effective dipole moment of the distribution is

$$\mu_e = \iiint z\rho(x,y,z)\,dx\,dy\,dz \tag{2-47}$$

The rectangular form above suggests an immediate explanation for the vanishing of nuclear dipole moments. If the distribution is symmetric relative to the plane defined by $z = 0$, that is, if $\rho(x,y,z)$ is an even function of z, then, since $z\rho(x,y,z)$ is an odd function of z, the integral vanishes identically. Deep-seated quantum-mechanical considerations,[12] indeed, show that a stationary-state distribution must be symmetric relative to any plane through its center of mass.

Next we consider an electrostatic field for which $\partial^2\phi/\partial^2 z$ is a constant C, and in which ϕ and the first derivatives of ϕ vanish at the origin and all third and higher derivatives of ϕ vanish identically. In arriving at an explicit potential, we might be tempted to set $\phi = \frac{1}{2}Cz^2$. However, recalling Laplace's equation from electrostatics, we must require that

$$\frac{\partial^2\phi}{\partial x^2} + \frac{\partial^2\phi}{\partial y^2} + \frac{\partial^2\phi}{\partial z^2} = 0 \tag{2-48}$$

The conditions which we specified and Laplace's equation can all be satisfied if

$$\phi = \tfrac{1}{2}(Ax^2 + By^2 + Cz^2)$$

providing that we let $A + B = -C$. If in addition we assume that the field has cylindrical symmetry relative to the z axis, we have immediately that $A = B = -C/2$, and hence the potential is

$$\phi = \frac{C}{4}(2z^2 - x^2 - y^2) = \frac{C}{4}(3z^2 - r^2) = \frac{1}{4}\frac{\partial^2\phi}{\partial z^2}(3z^2 - r^2) \tag{2-49}$$

Calculating the energy of the charge distribution in this potential, we find immediately that

$$W = \frac{1}{4}\frac{\partial^2\phi}{\partial z^2}\iiint(3z^2 - r^2)\rho(x,y,z)\,dV \tag{2-50}$$

Upon comparing this with Eq. (2-42), we see that the effective quadrupole moment associated with a symmetric distribution of charge is

$$Q = \iiint(3z^2 - r^2)\rho(x,y,z)\,dV \tag{2-51}$$

To bring out its implications, we might write this expression in the form

$$Q = 3\langle z^2\rangle - \langle r^2\rangle$$

where the averages are weighted with respect to the charge distribution. If the distribution were spherically symmetrical, we would have

$$\langle z^2\rangle = \langle x^2\rangle = \langle y^2\rangle = \tfrac{1}{3}\langle r^2\rangle$$

and the quadrupole moment would vanish. The quadrupole moment is positive when $3\langle z^2\rangle > \langle r^2\rangle$, in which case the nucleus acts like a prolate spheroid (stretched out along the z axis). The quadrupole moment is negative when $3\langle z^2\rangle < \langle r^2\rangle$, in which case the nucleus acts like an oblate spheroid (flattened out along the z axis).

In nuclear physics quadrupole moments are customarily defined as an area, or squared length, given by (using spherical polar coordinates)

$$Q = e^{-1} \iiint \rho_I(r,\theta,\varphi)[3(\cos^2 \theta) - 1]r^2 \, dV \tag{2-52}$$

where ρ_I is the nuclear charge density in the state for which $M_I = I$ and where the I axis is the intrinsic direction used for the measurement of the angles. This definition has been chosen because the constant so defined appears in the final quantum-mechanical formulas for the measured energy shifts associated with the interactions in atoms and molecules between the nuclear electric quadrupole moment and the electrostatic field set up at the nucleus by the electrons.

All measurements of nuclear quadrupole moments thus far indicate that the distortions from a perfect sphere which give rise to the nuclear quadrupole moments are relatively small. To obtain a qualitative indication of the magnitude of the distortions associated with actual nuclear quadrupole moments, let us assume that nuclei are uniformly charged ellipsoids of rotation with the semiaxis R_I along the axis of symmetry and the semiaxis R_P perpendicular to the symmetry axis. Let us further suppose that these axes are given by

$$R_I = R(1 + \epsilon) \tag{2-53}$$

and

$$R_P = R\left(1 - \frac{\epsilon}{2}\right) \tag{2-54}$$

where ϵ is a distortion parameter which is small compared to 1. These assumptions ensure that the volume of the distorted sphere to the first approximation (*i.e.*, neglecting terms in ϵ^2) is equal to that of the undistorted sphere; *i.e.*,

$$V = \tfrac{4}{3}\pi R_I R_P{}^2 \approx \tfrac{4}{3}\pi R^3$$

For a uniformly charged ellipsoid of revolution with charge Ze, Eq. (2-52) becomes

$$Q = \tfrac{2}{5}Z(R_I{}^2 - R_P{}^2) \approx \tfrac{6}{5}ZR^2\epsilon = \tfrac{6}{5}ZA^{\frac{2}{3}}b^2\epsilon \tag{2-55}$$

where in the last two forms we have used $R = bA^{\frac{1}{3}}$ and again we have neglected terms in ϵ^2. In a recent compilation[5] the largest positive quadrupole moment listed is 7×10^{-24} cm^2 for $_{71}\text{Lu}^{176}$, and the largest negative quadrupole moment is -1.2×10^{-24} cm^2 for $_{51}\text{Sb}^{123}$. The ϵ's computed for these extreme cases are

$$\epsilon(_{71}\text{Lu}^{176}) = 0.11 \qquad \text{and} \qquad \epsilon(_{51}\text{Sb}^{123}) = -0.035$$

Thus we see that the distortions of nuclei from the perfect sphere are relatively small.

It can be shown that nuclear quadrupole moments vanish identically[12] whenever $I = 0$ or $I = \frac{1}{2}$ but may have nonvanishing values whenever I is larger. The fact that the deuteron possesses a small quadrupole moment (0.00273×10^{-24} cm^2) is thought to be an important clue to the basic nature of nuclear forces.

2-8. Proton-Neutron Model of the Nucleus. We referred earlier to certain inconsistencies between the proton-electron model of the nucleus and experimental data. To illustrate these anomalies briefly in the light of recent data, we note that, according to the proton-electron model, the deuteron, *i.e.*, the nucleus of heavy hydrogen, should have three nuclear particles: two protons and an electron. Now it has been clearly established by spectroscopic studies that electrons and protons both possess a mechanical spin angular moment of $\frac{1}{2}$ [$|\mathbf{s}| = (\frac{1}{2} \cdot \frac{3}{2})^{\frac{1}{2}}\hbar$]. However, the deuteron nucleus is known to possess a total angular momentum of 1 [$|\mathbf{I}| = (1 \cdot 2)^{\frac{1}{2}}\hbar$]. According to a very basic principle of quantum mechanics an odd (even) number of spin $\frac{1}{2}$ particles can combine to form only an odd half-integral (integral) value for the total angular-momentum quantum number. Thus the experimental data suggest that the deuteron contains an even number of basic spin $\frac{1}{2}$ particles, in contradiction with the odd number (three) assigned by the proton-electron model. Similar discrepancies occur with other nuclei. The case of N^{14}, which has a net nuclear angular-momentum quantum number $I = 1$, was actually the first anomaly to be noted.[13]

The discovery by Chadwick[14] in 1932 of a neutral particle having approximately the mass of the proton led Heisenberg[15] to suggest the proton-neutron model of the nucleus. According to this model the additional mass needed to account for the difference between the mass number and the charge number consists of $A - Z = N$ neutrons. If neutrons are spin $\frac{1}{2}$ particles, it follows that nuclei of odd (even) mass number have an odd (even) number of nuclear particles and consequently have a total nuclear angular-momentum quantum number which is an odd half integer (integer). The total angular-momentum quantum number $I = 1$ for the nuclei of deuterium (2 particles) and nitrogen (14 particles) is obviously consistent with the results to be expected from the proton-neutron model. Indeed, no exception to this rule has been found among all the nuclei whose I values have been determined by experiment.

Another argument against the proton-electron model is based upon the Heisenberg uncertainty principle.[16] This principle may be expressed by the relation

$$\Delta x \, \Delta p \gtrsim \hbar \tag{2-56}$$

where Δx and Δp are the minimum simultaneous uncertainties possible in measurements of the position and momentum of a particle. Now, experimental results indicate that the radii of nuclei are about 7.5×10^{-13} cm, but an electron packet so localized would possess a spread in momentum corresponding to a very large average kinetic energy. To show this, we differentiate the extreme relativistic energy-momentum relationship $E = cp$ to obtain

$$\Delta E \approx c\, \Delta p \tag{2-57}$$

Letting $\Delta x \approx 7.5 \times 10^{-13}$ cm, we get $\Delta E \gtrsim 4 \times 10^{-5}$ erg ($\sim$ 25 Mev). Such a spread in energy implies that the average energy of a nuclear electron has an even greater magnitude. The total energies of nuclear electrons so calculated exceed by a large factor the known energies of nuclei.

A third argument against the proton-electron model runs as follows: Several theoretical considerations suggest that a bound fundamental particle cannot be localized within a region much smaller than its Compton wavelength, h/mc. Such an absolute limitation on the localization of a particle is thought to exist in addition to the limitation on the simultaneous determination of position and momentum specified by the Heisenberg uncertainty principle. As a qualitative basis for such a limitation one can show, by examining simple experimental arrangements such as the γ-ray microscope, that an absolute indeterminacy of this sort may be unavoidable. In the analysis of the γ-ray microscope it is found that the limiting simultaneous uncertainties in the position and momentum of a particle measured with the microscope are

$$\Delta x = \frac{\lambda'}{2 \sin \alpha} \tag{2-58}$$

and

$$\Delta p = \frac{2h \sin \alpha}{\lambda'} \tag{2-59}$$

where

$$\lambda' = \lambda + \frac{h}{mc}(1 - \cos \theta) \tag{2-60}$$

Here λ is the wavelength of the light used to illuminate the particle, λ' is the wavelength of the light scattered into the microscope, θ is the angle of scattering, and α is the half angle of the objective. If we seek to minimize the uncertainty in position at the expense of our knowledge of momentum, we should let the incident wavelength approach zero. This, however, leads to $\lambda' \approx h/mc$ for the scattered wavelengths entering the microscope around the angle $\theta \approx 90°$. The Compton wavelength of an electron is about 300 times the radius of a typical nucleus; hence if these rough considerations are accepted, we can dismiss the electron-proton model on the grounds that electrons cannot be squeezed into the nuclear volume.

2-9. Integral Nuclear Parameters. We shall henceforth accept the proton-neutron model of the nucleus. The term nucleon will be applied to either a proton or a neutron. The letter Z will be understood now to designate the number of protons in the nucleus; the letter N, the number of neutrons; and $A = N + Z$, the number of nucleons. In addition, we shall make considerable use of an integral number $D = N - Z$, which will be called the neutron excess. Species of atoms with equal Z will be called isotopes; those with equal N will be called isotones; those with equal A will be called isobars; and those with equal D will be called isodiaspheres.[(3)]

Since any two of these four symbols uniquely characterize a particular species of atoms, they may be used to label the nuclide. In addition to the symbols $_Z\mathrm{Sym}^A$, Sym^A, or Sym-A, we shall on occasion use less conventional labels such as (N,Z), (Z,A), (A,D), (A,N,Z), or even (A,D,N,Z). We record below a few obvious relations between the integral nuclear parameters.

$$A = N + Z = 2Z + D = 2N - D \tag{2-61}$$
$$D = N - Z = A - 2Z = 2N - A \tag{2-62}$$
$$N = \tfrac{1}{2}(A + D) \tag{2-63}$$
$$Z = \tfrac{1}{2}(A - D) \tag{2-64}$$

We shall also follow the practice of using the small letters a, d, n, and z to designate the integral parameters of very light nuclear particles such as the proton, deuteron, triton, etc.

2-10. Mass and Energy Parameters. In early work in precision mass spectroscopy Aston[(17)] introduced the quantity

$$\Delta = M - A \tag{2-65}$$

for representing the small deviations of actual atomic masses M from the integral mass numbers. Although he called this quantity the mass defect, we shall accept for it the name mass decrement to avoid confusion with the concept of atomic and nuclear energy. In view of the electron-nucleus model of the atom and the proton-neutron model of the nucleus, the total available atomic and nuclear energy may be defined as

$$E_{a,nucl} = M - Zm_p - Nm_n - Zm_e \tag{2-66}$$

where m_p is the mass of the proton and m_n is the mass of the neutron Mass and energy are here regarded as equivalent in accord with the relation $E = Mc^2$. In relating energy and mass parameters we shall, however, avoid the explicit introduction of the factor c^2. Instead we shall follow either the convention of expressing the energy in terms of the mass unit used for the mass parameters (such as the atomic mass unit) or the convention of expressing the masses in the energy unit (such as Mev) used for the energy parameters.

The difference given above between the total mass of an atom and the mass of its parts is, of course, a negative number, since it represents the mass or energy whose absence accounts for the binding of the parts of the atom. An energy or mass equal to the magnitude of $E_{a,nucl}$ is needed to disassemble the electronic structure and the nucleus of an atom completely. We may subdivide this total energy into the atomic (electronic) energy E_a and the nuclear energy E, which are defined by

$$E_a = M - M_{nucl} - Zm_e \tag{2-67}$$

and

$$E = E_{nucl} = M_{nucl} - Zm_p - Nm_n \tag{2-68}$$

where M_{nucl} is the mass of the bare nucleus. Since direct measurements of nuclear masses are not practical and since atomic energies are rather small compared to nuclear energies, it is customary to use for the calculation of nuclear energies the formula

$$E = M - Zm_{\text{H}} - Nm_n \tag{2-69}$$

where m_{H} is the mass of the neutral hydrogen atom. This definition automatically corrects for the mass of the electron; however, it neglects $E_a - ZE'$, where E' is the energy of an electron in the ground state of hydrogen (-13.5 ev or 14.5×10^{-9} MU). If one or two additional significant figures are attained in atomic-mass measurements, it will be necessary to consider this residual error in the calculation of the nuclear energy. We shall call the absolute magnitude of the nuclear energy, *i.e.*,

$$B = |E| = -E = Zm_{\text{H}} + Nm_n - M \tag{2-70}$$

the binding energy, or the true mass defect, of the nucleus.

Closely related to the mass decrement and to the nuclear energy are the quantities termed the packing fraction and the average nuclear energy. The packing fraction is defined by

$$f = \frac{M - A}{A} = \frac{\Delta}{A} \tag{2-71}$$

In Fig. 2-6 we show the packing fractions of stable nuclei. Note that, in accord with the definition, O^{16} has a zero packing fraction. This standard was chosen partly in an attempt to minimize the absolute values of packing fractions. The appropriateness of this choice should be apparent from the graph. Note that packing fractions are positive (0.6 to 0 mMU) for the stable nuclei from 1 to 20, negative (0 to -0.8 to 0 mMU) for nuclei from 20 to 170, and positive again (0 to 0.6 mMU) for the very heavy nuclei.

Average nuclear energy, or nuclear energy per particle, is defined by

$$\epsilon = \frac{E}{A} \tag{2-72}$$

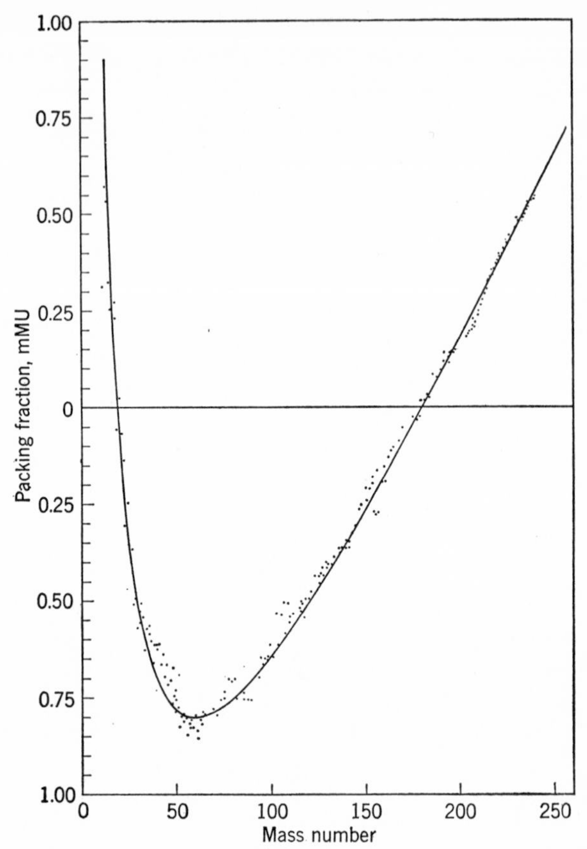

FIG. 2-6. Packing fractions for stable nuclides. The smooth curve is based upon an empirical equation given in Chap. 8.

This negative quantity varies only slightly for all known stable nuclei with the exception of the very lightest ones. To show that this is true, we make use of a relation between E and Δ which may be obtained very simply from the definitions. It follows from Eqs. (2-65) and (2-69) that

$$\begin{aligned} E &= \Delta - Z\Delta_{\mathrm{H}} - N\Delta_n \\ &= \Delta - \tfrac{1}{2}(\Delta_{\mathrm{H}} + \Delta_n)A - \tfrac{1}{2}(\Delta_n - \Delta_{\mathrm{H}})D \end{aligned} \tag{2-73}$$

where Δ_{H} and Δ_n are the mass decrements (and also the packing fractions) of the hydrogen atom and neutron, respectively. From the last equation and Eqs. (2-72) and (2-71), we find that

$$\epsilon = f - \frac{\Delta_{\mathrm{H}} + \Delta_n}{2} - \frac{D}{A}\frac{(\Delta_n - \Delta_{\mathrm{H}})}{2} \tag{2-74}$$

Since f and the last term are generally quite small, ϵ deviates only slightly from the constant $\frac{1}{2}(\Delta_{\mathrm{H}} + \Delta_n) = 8.562$ mMU.

We shall have many occasions to use two quantities which are the nuclear counterparts of the ionization energy of the valence electron in atomic physics. These quantities—B_n, the binding energy of the last neutron, and B_p, the binding energy of the last proton—are defined by

$$B_n(A,N,Z) = M(A - 1, N - 1, Z) + m_n - M(A,N,Z) \quad (2\text{-}75)$$
$$B_p(A,N,Z) = M(A - 1, N, Z - 1) + m_{\mathrm{H}} - M(A,N,Z) \quad (2\text{-}76)$$

where all masses refer to neutral atomic masses. In a similar way we may define the binding energy of any nuclear subgroup $x(a,n,z)$ by

$$B_x(A,N,Z) = M(A - a, N - n, Z - z) + m_x(a,n,z) - M(A,N,Z) \quad (2\text{-}77)$$

It is customary to give mass decrements and packing fractions in millimass units, whereas nuclear energies and binding energies are usually given in Mev. The conversion factors are

$$1 \text{ mMU} = 0.93115 \text{ Mev} \quad \text{and} \quad 1 \text{ Mev} = 1.07395 \text{ mMU} \quad (2\text{-}78)$$

A simple and accurate method for converting from one to the other with the use of a slide rule is contained in the rules: Subtract 6.89 per cent of the energy in millimass units to obtain the energy in Mev. Add 7.40 per cent of the energy in Mev to obtain the energy in mMU.

In Table 2-1 we give the values for the light nuclear particles of the static parameters which we have defined in this chapter.

TABLE 2-1. STATIC PARAMETERS OF VERY LIGHT NUCLEI

Particle		a	n	z	d	mMU		Mev				I	μ_I	g_I	Q†
						Δ	f	B	B/a	B_n	B_p				
n	n^1	1	1	0	1	8.982	8.982	0	0	0	0	$\frac{1}{2}$	−1.91280	−3.82560	0
p	H^1	1	0	1	−1	8.142	8.142	0	0	0	0	$\frac{1}{2}$	2.79255	5.58510	0
d	H^2	2	1	1	0	14.735	7.367	2.224	1.112	......	......	1	0.85735	0.85735	2.73
t	H^3	3	2	1	1	16.997	5.666	8.482	2.827	6.257	......	$\frac{1}{2}$	2.97864	5.95728	0
χ	He^3	3	1	2	−1	16.977	5.659	7.718	2.573	......	5.494	$\frac{1}{2}$	−2.12741	−4.25482	0
α	He^4	4	2	2	0	3.873	0.968	28.283	7.071	20.565	19.801	0	0	0	0

† In units of 10^{-27} cm^2.

PROBLEMS

2-1. According to Li *et al.* [*Phys. Rev.*, **83**, 512 (1951)], the isotopic weights of O^{16}, O^{17}, and O^{18} on the physical scale are 16.000,000, 17.004,533, and 18.004,878. Assuming the relative natural abundances 99.757, 0.039, and 0.204 per cent, what is the atomic weight of natural oxygen on the physical scale?

2-2. According to Eqs. (2-4) and (2-5), what are the approximate radii and volumes of nuclides with mass numbers 10, 100, and 240? If b and b_0 are uncertain to the extent of $\pm 0.3 \times 10^{-13}$ cm, what are the uncertainties in the radii and volumes of the above nuclides?

2-3. What accelerating voltages are needed to make the de Broglie wavelengths of an alpha particle, a proton, and an electron equal to the nuclear diameters for mass numbers 16, 125, and 216? (Assume $b = 1.22$.)

2-4. Negatively charged μ mesons ($q = -e$, $m_\mu = 207m_e$) are sometimes captured by atoms into hydrogenic types of orbits close to the nucleus. Assuming $Z \approx A/2$, at what value of A will the lowest Bohr orbit for the meson just graze the nuclear sphere?

2-5. Construct an energy-level diagram of the hyperfine structure of $3P_{\frac{1}{2}}$ and $3P_{\frac{3}{2}}$ states of Na^{23} ($I = \frac{3}{2}$, $\mu_I = 2.217$) showing the relative separations.

2-6. What is the Larmor precession frequency of a bare proton in a field of 1000 gauss? Of a bare electron?

2-7. Verify Eqs. (2-36) and (2-41).

2-8. Verify Eq. (2-55). (*Hint:* Use cylindrical coordinates.)

2-9. Using the data in Prob. 2-1, compute for O^{17} the mass decrement (in mMU), packing fraction (in mMU), nuclear energy (in Mev), binding energy (in Mev), nuclear energy per particle (in Mev), and binding energy of the last neutron (in Mev).

REFERENCES

1. Soddy, F.: *Trans. Chem. Soc.*, **99,** 72 (1911).
2. Thomson, J. J.: "Rays of Positive Electricity," Longmans, Green & Co., Inc., New York, 1913.
3. Kohman, T. P.: *Am. J. Phys.*, **15,** 356 (1947).
4. Crawford, M. F., and A. L. Schawlow: *Phys. Rev.*, **76,** 1310 (1949).
5. Klinkenberg, P.: *Revs. Mod. Phys.*, **24,** 64 (1952).
6. Pauling, L., and S. A. Goudsmit: "The Structure of Line Spectra," McGraw-Hill Book Company, Inc., New York, 1930.
7. White, H. E.: "Introduction to Atomic Spectra," McGraw-Hill Book Company, Inc., New York, 1935.
8. Condon, E. U., and G. Shortley: "The Theory of Atomic Spectra," Cambridge University Press, New York, 1935.
9. Herzberg, G.: "Molecular Spectra and Molecular Structure of Diatomic Molecules," Prentice-Hall, Inc., New York, 1939.
10. Dieke, G. H., and E. S. Robinson: *Phys. Rev.*, **80,** 1 (1950).
11. Good, W. E.: *Phys. Rev.*, **69,** 636 (1946).
12. Ramsey, N. F.: *Exptl. Nuclear Phys.*, **1,** 380 (1953).
13. Heitler, W., and G. Herzberg: *Naturwiss.*, **17,** 673 (1929).
14. Chadwick, J.: *Proc. Roy. Soc. (London)*, **A136,** 692 (1932).
15. Heisenberg, W.: *Z. Physik*, **77,** 1(1932).
16. Heisenberg, W.: "The Physical Principles of Quantum Mechanics," University of Chicago Press, Chicago, 1930.
17. Aston, F. W.: *Phil. Mag.*, **38,** 709 (1919).
18. Cohen, B. L., and R. V. Neidigh: *Phys. Rev.*, **93,** 282 (1954).
19. Lyman, E. M., A. O. Hanson, and M. B. Scott: *Phys. Rev.*, **84,** 626 (1951).
20. Hammer, C. L., E. C. Raka, and R. W. Pidd: *Phys. Rev.*, **90,** 341 (1953).
21. Hofstadter, R., H. R. Fechter, and J. A. McIntyre: *Phys. Rev.*, **92,** 978 (1953).
22. Schiff, L. I.: *Phys. Rev.*, **92,** 978 (1953).
23. Fitch, V. L., and J. Rainwater: *Phys. Rev.*, **92,** 789 (1953).
24. Green, A. E. S., and N. A. Engler: *Phys. Rev.*, **91,** 40 (1953). Also see Chap. 8 of this text.
25. Pake, G. E.: *Am. J. Phys.*, **18,** 438 (1950).

CHAPTER 3

ACCELERATORS

To a great extent, the growth of nuclear physics has depended upon the development of methods for producing beams of high-energy particles. Radioactive substances emit alpha particles (helium nuclei), beta particles (electrons), and gamma rays, which have been and still are used for nuclear projectiles. However, particle accelerators have greatly extended the range of intensities, energies, and types of particles which are available for research. For the most part light nuclear particles and gamma rays in the energy range from 0 to 25 Mev are the important projectiles for nuclear physics. Although research with very-high-energy accelerators will undoubtedly shed some light on the nature of nuclear forces, these accelerators have been developed primarily for research in fundamental-particle physics. This chapter will be devoted to a discussion of the principles underlying the important types of nuclear accelerators.

3-1. Voltage Multipliers. The transformer-rectifier-filter combination, familiar as a source of d-c voltage in radio, television, and X-ray equipment, is limited by insulation difficulties to voltages of the order of 100 kv. Several methods are available, however, for multiplying the limiting voltage obtainable from a single transformer. In the Cockcroft-Walton circuit[1] two banks of series capacitors are alternately connected by electronic switches (see Fig. 3-1) to give a limiting output voltage which is approximately equal to the number of capacitors times the peak transformer voltage. Starting with a completely discharged system, the operation of this circuit proceeds roughly as follows: During the first half cycle (see polarity in Fig. 3-1) capacitor a charges to the transformer voltage through tube A. During the negative half cycle,

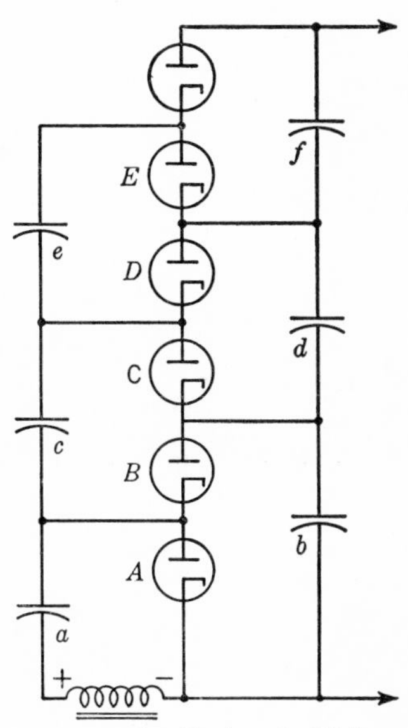

FIG. 3-1. The Cockcroft-Walton circuit.

tube A is nonconducting, however; the combined voltage of the transformer and the voltage now on capacitor a charges capacitor b through tube B. During the following half cycle, capacitor a recharges through tube A, and at the same time capacitor b partially discharges through tubes A and C into capacitor c. The analogous action in subsequent half cycles causes a net upward movement of charge until all the capacitors except capacitor a acquire the voltage $2V$. The output voltage is

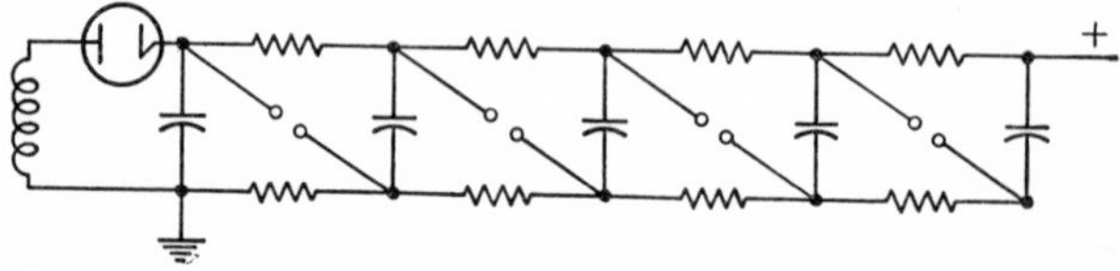

FIG. 3-2. The impulse voltage generator. *(From Brasch and Lange, Ref.* 3.)

approximately $2nV$, where n is the number of capacitors in series on the output side. The Cockcroft-Walton circuit has been used to reach voltages up to about 2 Mv. In Table 3-1 we give the characteristics of the Cockcroft-Walton generator at the Cavendish Laboratory.[2]

TABLE 3-1. CHARACTERISTICS OF 1-MV COCKCROFT-WALTON ACCELERATOR AT CAVENDISH LABORATORY, CAMBRIDGE†

Number of diodes	12
Number of capacitors (0.04 μf to 0.01 μf)	12
Peak-to-peak transformer voltage	220 kv
Maximum no-load voltage	1.25 Mv
Target current	To 100 μa
Frequency	200 cycles/sec
Energy spread with magnetic analyzer	10 kev

† From Jelley, Ref. 2.

The impulse generator (see Fig. 3-2) also utilizes capacitors for voltage multiplication. The output voltage of a half-wave rectifier charges all the capacitors in parallel through high resistances. Shortly before the peak voltage of the transformer is reached, a rapid succession of discharges through properly adjusted spark gaps effectively connects the capacitors in series. Consequently, the peak output voltage is the sum of the voltages across each capacitor, or approximately nV. Peak voltages up to 2.4 Mv have been obtained with impulse generators.

A third arrangement (see Fig. 3-3) for overcoming the limited voltage capabilities of a single transformer utilizes a cascade of transformers. The voltage output is equal to the sum of the secondary voltages developed by each transformer.

3-2. Electrostatic Generator.[5,6] The Van de Graaff[7] electrostatic accelerator is the most important type of accelerator currently used for obtaining projectiles with precisely defined energies up to about 10 Mev. This generator provides a means for converting into electrostatic energy the mechanical work that is expended in turning an endless belt against electrostatic forces.[61] A device consisting of needle points and a smooth plate maintained at 10 to 50 kv difference of potential sprays charges

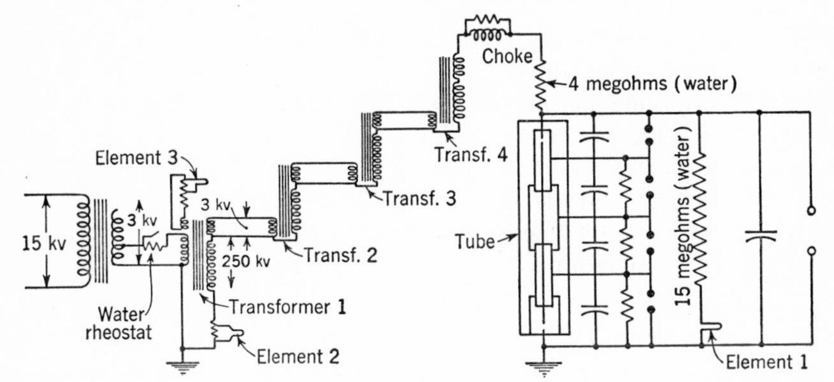

FIG. 3-3. Diagram of a cascade transformer set. (*From Lauritsen and Bennett, Ref.* 4.)

onto an endless nonconducting belt. The belt bodily transfers the charge to the interior of a metal sphere where a second spraying device transfers the charge to the sphere (see Fig. 3-4). In continuous operation

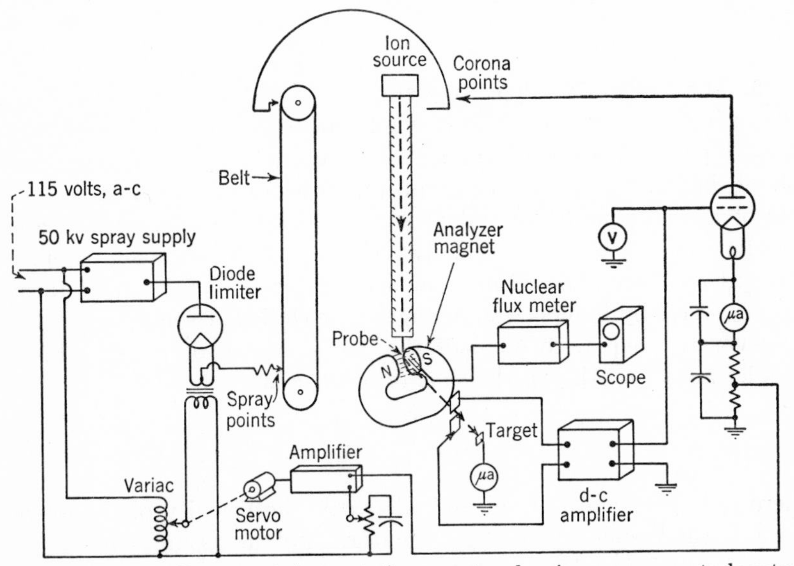

FIG. 3-4. Schematic diagram of electrostatic generator showing energy-control system. (*From Lamphere and Robinson, Ref.* 8.)

the sphere reaches a limiting potential relative to ground which is determined by the rate of transfer of charge by the belt and the leakage of charge by corona and by the beam current through the accelerator tube.

The most recently constructed electrostatic generators incorporate features which greatly increase the usefulness of this accelerator. To minimize corona losses, electrostatic generators are now generally enclosed in a tank which contains an inert gas mixture at high pressures. For this same purpose several equipotential metal shells may be used in conjunction with a voltage divider to maintain a favorable potential gradient. Precision electronic control equipment is employed to limit the voltage fluctuations. These and other improvements have made it possible to obtain beam currents of the order of 50 μa, with energies up to 8 Mev, and with energy spreads limited to a few kev. If beam current is sacrificed, even better energy definition is realized. In Table 3-2 we give the characteristics of the University of Wisconsin electrostatic accelerator.

TABLE 3-2. CHARACTERISTICS OF THE UNIVERSITY OF WISCONSIN ELECTROSTATIC GENERATOR†

Top usable voltage	4.5 Mev
Ion-beam current (protons or deuterons)	10 μa at 0.1% energy resolution
Neutron flux	$\sim 5 \times 10^7$ neutrons/sterad-sec with 40-kev spread
Pressure (90% air, 10% freon)	8 atm
Weight of accelerator and mount	7500 lb
Optimum resolution of analyzer	$\sim$0.02%

† From Adair, Ref 9.

3-3. The Linear Multiple Accelerator.[10] Sloan and Lawrence,[11] in 1931, using the first linear multiple accelerator, succeeded in accelerating charged particles to high energies by the application of many small voltage impulses. The linear multiple accelerator (see Fig. 3-5) consists of a set of hollow cylinders arranged along a line, with alternate cylinders joined together and driven by a high-frequency oscillator. Charged particles injected into the accelerator at one end drift through the successive cylinders, whose lengths are designed such that the time of traversal is equal to one-half the period of the oscillator. For the cylinder after the ith gap the time of passage is

$$\tau_i = \frac{L_i}{v_i} = \frac{1}{2f} \tag{3-1}$$

where L_i is the length of this cylinder, v_i is the velocity of the particle, and f is the frequency of the oscillator. Let us assume that at each gap the particle is subject to the average accelerating voltage $\bar{V}$. Therefore according to nonrelativistic dynamics the energy of a charge ze after the ith gap is

$$T_i = ize\bar{V} = \tfrac{1}{2}mv_i^2 \tag{3-2}$$

Combining Eqs. (3-1) and (3-2) we see that the cylinders must have the lengths

$$L_i = i^{\frac{1}{2}} \left(\frac{\bar{V}ze}{2m} \right)^{\frac{1}{2}} \frac{1}{f} \tag{3-3}$$

This equation indicates that, to minimize the total length of the accelerator for a given output, the frequency of the oscillator should be as high as possible. Using Eqs. (3-2) and (3-3), it can be shown that the voltage $\bar{V}$ should be as large as possible. The characteristics of the oscillators which were available in the early 1930's limited the linear multiple accelerator to energies of the order of 1 Mev. Since the cyclotron, which

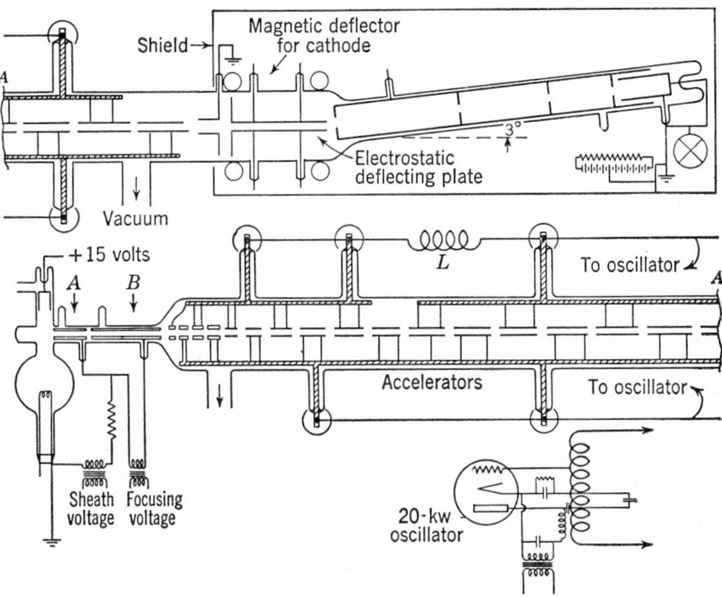

FIG. 3-5. Diagram of linear multiple accelerator. (*From Sloan and Lawrence, Ref.* 11.)

was developed by Lawrence about this time, provided a simpler and less cumbersome apparatus for accelerating nuclear particles to energies of this order, the linear-accelerator principle was not exploited widely. However, the development of very-high-frequency oscillators during World War II has led to a revival of interest in the linear accelerator. Under Alvarez[12] the University of California has constructed a 40-ft proton accelerator whose radio-frequency power is provided by twenty-eight 200-Mc oscillators. These oscillators are synchronized by feeding into a single resonant cavity, and the phase fed to each gap is adjusted to secure a radio-frequency field in the form of a standing wave. Protons injected at 4 Mev have been brought to 32 Mev.

The linear proton accelerator is rather inflexible, since it can give out only particles of a single energy; however, it has a great advantage in the high intensities attainable in the external beam. It is finding application to nuclear physics as a source of almost monoergic particles in the energy region above that accessible to the Van de Graaff accelerator. In Table 3-3 we give the characteristics of the Berkeley linear proton accelerator.

TABLE 3-3. THE UNIVERSITY OF CALIFORNIA LINEAR PROTON ACCELERATOR†

Length	40 ft
Diameter	39 in.
Number of drift tubes	47
Radio frequency	202.5 Mc
Power	2.5 Mw peak
Repetition rate	30 sec^{-1}
Duration of pulse	600 μsec
Injection energy	4 Mev (Van de Graaff)
Output energy	31.8 ± 0.1 Mev
Output current	0.25 μa (average); 16 μa (peak)
Beam diameter	3 mm
Beam divergence	1 milliradian

† From Alvarez *et al.*, Ref. 12.

The linear accelerator has also been applied to the acceleration of electrons to ultrarelativistic velocities. Most electron accelerators use frequencies of the order of 3000 Mc/sec with oscillators or radio-frequency power amplifiers coupled to produce a traveling wave field through a cylindrical waveguide. The electrons, which at injection are already traveling at very close to the velocity of light, are accelerated by the electric component of the traveling wave field. In contrast to the performance of a proton accelerator, the output energy of a given electron accelerator can be varied over wide limits. There is no apparent limit to the energies attainable with this type of machine.

Nuclear studies are under way with the electron beam itself, as well as with the high-energy X rays obtained from a target which is hit by the electron beam. In Table 3-4 we give the characteristics of the Stanford linear electron accelerator.

TABLE 3-4. CHARACTERISTICS OF STANFORD LINEAR ELECTRON ACCELERATOR†

Length (now completed)	220 ft
Number of independent sections	21
Radio frequency	2856 Mc
Radio-frequency power per section	$\sim$20 Mw
Repetition rate	60 sec^{-1}
Energy resolution (at 150 Mev)	1.5%
Pulse magnitude (at 150 Mev)	2×10^8 electrons (for 0.5 μsec)
Present design energy	380 Mev
Final design energy	1 Bev

† From Panofsky, Ref. 13.

3-4. The Cyclotron.[14–16] The cyclotron, invented by E. O. Lawrence,[17] is similar in principle to the linear multiple accelerator in that particles are subjected to multiple voltage impulses. The high-frequency alternating voltage is here applied between two hollow electrodes (dees), which are mounted between the poles of a huge magnet (see Fig. 3-6). An approximately uniform magnetic field bends the particle path into a circle having the radius

$$r = \frac{p}{Bze} = \frac{mv\gamma}{Bze} \tag{3-4}$$

The time interval from the moment of entry of the particle into one dee to the moment of emergence is

$$\tau_{\frac{1}{2}} = \frac{\pi r}{v} = \frac{\pi m\gamma}{Bze} \tag{3-5}$$

The fact that this is constant for nonrelativistic velocities ($\gamma \approx 1$) enables one to adjust the magnetic field or the radio frequency to obtain a resonance between the half period ($1/2f$) of the oscillator and the natural half period of the system, given by Eq. (3-5). At resonance, *i.e.*, when

$$f = \frac{Bze}{2\pi m\gamma} \tag{3-6}$$

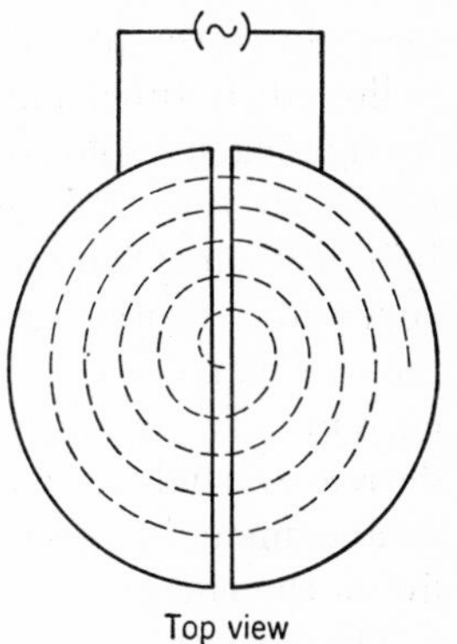

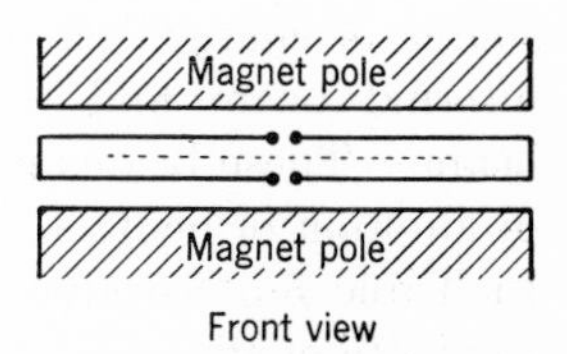

Fig. 3-6. Diagram showing multiple acceleration of ions in a cyclotron.

the electric field has the proper direction to increase the kinetic energy of the particle whenever it appears in the gap between the dees. After each traversal through the gap, the particle shifts to a slightly larger orbit until it finally reaches the outer radius R of the magnet. An electrostatic deflector here causes the particle to strike an internal or external target. The kinetic energy (nonrelativistic) attained by the particles is

$$T = \frac{p^2}{2m} = \frac{R^2B^2z^2e^2}{2m} = 2\pi^2f^2R^2m \tag{3-7}$$

For a given nuclear particle the maximum energy depends upon the radius of the cyclotron magnet and either the strength of the magnetic field or the frequency of the oscillator. For a given magnet the energy output varies with the particle parameters in a manner which depends upon how the resonance condition [Eq. (3-6)] is accomplished. If the oscillator frequency is varied to secure resonance with a fixed magnetic field, the energy attainable varies as z^2/m. Since this ratio is approximately the same for protons and alpha particles, these particles will be brought to the same energy. If, as is more customary and convenient, the magnetic induction is adjusted to achieve resonance with an oscillator having a fixed frequency, the energy attainable varies simply as m.

The designing of a cyclotron to obtain relativistic energies is complicated by the fact that γ in Eq. (3-5) is not constant. In consequence, as the particle moves to the outermost orbits, it arrives late at the gaps and gradually gets out of phase with the voltage pulses. This problem does not cause difficulty in the linear accelerator, since the lengths of the hollow drift tubes may be adjusted to satisfy the relativistic equations. An analogous solution for the cyclotron would be to shape the pole pieces so that B/γ is approximately constant, *i.e.*, so that the field becomes somewhat stronger at large radius. Unfortunately, such a slight curvature of the magnetic field will tend to defocus the particles from the median plane of the dee chambers and will result in a large loss of beam current. In fact, practical systems contain a magnetic field which decreases slightly with radius to secure focusing. Such a focusing arrangement in conjunction with the relativistic effect discussed above limits the energies attainable with a cyclotron to about 25 Mev.

The cyclotron is extremely important to nuclear physics as an intense source of charged particles, giving currents of the order of 1 ma in the internal beam and currents of the order of 50 μa in the external beam. These beams are used for the study of nuclear reactions, for the production of neutrons, and for the production of induced radioactivity. In Table 3-5 we give the characteristics of a cyclotron at the Nobel Institute of Physics.

TABLE 3-5. NOBEL INSTITUTE OF PHYSICS CYCLOTRON IN STOCKHOLM, SWEDEN†

Weight of magnet	400 tons
Weight of copper	27 tons
Pole-face diameter	88.5 in.
Power for 25-Mev deuteron	60 kw
Maximum power	240 kw
Radius of maximum orbit	90 cm
Field for 25-Mev deuteron	11,500 gauss
Maximum field	18,000 gauss
Oscillator frequency	8.7 Mc
Oscillator power	230 kw
Dee voltage	200 kv
Energy	25-Mev deuterons
Beam current (internal)	300 μa

† From Atterling and Lindstörm, Ref. 18.

3-5. The Synchrocyclotron.[15,19,20] In 1945 McMillan[21] and Veksler[22] independently suggested that the energy limitation of a cyclotron-like device may be removed by modulating the frequency of the oscillator. The idea was immediately reduced to practice at the University of

California in Berkeley. We know that a particle released in a cyclotron at the center of the field at $t = 0$ will gradually spiral around into larger and larger orbits. By calculating the radius of the orbit as a function of time, we may find the corresponding $\gamma[r(t)]$. If the magnetic field, for the purpose of focusing, also varies somewhat with r, we may compute $B[r(t)]$. If now the oscillator frequency is varied slightly to conform to the corresponding function of time given by Eq. (3-6), the resonance condition will always be satisfied. The desired frequency modulation of the oscillator may be obtained by attaching a rotating variable capacitor with appropriately shaped plates into the oscillator tank circuit. The output beam appears in periodic pulses, one for each frequency sweep.

For many purposes it is convenient to consider the modulation of the frequency as a means of expanding the stable orbit which would result at relativistic velocities with a radially decreasing magnetic field, if a fixed frequency were used. We see from Eq. (3-5) that, as γ increases and B decreases, the time of half transit increases. If the radio frequency were fixed, a gradual lag would take place between the time of arrival of the particle at the gap and the time of arrival of the peak voltage. When this lag is 90°, the voltage is zero, so that the particle acquires no additional energy during transit but instead merely continues to rotate at a fixed radius. Equation (3-6) with $B = B(r)$ and $\gamma = \gamma(r)$ may now be viewed as the equilibrium condition for stable resonance with a fixed frequency. When the frequency is slowly decreased with time, the radius of this stable orbit is expanded until the radius of the magnet is reached.

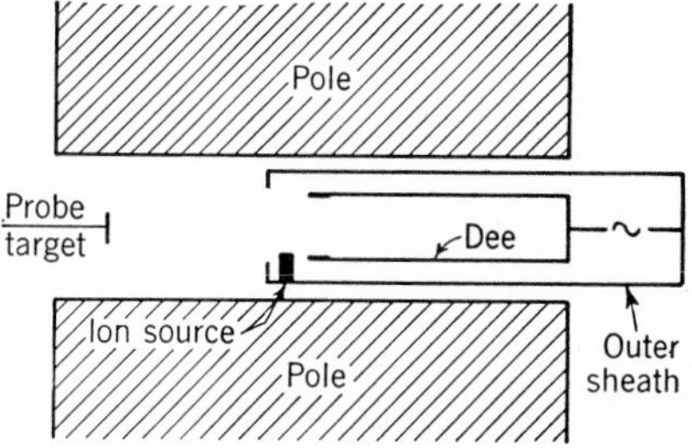

FIG. 3-7. Schematic diagram of synchrocyclotron, showing single-dee construction.

To ensure uniformity of the accelerating voltage along the radius under the circumstances when the oscillator wavelength is comparable to the dee dimensions, synchrocyclotrons are constructed with a single dee, and the accelerating voltage is applied between this dee and a grounded sheath (see Fig. 3-7). Particles of any energy less than the maximum may be chosen by adjusting the radial position of a probe target which is mounted in the space opposite the dee. Because of the pulsed character of the synchrocyclotron beam, the currents obtained are small, of the order of 1 μa for the internal beam and considerably less for the extracted beam. The synchrocyclotron principle has been incorporated into accelerators built at Berkeley, Rochester, Columbia, and elsewhere. In Table 3-6 we give some characteristics of the Berkeley 184-in. synchrocyclotron.

TABLE 3-6. UNIVERSITY OF CALIFORNIA 184-IN. SYNCHROCYCLOTRON†

Weight magnet, tons	4000 (steel); 300 (copper)
Pole-face diameter, in	184
Magnetic gap, in	15
Field, gauss	15,000 (center); 14,300 (at 80 in.)
Dee voltage, kv	17 (p); 12 (d); 12 (α)‡
Pulse rate, cycles/sec	60
Oscillator frequency, Mc/sec	22.9–15.8 (p); 11.5–9.8 (d, α)
Output energy, Mev	350 (p); 195 (d); 390 (α)
Average beam current, μa	0.75 (p); 0.75 (d); 0.1 (α)
Average deflected current, 10^{-9} amp	0.5 (p); 1 (d); 0.01 (α)

† From Heinrich *et al.*, Ref. 23.

‡ Where triple entries are given, the values refer to the particle whose symbol is given in parentheses.

3-6. The Betatron.[24] In the betatron, an instrument for accelerating electrons which was first successfully built by D. W. Kerst[25] in 1941, a changing magnetic flux in an electromagnet accelerates the electrons and at the same time holds them in an orbit having a fixed radius. The average force acting on the particle during a single revolution is the work (induced voltage multiplied by charge) divided by the distance ($2\pi R$). Equating this to the rate of change of momentum, we obtain, by using Faraday's law of induction,

$$\frac{e(\Delta\phi/\Delta t)}{2\pi R} = \frac{\Delta p}{\Delta t} = \frac{\Delta(BeR)}{\Delta t} \tag{3-8}$$

Letting R be constant and treating the finite increments as differentials, we obtain, upon integration between two instances of time,

$$\phi(t_2) - \phi(t_1) = 2\pi R^2[B(t_2) - B(t_1)] \tag{3-9}$$

This condition will automatically be satisfied if at all times the flux through the orbit and the magnetic induction at the orbit are related by

$$B(t) = \frac{\phi(t)}{2\pi R^2} \tag{3-10}$$

An electromagnet whose pole pieces are shaped so that the induction near the periphery decreases very rapidly will always have one radius which satisfies Eq. (3-10). A vacuum chamber, shaped like a doughnut, encloses this orbit (see Fig. 3-8).

In operation, an electron gun injects electrons of about 60 kev near the desired orbit at the start of the build-up of the magnetic field. During the build-up the electrons accumulate the kinetic energy

$$\Delta T = e\frac{\Delta\phi}{\Delta t} = \frac{e\,\Delta\phi}{2\pi(R/v)} \tag{3-11}$$

Since the electrons travel nearly at the velocity of light during the entire action of the force, we may replace v in Eq. (3-11) by c. Hence in one quarter cycle of the low-frequency magnet current, during which time the flux changes from ϕ_i to ϕ_f, the electrons acquire the energy

$$T = \frac{ec}{2\pi R}(\phi_f - \phi_i) = (B_f - B_i)Rce \qquad (3\text{-}12)$$

The energy obtainable is therefore limited by the radius and the peak strength of the magnet at the orbit. A large bank of capacitors is used

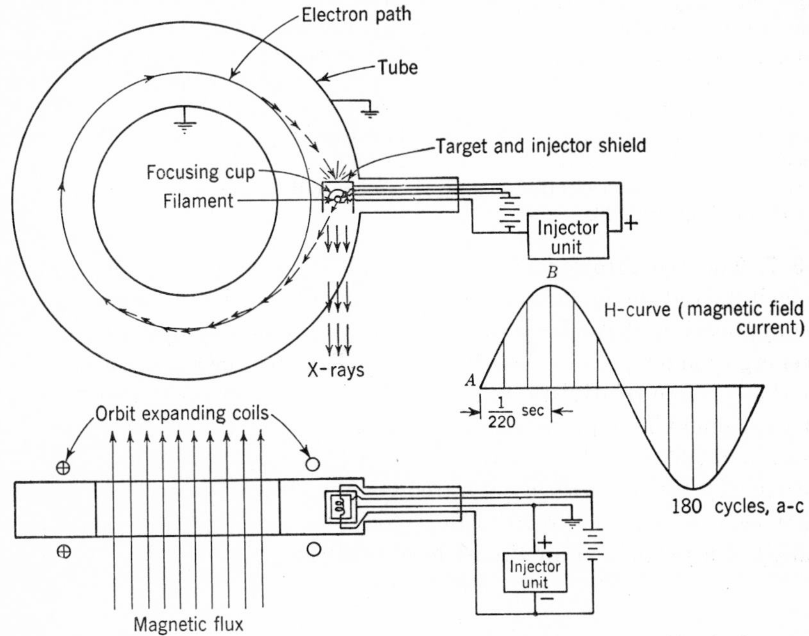

Fig. 3-8. The vacuum doughnut in which the electrons are accelerated in the betatron. Electrons passing from the injector to the equilibrium orbit actually circle the tube many times before reaching the orbit. The same is true for electrons leaving the orbit to hit the target. Electrons are injected at A, and the orbit is expanded at B in every cycle. (*From Kerst, Ref.* 25.)

to balance the inductive load, thus minimizing the average power input needed to provide the large energy absorbed by the magnetic field during every other quarter cycle.

The practical problems of focusing (see Sec. 3-8) and altering the beam at the end of a cycle to strike a target have been solved. The output is usually in the form of high-energy X rays, although some use has been made of the electron beam itself. Betatrons reaching to 25 Mev have been particularly useful for the study of photonuclear reactions. In Table 3-7 we give the characteristics of the betatron at the University of Saskatchewan.

Table 3-7. University of Saskatchewan Betatron†
Manufactured by the Allis-Chalmers Co.

Weight of betatron	5 tons
Voltage on magnet coils (at 22 Mev)	8,000–0–8,000 volts
Magnet coil current (at 22 Mev)	180 amp
Tuning capacity for betatron	10 μf
Power feed to resonant circuit (magnet and capacitor in parallel)	6000 volts, 8 amp
Equilibrium orbit	20 cm (7.9 in.)
Field index n [see Eq. (3-17)]	0.75
Injection voltage	60 kv
Volts per turn at equilibrium orbit	80 volts/turn (at 22 Mev)
X-ray yield	150 roentgens/min at 3 ft from target with betatron operating at 22 Mev
Magnetic field at orbit	4000 gauss
Magnetic field at center	11,000 gauss
Maximum energy	27 Mev
Variation in maximum electron energy	$\pm$5 kev (10–23 Mev)

† From Katz, Ref. 26.

3-7. The Synchrotron.[27–28] The high costs of the magnet and the capacitors and the inefficiency of induction acceleration have discouraged the application of the betatron principle to the acceleration of electrons to energies much greater than 100 Mev. The most promising accelerator for the extreme relativistic range of electron energies is the synchrotron, an instrument first proposed by Oliphant in 1943 (unpublished). This instrument, like the betatron, uses varying currents in the magnet and, like the cyclotron, uses a high-frequency voltage for accelerating the particles. At extreme relativistic velocities ($v \approx c$, $\gamma \gg 1$) the time of transit of a particle in an almost fixed orbit is

$$\tau = \frac{2\pi R}{v} = \frac{2\pi m\gamma}{zeB} \tag{3-13}$$

If B is now varied explicitly with time to cancel the variation of γ with time, resonance with a constant-frequency oscillator may be obtained. Since the radius expands only slightly ($R = v\tau/2\pi \rightarrow c\tau/2\pi$), it is possible to use an annular magnet (see Fig. 3-9) and thereby achieve a great saving in steel.

In the electron synchrotron the doughnut-shaped vacuum tube, which is silver-plated internally and externally, acts as a resonant cavity to the applied radio-frequency voltage. The high voltage between the edges of a gap in the coating accelerates the electrons whenever they pass through the gap. Electrons in synchrotrons are usually accelerated to a velocity very close to the velocity of light by betatron action during the initial phase of the accelerating cycle. Flux bars attached to the annular magnet provide the interior flux needed to satisfy the betatron

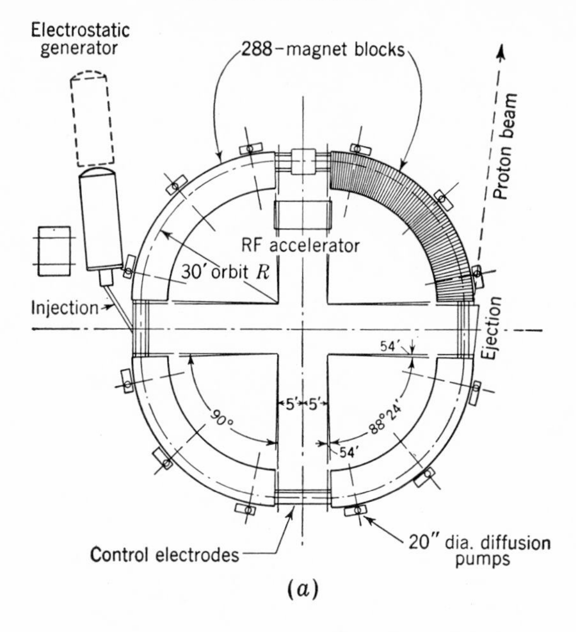

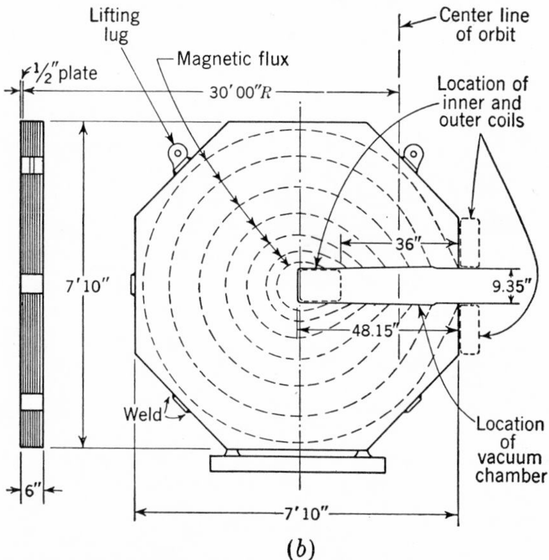

Fig. 3-9. (*a*) Plan view of the Brookhaven cosmotron, a proton synchrotron, showing the assembly of the magnet blocks. (*b*) Cross section of C magnets. (*From Livingston, Blewett, Green, and Haworth, Ref.* 29.)

condition. These flux bars saturate after a fraction of a millisecond, at which time the synchrotron operation starts. In Table 3-8 we give the characteristics of the electron synchrotron at Cornell University. An electron synchrotron at California Institute of Technology[30] has been designed to reach energies greater than 1 Bev.

TABLE 3-8. CORNELL UNIVERSITY ELECTRON SYNCHROTRON†

Weight of synchrotron	738 tons
Peak voltage on magnet coils	11.2 kv
Peak current in magnet coils	3500 amp
Pulse rate	30 sec^{-1}
Capacitor bank	1700 μf
Orbit radius	39.4 in.
Field index n	0.67
Oscillator frequency	47.5 Mc
Peak power of oscillator	5.5 kw
Operating gap voltage	1.9 kv
Peak magnetic field	1.0 weber/m
Injection energy	80 kv
End of betatron phase	2 Mev
Maximum energy at target	300 Mev
Central beam intensity	1600 roentgens/min at 1 m inside $\frac{1}{8}$-in. lead

† From Thomas, Kraushaar, and Halpern, Ref. 28.

The synchrotron principle is also being applied to the acceleration of protons to the billion-electron-volt (Bev) range. Because the initial protron velocity is not close to the velocity of light, even after injection at 4 to 10 Mev by a Van de Graaff or linear accelerator, the time of transit in a fixed orbit is not constant. In consequence, in addition to the increasing magnetic field, frequency modulation over a wide range of frequencies is needed to maintain an orbit of approximately constant radius. In Table 3-9 we give the characteristics of the proton synchro-

TABLE 3-9. CHARACTERISTICS OF THE BROOKHAVEN COSMOTRON†

Weight	288 steel blocks, 5.7 tons each; 70 tons copper bus bars
Peak current in magnet coils	7000 amp
Peak power	21,000 kva
Stored peak energy in flywheel	1.7×10^7 joules
Pulse rate	Once every 5 sec
Orbit radius	30 ft
Field range	300–14,000 gauss
Field index n	0.6
Frequency range	0.35–4.2 Mc
Radio-frequency oscillator voltage	2400 volts (0.35 Mc), 1400 volts (4.78 Mc)
Energy gain per turn	1000 ev
Injection energy	3.6 Mev (electrostatic accelerator)
Energy output	3.1 Bev (p), 2.5 Bev (d), 5.0 Bev (α)
Peak pulse current	1 ma (100 μsec)

† From Livingston, Blewett, Green, and Haworth, Ref. 29.

tron at the Brookhaven National Laboratory; this instrument is called the cosmotron. The proton synchrotron at the University of California has reached the 5- to 7-Bev range of energies.

The foregoing discussion covers the major types of particle accelerators now in use. Several other types have been developed, although in the main these accelerators have not been so important to nuclear physics as the types described above. Several comprehensive bibliographies[31–33] are available which list all the known particle accelerators and their major characteristics.

3-8. Geometric Focusing in Accelerators. We have thus far given attention to the principles which govern the energies attainable with accelerators. Other important aspects of accelerator design have to do with the properties of focusing and orbit stability. Machines having these properties to a high degree attain beams with larger intensity and better energy homogeneity than those which do not.

In linear electrostatic instruments, such as the voltage multipliers, the Van de Graaff accelerator, and the linear multiple accelerator, we identify radial focusing as the property of the system which restores to the axis those particles which tend to go off the axis. In magnetic instruments, such as cyclotrons, betatrons, synchrocyclotrons, and synchrotrons, we distinguish between axial and radial focusing. A system possesses axial focusing if particles which depart from the median horizontal plane tend to return to the median plane. A system possesses radial focusing if particles which depart from the equilibrium orbit are restored to this equilibrium orbit. Focusing in the betatron is particularly interesting, since the principles involved can be presented in rather simple and concrete terms. Let us therefore first consider the conditions which must be met for radial stability in a betatron.

In the equilibrium orbit (r_0) the outward centrifugal force is equal to the inward force of the magnetic field. Accordingly, the net radial outward force exerted upon the particle by the z component of the magnetic field is

$$\frac{pv}{r_0} - evB_z = 0 \tag{3-14}$$

Suppose now that the particle is displaced radially in the median plane so that its instantaneous radius is $r_0 + x$, where x is small compared to r_0 (see Fig. 3-10a). The net radial outward force acting on the particle is now

$$\begin{aligned} f_x &= \frac{pv}{r_0 + x} - ev\left(B_z + \frac{\partial B_z}{\partial r}x\right) \\ &\approx -ev\left(\frac{\partial B_z}{\partial r} + \frac{B_z}{r_0}\right)x \end{aligned} \tag{3-15}$$

where we have used the equilibrium condition [Eq. (3-14)] to eliminate pv.

We may write this force in the form

$$f_x = -\frac{evB_z}{r_0}(1 - n)x \tag{3-16}$$

where

$$n = -\frac{\partial B_z/\partial r}{B_z/r_0} \tag{3-17}$$

is a field parameter characterizing the variation of the field at the orbit. If $n < 1$, the outward radial force is negative; *i.e.*, the force acts in a

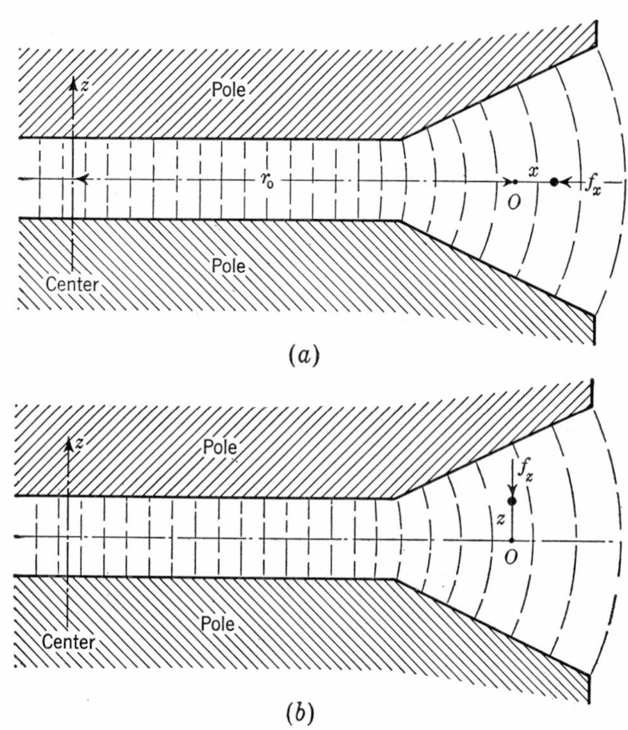

FIG. 3-10. Diagram showing (*a*) radial focusing property of fringing betatron field and (*b*) axial focusing property of fringing betatron field.

direction opposite to the displacement x. Equation (3-16), which relates to the radial motion about the equilibrium orbit, thus has precisely the form of Hooke's law. To a good approximation we may equate this force to $m\gamma\, d^2x/dt^2$, where the dependence of γ upon the orbital velocity is allowed but its dependence upon the radial velocity is ignored. Consequently we have

$$\frac{d^2x}{dt^2} + \frac{evB_z}{m\gamma r_0}(1 - n)x = 0 \tag{3-18}$$

or

$$\frac{d^2x}{dt^2} + \omega_0^2(1 - n)x = 0 \tag{3-19}$$

where we have used $\omega_0 = v_0/r_0 = evB_z/p$. Since this is precisely the differential equation for the motion of a harmonic oscillator, we may conclude that x varies harmonically with the angular frequency

$$\omega_r = \omega_0(1 - n)^{\frac{1}{2}} \tag{3-20}$$

We may apply a similar analysis to the vertical motion. In the median plane the magnetic field has only a vertical component; hence it exerts no vertical force. However, in a nonuniform field, which exists when the outer parts of the pole pieces open out, a small radial magnetic field exists above and below the median plane. This radial field is given approximately by

$$B_r = \frac{\partial B_r}{\partial z} z = \frac{\partial B_z}{\partial r} z \tag{3-21}$$

The last form is based upon the equality $\partial B_r/\partial z = \partial B_z/\partial r$, which follows from Maxwell's equation curl $B = 0$ (the magnetic field may be regarded as static in so far as the motion of the particle during a period of one revolution is concerned). Accordingly, we have for the vertical force on a vertically displaced electron (see Fig. 3-10*b*)

$$f_z = evB_r = ev\frac{\partial B_z}{\partial r} z = -\frac{nevB}{r_0} z \tag{3-22}$$

When $n > 0$, the force is opposite to the displacement. Reasoning as before, we may compare the motion in the z direction with the motion of a harmonic oscillator with the angular frequency

$$\omega_z = n^{\frac{1}{2}}\omega_0 \tag{3-23}$$

Accordingly, we see that to achieve both radial and vertical focusing the parameter n, which characterizes the variation of the field at the orbit, must satisfy the conditions

$$1 > n > 0 \tag{3-24}$$

The farther n is from zero, the stronger is the vertical restoring force. The farther n is from 1, the stronger is the radial restoring force.

If an electron is deflected in the radial direction or the vertical direction by a collision with a gas molecule, it will oscillate about the equilibrium orbit. Since for a harmonic oscillator with spring constant k the maximum energy is $\frac{1}{2}kx^2$, Eqs. (3-16) and (3-22) indicate that the ratio of the amplitudes of radial and vertical oscillators is

$$\frac{x}{z} = \left(\frac{n}{1 - n}\right)^{\frac{1}{2}} \tag{3-25}$$

In the original Kerst accelerator the vertical clearance was smaller than the radial clearance. Accordingly, the pole pieces were shaped to give an n closer to 1 than to 0 ($n \approx \frac{2}{3}$) in order to minimize the vertical excursions. Kerst and Serber[34] have shown by a more thorough treatment, in which consideration is given to the time variation of the magnetic field, that the amplitude of an oscillation varies as $B^{-\frac{1}{4}}$. The damping which results as B builds up leads to the useful result that the oscillating orbit gradually contracts to the equilibrium orbit. Care must be taken in the design and construction to avoid conditions which lead to antidamping. These may arise when azimuthal irregularities exist in the magnetic field and when resonances between the axial, radial, and orbital frequencies exist.

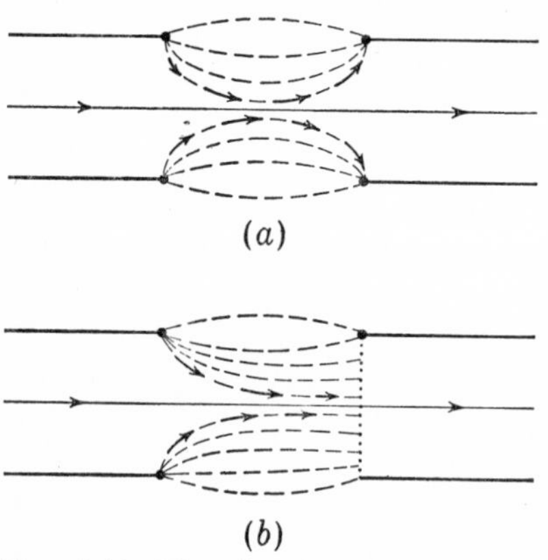

FIG. 3-11. The electric field between drift cylinders: (a) with symmetric gap; (b) when a grid is placed over the entrance.

The problem of geometric focusing in linear accelerators is entirely different. It can be shown by the use of electromagnetic theory that associated with the accelerating electrostatic field is an outward radial force tending to defocus the particles in the beam. Thus ion lenses must be incorporated not only to overcome this defocusing action but also to produce positive focusing. In proton accelerators the designs usually are based upon the lens action associated with the off-axis electrostatic field between the gaps. For a symmetrical gap (see Fig. 3-11a) this field has an inward component in the first half of the gap and an outward component in the second half. A focusing action automatically results from the fact that the accelerating particle spends a somewhat greater time in the first half of the gap than in the second half. Consequently, the net focusing force during a traversal of a gap is inward. This focusing action, however, is rather weak and is partially canceled by the fact (see discussion of phase stability in Sec. 3-9) that the electrostatic field builds up somewhat during the gap crossing. More positive focusing may be attained by shaping the field by use of metallic foils or screens at the entrance side of the drift tubes (see Fig. 3-11b).

The cyclotron, synchrocyclotron, and synchrotron afford natural opportunities for both electrostatic focusing and magnetic focusing. In the case of the cyclotron and synchrocyclotron the electrostatic field between the dees assists materially in axial focusing, particularly in the initial part of the acceleration (see Fig. 3-12a). This focusing action is enhanced by the fact that in these accelerators a particle crosses a gap during the decline of the voltage from the peak (see discussion of phase stability in Sec. 3-9). In the outer regions the cyclotron magnet is shimmed to give a slight radial decrease in magnetic field, thereby assisting in axial focusing (see Fig. 3-12*b*). A larger decrease can be tolerated in the synchrocyclotron, since here frequency modulation of the radio-frequency voltage is employed to maintain resonance. In the synchrotron, geometric focusing has depended mainly upon the magnetic effects discussed in connection with the betatron, and the electrostatic action at the gap is relatively unimportant.

Recently a strong axial and radial system has been proposed[35,36] which utilizes alternating-sector magnets with large positive and negative

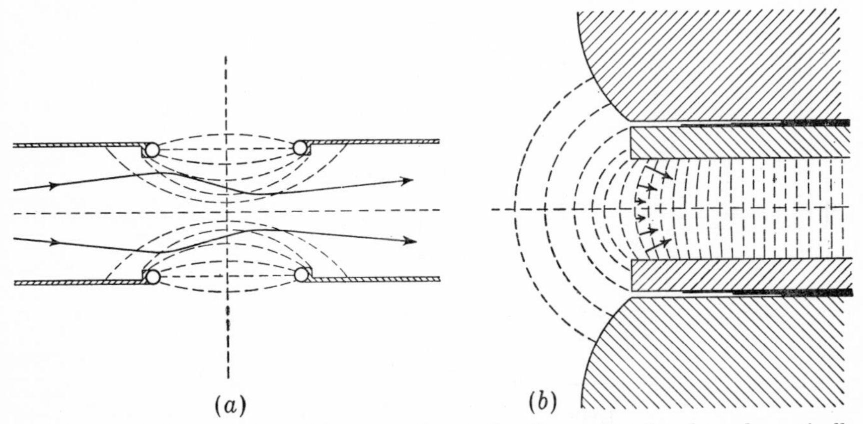

FIG. 3-12. (*a*) Cross section of dees near the acceleration region showing schematically the mechanism of electric focusing. (*b*) Representation of a fringing magnetic field and the focusing forces acting on ions off the central plane due to lines of force concave toward the center of the chamber. (*From Livingston, Ref.* 14.)

n values (see Fig. 3-13). This system will achieve a large reduction in the amplitude of radial and axial oscillations and consequently will require a relatively small magnet gap. The attractiveness of this proposal lies in the cost economy which might be achieved in accelerators in the range from 10 Bev upward. Design studies for high-energy machines based upon this proposal are being pursued aggressively at several research centers. A 25-Bev machine is under construction at Brookhaven National Laboratory.

Blewett[38] has shown that this same focusing principle is applicable to linear multiple accelerators. The application of this suggestion to the Berkeley proton linear accelerator by Numan and Watt[39] has shown considerable promise in increasing the beam current and decreasing the beam diameter.

3-9. Phase Stability in Multiple Accelerators. In addition to the geometric focusing which we have discussed, we may identify a focusing in multiple accelerators which is associated with the phase difference between the applied sinusoidal voltage and the time at which the particle crosses the gap. A phase-stable magnetic multiple accelerator possesses the property that particles which get ahead or behind will undergo oscillatory variations in angular velocity about the equilibrium angular velocity ω_0. A phase-stable linear multiple accelerator possesses the

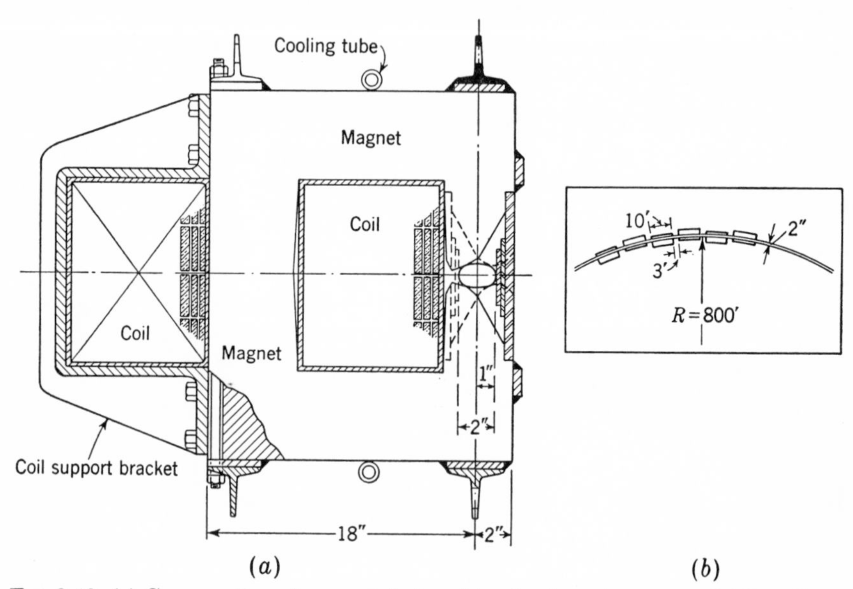

FIG. 3-13. (*a*) Cross section of magnet designed to give large transverse field gradients over 2- by $1\frac{1}{2}$-in. aperture. For focusing, alternate solid and dotted pole faces would be used. (*b*) Arrangement of alternate inside-C and outside-C magnets. (*From Livingston, Ref.* 37.)

property that particles which get ahead or behind tend to undergo oscillatory variations in traversal time through the drift tubes.

A necessary condition to achieve phase stability is that the peak available voltage V_p exceed the energy gain per gap crossing needed by the particle to keep in resonance. In Fig. 3-14*a* we plot the voltage vs. time of gap crossing for a single particle. In an accelerator designed so that particles receive the same voltage impulse $\bar{V}$ at each gap crossing, the design phase angle is ϕ given by

$$\bar{V} = V_p \sin \phi \qquad (3\text{-}26)$$

Particles which arrive at each gap at the instant corresponding to ϕ will, in accord with Eq. (3-3), always receive the appropriate impulse. A particle which has more (less) energy than that called for at a particular gap will necessarily arrive earlier (later). In consequence, this particle will receive a lesser (greater) energy impulse. After traversing several gaps, this particle will be brought to the stable phase and the resonant energy.

In a fixed-frequency cyclotron the region from 90 to 180° (see Fig. 3-14*b*) corresponds to the phase-stable region. This apparently reverse statement may be explained in the following way: Because $B(r)$ is a

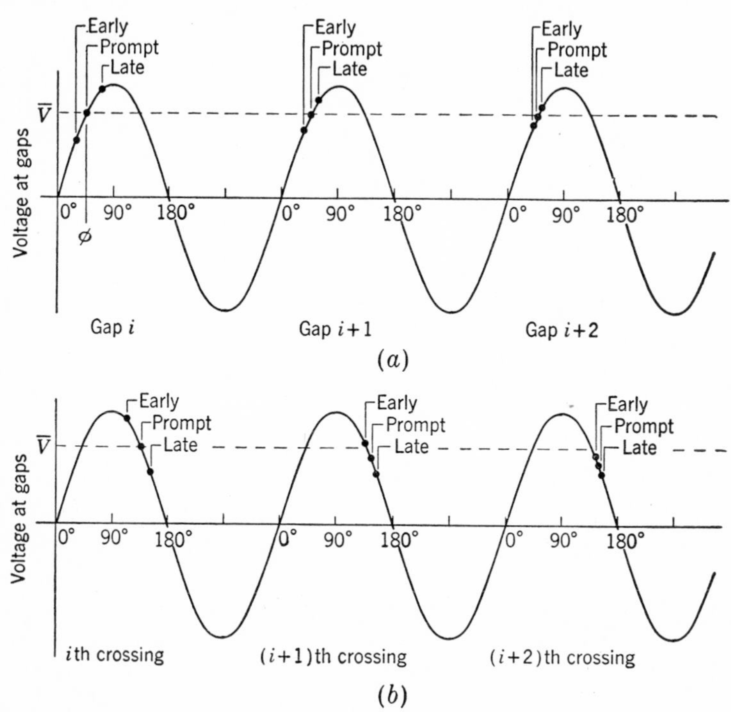

FIG. 3-14. Sketch showing (*a*) the phase relationship between the electric field, at the *i*th, $(i + 1)$th, and $(i + 2)$th gaps, and the time, with respect to an early, prompt, and late particle, showing phase-focusing property, and (*b*) the phase relationship between the electric fields, at the *i*th, $(i + 1)$th, and $(i + 2)$th crossings of the gap, between the dees in a fixed-frequency cyclotron. The phase-focusing property and the tendency of the central phase to drift toward 180° are shown schematically.

decreasing function (for geometric focusing) and $\gamma(r)$ is an increasing function, the time constant $\tau_{\frac{1}{2}}(r)$ is an increasing function of r. Consequently, a normal particle which starts out by crossing the gaps at 90° phase angle will gradually lose ground and drift toward 180° phase angle. If it reached this angle, the normal particle would simply circulate in an equilibrium orbit without further gain of energy. However, in a standard cyclotron the particles reach the target before they come to an equilibrium orbit. Suppose now that three particles arrive at the gap for a particular radius, one early, one on time, and the third late. The early (late) particle will receive a larger (smaller) energy impulse than the prompt particle and hence will take a greater (smaller) than normal increase in radius and time of half transit. Thus, accompanying the gradual drift of the particles toward the 180° phase angle, there will be a tendency for the phases to bunch or focus together. In the synchrocyclotron the period of the oscillator is increased to counteract the gradual drift of the phase toward 180°. In the electron synchrotron the magnetic field strength is increased to prevent the drift of the phase angle to 180°. In the proton synchrotron both the magnetic field and the period are increased. In each of these three cases phase focusing is still attained between 90 and 180° as long as the peak voltage is greater than that necessary for the particles to keep up with the magnetic field.

Because electrons in the betatron and synchrotron undergo central acceleration, they are continuously radiating energy. Theoretical and experimental studies[40] indicate that the radiation extends from the optical to the soft-X-ray range, and that the energy loss per revolution is given by

$$\Delta W = \frac{4\pi}{3} \frac{e^2}{R} \left(\frac{E}{mc^2} \right)^4 \tag{3-27}$$

where E is the total energy of the electron. This radiation loss will probably limit the application of the synchrotron principle in the acceleration of electrons above 1 Bev. However, the corresponding energy limitation for the proton, because of its greater mass, is in the range of hundreds of Bev. Apparently the only foreseeable limits to the energy attainable with accelerators are the financial resources behind the work. Recent developments in accelerator work have been summarized by Chu and Schiff[41] (see also Ref. 39).

3-10. Ion Sources. A source of ions or electrons is an essential component of every accelerator, and a wide variety of sources have been developed. The characteristics of an ion source which are desired in most particle accelerators are the following:

1. It should give a large, well-focused ion output to ensure as large a target current as possible and to minimize stray currents which contribute to power dissipation and electrode breakdown.

2. The energy spread should be small, particularly in constant-voltage types of accelerators, to minimize the energy spread of the projectiles coming out of the accelerator.

3. The source should be compact, rugged, dependable, and have a long life, to minimize repairs which involve breaking the vacuum and other time-consuming operations.

4. Wherever possible, the source should be designed such that final

adjustments of the position of the entire unit or perhaps components of it can be made by external manipulations.

5. In positive-ion sources the ratio of molecular ions to the desired atomic ions should be small, to minimize space charge and power dissipation.

6. The efficiency of the positive-ion source (ratio of atomic-ion output to neutral-gas output) should be large, to simplify the problem of maintaining a vacuum and to reduce the gas consumption. This latter consideration is particularly important in the use of H^3 and He^3 ions.

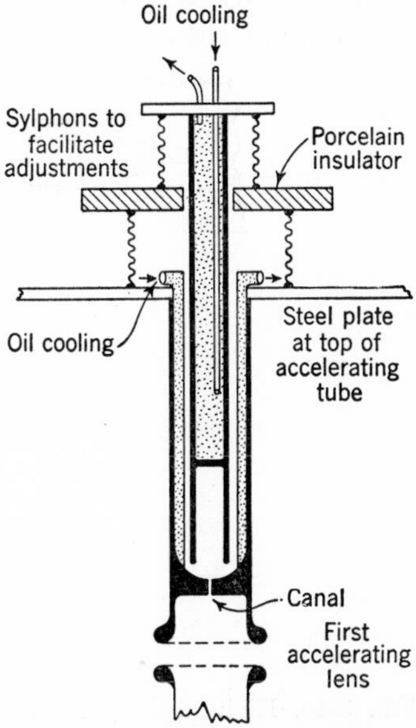

Sources of electrons for betatrons, synchrotrons, and linear electron accelerators are usually simple modifications of the electron guns which have been developed for high-powered radio, television, and X-ray tubes. Such sources are electron emitters in the form of a hot filament or indirectly heated cathode. An accelerating anode and a set of focusing or anode grids, which are maintained at a moderately high voltage, serve to form the electron beam. Electron-gun types of sources can readily be designed to provide electron currents as high as 100 ma or higher. Since the current or power capacities of most electron accelerators are usually of the order of hundreds of microamperes, the design of the electron source usually does not pose any difficult problem in an electron accelerator.

FIG. 3-15. Schematic diagram of cold-cathode high-voltage-discharge ion source. Positive ions move through the canal into the accelerating column. (*From Jelley, Ref.* 2; *Leonard Hill, Ltd., London, by kind permission.*)

Electron emitters are also an essential component of most sources of positive ions, although the form of the source of electrons varies widely depending upon the type of discharge phenomenon involved in the ion source. Here again, there is no difficulty in obtaining a sufficiently strong stream of electrons, but instead the problem is to utilize these electrons efficiently for the production of positive ions.

The earliest positive-ion sources were based upon high-voltage ($\sim$1000 volts) gaseous discharges in cold-cathode tubes maintained at a pressure of about 10^{-3} mm Hg (Fig. 3-15). Because of the large energy spread, the relatively small ion currents, and the rapid erosion of the electrodes, this type of source is no longer used widely.

A low-voltage capillary-arc gaseous discharge[42] provides the basis for a variety of ion sources in wide use, particularly for Van de Graaff and Cockcroft-Walton accelerators. The pressure in the discharge chamber is maintained at about 0.1 mm Hg. When used with hydrogen, these sources characteristically give off monatomic, diatomic, and triatomic hydrogen in about equal proportions. The energy spread is fairly small, and the ion currents in practice usually of the order of 10 μa. In some low-voltage-arc ion sources[43] a high-voltage probe is used to extract the ions from the discharge chamber and thereby increase the flow of ions relative to hydrogen molecules. The added source efficiency, however, is usually at the expense of energy spread and stray-ion current.

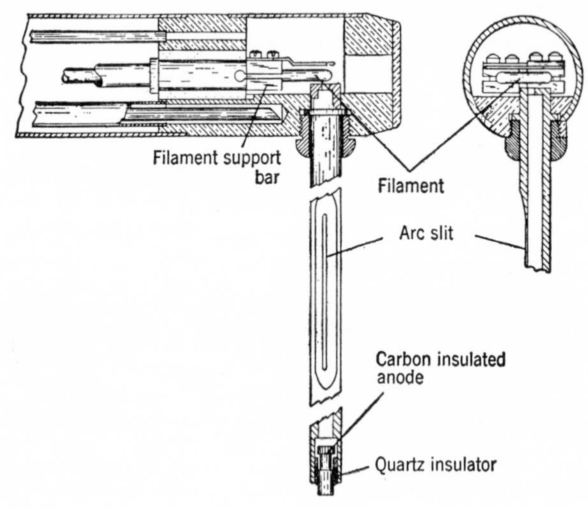

FIG. 3-16. High-intensity ion source for cyclotrons. (*From Livingston and Jones, Ref.* 44.)

In a type of ion source which is frequently used in cyclotrons the gas is channeled into a region near a hot filament where it is ionized by electron bombardment. These ions leak through exit holes into the central region between the dees, from which they are drawn each half cycle by the radio-frequency dee voltage. In most of the recent filament-type cyclotron sources the axial magnetic field of the cyclotron serves, in conjunction with electric fields set up by the anode and cathode, to constrain the electrons to oscillate along the axis of the source. Efficient ionization of the gas is accomplished in the central region, and rather large ion currents are obtained ($\sim$300 μa).

Recently Livingston and Jones[44] have developed an arc-discharge ion source for cyclotrons which provides ion currents as intense as can be handled by existing cyclotrons. The distinguishing features of this ion source (see Fig. 3-16) are its arc chamber of carbon, its heavy tantalum filament heated with direct current, and its use of a specially shaped accelerating electrode. The electrons emitted by the filament are accelerated to the anode by a potential of 100 to 300 volts and collimated by the magnetic field. Ions are formed in the hollow arc chamber in the intense gaseous discharge, which occurs at a few microns pressure. An accelerating slit (not shown) attached to one dee extracts ions through the long narrow slit in the arc chamber. Under d-c tests this type of source gives ion currents as high as 500 ma. Ion efficiencies as high as 95 per cent have been obtained, with protons constituting as much as 70 to 95 per cent of the current. In actual operation in 1.5-Mev and 22-Mev cyclotrons, proton current of 3 ma have been obtained. This type of ion source could probably be developed to yield still larger currents should the need arise.

Setlow,[(45)] using a hot-cathode source with an external axial magnetic field, designed for use in a linear accelerator, obtains peak ion currents of 100 ma when the electron beam is pulsed, for 250 μ sec, 60 times a second. At 25 μ Hg pressure the proton content of the beam averages about 35 per cent.

Another recent type of ion source is based upon discharge maintained in an electrodeless pyrex or quartz chamber by radio-frequency power inductively fed by a radio-frequency oscillator. An axial magnetic field ($\sim$1000 gauss) is often used to help constrain the electrons to oscillate within the discharge chamber. A source of this type developed by Hall[(46)] uses a 450-Mc/sec oscillator with 60-watt output. This source gives a beam current of 400 μa containing 60 per cent protons with a pin-point target spot and relatively few stray ions. Moak, Reese, and Good[(47)] utilize a 60-watt 100-Mc oscillator and a 5-kv-probe extracting system (see Fig. 3-17). Their source delivers 1.25 ma of positive ions, over 90 per cent of which are protons. Their final target spot has a diameter of 3 mm.

Several special sources or techniques have been developed which have particularly low gas consumption in relation to the number of atomic ions produced. Swann and Swingle[(48)] have developed a radio-frequency ion source which uses a transverse magnetic field for constraining the electrons. They obtain 50 μa of ions with a gas flow of less than 1 cm^3/hr (measured at atmospheric pressure). Arnold[(49)] finds that by mixing 1 cm^3 of T_2 with 49 cm^3 of He^4 he could obtain a 1-μa T^+ beam for 50 hr. Pool *et al.*,[(50)] using a remarkable vacuum system, conserve He^3 by trapping and recovering the unused gas and recycling it to the source.

Sources of minute currents of negative ions such as H^- (proton with two electrons), D^-, etc., have been known for some time;[(51)] however, only recently has a method been found to obtain substantial currents ($\sim$100 μa).[(52)] The method is based upon the passing of low-energy

(~10 kev) protons and deuterons through thin aluminum foils. About 25 per cent of the original positive ions emerge as negative ions. This recent development of sources of negative hydrogen and deuterium ions has prompted Alvarez[53] to suggest a scheme for doubling the energy obtainable with a constant-voltage accelerator. The negative ions are accelerated from ground to a high positive potential, where they pass through a second thin foil. This thin foil converts the high-energy negative ions to positive ions by stripping off the electrons. The particles then continue to gain energy in accelerating to ground potential. The

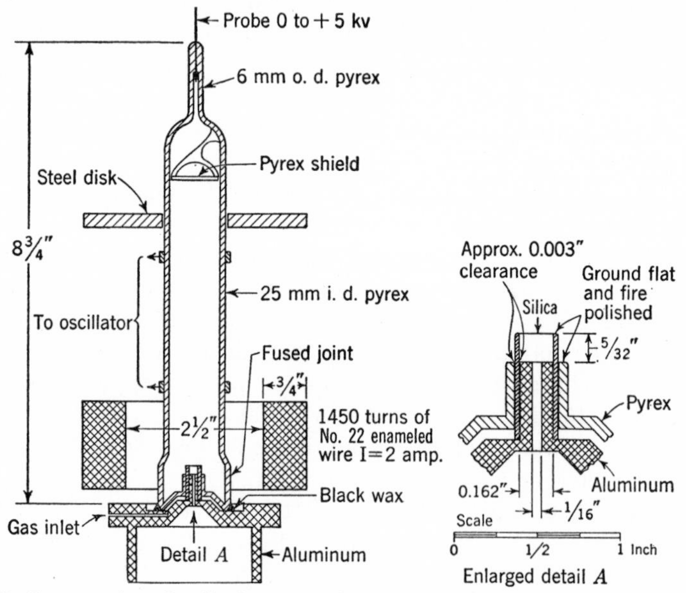

FIG. 3-17. Cross section of radio-frequency ion source and completed assembly of glass vessel and aluminum base. Details of extraction geometry are shown in enlarged view. (*From Moak, Reese, and Good, Ref.* 47.)

fact that both the ion source and target are at ground potential is a highly convenient feature of this type of arrangement.

The use of multiply ionized atoms heavier than He^4 has long been regarded as a possibility, although only recently has this possibility been realized. Beams of C^{12} (+6) have been produced in the 60-in. cyclotron at the University of California,[54] where internal currents of 0.2 μa with energies greater than 100 Mev have been realized. Other ions which have been accelerated at Berkeley and elsewhere include N^{14} (+3), C^{13} (+6), Ne^{20} (+9), Be^9 (+4), N^{14} (+6), C^{12} (+5), C^{13} (+5), and O^{16} (+6). These ions can conveniently be accelerated at the fundamental or various odd harmonics of the oscillator frequency. A natural internal mechanism apparently exists in cyclotrons which converts ions from the $\mathfrak{z}$ state of ionization to the $3\mathfrak{z}$, for example C (+2) to C (+6). If a cyclotron is tuned so that the fundamental frequency accelerates particles with charge $3\mathfrak{z}$, then the first odd harmonic will accelerate ions with $\mathfrak{z}$ (see Prob. 3-6). Apparently these lower-order ions are stripped by multiple bombardment by high-energy electrons which oscillate between the dees or possibly by collisions with gas molecules. Internal production of C (+6) from C (+2) and N (+6) from N (+2) has been observed.

The fact that the ions produced by collisions between the dees do not have a common center of rotation results in small beam intensity, large energy spread, and great difficulties in deflection. For these reasons a centrally located source of multiply ionized particles is quite advantageous. Jones and Zucker[55] have recently developed ion sources which produce milliampere currents of N (+1), N (+2), N (+3), and N (+4).

Experiments with stripped and multiple ions are now under way, and a number of unusual types of nuclear reactions have already been induced.

Sources of ions of many elements and compounds are needed in the field of mass spectroscopy (see Chap. 4). A description of the major sources used has been given by Inghram.[56] The most widely used sources are essentially of the electron-bombardment type used for particle accelerators. When the substance to be analyzed is normally in gaseous form, the same techniques used for hydrogen- and helium-ion sources are employed. For substances in the form of a solid or liquid, an oven serves to vaporize the source material to form a stream of gas for the discharge chamber. Electron-bombardment sources have the important advantages of low energy spread and high stability, which make them suitable for precision mass spectroscopy.

The hot-anode ion source used in mass spectroscopy is based upon the principle that, when two substances are heated together, the substance with a higher affinity for electrons will ionize the other substance. Accordingly, the source material is applied directly to filaments of tungsten or platinum (materials with relatively high work functions). When the filament is raised to a high temperature, ions of the source material are formed; these are then collimated and focused by the ion-accelerating system of the mass spectrograph. A variation of the hot-anode source has the anode in the form of a crucible which contains the source material and which is heated by electron bombardment. The hot-anode source also has the great advantage of producing ions with a very small energy spread.

The hot-spark ion source, which is perhaps the most widely used source in low-resolution mass spectroscopy (as well as in optical spectroscopy), is based upon the ionizing and vaporizing action at the high temperatures produced by a spark discharge. The discharge is usually maintained by a radio-frequency oscillator, and one of the electrodes either is made of the material to be analyzed or else is packed with this material. The ions emanating from this primary electrode are formed into a beam by the collimating and accelerating system.

Ion sources which are based upon a low-voltage arc have high current capabilities, and because of this they have found application to the separation of isotopes.[57] A form of mass spectroscope known as the calutron was developed extensively during World War II in connection with the electromagnetic separation of U^{235} from U^{238}. The method has now been developed to the point that most elements can now be separated into pure isotopic forms. The arc-discharge and the hot-spark types of ion sources are not usually used in precision mass spectroscopy, because the large energy spread would necessitate the use of velocity focusing or a velocity selection (see discussion in Sec. 4-9).

3-11. Neutron Sources.[58,59] Studies using the neutron as a nuclear projectile have been among the most informative in nuclear physics, and considerable effort has been expended to obtain beams of neutrons with precisely defined energies. Since the neutron is uncharged, the problem is quite different from the problem of obtaining beams of charged particles. For precision studies the most useful means of obtaining neutron beams are based upon neutron-yielding reactions induced by light charged nuclear particles which have been obtained from an accelerator. In many instances knowledge of the incident kinetic energy, the reaction energy, and the angle of the neutron beam relative to the incident charged-particle beam leads to a unique determination of the neutron energy (see Sec. 7-3). Among the more useful reactions for this purpose are

$$p + \mathrm{Li}^7 \rightarrow n + \mathrm{Be}^7 \tag{3-28}$$
$$p + \mathrm{H}^3 \rightarrow n + \mathrm{He}^3 \tag{3-29}$$
$$d + \mathrm{C}^{12} \rightarrow n + \mathrm{N}^{13} \tag{3-30}$$
$$d + \mathrm{H}^2 \rightarrow n + \mathrm{He}^3 \tag{3-31}$$

These reactions have been used to provide neutrons with precisely defined energies in the range from several kev to several Mev. The highly exoergic reaction

$$d + \mathrm{H}^3 \rightarrow n + \mathrm{He}^4 \tag{3-32}$$

has been particularly useful for obtaining neutrons in the 14- to 20-Mev range when only a low-voltage machine such as a Cockcroft-Walton or Van de Graaff accelerator is available.

Photoneutron reactions using high-energy gamma rays obtained from betatrons have also been employed to obtain neutrons for many studies.

The fact that these gamma rays have a continuous range of energy results in a heteroenergetic neutron beam. For this reason neutrons from such sources are not so desirable as neutrons obtained from charged-particle accelerators.

The earliest sources of neutrons made use of alpha particles obtained from naturally radioactive sources such as polonium or radon to induce a neutron-yielding nuclear reaction. The most commonly used reaction is

$$\alpha + \mathrm{Be}^9 \rightarrow \mathrm{C}^{12} + n \tag{3-33}$$

Such sources usually consist of an intimate chemical or mechanical mixture of beryllium and the alpha emitter. Because the neutrons emerge in all directions and because C^{12} is frequently left in an excited state, such sources yield neutrons ranging in energies from less than 1 Mev to about 10 Mev. Neutron sources utilizing radioactive gamma-ray sources in conjunction with deuterium or beryllium are also used in many practical sources. These are based upon the reactions

$$\gamma + \mathrm{H}^2 \rightarrow n + p \tag{3-34}$$

and

$$\gamma + \mathrm{Be}^9 \rightarrow n + 2\mathrm{He}^4 \tag{3-35}$$

For reasons of intensity the gamma-ray source is surrounded by beryllium or deuterium, and neutrons emerging in all directions are utilized. Because of this, as well as other causes, such as neutron scattering, the neutrons emerge with an appreciable energy spread.

The nuclear reactor provides the most intense source of neutrons now available with fluxes as great as 10^{14} neutrons/cm²-sec[60] attainable in the center of a high-powered reactor. Here again a difficulty arises in doing precise work in that the neutrons have energies ranging from a fraction of an ev to several Mev. In the very-low-energy range (0 to 1000 ev) mechanical and crystal neutron spectrometers are available to "monochromatize" the beam into various desired energy components. However, as yet this technique is not easily used in the Mev range of energies. The intense neutron beams obtained from a nuclear reactor have been extremely useful in the production of new stable and radioactive nuclides, and a tremendous quantity of information has been obtained from such studies.

Neutrons in the 100-Mev range of energies have been obtained by using deuterons and protons from synchrocyclotrons. When deuterons are used, one takes advantage of a stripping reaction in which the proton is captured by a light target nucleus while the neutron continues with approximately half of the deuteron energy. When protons are used, the process is essentially a direct collision between the proton and neutron within the target nucleus, and the neutron emerges with the major portion of the proton energy. Neutrons in the Bev range of energies are naturally available in cosmic rays, and these have been used in many studies, particularly in elementary-particle physics.

PROBLEMS

3-1. A section of a linear proton accelerator has five drift tubes and is driven by a 50-Mc oscillator. Assuming the protons are injected into the first drift tube at 100,000 volts and gain 100,000 volts in every gap crossing, (*a*) what is the output after the fifth drift tube? (*b*) What is the length of the section (ignore gap widths)?

3-2. A fixed-frequency 60-in. cyclotron is powered by a 50,000-volt 5-Mc radio-frequency power supply.

(*a*) What magnetic fields will secure resonance for protons, deuterons, and alpha particles?

(*b*) What energies will these particles attain (in Mev)?

***3-3.** The magnet of a frequency-modulated cyclotron is shimmed to give a magnetic field which varies approximately as $15{,}000(1 - 0.05r/r_0)^2$, where r_0 is 80 in. Allowing for relativistic effects, what is the resonance frequency for protons at 0, 25, 50, 60, 70, and 80 cm radius? Assuming a voltage gain of 10,000 volts per gap crossing, plot the approximate variation of radius with time and of resonant frequency with time during an acceleration cycle.

3-4. A betatron is designed to the following specifications: $R = 20$ cm; $B = 4000$ gauss (peak field at orbit); frequency, 60 cycles/sec; $n = \frac{1}{2}$; internal target.

(*a*) What are the kinetic energy (in Mev) and momentum of the output electrons?

(*b*) Approximately how many revolutions does an electron make during the accelerating period?

(*c*) What is the de Broglie wavelength of these electrons?

(*d*) What is the shortest wavelength of the emitted X rays?

(*e*) Show that electrons which depart from the equilibrium orbit in either the radial or vertical directions will return to these orbits after turning through $(2\pi)^{\frac{1}{2}}$ radians.

3-5. Assuming a guide field of 15 kilogauss is attainable, what radius is needed in a proton synchrotron to reach 10 Bev? 100 Bev? What are the resonance frequencies at the ends of the accelerating cycles in these cases?

3-6. (*a*) What relationship between the magnetic field of a cyclotron and the oscillator frequency f must be satisfied for a $\mathfrak{z}$-fold ionized atom of mass number a to rotate at the subharmonic orbital frequency $f/(2n + 1)$?

(*b*) How is the energy attained by such particles related to the radius and magnetic field strength?

(*c*) A 60-in. cyclotron is tuned to accelerate deuterons to 20 Mev at the fundamental frequency. List all the ions of stable nuclides or long-lived radionuclides up to mass number 16 which would be in resonance at various subharmonics, and give the energies attainable by each.

†**3-7.** Prepare a list of particle accelerators now in operation which yield energies exceeding 100 Mev.

REFERENCES

1. Cockcroft, J. D., and E. Walton: *Proc. Roy. Soc. (London)*, **A136**, 619 (1932).
2. Jelley, J. V.: *Atomics*, **3**, 61 (1952).
3. Brasch, A., and F. Lange: *Z. Physik*, **70**, 10 (1931).
4. Lauritsen, C. C., and R. D. Bennett: *Phys. Rev.*, **32**, 850 (1928).
5. Fortescue, R. L.: *Prog. Nuclear Phys.*, **1**, 21 (1950).
6. Van de Graaff, R. J., *et al.*: *Repts. Prog. Phys.* **11**, 1 (1947).

7. Van de Graaff, R. J.: *Phys. Rev.*, **38**, 1919 (1931).
8. Lamphere, R. W., and G. P. Robinson: *Nucleonics*, **10**(10), 31 (1952).
9. Adair, R. K.: private communication.
10. Slater, J. C.: *Ann. Rev. Nuclear Sci.*, **1**, 199 (1952).
11. Sloan, D. H., and E. O. Lawrence: *Phys. Rev.*, **38**, 2021 (1931).
12. Alvarez, L. W., *et al.*: *U.S. Atomic Energy Comm. Document AECU* 120, 1948.
13. Panofsky, W. K. H.: personal communication.
14. Livingston, M. S.: *J. Appl. Phys.*, **15**, 2 (1944).
15. Pickavance, T. G.: *Prog. Nuclear Phys.*, **1**, 1 (1950).
16. Livingston, M. S.: *Ann. Rev. Nuclear Sci.*, **1**, 157 (1952).
17. Lawrence, E. O., and N. E. Edlefsen: *Science*, **72**, 376 (1930).
18. Atterling, H., and G. Lindström: *Arkiv Fysik*, **4**, 559 (1952).
19. Livingston, M. S.: *Ann. Rev. Nuclear Sci.*, **1**, 163 (1952).
20. Livingston, M. S.: *Advances in Electronics*, **1**, 269 (1948).
21. McMillan, E. M.: *Phys. Rev.*, **68**, 143 (1945).
22. Veksler, V.: *J. Phys.* (*U.S.S.R.*), **9**, 153 (1945).
23. Heinrich, L. R., *et al.*: *Rev. Sci. Instr.*, **20**, 887 (1949).
24. Kerst, D. W.: *Am. J. Phys.*, **10**, 221 (1942).
25. Kerst, D. W.: *Phys. Rev.*, **60**, 47 (1941).
26. Katz, L.: personal communication.
27. Livingston, M. S.: *Ann. Rev. Nuclear Sci.*, **1**, 169 (1952).
28. Thomas, J. E., Jr., W. L. Kraushaar, and I. Halpern: *Ann. Rev. Nuclear Sci.*, **1**, 175 (1952).
29. Livingston, M. S., J. P. Blewett, C. K. Green, and L. J. Haworth: *Rev. Sci. Instr.*, **21**, 7 (1950).
30. Bacher, R.: private communication.
31. Thomas, E., P. Mittelman, and H. H. Goldsmith: *U.S. Atomic Energy Comm. Document BNL-L*-101, 1948.
32. Cushman, B. E.: *U.S. Atomic Energy Comm. Document UCRL* 1238, 1951.
33. Schewchuck, S.: *U.S. Atomic Energy Comm. Document UCRL* 1481, 1951.
34. Kerst, D. W., and R. Serber: *Phys. Rev.*, **60**, 53 (1941).
35. Christophilos, W.: unpublished.
36. Courant, E. D., M. S. Livingston, and H. S. Snyder: *Phys. Rev.*, **88**, 1190 (1952).
37. Livingston, M. S.: *Nucleonics*, **11**(1), 13 (1953).
38. Blewett, J. B.: *Phys. Rev.*, **88**, 1197 (1952).
39. "Notes on the High Energy Accelerator Conference, Dec. 16–17, 1952," *U.S. Atomic Energy Comm. Document BNL* 213 (c-16).
40. Corson, D. R.: *Phys. Rev.*, **90**, 748 (1953).
41. Chu, E. L., and L. I. Schiff: *Ann. Rev. Nuclear Sci.*, **2**, 79 (1952).
42. Lamar, E. S., and O. Luhr: *Phys. Rev.*, **44**, 947 (1933); **46**, 87 (1934).
43. Tuve, M. A., O. Dahl, and L. F. Hafstad: *Phys. Rev.*, **48**, 243 (1935).
44. Livingston, R. S., and R. J. Jones: personal communication.
45. Setlow, R. B.: *Rev. Sci. Instr.*, **20**, 558 (1949).
46. Hall, R. N.: *Rev. Sci. Instr.*, **19**, 905 (1948).
47. Moak, C. D., H. Reese, Jr., and W. M. Good: *Nucleonics*, **9**(3), 20 (1951).
48. Swann, C. P., and J. P. Swingle, Jr.: *Rev. Sci. Instr.*, **23**, 636 (1952).
49. Arnold, W. R., Jr.: *Rev. Sci. Instr.*, **23**, 97 (1952).
50. Kundu, D. W., T. W. Donaven, M. L. Pool, and J. K. Long: *Phys. Rev.*, **89**, 1200 (1953).
51. Bennett, W.: *Phys. Rev.*, **49**, 97 (1936).
52. Tuck, J.: private communication to L. W. Alvarez (Ref. 53).
53. Alvarez, L. W.: *Rev. Sci. Instr.*, **22**, 706 (1951).

54. Rossi, C. B., *et al.*: *Phys. Rev.*, **93**, 256 (1954).
55. Jones, J., and A. Zucker: in press.
56. Inghram, M. G.: *Advances in Electronics*, **1**, 219 (1948).
57. C. P. Keim: *Am. Rev. Nuclear Sci.*, **1**, 263 (1952).
58. Hanson, A. O., R. F. Taschek, and T. H. Williams: *Revs. Mod. Phys.*, **21**, 4 (1949).
59. Feld, B. T.: *Exptl. Nuclear Phys.*, **2**, 208 (1953).
60. *Nucleonics*, **12** (4), 1954. This issue is devoted to reports given at the Research Reactor Conference at Oak Ridge in February, 1954.
61. Simon, A. W.: *Am. J. Phys.*, **22**, 318 (1954).

CHAPTER 4

PRECISION INSTRUMENTS AND METHODS

The impact upon nuclear physics of the relatively recent development of precision nuclear instruments is still not clear. This work is transforming nuclear physics from a science based upon semiquantitative data to a science based upon data as precise as those available to almost any other branch of physics. Certainly the chances of discovering exact laws of nuclear physics have been immeasurably enhanced by this work.

This chapter will be devoted to the presentation of the principles underlying various types of "precision" nuclear "spectroscopes." We use here the term "precision" to signify an instrument which gives results with at least two significant figures. We use the word "spectroscope" as a broad term which includes not only instruments which separate electromagnetic wavelengths but also instruments which separate particles according to their kinetic energies, masses, and other dynamical parameters. The word "spectroscope" will also be used as a more general term which includes spectrometers (meter detection) and spectrographs (emulsion detection).

4-1. Figures of Merit for Precision Energy Analyzers.[1] The precise determination of the kinetic energies or momenta of particles is usually based upon the direct measurement of various trajectory parameters in known electrostatic or magnetic fields. Other methods which are useful are based upon the measurement of time of flight over a known path or the resonance of some oscillation with a precisely known radio-frequency wave. The main physical considerations which determine the suitability of any one method are (1) the resolution attainable and (2) the extent of utilization of the particles. Of course, cost, difficulty of construction, and other practical considerations also determine which type of instrument is used. The momentum and energy resolutions of an instrument are defined by

$$R_p = \frac{p}{\Delta p} \tag{4-1}$$

and

$$R_T = \frac{T}{\Delta T} \tag{4-2}$$

where Δp and ΔT are the inherent uncertainties in momentum and energy. These uncertainties usually signify the momentum or energy width (distance between the half-maximum points) of a line corresponding to monoergic incident particles. In some instances the resolution is independent of the energy or momentum. In other instances the resolution depends upon energy or momentum, so that an average figure of merit must be given for the instrument. Frequently the resolving power is characterized by the reciprocal of R expressed in per cent.

The figure of merit which is used to measure the extent of utilization of the particles within the energy or momentum interval ΔT or Δp depends upon the nature of the source and other features of the instrument. When the source may be treated as a point, a useful figure of merit is the "gathering power," which is defined by

$$G = \frac{\Omega}{4\pi} \tag{4-3}$$

where Ω is the solid angle into which particles may be accepted. Frequently this quantity is expressed in percentage and called the transmission. When extended sources are used, the luminosity is a useful figure of merit; it is defined by

$$L = GS \tag{4-4}$$

where S is the area of the source. For a given instrument an inverse relation exists between the gathering power or luminosity and the resolution. However, the relation between luminosity or gathering power and resolution differs greatly from one instrument to another, in the sense that the best-designed instruments attain high resolution and high luminosity simultaneously.

4-2. Electrostatic Analyzers.[2-4] The direct measurement of an accelerating or retarding voltage may be used to determine the kinetic energy of a particle ($T = \mathfrak{z}eV$). The voltage-measuring system consists of a voltage-dividing network containing precision high and low resistors in series across the voltage supply and a potentiometer across the low resistor. The high resistance in the voltage divider must be as large as possible to avoid draining too much power into the measuring system. This method becomes impractical for voltages much greater than 0.1 Mv because very high resistors with stable characteristics are not available.

Voltage measurements with low-voltage measuring equipment may be used for kinetic energies which are equivalent to high accelerator voltages by arrangements which may be characterized as dynamic voltage dividers. One such arrangement requires the measurement of the deflection of a beam of monoergic charged particles in a uniform electrostatic field. If a beam of positively charged particles with charge $\mathfrak{z}e$ and mass m is directed with a velocity v perpendicularly to a uniform electric field $\mathcal{E}$, the linear deflection y in the direction of the field is

$$y = \frac{1}{2} a_y t^2 = \frac{\mathfrak{z}e\mathcal{E}L^2}{2mv^2} = \frac{\mathfrak{z}eL^2\mathcal{V}}{4dT} \qquad (4\text{-}5)$$

where a_y is the vertical acceleration, t is the time of traversal, L is the horizontal distance traversed, $\mathcal{V}$ is the voltage between two plates, and d is the separation. Since $T = \mathfrak{z}eV$, where V is the equivalent accelerator voltage, we have

$$V = \frac{L^2}{4dy} \mathcal{V} \qquad (4\text{-}6)$$

$L^2/4dy$ can be made sufficiently large that $\mathcal{V}$ is within the range of a reliable voltage divider–potentiometer system.

An inwardly directed radial electrostatic field may also be used as the basis of energy measurement. Let us suppose the field $\mathcal{E}_0$ is needed to maintain a particle precisely in a path of radius r_0. Using Eq. (1-29) for the centrifugal "force," we see that $\mathcal{E}_0$ must satisfy

$$\mathcal{E}_0 \mathfrak{z} e = \frac{pv}{r_0} = \frac{mv^2}{r_0} = \frac{2T}{r_0} \qquad (4\text{-}7)$$

where the last forms are for the nonrelativistic case. Letting $T = V\mathfrak{z}e$, where V is the accelerator voltage, we find that the necessary field is

$$\mathcal{E}_0 = \frac{2V}{r_0} \qquad (4\text{-}8)$$

A radially directed electrostatic field of this magnitude can be obtained by placing a voltage $\mathcal{V}$ between two closely spaced (separation d) coaxial cylindrical plates or concentric spherical plates which have the average radius r_0. For these cases the field at the mean radius r_0 is given approximately by $\mathcal{E}_0 = \mathcal{V}/d$, so that the accelerator voltage is

$$V = \frac{r_0}{2d} \mathcal{V} \qquad (4\text{-}9)$$

Usually $r_0/2d$ is a very large number, so that relatively low voltage equipment suffices for the measurement of $\mathcal{V}$.

Electrostatic systems based upon cylindrical or spherical electrostatic fields can be used to obtain direction focusing over limited ranges of angles. A system which possesses direction focusing may be regarded as an analogue of an optical lens-prism combination, in that it achieves dispersion in energies (color) which over a range of angles is independent of the direction (rays). To indicate how the focusing property may be achieved, let us consider the nonrelativistic motion of particles in a cylindrical field which has the magnitude

$$\mathcal{E} = \mathcal{E}_0 \frac{r_0}{r} \tag{4-10}$$

We shall accept the z axis as the axis of symmetry (see Fig. 4-1). From our previous discussion we know that particles with charge $\mathfrak{z}e$ with the kinetic energy $T = \mathcal{E}_0 r_0 \mathfrak{z}e/2$ will move in an equilibrium orbit of radius r_0. Hence, treating the inertial force as a real force (d'Alembert's prin-

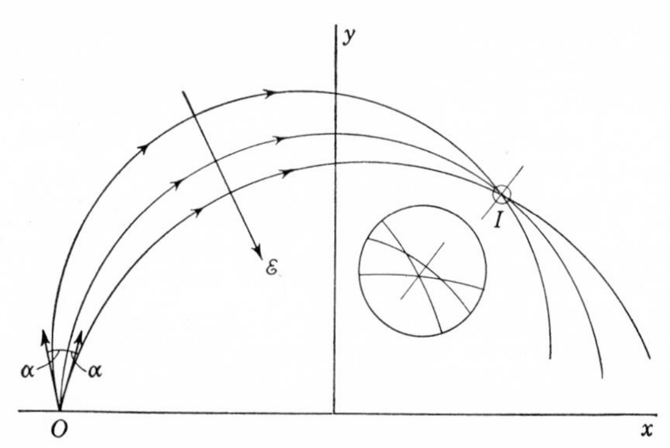

FIG. 4-1. Schematic diagram showing the focusing properties of a cylindrical electrostatic field. The insert is an enlarged view of the image point, indicating the small aberrations associated with the noncentral rays.

ciple), we may state that there is no net radial force on a "central ray," *i.e.*,

$$f_r = \frac{mv_0^2}{r_0} - \mathcal{E}_0 \mathfrak{z}e = 0 \tag{4-11}$$

Let us now suppose that a particle with the initial velocity v_0 leaves an object point O in the xy plane at a small angle α with respect to the central ray. The net force acting on this particle when it is instantaneously moving with the velocity v in a path of radius r will produce a radial acceleration $\ddot{r}$ which satisfies

$$m\ddot{r} = \frac{mv^2}{r} - \mathfrak{z}e \frac{\mathcal{E}_0 r_0}{r} \tag{4-12}$$

Since the force is radially directed, the angular momentum around the z axis is conserved, and hence

$$mvr = mv_0 r_0 \cos \alpha \approx mv_0 r_0 \left(1 - \frac{\alpha^2}{2} + \cdots \right) \tag{4-13}$$

Using this to eliminate v from Eq. (4-12), we find

$$m\ddot{r} = \frac{m^2 v_0^2 r_0^2 \cos^2 \alpha}{r^3} - \frac{\mathfrak{z}e\mathcal{E}_0 r_0}{r}$$

Letting $r = r_0 + x$, we may set

$$r^n = (r_0 + x)^n = r_0^n \left[1 + n\frac{x}{r_0} + \frac{n(n-1)}{2}\left(\frac{x}{r_0}\right)^2 + \cdots\right] \qquad (4\text{-}14)$$

It immediately follows, when we discard terms of order α^2 and terms of order x^2/r^2 and make use of Eq. (4-11), that

$$\ddot{x} = -2\frac{v_0^2}{r_0^2}x = -2\omega_0^2 x \qquad (4\text{-}15)$$

where $\omega_0 = v_0/r_0$. This is precisely the differential equation which governs the motion of a harmonic oscillator. The general solution of this differential equation is

$$x = A \sin \sqrt{2}\,\omega_0 t + B \cos \sqrt{2}\,\omega_0 t \qquad (4\text{-}16)$$

If $t = 0$ represents the instant at which the particle leaves O, the initial conditions are $x(0) = 0$ and $\dot{x}(0) = v_0 \sin \alpha \approx v_0\alpha$. Using these conditions to evaluate A and B, we find that the appropriate equation of motion is

$$x = \frac{r_0\alpha}{\sqrt{2}} \sin \sqrt{2}\,\omega_0 t \qquad (4\text{-}17)$$

The fact that, in the first order in α, the period of radial oscillation is independent of α accounts for the focusing properties of this field arrangement. The deviation parameter x, which vanishes at $t = 0$, also vanishes for any small α when $\sqrt{2}\,\omega_0 t = \pi$ or at the angle $\varphi = \omega_0 t = \pi/\sqrt{2}$. Accordingly, it follows in a first-order analysis that all particles which leave O with the velocity v_0 at a small angle relative to the central ray are refocused to an image point at an angle $\pi/\sqrt{2} = 127°17'$ away. This property of a cylindrical electrostatic lens was first pointed out by Hughes and Rojansky.[5] A more complicated analysis[3] carried out to the second order in α and x/r reveals the existence of aberrations which give rise to an image width. When consideration is also given to the finite size of the source or the width of the object-defining slit (W_O), it is found that the image width (W_I) for the cylindrical case is approximately

$$W_I = \tfrac{4}{3}r_0\alpha^2 + W_O \qquad (4\text{-}18)$$

To determine the dispersion of a cylindrical analyzer, let us now consider a "central ray" which has the initial velocity $v_0 + \Delta v$. Again eliminating the instantaneous velocity by use of conservation of angular momentum, it follows to the first order in $\Delta v/v_0$, x/r_0, and α that

$$\ddot{x} = -2\omega_0^2 x + 2\omega_0\,\Delta v \qquad (4\text{-}19)$$

The solution of this equation which satisfies the initial conditions $x(0) = 0$ and $\dot{x}(0) = 0$ is

$$x = \frac{\Delta v}{v_0} r_0(1 - \cos \sqrt{2}\, \omega_0 t) \tag{4-20}$$

At the focusing angle $\sqrt{2}\, \omega_0 t = \pi$ the particle with anomalous velocity $v_0 + \Delta v$ is displaced a distance (see Fig. 4-2)

$$Y = 2 \frac{\Delta v}{v_0} r_0 \tag{4-21}$$

The ratio of this distance to the image width [Eq. (4-18)] determines the velocity-resolving power of the system.

Focusing is attainable with cylindrical plates subtending smaller angles than $\pi/\sqrt{2}$, providing that the image and object points are placed at

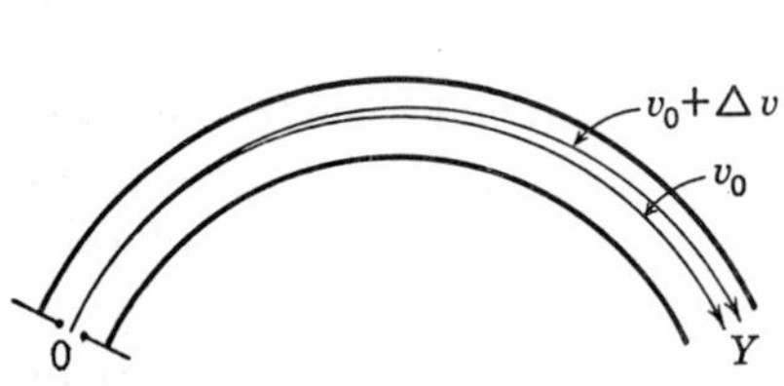

FIG. 4-2. Diagram showing a 127°17′ cylindrical analyzer, indicating the velocity dispersion for "central rays."

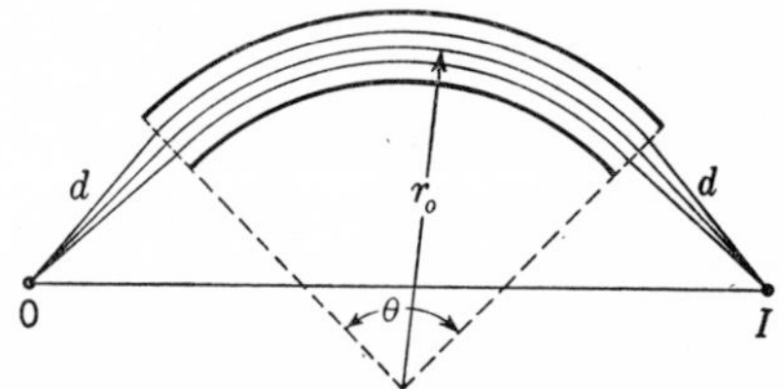

FIG. 4-3. Diagram illustrating the focusing properties of a cylindrical electrostatic lens when the source and image point lie outside the field.

critical locations outside the field. It can be shown that, in the symmetrical case illustrated in Fig. 4-3, the distance from the source and image to the faces of the cylindrical lens, which subtends the angle θ, is given by

$$d = \frac{r_0}{\sqrt{2}} \cot \frac{\theta}{\sqrt{2}} \tag{4-22}$$

We note that this distance reduces to zero when $\theta = \pi/\sqrt{2}$, which corresponds to the special case studied by Rojansky and Hughes. Cylindrical analyzers with $\theta = 90°$ are used in many practical systems.

The focusing properties of a spherical electrostatic field may be treated in a similar way. In this case the spherical field is characterized by

$$\mathcal{E} = \mathcal{E}_0 \frac{r_0^2}{r^2} \tag{4-23}$$

The analysis of the motion of a particle in a plane defined by its initial velocity and passing through the center of the sphere is almost identical with the cylindrical case. The analysis leads immediately to the equation of motion

$$x = r_0 \alpha \sin \omega_0 t \tag{4-24}$$

Consequently the focusing angle is $\varphi = \pi = 180°$. The velocity dispersion is found to be

$$Y = 4 \frac{\Delta v}{v_0} r_0 \tag{4-25}$$

An analysis of the aberrations[6] leads to the image width

$$W_I = 2r_0\alpha^2 + W_O \tag{4-26}$$

Purcell[6] by an analysis of trajectories has shown that a sector-type spherical electrostatic analyzer satisfies a focusing condition which is embodied in the rule that the image and object points lie along a line which contains the center of the spherical plates. In the symmetrical case (see Fig. 4-4) the distances to the openings and the object and image distances are given by

$$d = r_0 \cot \frac{\theta}{2} \tag{4-27}$$

and

$$P = Q = r_0 \csc \frac{\theta}{2} \tag{4-28}$$

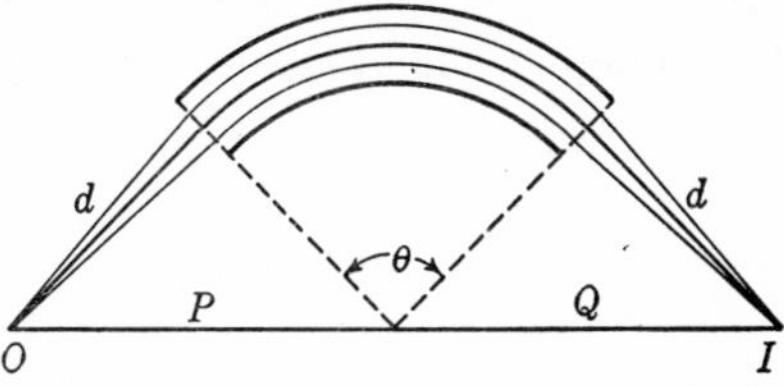

FIG. 4-4. Diagram illustrating one of the focusing properties of a spherical electrostatic lens. The second focusing property follows from the symmetry of the figure about the O-I axis.

When particles leave a point source within a slight range of angles with respect to an axis passing through the common center of the spherical plates, they are brought to an image point which lies on this axis, as indicated by Fig. 4-4. This planar-type focusing is also possessed by the cylindrical analyzer. However, the spherical analyzer in addition has the feature that particles leaving in any plane containing the principal axis will be refocused to the same image point. This conical focusing property, which is an automatic consequence of the symmetry of the apparatus about the principal axis, greatly enhances the gathering power of the instrument.

Cylindrical and spherical electrostatic energy analyzers have been used for light, charged nuclear particles and for massive ions but not for beta particles. A relativistic treatment shows that large systems would be required and that the attainment of focusing would be difficult in the relativistic case for beta particles.

4-3. Magnetic Analyzers.[2-4] Analyzers which are based on the measurement of the trajectories of charged particles in known magnetic fields may be divided into two general classes: flat, or prism, spectroscopes and helical, or lens, spectroscopes. In flat instruments the particles move approximately in a plane which is perpendicular to the magnetic field. If the field is uniform, the particles move in circular paths with a common radius of curvature, which is given by Eq. (1-30). For these cases the focusing properties may be derived by well-known methods of analytical geometry.

The simplest example of such an analyzer is the 180° spectroscope, whose focusing properties are shown in Fig. 4-5. The fact that a 180° spectroscope has direction focusing is an automatic geometric property of the semicircle, which the reader may test experimentally, using a compass and a straightedge. Alternatively, we may analyze the trajectory using d'Alembert's principle. The radial differential equation in this case is

$$m\gamma\ddot{r} = \frac{mv^2\gamma}{r} - evB \tag{4-29}$$

Here, however, B is constant, and since no work is done on the particle by a magnetic field, v and $\gamma(v)$ are also constant. It follows immediately

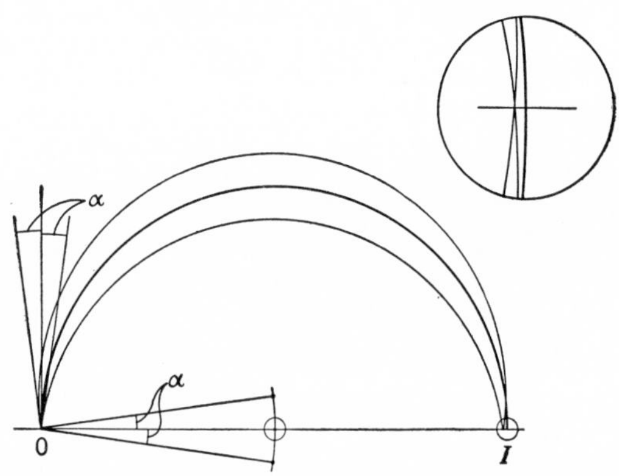

FIG. 4-5. Diagram showing natural focusing property of 180° spectroscope. Insert is an enlargement of image showing second-order aberrations.

that the deviation coordinate satisfies the differential equation

$$\ddot{x} = -\omega_0{}^2x \tag{4-30}$$

where $\omega_0 = v/r_0$.

The remaining discussion is similar to that for electrostatic analyzers. We find the focusing angle is 180°, and the dispersion in the nonrelativistic case is

$$Y = 2\frac{\Delta p}{p_0}r_0 = 2\frac{\Delta v}{v_0}r_0 \tag{4-31}$$

The image width is

$$W_I = r_0\alpha^2 + W_O \tag{4-32}$$

The justification for the aberration term in the image width is particularly simple in this case. We see in Fig. 4-5 that the noncentral rays taking off at $\pm\alpha$ arrive at a point whose distance from O is equal to $2r_0 \cos \alpha \approx 2r_0(1 - \frac{1}{2}\alpha^2)$. This differs from the central ray $(2r_0)$ by the distance $r_0\alpha^2$.

The focusing properties of wedge-shaped magnets are based upon the intrinsic properties of circles and triangles. The fact that the extended tangents to circular arcs which are terminated by a wedge will converge may be verified by the use of a compass and straightedge. A dynamical analysis also reveals this same property, providing that one neglects the effect of the fringe field upon entering and leaving the wedge. An approximate correction for the effect of the fringe field may be made by assuming that the magnetic field extends about one gap width beyond the actual face of the magnet.

Some of the focusing and dispersion relations for wedge-shaped spectroscopes can be summarized in simple terms by virtue of certain geometric

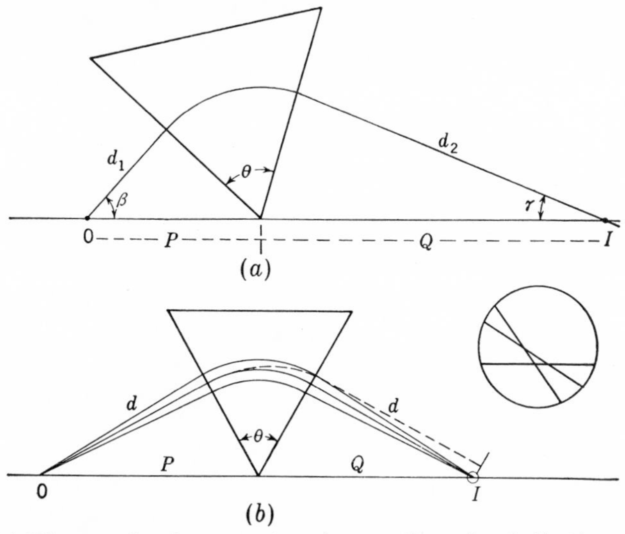

FIG. 4-6. (*a*) Diagram showing geometry of magnetic wedge, indicating the location of source and image according to the rule of Barber and Stephens. (*b*) The focusing of paths in the symmetric wedge. Insert shows enlargement of image. (*Adapted from Stephens, Ref.* 8.)

conditions which have been shown, by Barber[7] and Stephens,[8] to follow from analyses of trajectories. When the field is adjusted such that the central particle enters and emerges from a magnetic wedge perpendicular to the faces, then the conjugate image and object points lie along the line which contains the effective vertex of the wedge (see Fig. 4-6*a*). The relationships between the distances P, Q, d_1, d_2, the angles β and γ shown in Fig. 4-6*a*, the angle θ of the wedge, and the radius r_0 may be determined by studying the geometry of the situation. To simplify the discussion, let us again consider only the symmetrical case, *i.e.*, the case when $P = Q$ and $\beta = \gamma = \theta/2$ (see Fig. 4-6*b*). For this case it is readily apparent that

$$P = Q = r_0 \csc \frac{\theta}{2} \tag{4-33}$$

and that

$$d = r_0 \cot \frac{\theta}{2} \tag{4-34}$$

We note that, when θ is 180°, d vanishes and P becomes simply r_0. This is the case for the well-known 180° analyzer.

The term in the aberration width for wedge magnets which is proportional to the angular opening is a purely geometric effect. By appropriately modifying the fields acting upon noncentral rays, it is possible to reduce this term or eliminate it altogether. For example, the intrinsic focusing property of a 180° instrument may be improved by shaping the field slightly so that particles going on the inside and outside of the central

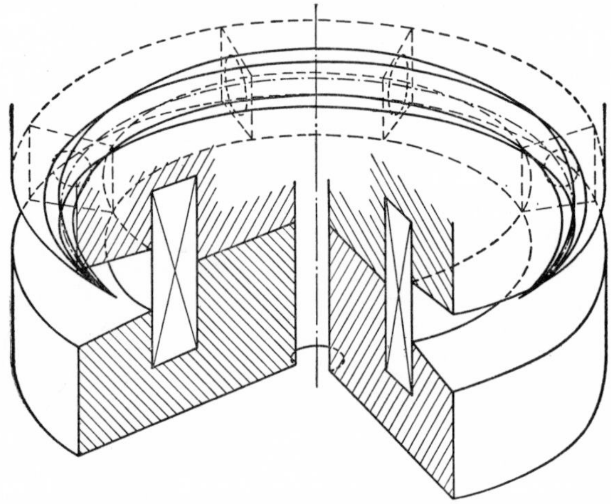

FIG. 4-7. A diagram showing the double-focusing property of a 254°33′ magnetic field with $n = \frac{1}{2}$. *(From Siegbahn and Svartholm, Ref.* 11.)

radius travel on the average in a slightly weaker field than those moving in the center.

Wedge-shaped magnets with nonuniform fields may be used to attain focusing in two directions,[9] by allowing the particles to impinge at an angle to the wedge which is smaller than 90°. The fringing action of the field causes the axial focusing more or less as it does in the betatron case. Using the focusing principles of the betatron, Siegbahn and Svartholm[10] have developed a "flat" spectroscope which has a radially decreasing magnetic field with the field parameter $n = \frac{1}{2}$. The angular frequencies of the vertical and radial oscillations in this case are both equal to $\omega_0/\sqrt{2}$. Consequently, particles emitted from a point source with a slight range of angles in the median and vertical planes are refocused to an image point at an angle $\sqrt{2}\,\pi$ or 254°33′ from the source (see Fig. 4-7).

By shaping the boundaries of a uniform magnetic field or by shaping the pole pieces to obtain any desired variation of the field, it is possible to achieve a great variety of focusing properties. In Fig. 4-8 we show a special type of lens with an indication of its focusing properties. The analysis of trajectories in cases of inhomogeneous fields and shaped boundaries usually is quite difficult. Flat spectroscopes have been developed for beta rays, for light, charged nuclear particles, and for massive ions.

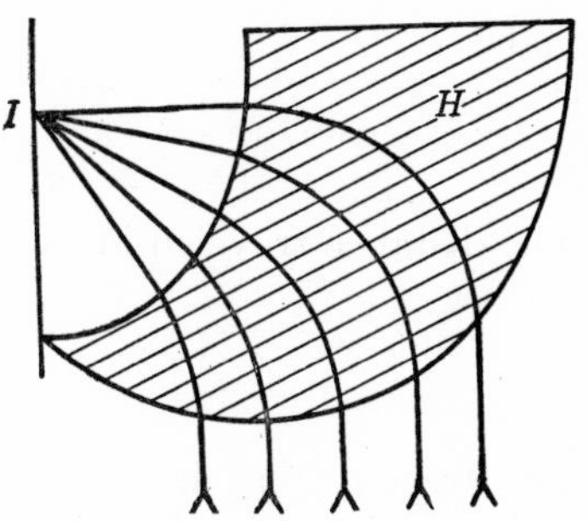

FIG. 4-8. Diagram illustrating how a special focusing property may be achieved by shaping boundary of magnetic. field. (*From Smythe, Rumbaugh, and West, Ref.* 12.)

Helical, or lens, spectroscopes are based upon the motion of particles in an axially symmetric field when the initial velocity of the particles makes an angle with respect to the field axis which is much less than $\pi/2$ (see Fig. 4-9*a*). The component of the velocity vector parallel to the magnetic field is unaffected by the field. The component of velocity perpendicular to the magnetic field gives rise to a circular motion which is described by Eqs. (1-29) and (1-30). If the field is uniform, the motion is a combination of uniform circular motion in a plane perpendicular to the magnetic field and uniform linear motion in the direction of the field. Such a trajectory is a helix.

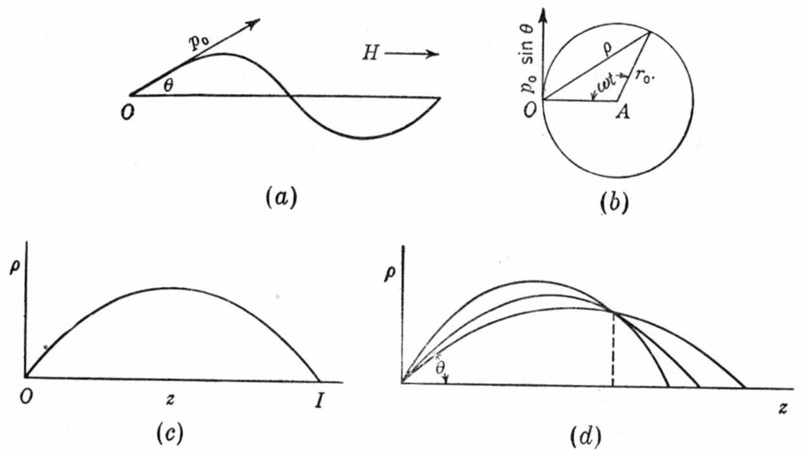

FIG. 4-9. (*a*) Side projection of helical trajectory; (*b*) end-on view of helical trajectory; (*c*) the trajectory as projected in a plane rotating with the particle around *O-I* axis; (*d*) diagram indicating the formation of a ring-type image.

In Fig. 4-9*b* we show an end-on view of the trajectory of a particle which at $t = 0$ is at point O and has a vertical component of momentum $p_0 \sin\theta$ and a component in the direction of the field $p_0 \cos\theta$. The radius of the projected path about the axis A and the angular velocity of rotation are given by

$$r_0 = \frac{p_0 \sin \theta}{B_z e} \tag{4-35}$$

and

$$\omega = \frac{B_z e}{m\gamma} \tag{4-36}$$

The distance traveled in the z direction in a time t is

$$z = \frac{p_0 \cos \theta}{m\gamma} t \tag{4-37}$$

The trace ρ, that is, the instantaneous distance between the particle and an axis in the direction of B going through point O (see Fig. 4-9c), is a sinusoid given by

$$\rho = 2r_0 \sin \frac{\omega t}{2} = \frac{2p_0 \sin \theta}{B_z e} \sin \frac{B_z e z}{2p_0 \cos \theta} \tag{4-38}$$

When $t = 2\pi/\omega$, the particle has turned through one complete revolution and consequently has advanced a distance

$$d = \frac{p_0 \cos \theta}{m\gamma} \frac{2\pi}{\omega} = \frac{2\pi p_0 \cos \theta}{B_z e} \tag{4-39}$$

Hence for a fixed B and θ the distance between O and I indicated in Fig. 4-9c is a measure of p_0.

The magnetic field in helical spectroscopes is usually established by means of a cylindrically symmetrical solenoid. By virtue of this cylindrical symmetry the distance OI in Fig. 4-9c is independent of the orientation of the plane formed by the initial velocity vector and the magnetic field. The helical spectrometer thus automatically possesses a focusing property such that all particles of a given momentum which are emitted along a cone defined by the angle θ will be focused to a single point along the axis. In addition to the intrinsic focusing property associated with the cylindrical symmetry, helical spectroscopes can also focus particles ejected within a range of angles. For a given resolution this range of angles can be greatly extended if a ring-type image slit is placed forward of the point focus (see Fig. 4-9d). The investigation of this focusing condition may be carried out in a straightforward manner by considering the traces for particles which take off at the angles $\theta \pm \alpha$, where α is small (see Prob. 4-4). Helical spectrometers which utilize the ring image have very high gathering power and are coming into wide use.

Many helical spectrometers are based upon a short axial coil (thin lens) or several short axial coils. In these cases the traces are not sinusoids, and the trajectory analysis is far more complicated. Nevertheless such spectroscopes are relatively simple to construct and to calibrate and are quite widely used.

One of the limiting factors in the use of magnetic instruments has been the inability to make precise absolute determinations of the magnetic field. To take full advantage of the relative precision attainable with a magnetic analyzer, the instrument is generally calibrated internally by the use of particles with precisely known energies. These energies must be determined by another method which lends itself to an absolute determination. Recently a technique for measuring magnetic fields has been developed which is based upon the direct measurement of the Larmor precession frequency of the proton. The use of this method promises to permit precise absolute determinations of magnetic fields with an accuracy of the order of 1 part in 10,000.

The focusing properties of various types and arrangements of electric and magnetic fields have been given considerable study. Current activity in the field, however, suggests that the subject is far from exhausted.(4,13,14)

4-4. Energy Analyzers for Light, Charged Nuclear Particles. The precise energy definitions obtainable with the Van de Graaff accelerator and other accelerators are due largely to the use of precision analyzers, which measure the energy of the charged particles and regulate the output to a desired energy. The electrostatic analyzer and control device of the Van de Graaff accelerator at the California Institute of Technology(15) is a high-resolution, 90° cylindrical instrument which maintains the energy of the incident beam within 2 parts in 10,000 of the selected value. In proton or deuteron acceleration a coarse magnetic analyzer is used to separate the molecular-hydrogen ions from the proton or deuteron beam. The desired particles are focused on a split detector located at the image point of the cylindrical electrostatic lens. If the output voltage is exactly the desired value, both halves of the detector receive the same current. However, if the voltage changes, a differential current develops. A signal based upon this differential current is amplified and fed back to one or more control points in such a manner as to secure a corrective change in the accelerator voltage. In Fig. 4-10 we show the analyzer part of the control device.

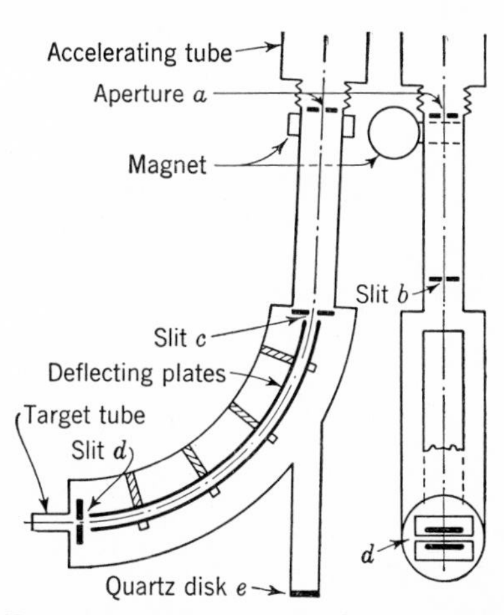

FIG. 4-10. Schematic diagram of electrostatic analyzer. (*From Fowler, Lauritsen, and Lauritsen, Ref.* 15.)

Electrostatic analyzers also have been used to measure the energies of the charged products of nuclear reactions. A spherical electrostatic analyzer which has been constructed for this purpose at the University of Wisconsin[16] has an energy resolution of 650.

The energy of the charged products of nuclear reactions may also be measured precisely with a magnetic spectroscope. C. W. Snyder *et al.*[17] have devised an analyzer for massive charged particles based upon the

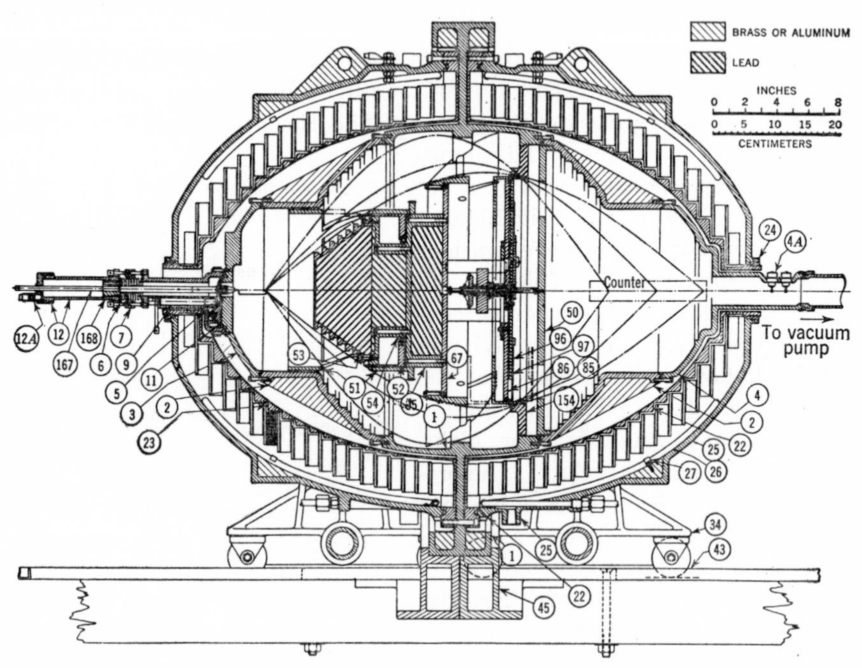

Fig. 4-11. Diagram of high-resolution, high-luminosity beta-ray spectroscope. (*From DuMond et al., Ref.* 20.)

Siegbahn-Svartholm double-focusing spectroscope. To keep the source and detector in a field-free region and to simplify the construction, they use a 180° field instead of a 254°33′ field, sacrificing some dispersion and resolution. They obtain a momentum resolution of 1000.

4-5. Beta-ray Spectroscopes. Precision instruments for measuring the kinetic energies of beta particles are mostly of the magnetic type, and all of them incorporate focusing features. The 180° instrument of Langer and Cook[18] with 40-cm radius achieves almost perfect directional focusing in the horizontal plane by the use of a shaped field. When a source 0.4 mm wide is used, a transmission of 0.1 per cent and a line width of 0.5 per cent are achieved with this instrument. A Siegbahn-Svartholm beta-ray spectrometer[19] with 50-cm radius, using a 5-mm-wide source, achieves a transmission of 1 per cent and a line width of 0.9 per cent.

Most helical spectroscopes are long and narrow, with the magnetic field in the form of a long solenoid, a short axial coil, or several closely spaced axial coils. However, it has been shown that optimum luminosity for a given energy resolution is achieved if the half angle of the cone of the beta particles runs between 30° and 60°. In Fig. 4-11 we show an instrument[20] which has both high energy resolution and high luminosity.

The energy resolution of beta-ray spectroscopes falls off rapidly above a few Mev.

4-6. Gamma-ray Spectroscopes. In recent years DuMond and his group[21] have extended the precision measurement of electromagnetic wavelengths to the 500-kev gamma-ray region by the use of a large curved-crystal spectrometer. The usual Bragg formula for the wavelength in terms of the lattice spacing, diffraction angle, and order number is still applicable; however, the angles of the diffraction maxima for gamma rays are exceedingly small. Despite this it is possible to use this instrument with very strong sources for the precision measurement of energies up to about 2 Mev.[22] In Fig. 4-12 we illustrate the geometry of a curved-crystal gamma-ray spectrometer.

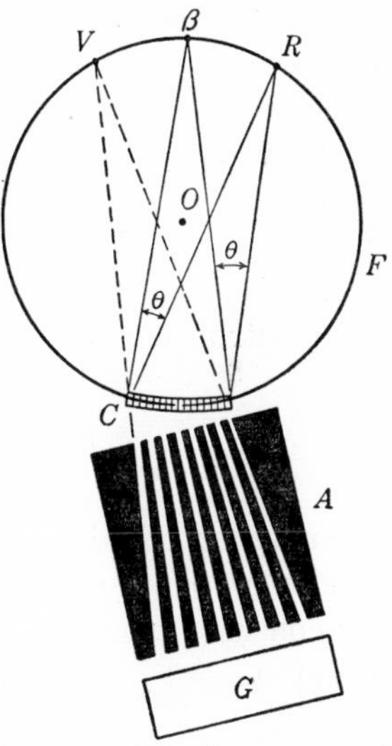

FIG. 4-12. Geometry of gamma-ray spectrometer. The crystal appears at C and the source at R on the focal circle F. The reflected radiation appears to diverge from the virtual focus V as it passes through the collimater A to the detector at G. (*From DuMond et al., Ref.* 23.)

Beta-ray spectrometers may be used to measure the energies of gamma rays if the gamma rays are first converted into high-speed electrons, either by the external photoelectric effect or by an internal photoelectric effect. In the former case gamma rays striking a target eject some electrons from the inner shells of the target atoms. The electrons ejected from the ith shell by monoenergetic gamma rays with the energy E_γ possess the kinetic energy

$$T_i = E_\gamma - W_i \tag{4-40}$$

where W_i is the critical energy necessary to remove an electron from the ith shell. Since these critical energies are known precisely from X-ray studies, one may infer the original gamma-ray energy from the discrete beta-ray spectrum.

In certain cases of radioactivity, gamma rays are accompanied by beta rays having discrete energies; the beta rays are attributed to an internal photoelectric effect (internal conversion). The process is viewed roughly as one in which a nuclear gamma ray is captured by an extra-nuclear electron of the same atom. This electron is ejected from the atom with the kinetic energy given by Eq. (4-40), where W_i represents the critical energy for the same atom. Using the known critical excitation energies, one may infer the energies of the gamma rays.

A magnetic spectrometer for gamma-ray energy and intensity measurements based upon the measurement of the momentum distribution of Compton electrons has been constructed recently.[67] It covers the range of energies from 0.2 to 12 Mev with an energy resolution of the order of 5 per cent.

The production of electron-positron pairs by gamma rays, a perfect example of the materialization of energy, has also been used to provide a means for measuring high-energy gamma rays. According to the conservation-of-energy principle, the energies of the gamma-ray electron and positron must satisfy [Eqs. (1-15) and (1-14)]

$$E_\gamma = mc^2\gamma_- + mc^2\gamma_+ = \frac{p_-c^2}{v_-} + \frac{p_+c^2}{v_+} \tag{4-41}$$

The magnetic rigidities of the electron and positron, as determined with a cloud chamber in a magnetic field, may be used to calculate the momenta and consequently E_γ. In the region of very high, almost equally divided energy, $v_- \approx v_+ \approx c$ so that

$$E_\gamma \approx p_-c + p_+c = Bec(r_- + r_+) \tag{4-42}$$

The sum of the two radii, therefore, gives the energy of the gamma ray. Arrangements of coincidence counters in a 180° magnetic spectroscope have been used[24] to obtain stepwise measurements of the sum of these two radii without measuring the radii themselves. In the pair spectrometer of Kinsey and Bartholomew[24] the field is varied until coincidences are recorded between counters with sharply defined slits. When certain corrections are made, it is possible to attain an accuracy of the order of 0.1 per cent in the energy range from 2 to 10 Mev. Figure 4-13 is a schematic diagram of this instrument.

Helical-type beta-ray spectrometers, which have inherently greater gathering power, have also been applied as pair spectrometers. The orbits of the electron and positron differ in the sense of their rotation relative to the axial magnetic field. Usually a baffle system is used, so that only pairs of nearly equal energies are selected. Instruments of this type can measure gamma-ray energies from 4 to 20 Mev with an accuracy of about 1 per cent in the lower-energy range.

At this time there are no truly precise instruments for the measurement of gamma-ray energies above, say, 10 Mev. In the 10- to 20-Mev region, methods based upon threshold reactions have been used; these give almost two significant figures. These methods are based upon the detection of the onset of some photonuclear reaction whose threshold is precisely known. Reactions in which gamma rays eject neutrons are the most useful, since many photoneutron thresholds in the range from 2 to 20 Mev are known accurately. In such arrangements a detector of low-energy neutrons is used to determine whether the gamma rays can eject neutrons from a sequence of substances which lie at precisely known points on a scale of gamma-ray energies. Some interpolation between thresholds is possible by making use of the rapid change in neutron yield which takes

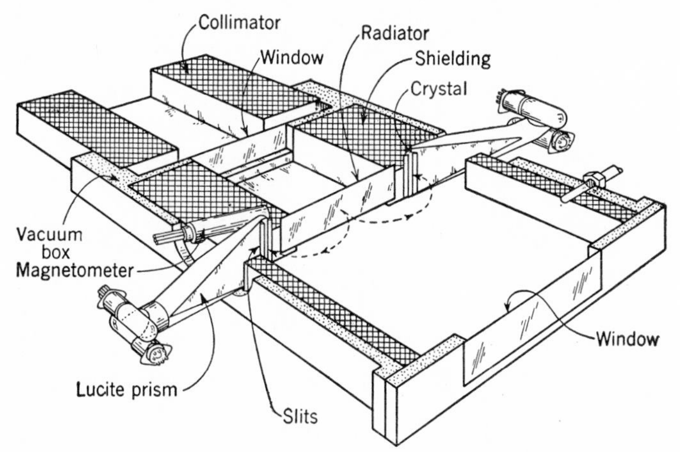

FIG. 4-13. Schematic diagram of a pair spectrometer. (*From Kinsey and Bartholomew, Ref.* 24.)

place immediately above the threshold of a particular photoneutron reaction. Photoproton reactions and photofission reactions also have convenient thresholds and are useful for energy determinations. The photoproton reaction of deuterium provides a convenient way of converting the gamma ray to a particle whose energy is more easily determined. Gamma-ray spectrometers based upon these reactions promise to be as reliable as pair spectrometers.

4-7. Neutron-energy Measurement. Neutron kinetic energies can be measured precisely by two methods, both of which have been limited until recently to the low-energy region. Crystal spectrometers (see Fig. 4-14) are suitable for measuring the de Broglie wavelengths of neutrons with kinetic energies between 0.01 and 100 ev.

Time-of-flight measurements of pulses of neutrons have been carried out extensively in the energy range 0.01 to 10,000 ev, with path lengths running of the order of a few meters. In one type of time-of-flight instrument a neutron beam is pulsed by a mechanical shutter (see Fig. 4-15). In a second type, the charged-particle accelerator which produces the neutron beam is pulsed. Electronic timing methods are used in both

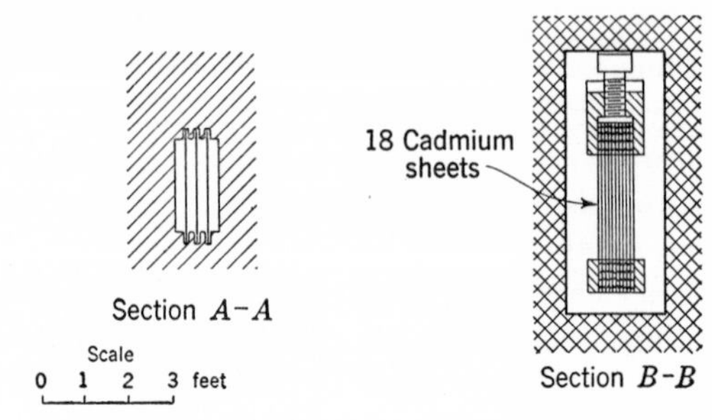

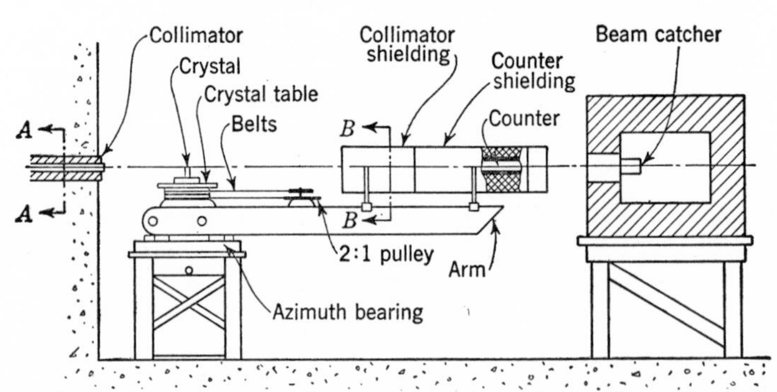

FIG. 4-14. General arrangement of neutron spectrometer. (*From Hurst, Pressesky, and Tunnicliffe, Ref.* 25.)

types of instruments. The recent development of electronic timing methods with uncertainties measured in millimicroseconds has permitted the extension of the pulsed-accelerator method to the Mev range of energies[27,68] and even the 100-Mev range of energies.[28] At these high energies, path lengths from 1 to 150 m are used. Other techniques for measuring neutron energies above 10 kev will be discussed in the next chapter.

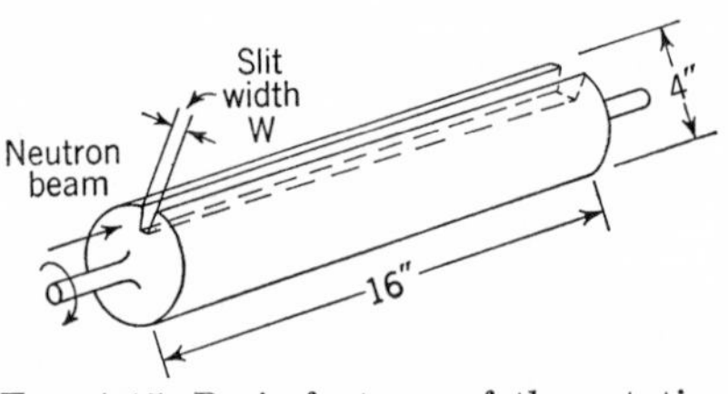

FIG. 4-15. Basic features of the rotating shutter. (*From Selove, Ref.* 26.)

4-8. Mass Spectroscopes.[4,29–33] Mass spectroscopes are essentially instruments for measuring the charge-to-mass ratios of ions. Since the charge is simply the charge of the electron times a small integer, which can usually be inferred, the mass can readily be calculated.

The determination of the mass of particles in a sharply collimated monoergic beam can be accomplished by measuring the kinetic energy and momentum of the particles ($M = p^2/2T$). These two variables may be determined by measuring deflection parameters in electric and magnetic fields. Most mass spectroscopes are instruments which combine the energy and momentum measurements in such a way as to give a result which depends directly upon the mass alone. When the beam of particles is not sharply collimated or monoergic, the determination of mass is more difficult. The mass spectroscope must be carefully designed so that differences in the velocities of the particles or differences in their directions are not interpreted as differences in mass. The ideal mass spectroscope would take all particles emanating from a small source opening or object point, regardless of their direction or velocity, and bring them to sharp image points spread out on a scale which is related to the mass. Practical instruments achieve these ideals only to a limited extent, and to obtain the desired resolution, it is necessary to sacrifice some of the particles leaving the source, by using a collimator and an energy, momentum, or velocity discriminator. We have already noted several arrangements for achieving direction focusing and velocity, energy, or momentum dispersion by means of electric and magnetic fields. In most mass spectroscopes both electric and magnetic fields are used to secure mass dispersion; hence combinations are possible, so that for a limited range of angles and velocities the second element approximately counteracts the velocity dispersion due to the first element.

In seeking focusing arrangements, it is profitable to consider the optical analogue of a mass spectroscope. Particles of a given mass and charge, which diverge from a source with a range of directions and velocities, may be compared with light rays which diverge from a source with a range of directions and wavelengths. We may then treat certain arrangements of an electric or magnetic field as equivalent to a prism-lens combination which focuses identical particles diverging with the same velocity (direction focusing) but which brings particles with different velocities to different image points (velocity, momentum, or energy dispersion). Recalling that an achromatic lens brings all rays leaving an object point to a given image point, no matter what the angle or wavelength, we see that a velocity- and direction-focusing mass spectroscope may be viewed as an achromatic-lens combination for each mass component. The mass spectroscope, however, achieves mass dispersion, a property which has no simple optical analogue.

Mass spectroscopes may be divided into two general classes, (1) low-resolution instruments and (2) precision instruments. Low-resolution instruments are designed to resolve mass differences of 1 MU. These are used primarily to detect particular ions and to measure the abundance of isotopes. Most precision instruments are designed to measure as accurately as possible the differences between the masses of atoms or molecules which would come to a single point on an instrument of low resolution. The best of these instruments are capable of resolving mass differences which are a small part of 1 mMU.

4-9. Low-resolution Mass Spectroscopes. Thomson,[34] in his instrument (see Fig. 4-16), used a narrowly collimated beam with a source (a gaseous-discharge tube) which yielded ions with large variations of energy. To avoid error due to this inhomogeneity, the beam was passed through a velocity discriminator consisting of parallel electric and magnetic fields. To analyze the operation of this instrument, let us assume that the fields are uniform and that both extend over the same length L.

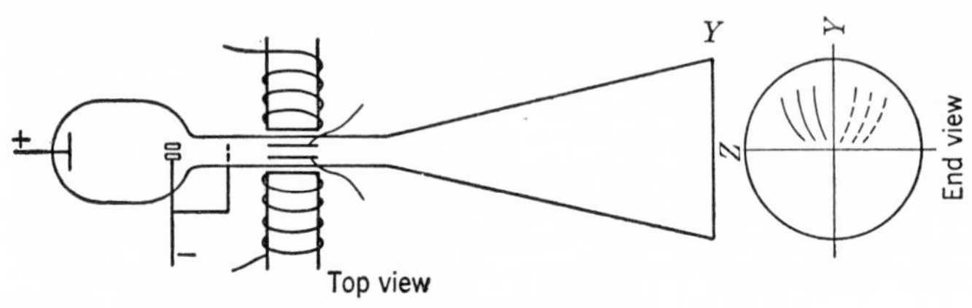

Fig. 4-16. Thomson's mass spectroscope, illustrating the formation of parabolas. Dotted curves are generated when the magnetic field is reversed.

Using the nonrelativistic equations and assuming both deflections to be small and perpendicular to the original line of motion, we find that

$$y = \frac{1}{2} a_y t^2 = \frac{\mathfrak{z} e \mathcal{E} L^2}{2Mv^2} \tag{4-43}$$

and

$$z = \frac{1}{2} a_z t^2 = \frac{B \mathfrak{z} e L^2}{2Mv} \tag{4-44}$$

These equations may be viewed as parametric equations relating y and z through the variable v. If v is eliminated, we obtain

$$z^2 = \frac{L^2 B^2}{2\mathcal{E}} \frac{\mathfrak{z} e}{M} y \tag{4-45}$$

The observed deflections are noted on a photographic plate or fluorescent screen at a distance from the region of the fields so that y and z are both magnified to Y and Z by a factor ρ, which depends upon the geometry of the apparatus. The final locus of points due to particles having a given $\mathfrak{z}e/M$ ratio satisfies the equation (see Fig. 4-16)

$$Z^2 = \frac{k \mathfrak{z} e}{M} Y \tag{4-46}$$

where

$$k = \rho \frac{L^2 B^2}{2\mathcal{E}} \tag{4-47}$$

Using such an instrument, Thomson in 1913 showed that associated with natural neon ($M = 20.183$ CMU) are ions having masses approximately equal to 20.0 and 22.0.

Dempster[35] in 1918 designed a mass spectroscope incorporating a 180° magnetic field which within a limited range possessed the property of direction focusing. In this instrument heated salts bombarded by electrons are usually used as the source of positively charged ions. A large voltage (~50 kv) accelerates these ions to the energy

$$V\mathfrak{z}e = T = \tfrac{1}{2}Mv^2 \tag{4-48}$$

The magnetic field then bends the ions into a semicircle having the radius determined by

$$B\mathfrak{z}ev = \frac{Mv^2}{R} \tag{4-49}$$

It follows immediately that the masses are given by

$$M = \frac{\mathfrak{z}eB^2R^2}{2V} \tag{4-50}$$

In the actual instrument, B and R are fixed, and the voltage is adjusted to bring particles of a particular mass into the detecting slit. Since this voltage is usually large, compared to the initial distribution of energies at the source, the energies of the particles of a given mass are quite homogeneous.

In another early instrument, due to Bainbridge,[36] which incorporates a 180° magnetic field, particles are accelerated by a large voltage and first sent through a velocity selector which passes only particles with the velocity $v = \mathcal{E}/B$. The radius of curvature in the same magnetic field is measured. The linear relation

$$M = \frac{R\mathfrak{z}eB^2}{\mathcal{E}} \tag{4-51}$$

between M and R is the desirable feature of this instrument.

A variety of low-resolution instruments, including those described above, are currently being used for mass analysis and the separation of isotopes. A design first proposed by Bleakney and Hipple[37] is based upon the trajectory of particles in a perpendicular combination of uniform electric and magnetic fields. Particles which initially are directed in a plane normal to the magnetic field move in a periodic trochoidal trajectory. For a given $\mathfrak{z}e/M$ these trajectories have a series of focal points which are independent of the initial directions and velocities of the particles. Hence the system gives perfect direction and velocity focusing in a single plane.

A spectrometer based upon the lens design shown in Fig. 4-8 has been used for isotope separation by Rumbaugh.[38] Glenn[39] has recently designed and constructed a strictly electrostatic mass spectrograph based upon time-of-flight differences of ions. The instrument is an outgrowth of a method for separating isotopes proposed in 1941 by R. R. Wilson.[40] The ions leaving the source are accelerated by a common voltage, bunched together, and sent into a drift tube (66 cm long). These bunches arrive at the detecting end of the drift tube at times that correspond to their masses. Here a grid system passes the ions with a predetermined transit time and repels the remainder. By controlling the accelerating voltage any desired mass can be passed. The instrument has a resolution substantially less than 1 MU and a transmission for the desired particles of the order of 20 per cent. It will probably be very useful for the rapid separation of artificially produced radioactive isotopes. Another recent time-of-flight instrument has been reported by Wolff and Stephens.[69]

4-10. Precision Mass Spectroscopes. The precision mass spectroscopes designed by Aston,[41] Dempster,[42] Bainbridge,[43] Mattauch,[44] Nier,[45] and others are used to compare masses by the so-called "doublet method." This method is based on the small differences between the masses of ions which correspond to the same mass number; these differences are utilized to arrive at the mass decrements. To illustrate the basis of the doublet method, let us consider the manner in which the precise masses of the substandards H^1, H^2, and C^{12} have been established precisely in terms of the primary standard O^{16}. Let us denote the mass difference between CH_4^+ and O^+ at mass number 16 as α, between D_3^+ and C^{++} at mass number 6 as β, and between H_2^+ and D^+ at mass number 2 as γ. These mass differences may be regarded as applying to the neutral atoms or molecules. The basis for this is obvious when we compare pairs of positive ions which lack the same number of electrons, such as H_2^+ and D^+ or CH_4^+ and O^+. There is a slight error in the mass difference ($\sim 10^{-6}$ mMU) due to the fact that the last electrons in the two neutral atoms or molecules are not bound with precisely the same strength, but this error may be neglected. For doubly, triply, etc., ionized particles the instrument really measures $\frac{1}{2}M$, $\frac{1}{3}M$, etc.; hence even in these cases the masses of the missing electrons cancel in the difference. We may, therefore, write for the above doublets

$$\Delta(\text{C}) + 4\Delta(\text{H}) - \Delta(\text{O}) = \alpha \tag{4-52}$$

$$3\Delta(\text{D}) - \tfrac{1}{2}\Delta(\text{C}) = \beta \tag{4-53}$$

$$2\Delta(\text{H}) - \Delta(\text{D}) = \gamma \tag{4-54}$$

Since $\Delta(\text{O}) = 0$, we have three linear equations in three unknowns. These lead to the solutions

$$\Delta(\text{H}) = \tfrac{1}{16}\alpha + \tfrac{1}{8}\beta + \tfrac{3}{8}\gamma \tag{4-55}$$

$$\Delta(\text{D}) = \tfrac{1}{8}\alpha + \tfrac{1}{4}\beta - \tfrac{1}{4}\gamma \tag{4-56}$$

$$\Delta(\text{C}) = \tfrac{3}{4}\alpha - \tfrac{1}{2}\beta - \tfrac{3}{2}\gamma \tag{4-57}$$

Accordingly, we may obtain the mass decrements Δ(H), Δ(D), and Δ(C) with approximately the same number of significant figures as the measured differences α, β, and γ. In a similar way measurements of other mass

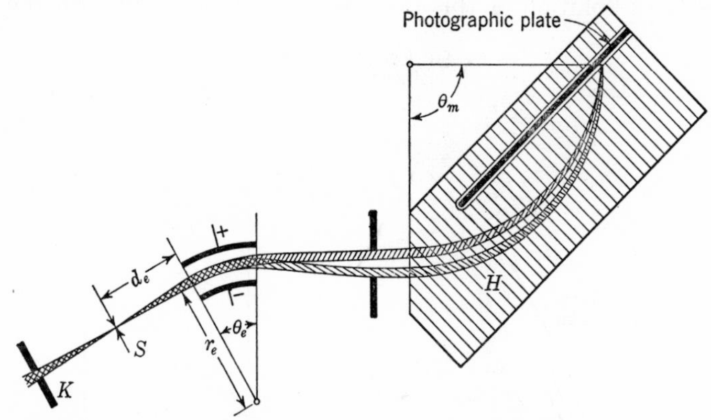

FIG. 4-17. The arrangement of fields in the precision mass spectroscope of Mattauch, showing the direction- and velocity-focusing properties achieved.

doublets lead to the mass decrements of other nuclides in terms of the basic standard and the substandards discussed above.

Recent precision instruments are capable of resolving mass differences of the order of 1 μMU for light nuclides. In consequence, we know numerous atomic masses to a relative accuracy of the order of 1 part in 10^6. In Figs. 4-17 and 4-18 we show a schematic drawing of the arrangement of fields in the precision spectroscopes of Mattauch[44] and Dempster.[42] In Fig. 4-19 we show a schematic drawing of the recent precision mass spectrometer of Nier and Roberts.[45] This instrument achieves first-order velocity focusing and second-order angular focusing by using a 90° electrostatic analyzer and a 60° magnetic analyzer. An auxiliary spectrometer serves as a control device to stabilize the magnetic and electric fields. An electrometer, an electron multiplier, and a magnetic oscillograph are used to detect, amplify, and record the ion currents. The mass difference between two ions with the same mass number is given by

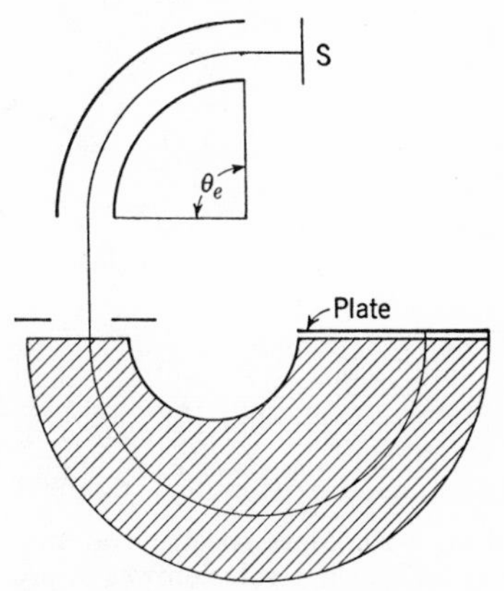

FIG. 4-18. The arrangement of fields in the precision mass spectroscope of Dempster.

$$\frac{\Delta M}{M} = \frac{G\,\Delta R}{R(G+1)} \tag{4-58}$$

where G is the open-circuit gain of the feedback loop, R is the resistance corresponding to a tapping point of a voltage divider, and ΔR is the difference in resistance corresponding to the two masses. Figure 4-20 indicates the resolution of this instrument in connection with the mass

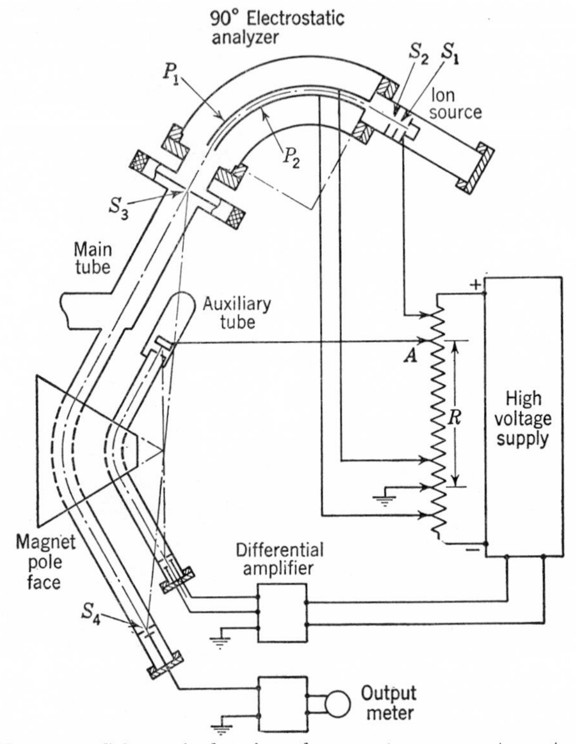

FIG. 4-19. Schematic drawing of a recent mass spectrometer.

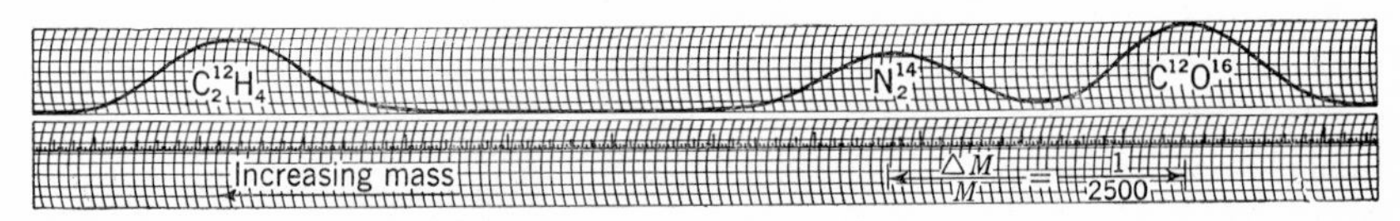

FIG. 4-20. Mass spectrum at mass number 28, showing $C^{12}{}_2H_4$, $N^{14}{}_2$, and $C^{12}O^{16}$. Actually, the resolution was improved after the print was made, and for most of the work in the paper cited $N^{14}{}_2$ and $C^{12}O^{16}$ were completely resolved. (*From Collins, Nier, and Johnson, Ref.* 46.)

spectrum of several ions with mass number 28. A modified and enlarged version of this instrument[70] has recently been completed which achieves a resolution ten times greater than that shown in Fig. 4-20.

Recently several instruments have been constructed for the purpose of precision mass measurement which are based upon principles differing substantially from those used in the doublet-type mass spectrographs.

An instrument called the "chronotron," proposed by Goudsmit,[47] measures the time of flight of an ion taking a helical path in a uniform magnetic field. The instrument constructed by Hays, Richards, and Goudsmit[48] satisfies the characteristic equation

$$T = \frac{652NM}{B} \tag{4-59}$$

where N is the number of revolutions, M is the mass in atomic mass units, and B is the field in gauss. Values of time of flight for several (five to seven) revolutions are measured, using an electronic timing system. Mass measurements good to about 1 mMU have been attained with the instrument. For heavy masses this represents an accuracy of 1 part in 2×10^5, which is of the same order as that obtained by doublet methods.

Hipple, Sommer, and Thomas[49] have developed an instrument called the "omegatron," which utilizes the cyclotron resonance condition as a means of measuring the $\mathfrak{z}e/M$ ratio of atomic particles. This method promises to provide precise atomic masses in the low-mass range. Smith and Damm[50] have constructed an instrument which in its present form is also based upon cyclotron resonances of ions. The frequency difference between high harmonics (140 to 160) of two components of a mass doublet is measured precisely with the aid of an ingenious peak-matching scheme. The percentage frequency difference corresponds to the percentage mass difference. The instrument appears to be capable of assigning masses with greater precision than the usual types of mass spectrometers.

4-11. Microwave Spectroscopy.[51,52] The study of molecular spectra with the microwave techniques which were developed in World War II has yielded mass data with precision approaching that attainable with conventional mass spectroscopes. As an example, Townes and Low[53] have investigated lines, in the microwave region of the electromagnetic spectrum, associated with the $l = 0 \rightarrow 1$ transition of ICl^{35} and ICl^{37}; they report the mass ratio $M(Cl^{35})/M(Cl^{37}) = 0.9459906 \pm 120$. Numerous other mass measurements have been made by microwave techniques.

The most important applications of microwaves (30 to 0.3 cm, or 10^9 to 10^{11} cycles/sec) to nuclear physics have been in the precise measurement of nuclear moments. We have already discussed the fact that the nucleus causes small shifts and splittings (hyperfine structure) of the optical and infrared lines in atomic and molecular spectra. In the measurement of these shifts most of the accuracy of spectroscopic measurements is lost in the difference steps which must be taken to bring out the nuclear effects. Thus despite the high inherent accuracy of usual spectroscopic methods, they are not well suited to the study of nuclear effects. In contrast, microwave methods are particularly suited to the study of these effects, since transitions between members of hyperfine multiplets often correspond to wavelengths in the microwave region. Consequently, the significant data obtained from microwave measurements have almost the full accuracy of microwave frequency measurements ($\sim$1 part in 10^5). A further advantage of microwave technique is the fact that it is possible, by using gaseous absorbers at low temperatures and pressures, to reduce significantly the factors which tend to broaden spectral lines, whereas in optical spectra the minimum line width attain-

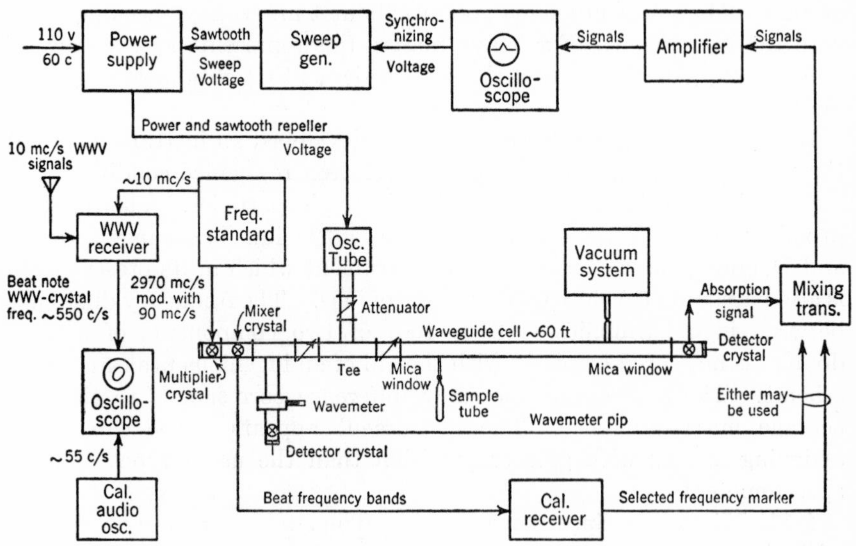

FIG. 4-21. Diagram of the Duke millimeter-wave spectrometer. (*From Gordy, Ref.* 54.)

able is almost comparable, on a wavelength scale, to the shifts due to nuclear effects.

The techniques employed in microwave spectroscopy are vastly different from those used in X-ray, ultraviolet, optical, and infrared spectroscopy. Much of this difference is occasioned by the fact that the fundamental entity which is measured in microwave work is the frequency, which is determined by comparison with frequency standards. In other spectral regions the wavelength is the basic entity measured, and this is accomplished by comparing wavelengths with the repeat distances of ruled gratings or crystals. The components of a microwave spectrograph consist basically of an oscillator, a waveguide absorption cell containing the gas to be investigated, and a frequency-measuring detector system. In some arrangements the oscillator, usually a reflection klystron, is frequency-modulated over a slight range, and the output is indicated on a cathode-ray oscilloscope whose sweep is synchronized with the modulating frequency. This arrangement provides a visual pattern of the spectral lines under investigation. In some systems a recording oscillograph gives the spectral pattern. In Fig. 4-21 we give a schematic diagram of the microwave spectrograph at Duke. In Fig. 4-22 we show the hyperfine structure of the rotational transition of ICN at 5.81 mm wavelength.

The general theory of the interaction between nuclear quadrupole moments and the molecular field has been developed by Casimir[56] and has been applied to various types of molecules by different investigators. The theory leads to formulas for the spectral pattern in terms of quantum

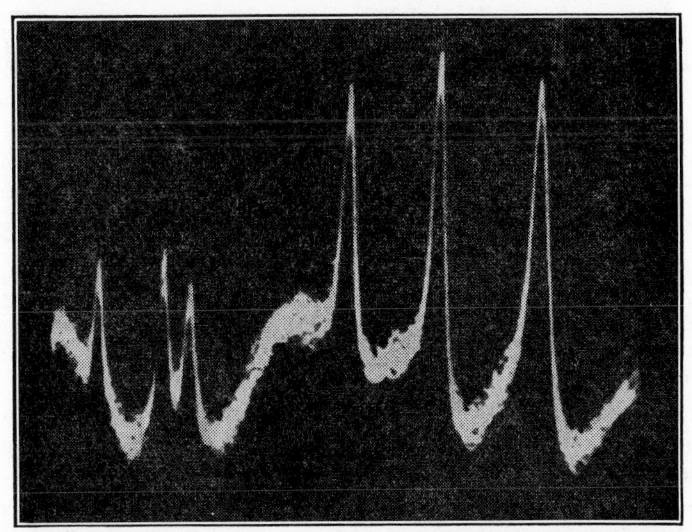

FIG. 4-22. Hyperfine structure of a rotational line of ICN at 5.81 mm wavelength. (*From Gordy, Ref.* 55.)

numbers which characterize the multiplets and their substates. The formulas contain certain parameters which are directly related to the quadrupole moments. For example, for a diatomic molecule with a single interacting nucleus the interaction energy[54] is

$$W_Q = -eQ \frac{\partial^2 V}{\partial z^2} \frac{\frac{3}{4}C(C+1) - I(I+1)J(J+1)}{2(2J+3)(2J-1)I(2I-1)} \tag{4-60}$$

where

$$C = F(F+1) - I(I+1) - J(J+1) \tag{4-61}$$

$$\mathbf{F} = \mathbf{J} + \mathbf{I} \tag{4-62}$$

Q is the nuclear quadrupole moment, and $\partial^2 V/\partial z^2$ is the divergence of the electrostatic field along the axis of the molecule at the interacting nucleus. More complicated formulas apply to more complicated molecules. If the quantum numbers in these formulas can be identified on the basis of the multiplet structure or other considerations and if $\partial^2 V/\partial z^2$ can be evaluated on the basis of the molecular theory, the quadrupole moment Q may be computed from the observed energy shifts. The theoretical analysis which establishes the field at the nucleus limits the evaluation of quadrupole moments to two to four significant figures.

4-12. Radio-frequency Spectroscopy.(57) The long-wavelength side of the microwave region as well as the high-frequency radio-wave region (10^3 to 1 Mc or 30 cm to 300 m) also provide useful information concerning nuclear moments. The apparatus employed in "radio-frequency spectroscopy" differs in many respects from microwave apparatus. In

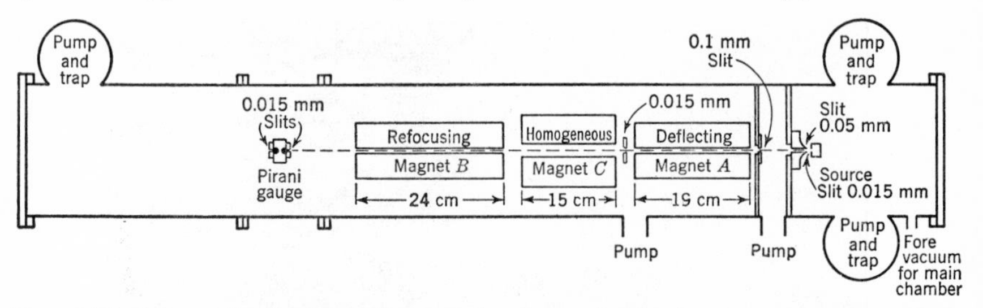

FIG. 4-23. Schematic diagram of apparatus for molecular-beam resonance method. Longitudinal dimensions from source to detector are drawn to scale. Flattened copper tubes, 13.5 cm long, to carry radio-frequency current, are not shown. They should appear between the pole pieces of magnet C. *(From Kellogg, Rabi, Ramsey, and Zacharias, Ref.* 58.)

the first place high-radio-frequency oscillators and transmission lines are used in place of cavity oscillators and waveguides. The most important difference, however, has to do with the methods of detecting the transitions which are induced by the radio-frequency field. Accordingly, these detection methods characterize the particular radio-frequency spectroscope.

Rabi *et al.*(58) have devised a method known as the molecular-beam resonance method which gives quite accurately the magnetic moments of the nuclei contained in molecules. Their arrangement (see Fig. 4-23) consists of two identical inhomogeneous fields, whose gradients are oriented in the z and $-z$ directions, and a central uniform field oriented in the z direction. The first field exerts a deflecting force upon the molecule which is given by

$$f = \frac{\partial H}{\partial z} \mu_z \tag{4-63}$$

where μ_z is the projection of the magnetic moment of the molecule upon the z axis. A slit at the exit of the first inhomogeneous field eliminates all particles except those whose initial angle and velocities lead to trajectories which are symmetrical relative to the source and the slit. Since the central field is uniform, no deflecting force acts upon the molecule. However, the torque, due to the magnetic field, causes the magnet to precess around the z axis at the Larmor frequency. Since this precession does not change the projected moment of the molecule, the particles, after entering the second inhomogeneous field, experience a deflecting force exactly opposite to that which acted in the first inhomogeneous magnetic field. In consequence, particles which pass through the first slit are all refocused to the detector unless the trajectory is disturbed in some way. In the molecular-beam apparatus the central field is modulated by a radio-frequency field which is perpendicular to H_0. When the magnetic field or the radio frequency is adjusted to resonate with the natural Larmor precessional frequency of the system, a large interaction takes place in the center of the instrument. As a result of the change in orientation caused by this interaction, the magnetic dipoles are no longer refocused to the detector. The frequency ν corresponding to the minimum of the detector current therefore gives the Larmor precession frequency. The magnitude of ν/H_0 then yields the g factor and the magnetic moment of the molecule.

If only one nucleus in the molecule possesses a magnetic moment and if the electronic and molecular motions produce negligible magnetic fields at this nucleus, the entire molecular moment may be assigned to this nucleus. The measured resonance frequency then gives directly the g_I factor for this nucleus. In most cases, however, one cannot assume simply that one nucleus interacts independently with the external field. When we consider the local magnetic field acting on a nucleus due to the electronic and molecular motion as well as that due to the moments of neighboring nuclei, we are led to expect a fine structure in the radio-frequency spectrum. If the atomic and molecular wave functions and moments of the nuclei are known, one may predict the location of these radio-frequency lines. Such calculations generally give the results to be expected in terms of the values of the nuclear moments. Thus the experimental radio-frequency spectrum for molecular-beam resonances may be used to infer these moments.

Since the precision of magnetic-field measurements is rather poor compared to the precision of frequency measurements, the molecular-beam technique has been developed so that the Larmor frequencies of two nuclei in the same magnetic field can be measured simultaneously. Such "common-field" instruments give the ratio of the two magnetic moments with a precision of a few parts in 10^5. A collection of these ratios, in conjunction with the absolute determination of one nuclear magnetic moment, then give the absolute magnetic moments of the remaining nuclei.

Extensive efforts have been made to establish the absolute magnetic moment of the proton. These have been based upon methods for comparing the proton moment to the electron moment. Taub and Kusch[59] and Gardner and Purcell,[60] using very different methods, have obtained for the proton moment

$$\mu_p = (15.2100 \times 10^{-4})\mu_B \tag{4-64}$$

where μ_B is the Bohr magnetron.

Bloch, Nicodemus, and Staub,[61] using a beam of neutrons along with ingenious modifications of Rabi's beam techniques, have measured the magnetic moment of the neutron.

Studies of the radio-frequency spectrum of the deuterium molecule carried out by Rabi *et al.*[58] indicated a rather serious disagreement between the theory of the nuclear magnetic interaction and the experimental results. This disagreement was resolved when the assumption was made that the deuteron possesses an electric quadrupole moment (i.e., if the deuteron is assumed to have the form of a prolate spheroid). The observed radio-frequency spectrum then led to a quantitative value for the quadrupole moment of the nucleus.

A second type of radio-frequency spectroscope is based upon the phenomenon of paramagnetism.[62] This phenomenon is attributed to the existence of permanent magnetic moments in atoms which are brought into alignment by the application of a magnetic field. The additional contribution to the magnetic induction is given by the well-known formula

$$B = H(1 + 4\pi\chi) \tag{4-65}$$

where χ is the magnetic susceptibility. The theory of paramagnetism due to atomic moments indicates that the susceptibility depends quadratically upon the dipole moments of atoms. If nuclear moments affect susceptibility in a similar way, their contributions should be of the order of one millionth of the contributions of atomic moments. Despite this, Purcell, Torrey, and Pound[63] and Bloch, Hansen, and Packard[64] succeeded independently in detecting nuclear contributions to paramagnetism. By so doing, they provided a precise method for measuring nuclear moments which supplements the molecular-beam method. The method of Purcell is based upon resonance absorption phenomena in solids and liquids which were explored earlier but without success by Gorter and Broer.[65]

In nuclear-paramagnetism studies a coil filled with the material to be investigated is placed in (and perpendicular to) a magnetic field H_0. The coil is connected in parallel with a capacitor and excited to a-c resonance by a radio-frequency oscillator (see Fig. 4-24). The Q of this LC circuit is found to vary slightly when H_0 is adjusted so that the Larmor frequency resonates with the resonant frequency of the LC circuit. The effect is due to the energy absorption by nuclei at the doubly resonant frequency. To accentuate this effect, a balanced bridge circuit is employed containing a "dummy" coil. With such an arrangement a change of the order of 50 per cent in the output of the bridge occurs in passing through the resonant condition. The apparatus used in this technique is simpler than molecular-beam apparatus, and at the same time the method is capable of giving magnetic moments with greater precision.

As a physical consequence of the absorption of energy, the system of spinning nuclei increases in temperature more rapidly than its surroundings. A decrease in the rate of absorption of energy therefore results

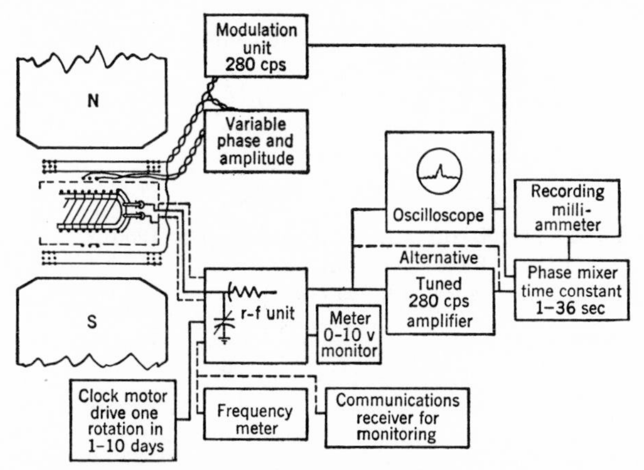

FIG. 4-24. Block diagram of the arrangement of components of a radio-frequency spectrometer. (*From Pound and Knight, Ref.* 66.)

until equilibrium with the surrounding lattice is reestablished. These so-called "relaxation" times are of the order of 10^{-4} to 10 sec. Relaxation times and the shapes and widths of the resonance absorption curves provide information of considerable theoretical interest in studies concerning the liquid and solid states.

The method of Bloch, usually called nuclear induction, utilizes a somewhat different arrangement for detecting nuclear resonances but achieves the same order of precision as the method of Purcell.

PROBLEMS

4-1. What voltage must be applied between the plates of a 1-m (radius) cylindrical analyzer (with separation 0.5 cm) in order to pass 1-Mev protons?

4-2. Verify Eqs. (4-24) and (4-25) for the spherical electrostatic analyzer.

***4-3.** Verify Barber's rule for a 60° symmetrical analyzer (Fig. 4-6*b*) by graphical construction and by the use of analytical geometry. Derive an expression for the shift in image position associated with a small change in momentum.

***4-4.** Find the location of the radius and the axial distance of the image ring for a helical spectroscope for rays which leave a point source at the angles $\theta \pm \alpha$, where α is of the order of 1° and θ is between 15° and 75°.

4-5. What is the time of flight of 1-Mev neutrons over a 1-m path length? To what precision must a time-interval measurement be made in order to assign energies to 1 per cent?

4-6. What is the significance of the fact that the traces do not extend to the vertex of the Thomson parabolas, and what may be learned from the coordinates of the points which lie closest to the vertex?

4-7. What neutron energies can be measured with a curved-crystal spectrometer which can measure the wavelengths of 2-Mev gamma rays?

4-8. Mass assignments for H^1 and C^{12} reported in 1951 are $H^1 = 1.008146 \pm 3$ and $C^{12} = 12.003842 \pm 4$ (Ref. 46), and $H^1 = 1.008142 \pm 3$ and $C^{12} = 12.003804 \pm 17$ (Ref. 6 of Chap. 7). What effect do these as yet unresolved discrepancies have upon the assignment of the mass of heavy nuclides based upon doublets with complex hydrocarbons [*e.g.*, $M(C_8H_{16}) - M(Cd^{112}) = 224.43 \pm 0.09$ mMU]?

***4-9.** Show how the masses of H^1 and C^{12} may be deduced from the doublets H_2-D, $C^{12}H_4$-O^{16}, D_2O^{16}-$\frac{1}{2}A^{40}$, and C_3H_4-A^{40}.

4-10. What is the maximum deflection of a 1-ev proton traversing a distance of 50 cm in an inhomogeneous field of 50,000 gauss/cm whose gradient is perpendicular to the initial line of motion?

REFERENCES

1. Persico, E., and C. Geofrian: *Rev. Sci. Instr.*, **21,** 945 (1950).
2. Herzog, G.: *Z. Physik*, **89,** 447 (1934).
3. Henneberg, W.: *Ann. Physik*, **19,** 335 (1934).
4. Bainbridge, K. T.: *Exptl. Nuclear Phys.*, **1,** 559 (1953).
5. Hughes, A. L., and V. Rojansky: *Phys. Rev.*, **34,** 284 (1929).
6. Purcell, E. M.: *Phys. Rev.*, **54,** 88 (1938).
7. Barber, N. F.: *Proc. Leeds Phil. Lit. Soc. Sci. Sect.*, **2,** 427 (1933).
8. Stephens, W. E.: *Phys. Rev.*, **45,** 53 (1934).
9. Gross, W. G.: *Rev. Sci. Instr.*, **23,** 717 (1952).
10. Siegbahn, K., and N. Svartholm: *Nature*, **157,** 872 (1946).
11. Siegbahn, K., and N. Svartholm: *Arkiv. Mat. Astron. Fysik*, **33**(21) (1946).
12. Smythe, W. R., L. H. Rumbaugh, and S. S. West: *Phys. Rev.*, **45,** 724 (1934).
13. Johnson, E. G., and A. O. Nier: *Phys. Rev.*, **91,** 10 (1953).
14. Verster, N. F.: *Progr. Nuclear Phys.*, **2,** 1 (1952).
15. Fowler, W. A., C. C. Lauritsen, and T. Lauritsen: *Rev. Sci. Instr.*, **18,** 818 (1947).
16. Brown, C. P., D. S. Craig, and R. Williamson: *Rev. Sci. Instr.*, **22,** 953 (1951).
17. Snyder, C. W., S. Rubin, W. A. Fowler, and C. C. Lauritsen: *Rev. Sci. Instr.*, **21,** 852 (1950).
18. Langer, L. M., and C. S. Cook: *Rev. Sci. Instr.*, **19,** 257 (1948).
19. Hedgran, A., K. Siegbahn, and N. Svartholm, *Proc. Phys. Soc. (London)*, **A63,** 690 (1950).
20. DuMond, J. W. M., *et al.*: *Norman Bridge Lab. Phys. Special Tech. Rept.* 16, California Institute of Technology, 1952.
21. DuMond, J. W. M.: *Rev. Sci. Instr.*, **18,** 626 (1947).
22. Hoyt, H. C., J. J. Murray, and J. W. M. DuMond: *Phys. Rev.*, **90,** 169 (1953).
23. Miller, D. E., H. C. Hoyt, D. J. Klein, and J. W. M. DuMond: *Phys. Rev.*, **88,** 775 (1952).
24. Kinsey, B. B., and G. A. Bartholomew: *Can. J. Phys.*, **31,** 555 (1953).
25. Hurst, D. G., A. J. Pressesky, and P. R. Tunnicliffe: *Rev. Sci. Instr.*, **21,** 705 (1950).
26. Selove, W.: *Phys. Rev.*, **84,** 870 (1951).
27. Jennings, B., and G. L. Griffith: *Phys. Rev.*, **91,** 440 (1953).
28. Ragent, B., and W. I. Linlor: *Phys. Rev.*, **91,** 440 (1953).

29. Mattauch, J., and R. Herzog: *Z. Physik*, **89**, 794 (1934).
30. Aston, F. W.: "Mass Spectra and Isotopes," Edward Arnold & Co., London, 1942.
31. Barnard, G. P.: "Modern Mass Spectrometry," The Institute of Physics, London, 1953.
32. Mayne, K. I.: *Repts. Progr. Phys.*, **15**, 24 (1952).
33. Inghram, W., *Advances in Electronics*, **1**, 219–268 (1948).
34. Thomson, J. J.: "Positive Rays," Longmans, Green & Co., Inc., New York, 1913.
35. Dempster, A. J.: *Phys. Rev.*, **11**, 316 (1918).
36. Bainbridge, K. T.: *Phys. Rev.*, **40**, 130 (1932).
37. Bleakney, W., and J. A. Hipple, Jr.: *Phys. Rev.*, **53**, 521 (1938).
38. Rumbaugh, L. H.: *Phys. Rev.*, **49**, 882 (1936).
39. Glenn, W. E., Jr.: *U.S. Atomic Energy Comm. Document* 3371, Jan. 8, 1952.
40. Wilson, R. R.: *U.S. Atomic Energy Comm. Document* 3373, May 9, 1952.
41. Aston, F. W.: *Proc. Roy. Soc.* (*London*), **A115**, 487 (1927); **A163**, 391 (1937).
42. Dempster, A. J.: *Proc. Am. Phil. Soc.*, **75**, 755 (1935).
43. Bainbridge, K. T., and E. B. Jordan: *Phys. Rev.*, **50**, 283 (1936).
44. Mattauch, J.: *Phys. Rev.*, **50**, 617 (1937).
45. Nier, A. O., and T. R. Roberts: *Phys. Rev.*, **81**, 504 (1951).
46. Collins, T. L., A. O. Nier, and W. H. Johnson, Jr.: *Phys. Rev.*, **84**, 717 (1951).
47. Goudsmit, S. A.: *Phys. Rev.*, **74**, 622 (1948).
48. Hays, E. E., P. T. Richards, and S. A. Goudsmit: *Phys. Rev.*, **84**, 824 (1951).
49. Hipple, J. A., H. Sommer, and H. A. Thomas: *Phys. Rev.*, **76**, 1877 (1949).
50. Smith, L. G., and C. C. Damm: *Phys. Rev.*, **90**, 324 (1953).
51. Gordy, W., W. V. Smith, and R. Trambarulo: "Microwave Spectroscopy," John Wiley & Sons, Inc., New York, 1953.
52. Dieke, G. H.: *Ann. Rev. Nuclear Sci.*, **1**, 363 (1952).
53. Townes, C. H., and W. Low: *Phys. Rev.*, **80**, 608 (1950).
54. Gordy, W., *Revs. Mod. Phys.*, **20**, 668 (1948).
55. Gordy, W.: *Phys. Today*, **5**(12), 6 (1952).
56. Casimir, H. B. G.: "On the Intersection between Atomic Nuclei and Electrons," Teyler's Tweede Genootschop, Haarlem, 1936.
57. Ramsey, N. F.: *Exptl. Nuclear Phys.*, **1**, 385 (1953).
58. Kellogg, J., I. Rabi, N. F. Ramsey, and J. Zacharias: *Phys. Rev.*, **56**, 730 (1939).
59. Taub, A. H., and P. Kusch: *Phys. Rev.*, **75**, 1477 (1949).
60. Gardner, J. H., and E. M. Purcell: *Phys. Rev.*, **76**, 126 (1949).
61. Bloch, F., D. Nicodemus, and H. H. Staub: *Phys. Rev.*, **74**, 1025 (1948).
62. Pound, R. V.: *Progr. Nuclear Phys.*, **2**, 21 (1952).
63. Purcell, E. M., H. C. Torrey, and R. V. Pound: *Phys. Rev.*, **69**, 37 (1946).
64. Bloch, F., W. Hansen, and M. Packard: *Phys. Rev.*, **69**, 127 (1946).
65. Gorter, C. J., and L. J. F. Broer: *Physica*, **9**, 591 (1942).
66. Pound, R. V., and W. D. Knight: *Rev. Sci. Instr.*, **21**, 220 (1950).
67. Motz, J. W., *et al.*: *Rev. Sci. Instr.*, **24**, 929 (1953).
68. Snyder, C. W., and V. E. Parker: *Bull. Am. Phys. Soc.*, **29**(4), 47 (1954).
69. Wolff, M. M., and W. E. Stephens: *Rev. Sci. Instr.*, **24**, 616 (1953).
70. Collins, T. L., T. T. Scolman, and A. O. Nier: *Bull. Am. Phys. Soc.*, **29**(4), 27 (1954).

CHAPTER 5

DETECTORS AND NUCLEAR TECHNIQUES

The character of nuclear physics has been transformed to such an extent in recent years by the extensive application of precision instruments that most of the early work based upon semiquantitative techniques is now obsolete. Nevertheless, there are still areas in nuclear physics in which the data obtained with instruments or techniques giving results accurate to two or even one significant figure assist in the understanding of nuclear phenomena. Such instances arise (1) when an exploratory study is needed upon which to base the design of a precise study, (2) when no precision methods are available for the particular study, (3) when the successful application of a precision instrument is prohibited by a practical difficulty such as lack of source intensity or the shortness of the lifetime of the source, and (4) when discrimination between conflicting theories requires only limited accuracy. In many instances a coarse instrument is used in conjunction with a precision instrument to reduce interfering background effects due to cosmic rays or to eliminate other types of unwanted radiations.

This chapter will be devoted to a discussion of detectors of nuclear particles and to some of the key semiquantitative techniques used in nuclear physics, particularly in connection with energy measurements. In early applications of many of these techniques it was necessary to go rather deeply into the theory of each technique to interpret the data obtained. Since sources of almost monoergic particles are now available with energies covering most of the range of interest in nuclear physics, almost all semiquantitative energy-measuring techniques may be calibrated experimentally by means of precision techniques. Consequently, in so far as nuclear physics is concerned, the theoretical results are now mainly of interest as interpolating formulas between experimentally calibrated points. The material in this chapter will be presented with this in mind.

5-1. Detectors and Counters.[1,2,66] Practically every nuclear apparatus has a component whose function is to detect particles. The most elementary type of detection device simply indicates the arrival of a particle at a physically specified area by a signal which is directly or indirectly intelligible to the observer. The signals given off by detectors of photons, electrons, positrons, and charged nuclear particles usually result from the electromagnetic interaction of these particles with atomic electrons. The resulting excitation and ionization of atoms in the detector may be rendered observable in a variety of ways. Some detectors, however, depend upon the direct interactions between the particles and nuclei. These interactions generally produce secondary effects which cause atomic ionization. Detectors of neutrons and neutral mesons depend upon such two-step processes.

Simple detectors (which are usually called counters) are used in conjunction with systems for counting the number of signals arriving in a specified time. In the most primitive arrangement the observer himself acts as the counter. The accumulation of useful data by such means is a long and tedious task, and the possibility of human error is great, particularly if successive signals are separated by less than 0.5 sec. Human fallibility may be eliminated, however, by the use of electromechanical counters. Accordingly, in almost all present-day arrangements the signal is converted by one means or another into a current pulse which drives an electromechanical counting device. Electromechanical counters can register signals separated by as little as 0.01 sec.

When signals arrive separated by still smaller time intervals, even electromechanical counters will miss counts; hence, to extend the range of counters still further, electronic methods are utilized to record the first few digits, and electromechanical methods record only the higher powers of 10 (or powers of 2, if the binary system of numbers is used). Such electronic systems are called scalers.

Efforts to count individual pulses separated by exceedingly short time intervals require very careful design of the components of the detector-counter system. After detecting a particle and recording a count, the complete system must return rapidly to its normal condition to be ready for the next pulse. Using electronic systems (see Sec. 5-5) which contain only "hard" vacuum tubes, it is possible to register pulses spaced of the order of 10^{-9} sec apart. The recovery time of the detector itself, however, usually limits the resolution time of the detector-counter systems. The resolution time τ of a detector-counter system is the period immediately following an event during which the system is insensitive to a second event. If this resolving time is comparable to the average time interval between events, then many counts are lost. A correction can be made for counting losses, when they are relatively small ($\sim$10 per cent), based upon the following considerations: Let n be the number of actual events per second and m be the number of observed counts per second. Since the total dead time in 1 sec is $m\tau$, the probability of a single actual event falling within this total dead time is $m\tau/1$. Consequently, the total number of events which fall within this dead time in 1 sec, or the counting loss per second, is

$$n - m = n(m\tau) \tag{5-1}$$

Therefore

$$n = \frac{m}{1 - m\tau} \tag{5-2}$$

When the time interval between pulses is smaller than the resolution time of a detector-counter system, it is more practical to use detecting devices which give a signal proportional to the flux, or number of particles per second striking a specified area. The ionization chamber in steady operation is an example of such an instrument.

In many different phases of nuclear physics valuable information is provided by the investigation of coincidences between nuclear events. Coincidences between particles emitted in radioactive decay are clues to energy-level structures and decay schemes. Coincidence techniques are the basis of many systems for collimating particles. Delayed coincidences are used in certain time-of-flight investigations. In applications of detectors to coincidence investigations the response time of the detector rather than the recovery time largely determines its suitability for an investigation. We may define a characteristic coincidence-resolving time τ_c as the maximum time separation between two independent pulses which are recorded as a spurious coincidence. The number of spurious coincidences which occur when m_1 and m_2 are the *independent* counting rates of the two counters may be deduced by simple probability considerations. In 1 sec the total time during which pulses in the first counter can record a coincidence with an independent pulse in the second counter is $2\tau_c m_1$. The probability of a single coincidence therefore is $2\tau_c m_1/1$. The total number of *accidental* coincidences when the second counter registers m_2 counts therefore is

$$n_c = 2\tau_c m_1 m_2 \tag{5-3}$$

Accordingly, to minimize the number of accidental coincidences, the coincidence-resolving time of the system must be as small as possible. An external electronic circuit can always be used to "clip" a long pulse into a short one, providing that the output of the detector itself builds up rapidly, *i.e.*, that the detector responds rapidly to the incident particle. Thus detectors with long resolving times but with short rise times can still be used in coincidence work when the background and the coincidence counting rates are small.

Detectors frequently serve other uses in addition to signaling the arrival of a particle upon a specified area or determining the flux of particles. When the signal emitted by the detector depends appreciably upon the type of particle (*e.g.*, electrons are lightly ionizing compared to protons of the same energy), the detector can be used to identify the particle or discriminate between particles. Detectors which yield signals depending upon the energy of the incident particle can be used to measure this energy. Such detectors, known as proportional counters, are used in conjunction with pulse analyzers which count the output pulses falling into various amplitude intervals.

5-2. Ionization Chambers.[3–7] The ionization chamber is perhaps the most widely known and widely used particle detector. Usually it consists of a gaseous chamber containing a cathode and a collector-type anode. This general type of system may be used as a flux indicator, a simple detector (a Geiger counter), or a proportional counter. The basic physical phenomenon upon which ionization chambers are based is the fact that a charged particle in passing through a gas leaves in its wake a large number of ion pairs, most of which consist of an electron and a positively charged molecule. For typical field conditions the electrons drift at velocities of the order of 10^6 cm/sec, whereas the ions drift at velocities of the order of 10^4 cm/sec. The detailed nature of the migrations, the recombinations, and the secondary processes caused by these primary electrons and ions depends in a complex way upon the physical design of the chamber, the applied voltage, the gaseous filling, and the auxiliary circuits. Several extensive monographs on ionization chambers are available to which we refer the reader for detailed discussions. We shall here consider a cylindrical ionization chamber containing a simple gas such as nitrogen, hydrogen, argon, etc., connected as shown in Fig. 5-1, and shall simply indicate in an elementary way the manner in which it responds to the passage of a charged particle through the chamber.

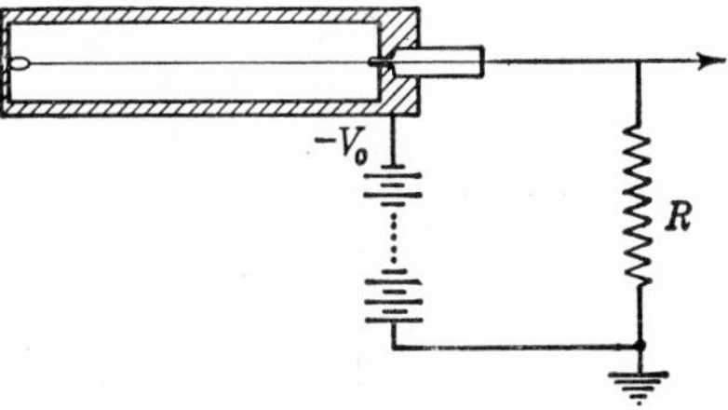

FIG. 5-1. Schematic diagram of a cylindrical ionization chamber connected to give a negative voltage pulse.

For the case illustrated in Fig. 5-1, let us tentatively assume that (1) the incident charged particle creates n ion pairs in the chamber; (2) the time constant RC, where C is the capacitance of the chamber, is large compared to the migration time of electrons and ions, (3) the voltage V_0 is large enough that no appreciable recombination takes place; (4) the voltage V_0 nevertheless is small enough that no appreciable secondary ionization takes place. Under these circumstances the magnitude of the output voltage $|V_a(t)|$ will appear approximately as shown in Fig. 5-2. The sharp rise of $|V_a(t)|$ may be ascribed to the rapid migration of the electrons to the anode and the slower continued increase to the migration of positive ions to the outer cathode. When RC is much greater than the migration time for the positive ions, the peak voltage is approximately equal to ne/C. This is to be expected since in effect we have transferred a positive and negative charge of magnitude ne to opposite plates of a capacitor. The decay of $|V_a(t)|$ is due to the discharge of the chamber through the external resistance R. By lowering this resistance the decay time may be shortened. If the time is lowered to the point that it is comparable to the migration time for the positive ions, the peak of the voltage pulse will be lower than ne/C. If the time constant is made very small, of the order of the migration time for the electrons, say, the peak voltage will be a very small fraction of ne/C. Nevertheless, for

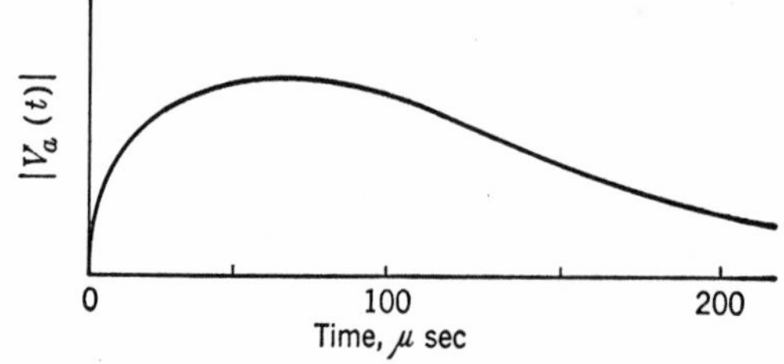

FIG. 5-2. Voltage output vs. time for a typical cylindrical chamber.

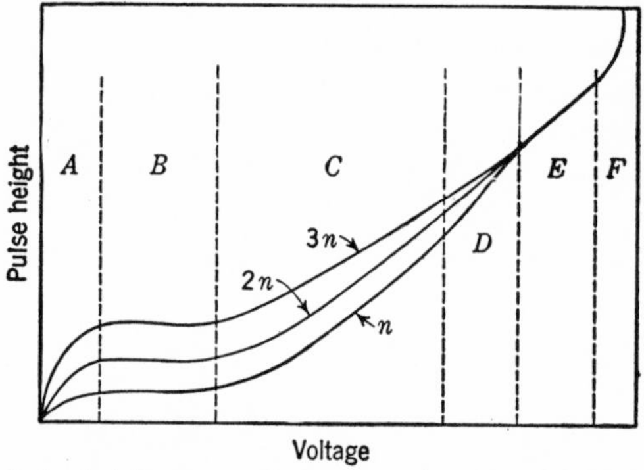

FIG. 5-3. Pulse height vs. applied voltage for three initial conditions.

the voltage conditions which we specified this peak output voltage will be proportional to the number of ions originally formed.

To explain the more general characteristics of this type of ionization chamber, let us now suppose that three incident charged particles passing through the chamber produce almost instantly n ion pairs, $2n$ ion pairs, and $3n$ ion pairs, and let us now allow the voltage V_0 to be varied. In Fig. 5-3 we show schematically the manner in which magnitude of the peak anode voltage depends upon the applied voltage V_0 in these three cases. The curve of pulse height vs. voltage may be divided into several characteristic regions, which we have indicated on this diagram. In the very-low-voltage region (A) the charge collected varies markedly with voltage and is less than ne, $2ne$, $3ne$. In this region significant recombination of electrons and positive ions takes place before the ions are collected. On the other hand in region B, which usually corresponds to field strengths of the order of 20 to 50 volts/cm, all the ions initially formed are collected, and neither recombination nor secondary ionization is appreciable. This region of operation is used in ionization chambers in steady operation to measure the flux of particles. In region C, the proportional region, more ions are collected than are initially formed. The additional ions are produced by a phenomenon sometimes referred to as gas multiplication, which is due to the intense electric fields which exist in the neighborhood of the anode. This field in the case of a cylindrical counter is given approximately by

$$\mathcal{E} = \frac{V}{r \ln (r_c/r_a)} \tag{5-4}$$

where r_a and r_c are the radii of the anode wire and the cathode cylinder. As an electron, which was created during the primary ionization process, drifts into the immediate vicinity of the anode, it accelerates rapidly until it has sufficient energy to ionize an additional gas molecule. The original electron and the secondary electron both accelerate rapidly to the anode and cause additional ion pairs. If the voltage is high enough, an "avalanche" occurs in the immediate neighborhood of the wire such that each primary electron finally reaches the anode accompanied by a large number (10 to 10^6) of additional electrons. Consequently in this region the pulse height is proportional to the initial number of ions.

At the higher end of region C and in the transition region D, proportionality between pulse height and the initial number of ions gradually is lost. For still higher voltages the region E is reached, in which pulse height is very large and also substantially independent of the initial number of ions. This is the well-known Geiger-Müller region of operation. The next region F is associated with a continuous glow, or arc discharge, which is indifferent to the presence of incident charged particles and thus has no interest here.

In the Geiger region the avalanche associated with the drift of a single electron to one point on the anode initiates avalanches over the entire anode length. Photons emitted during the course of one avalanche act to spread the discharge over the entire tube. The rapid collection of electrons by the anode in a time which is usually of the order of 1 μsec momentarily leaves a sheath of positive ions surrounding the anode, which tends to cancel the field and finally limit the avalanching of electrons to the anode. This sheath then spreads out radially and reaches the cathode in a time of the order of 100 μsec. The remainder of the discharge process depends upon the gaseous filling and the external circuit.

The discharge in the Geiger region associated with an initial particle can readily be regenerated if a gas ion, upon striking the cathode, releases a new electron which is then accelerated to the anode, initiating a second avalanche. The regeneration process will continue unless the voltage is reduced in some way below the Geiger threshold. Several external circuits are available for "quenching" the discharge by lowering the voltage. We refer the reader to standard works on electronics for discussions of such quenching circuits.

The inclusion in the chamber of a small quantity (~10 per cent) of ethyl alcohol, ethane, amyl acetate, or other polyatomic gas results in a self-quenching action. These molecules, whose ionization potentials are lower than that of the simple-gas filling, apparently neutralize the simple ions in the outspreading sheath so that finally only complex ions reach the wall. Here they give up their ionization energy by dissociation into simpler molecules rather than by the initiation of new electrons. This dissociation gradually exhausts the polyatomic-gas filling, so that a new filling or a new counter is needed after a certain number of counts (~10^{10} counts in a typical system). Counter tubes are also manufactured containing a halogen quenching agent. The halogen gas acts in conjunction with the cathode surface to convert the pulse energy into heat without consuming the quenching agent. The counting life of such tubes is apparently unlimited.

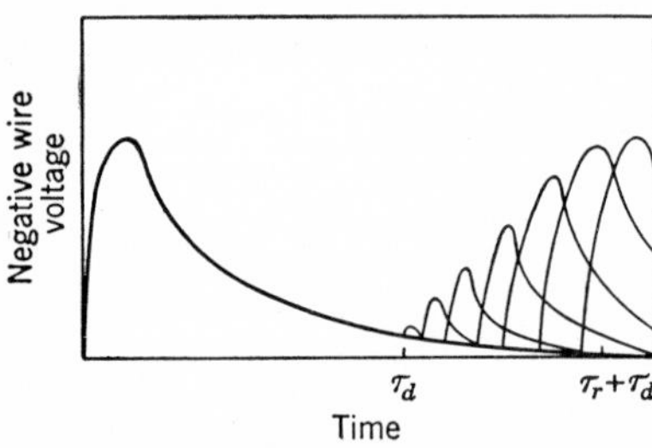

FIG. 5-4. Drawing of oscilloscope pattern showing the dead time τ_d and the recovery time τ_r. The time $\tau_d + \tau_r$ corresponds to the arrival of the positive-ion sheath at the cylinder. The time τ_d corresponds to the point in the transit of the positive ions at which the field about the wire has returned to threshold field. (*From Stever, Ref.* 8.)

During the period of migration of the ion sheath to the cathode the Geiger counter is insensitive or only partially sensitive to additional primary ionizing particles. A method devised by Stever[8] reveals this phenomenon very clearly. A particle pulse triggers an oscilloscope sweep of about 500 μsec. Should a second particle enter the chamber during this time, the output pulse associated with it, if any, will also appear on the oscilloscope. A time-exposed photograph of many records of two pulses gives a clear picture of the sensitivity of the Geiger counter to a second particle during the migration of the ion sheaths resulting from the first particle. In Fig. 5-4 we show schematically the results of an experiment in which the output associated with the primary particle is indicated by a dark curve and the outputs associated with secondary particles with various delays are shown with light curves. Clearly any secondary particle which arrives within the time interval indicated by τ_d, the dead time, will not register. The time τ_r indicated on the diagram is known as the recovery time. The time $\tau_d + \tau_r$ must elapse before the system will give an output pulse for the second particle equal to the output pulse of the primary particle.

The fact that the resolving time of a Geiger counter is of the order of several hundred microseconds prevents the application of Geiger counters to high counting rates. However, the initial response of the Geiger counter is quite fast, since it depends upon the motion of electrons in the neighborhood of the anode. Consequently the coincidence-resolving time attainable with small Geiger counters is of the order of 0.1 μsec.

One of the important characteristics of a Geiger-Müller counter is its relative insensitivity, within a range which is known as the plateau, to

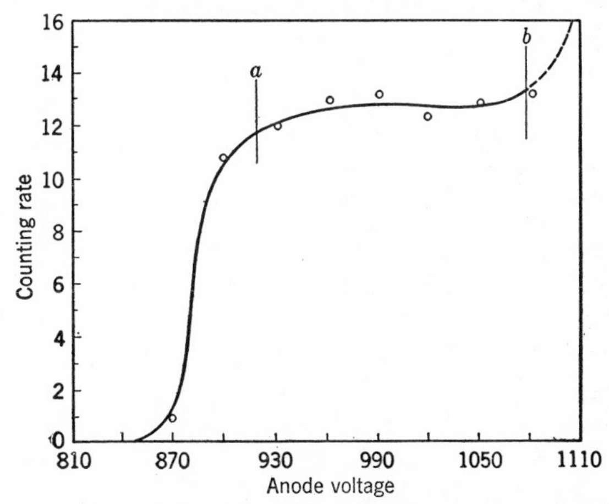

FIG. 5-5. Counting rate vs. anode voltage for a constant source of radiation. (*From Rossi and Staub, Ref.* 3.)

variations of anode voltage. In Fig. 5-5 we show a curve which indicates the observed counting rate corresponding to a constant source of radiation as a function of the anode voltage. The useful operating region lies between points a and b on the curve.

We have indicated that, in region C of Fig. 5-3, the maximum height of the voltage pulse is approximately proportional to the number of ions initially formed in the sensitive region of the chamber, that is, $|V_{am}| \approx n$. If the chamber is long compared to the ranges of a particular type of charged particle under study, the entire kinetic energy of the charged particle will be dissipated within the chamber. Since the energy necessary to form an ion pair in gases is almost independent of the energy of the incident particle, we see that $n \approx T/w$, where w is the energy necessary for the incident particle to form an ion pair (in most gases w runs between 21 and 37 ev for charged particles). Consequently, for long chambers in the proportional region of operation, $|V_{am}| \approx T$. The extent to which the output pulse will be proportional to the energy of the incident particle depends upon the care exercised in the design and construction of the ionization chamber. Since the field in the multiplication region around the anode must be very uniform, the anode wire must be uniform, and the supporting and insulating structures must be constructed to minimize distortion. Many of the considerations concerning gas filling and response time for Geiger counters are also applicable to proportional counters.

Proportional counters have long been used with success with charged nuclear particles, whose range is relatively small and which produce a large number of ions. Recently, proportional counters have been developed for β particles. The use of Geiger and proportional counters for gamma rays is mainly based upon the conversion of these gamma rays into electrons in the wall of the tube. The over-all efficiency of this type of detector varies somewhat with energy and with the atomic number of the wall material. However, at best, *i.e.*, with walls of heavy metals, it is rather low ($\sim$2 per cent).

Chambers based upon steady ionization currents have been made in a great variety of forms, depending upon the particles to be detected and the purpose of the investigation. Chambers may roughly be divided into "small" and "large" chambers, where these words apply in relation to the intrinsic range of the particle rather than to any absolute length. In large chambers either the incident particle comes to rest within the chamber, or else a very substantial portion of its original energy is expended in the chamber. In small chambers only a fraction of the energy of the particle is lost.

Since ionization currents are small in spite of gas multiplication, a d-c amplifier is generally used between the ionization chamber and the galvanometer or electrometer. A frequently used arrangement passes the ion current through a very high resistance and measures the potential drop with an electrometer. Instead of measuring the steady ionization current through a high resistance, some ionization chambers are connected to a sensitive electrometer which measures the rate of discharge of an initially charged system. Electroscope types of ionization chambers are characterized by the fact that the anode itself is the flexible member which indicates the charge of the system. In the Lauritsen electroscope, a compact form of this device, a flexible quartz fiber serves as the moving element. The position of the fiber in relation to a graduated scale is read with the small microscope, which is a part of the instrument.

5-3. The Scintillation Detector.[7,9–11,67,68] In the scintillation detector the incident particle induces the detector to emit a light pulse which serves as the signal for a count. In earliest applications of this type of detecting system a thin layer of ZnS was used as a phosphor for indicating alpha particles. The observer viewed the coated area through a microscope and simply counted the number of light flashes in a chosen interval of time. In recent scintillation detectors a photomultiplier is used to change the light pulse into a large burst of electrons. These recent counters make use of efficient phospors which are transparent to their own radiation. The organic compounds anthracene, stilbene, phenanthrene, and naphthalene and the inorganic crystals NaI and KI (activated with Tl), NaCl activated with Ag, and thin layers of $CaWO_4$ possess these desirable properties. Recently scintillators have been made of organic phosphors in liquid solution and in solid solutions, which are easily obtainable in desired sizes and shapes.

Scintillation counters have several advantages over Geiger counters and are now replacing Geiger counters in many applications. Some of these advantages are (1) high efficiency, (2) short rise and recovery times, and (3) long or indefinite usable life. The inorganic crystals tend to have the highest efficiencies ($\sim$20 per cent for α, p, β, and γ particles) for the conversion of particle or γ-ray energy into light energy. Their rise and recovery times run of the order of 1 μsec. Organic crystals are lower in efficiency ($\sim$10 per cent for γ and 1 per cent for α and p) but have rise and recovery times of the order of 10 mμsec. Liquid and solid solutions of phosphors tend to have still smaller efficiencies, but also smaller rise and recovery times.

The detailed nature of the scintillation process is related to the complex phenomena of fluorescence and phosphorescence and is still not well understood. Qualitatively speaking, we may describe the process as one in which the ionizing particle excites the atoms or molecules in the phosphor by raising their electrons to higher energy states. Photons are emitted when these electrons return to their normal state, unless the atoms or molecules dissipate this energy by nonradiative collisions. In delayed light emission, or phosphorescence, the atom or molecule is raised into a metastable state from which it cannot decay directly. However, thermal motion after a time may raise it further to an ordinary excited state, from which it decays almost instantly.

"Activators," such as crystal imperfections and impurities, play an important but complex part in fluorescence and phosphorescence, acting as centers for decay by photon emission. The over-all action of a phosphor is to convert into photons the energy lost during the passage of the ionizing particle. Estimates of the amount of energy required to produce a photon in a typical phosphor vary from 10 to 100 ev, with recent work indicating the higher figure. Since a typical energy loss by a charged particle in a phosphor runs of the order of 10^5 to 10^6 ev, many photons are produced.

The photomultiplier, an intrinsic part of the scintillation counter-detector system, consists of a photocathode and an electron multiplier. The cathode is usually coated on the inside of the end of the tube. For maximum efficiency it is important that the spectrum of the light emitted by the phosphor match the spectral-sensitivity curve of the photomultiplier. In the photomultiplier an electron released by a photon is accelerated to the first dynode by a high potential difference. A number of

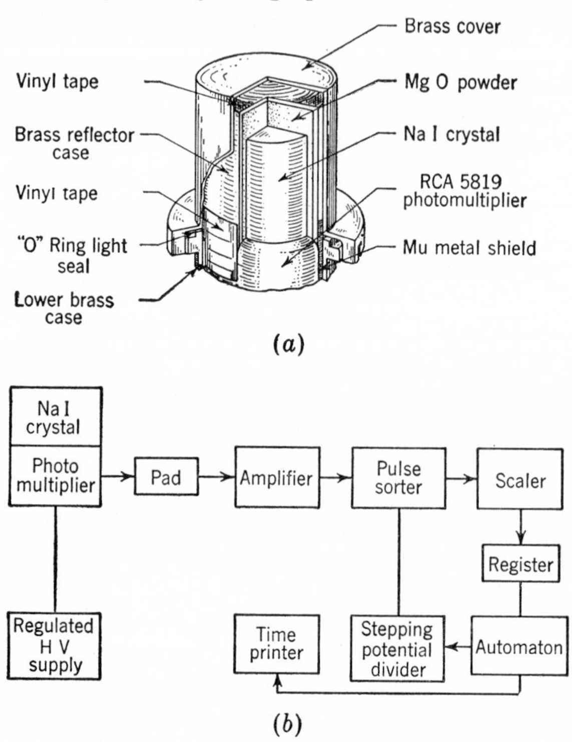

FIG. 5-6. (*a*) Crystal-photomultiplier assembly. The crystal is optically connected to the glass of the photomultiplier tube by a film of Dow-Corning stopcock grease and is surrounded by a high-efficiency reflector of MgO powder. Hermetic seals are made with vinyl tape. The outer enclosure makes the assembly light tight. (*b*) Block diagram of the spectrometer. Arrowheads show the direction of transmission of pulse signals. (*From Strickler and Wadey, Ref.* 12.)

secondary electrons are released and accelerated to the next dynode. This process avalanches until finally a burst of electrons reaches the collector anode. Usually some type of light-collection system is used to "pipe" the light from the phosphor to the photocathode. In many instances a Lucite plug not only serves as a light guide but also helps to protect the phosphor (NaI is hygroscopic and must be hermetically sealed). For example, a reflector consisting of aluminum foil is sometimes used around the crystal, light guide, and photomultiplier to reduce light loss. In Fig. 5-6 we show a typical scintillation-counter arrangement.

A figure of merit which is sometimes applied to the phosphor-light collector and the photoelectric surface of the photomultiplier is the energy loss in the phosphor for a single photoelectron emitted. Typical figures of merit run of the order of 1 kev per photoelectron. This is much larger than the energy loss per electron produced in gaseous chambers (~30 ev). Despite this, the scintillation counter has a great advantage over ionization chambers, when applied to high-energy gamma rays and beta particles, since the energy loss per unit length of track in a solid or liquid scintillator is immensely greater than in a gas. For this reason scintillation counters are replacing Geiger counters as beta- and gamma-ray detectors. Typical scintillation counters register about 20 per cent of the gamma rays impinging upon the sensitive area, as compared to about 1 or 2 per cent for Geiger counters.

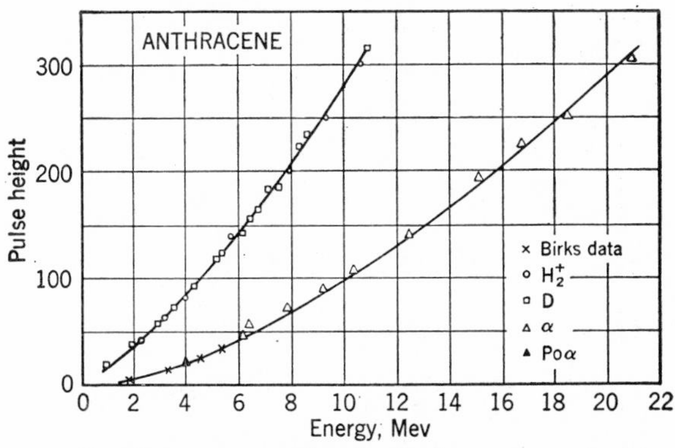

FIG. 5-7. Response of anthracene to molecular-hydrogen ions, deuterons, and alpha particles. (*From Taylor et al., Ref.* 13.)

Scintillation detectors are also coming into wide use as energy-proportional counters for gamma rays, beta rays, and charged nuclear particles. This use is based upon experimental observations of the dependency of pulse height upon particle energy. In all cases the pulse height has a simple, almost linear, relationship to the incident energy, provided that the incident particle or photon is absorbed in the scintillator. In Fig. 5-7 we show the response of anthracene to several types of charged particles. In Fig. 5-8 we show the response of anthracene, stilbene, and sodium iodide to electrons. The theoretical explanation for these simple response curves has yet to be given.

The response of a scintillation counter to gamma rays is more complicated; nevertheless it may still be used for energy measurement, if the gamma spectrum is not very complex. Difficulties arise with complex spectra because various subsidiary peaks are introduced into the spectra in the scattering process (see Sec. 7-9). In Fig. 5-9 we show the pulse-height distributions of NaI and anthracene due to 1.38- and 2.76-Mev γ rays from Na^{24}.

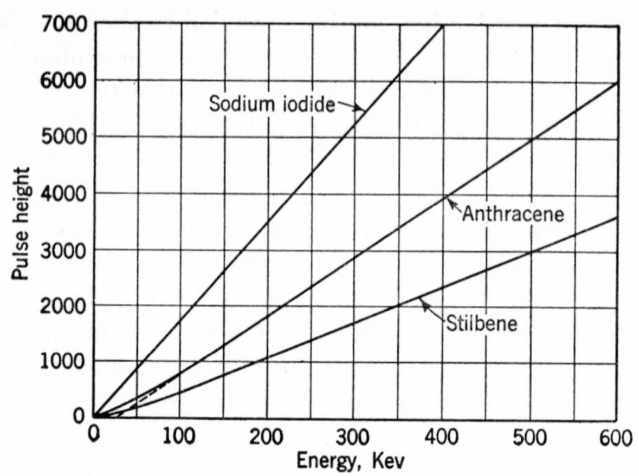

FIG. 5-8. Response of anthracene, stilbene, and sodium iodide to electrons. (*From Taylor et al., Ref.* 13.)

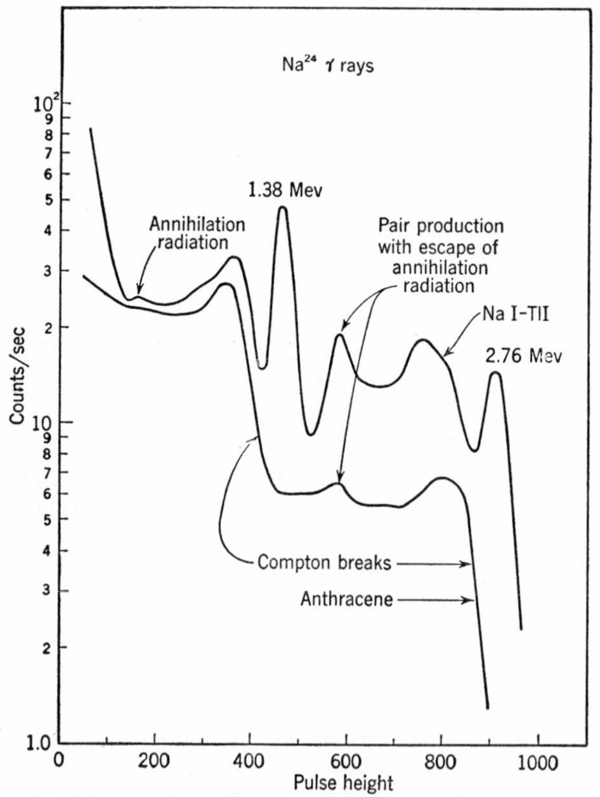

FIG. 5-9. A comparison of the pulse-height distributions of NaI and anthracene to Na^{24} γ rays. (*From Jordan and Bell, Ref.* 10.)

Scintillation spectrometers are finding even more useful applications in beta-ray spectroscopy. The resolution is not comparable with that of magnetic spectrometers; however, scintillation spectrometers may be used with much weaker sources, since a large fraction of the beta particles are counted. Scintillation spectrometers have also been used recently for measuring the energy spectrum of massive charged particles, which result from certain nuclear reactions. In Fig. 5-10 we give the proton spectrum resulting from the bombardment of magnesium with protons, as it appears in an oscilloscope pulse analyzer (see Sec. 5-5). The intensities of the traces are rough measures of the relative intensities of proton groups emitted in the reaction being studied. The error in the assignment of the energy of the individual proton groups, on the basis of this

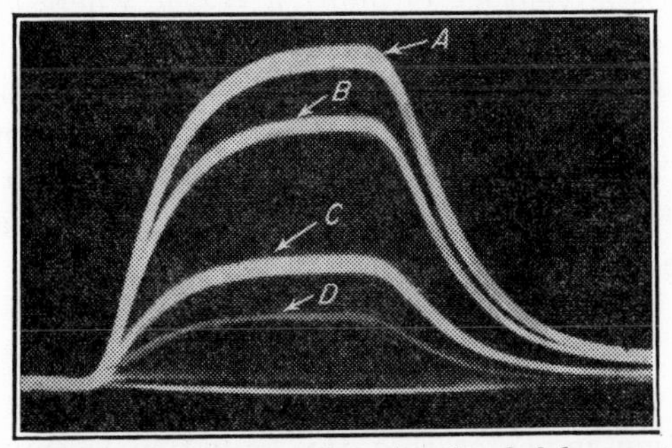

FIG. 5-10. Pulses resulting from magnesium bombarded by protons. The largest pulses come from the elastically scattered protons (*A*). This group appears to be broader than the others because it is considerably overexposed. The other two strong groups result from the excitation of Mg^{24} to the well-known energy levels of 1.38 and 4.14 Mev. A fainter group (*D*) is seen which corresponds to a level at 5.10 Mev. Note that the oscilloscope trigger cuts off just before the thin, dense base line, which is artificially inserted immediately after the run. (*From Stoddart and Gove, Ref.* 14.)

photograph, is ± 40 kev. Although this is considerably larger than the error of magnetic methods, nevertheless the technique is useful in instances where efficiency is important.

Because of the short resolving time, scintillation spectrometers are particularly useful for the measurement of coincidences of particles emitted by radioactive nuclides. Coincidence scintillation spectrometers have been used for studying correlations in beta and gamma decay.

In some instances a scintillation spectrometer is used in conjunction with a precision magnetic spectrometer as a biased detector, which rejects all particles except those which satisfy the energy setting of the precision spectrometer. In this way background counts are reduced considerably.

5-4. The Crystal,[15,69] Cerenkov,[70,71] and Spark Detectors. The crystal detector consists of a suitable crystal placed between electrodes which are maintained at a high difference of potential. Although normally a good insulator, the crystal becomes conductive for a brief interval of time ($\sim 10^{-8}$ sec) after a fast charged particle passes through it. Certain small diamonds, silver chloride, and cadmium sulfide crystals possess this useful property.

The electronic circuitry associated with conduction-type crystal counters is somewhat simpler than that needed for the scintillation counter, and no light collection problem exists. Unfortunately polarization effects, due to the entrapment of charges within the crystal lattice, change the sensitivity of the crystal. An additional disadvantage is the fact that most crystal detectors must be kept at low temperatures and in a vacuum. For these reasons crystal counters are not yet used extensively.

If a very fast particle passes through a transparent solid medium whose characteristic velocity of light ($u = c/n$, where n is the index of refraction) is less than the velocity of the particle (v), this particle emits an electromagnetic radiation known as Cerenkov[16] radiation. The effect is analogous to the emission of a shock wave by a bullet moving faster than sound. The detailed theory of this effect has been worked out by several writers.[17, 18] The theory indicates that the radiation is confined to a cone whose half angle is given by

$$\cos\theta = \frac{u}{v} = \frac{c}{nv} \tag{5-5}$$

This last equation indicates that this radiation is emitted only when $v > c/n$. Since the index of refraction of typical transparent materials runs of the order of 1.5, we see that this type of radiation might be useful for detecting particles with $v > 2 \times 10^{10}$ cm/sec. Such velocities correspond to kinetic energies equal to about 0.35 times the rest energy of the particle ($\sim$0.2 Mev for electrons, $\sim$300 Mev for protons). Cerenkov radiation is finding application both as a signal for the indication of high-speed particles and as a means for measuring the energy of these particles. In the latter connection several suggestions[19,20] have been made for measuring the conical angle to obtain a direct estimate of the kinetic energy.

The various forms of spark counters which have been developed exploit the fact that air under a sufficiently intense electric field breaks down when a charged particle passes through it. To secure intense fields with reasonable voltages, the earliest spark counters made use of point electrodes. This form, however, has the disadvantage of having too small a sensitive volume. This deficiency is overcome in wire counters, which in their original form consisted of a thin wire stretched parallel to a flat plate at a distance of the order of 1 mm. A multiple-wire spark counter due to Rosenblum[21] has several particular advantages for alpha counting. Recent forms of this detector described by Eichholz[22] are simple and rugged, have short recovery time (~1 μsec), and have desirable directional properties. Pidd and Madansky[23] have developed parallel-plate spark counters, which have even greater detecting volumes. While these give very short delay times, they have not come into wide use because of difficulties with reproducibility and construction.

5-5. Electronic Instruments.[6,24–27] In this section we shall describe briefly some of the major electronic instruments which are used to amplify, count, detect the coincidences, or measure the amplitude of the pulses which are obtained from particle detectors. We shall assume that the reader is already familiar with the elementary concepts of electronics.

For use in nuclear physics a pulse amplifier must deliver an output pulse which is large enough (~10 to 100 volts) to actuate a recording instrument. Since the different detectors afford a large range of input signals, the amplification needed to bring a pulse up to the desired output level may run anywhere from 1 to 10^6. Gains much greater than 10^6 are usually impractical because of the spurious signals (noise) which are inherent in any electron-tube device. These inherent noises are (1) the shot noise associated with the random emission of electrons by the cathode of the input tube, (2) the resistor noise associated with the thermal motion of electrons in the input resistance, and (3) the grid-current noise associated with small positive-ion grid currents. Spurious signals may also be introduced by external causes such as the house current, which gives rise to 60-cycle hum, transient electrical disturbances, or transient mechanical disturbances. These external noises, however, may be minimized by careful shielding and mechanical mounting. Practical experience with pulse amplifiers shows that the peak noises cannot be reduced appreciably below 10 μv. This figure sets an approximate lower limit upon the size of usable signals from detectors and an upper limit on the usable gains of pulse amplifiers.

Apart from raising the voltage level of a pulse, a pulse amplifier changes the shape of a pulse in a manner which depends upon the components of the amplifier. The effect of a pulse amplifier on input pulses of various shapes may best be determined if the voltage response of the amplifier to a unit-step voltage is known. Such a voltage is shown in Fig. 5-11. The response $e(t)$ of a typical pulse amplifier to a step-function voltage is indicated schematically in Fig. 5-12. If this step-function response curve is known for a particular amplifier, the output pulse for an arbitrary input pulse V_i may be calculated using

$$V_o(t) = \int_0^\infty V_i(t - t') \frac{de}{dt'} dt' \tag{5-6}$$

Several parameters may be used to characterize the response curve $e(t)$. The delay time T_d may be defined as the time required for $e(t)$ to rise to one-half of its peak value. The rise time T_r may conveniently be defined as the time required for $e(t)$ to rise from 10 to 90 per cent of its peak value. The clipping time T_c is the time constant which characterizes the rate of decay of the output pulse. This decay is commonly of an exponential form with a time constant determined by a short RC coupling constant which usually is associated with an intermediate stage of the amplifier. For fast counting applications the clipping time should be approximately of the same magnitude as the rise time in order to prevent the "pile-up" of pulses. The exponential pulse shape is then undesirable, not only because of its long tail but because the peak magnitude of the pulse is greatly reduced when the decay time is shortened to be comparable to the rise time. Fortunately, several methods are available for transforming a

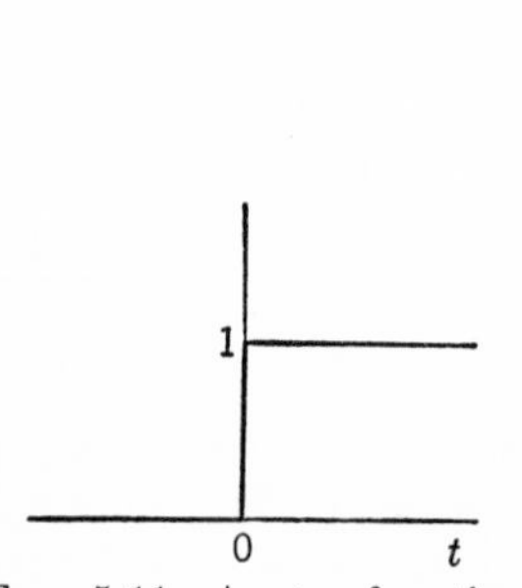

FIG. 5-11. A step-function voltage.

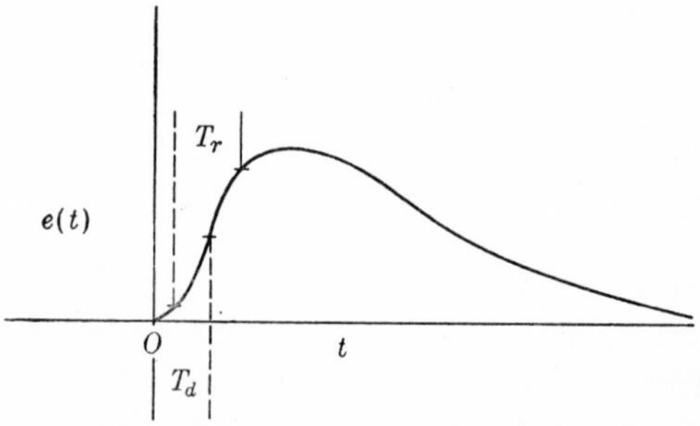

FIG. 5-12. The response of a typical pulse amplifier to a step-function voltage.

pulse into an approximately square shape, which is the ideal form for accurate pulse-height measurement at fast counting rates.

The rise time of a resistance-coupled amplifier is given by

$$T_r = \sqrt{2\pi}\, RC \tag{5-7}$$

where R is the resistance in the plate circuit and C is the total parasitic capacitance shunting this resistance. Since it is difficult to reduce these stray capacitances much below 10 $\mu\mu$f, relatively small values of R are used in fast multistage amplifiers. The gain of an amplifier stage, however, is given by

$$G = g_m R \tag{5-8}$$

where g_m is the transconductance of the tube. Accordingly one cannot reduce R very far without requiring an impractical number of amplifying stages. Some improvements in the speed of response of an amplifier may be achieved without sacrificing gain by incorporating small compensating inductances in series with the plate resistor. The inductance which leads to the shortest rise time is given by

$$L = \frac{R^2C}{4} \tag{5-9}$$

In a multistage amplifier the net rise time can be shown to be the geometric mean of the rise times for each stage, and this net rise time is a minimum when every stage has the same rise curve.

A typical nuclear amplifier has a preamplifier, which is built into a compact unit with the detector. A cathode follower is used in the output of the preamplifier because of the capacitative load of the cables to the main amplifier. In Fig. 5-13 we show a recently designed preamplifier. Most pulse amplifiers incorporate inverse feedback to improve the linearity in amplification and to minimize the effects of changes in line voltage and changes in the characteristics of the circuit elements. However, when the shortest rise time is desired, feedback circuits are avoided; instead circuits with inductive compensation are used. In Fig. 5-14 we show a recently designed pulse amplifier.

For counting, the output of the pulse amplifier is usually fed to a scaling circuit, which divides the number of counts by a fixed factor such as 64, 100, etc. The basic component of most scalers is a "flip-flop" circuit, which gives one output pulse for every two input pulses. The Higenbotham circuit (see Fig. 5-15) is widely used for this purpose. The cathode bias, the anode potentials, and the cross couplings between the triodes are chosen to make this circuit stable when either tube *A* or tube *B* is conducting but not when both are conducting. To describe the action of this circuit, let us suppose tube *B* is conducting and tube *A* is cut off. In consequence of the voltage drop in the plate resistor of tube

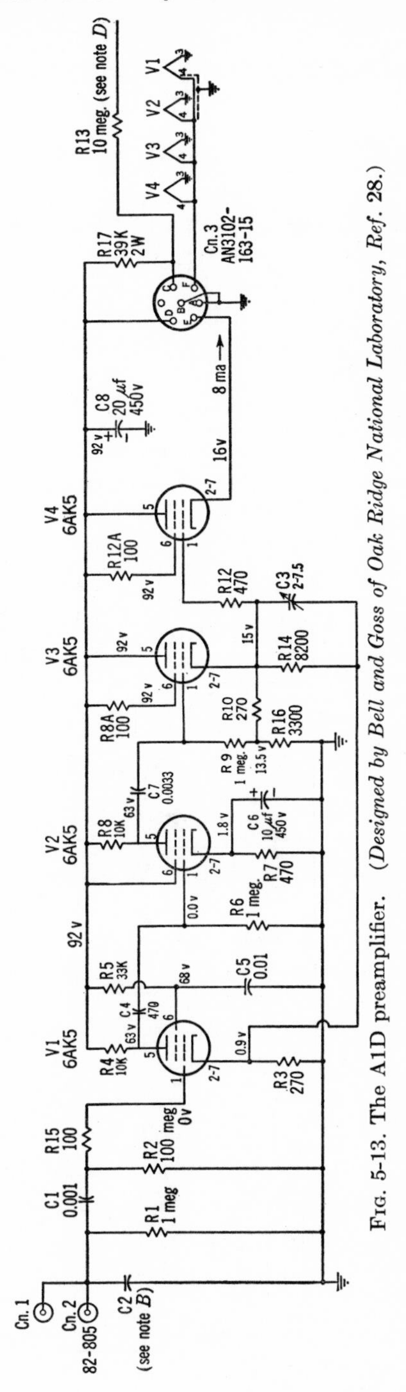

FIG. 5-13. The A1D preamplifier. (*Designed by Bell and Goss of Oak Ridge National Laboratory, Ref.* 28.)

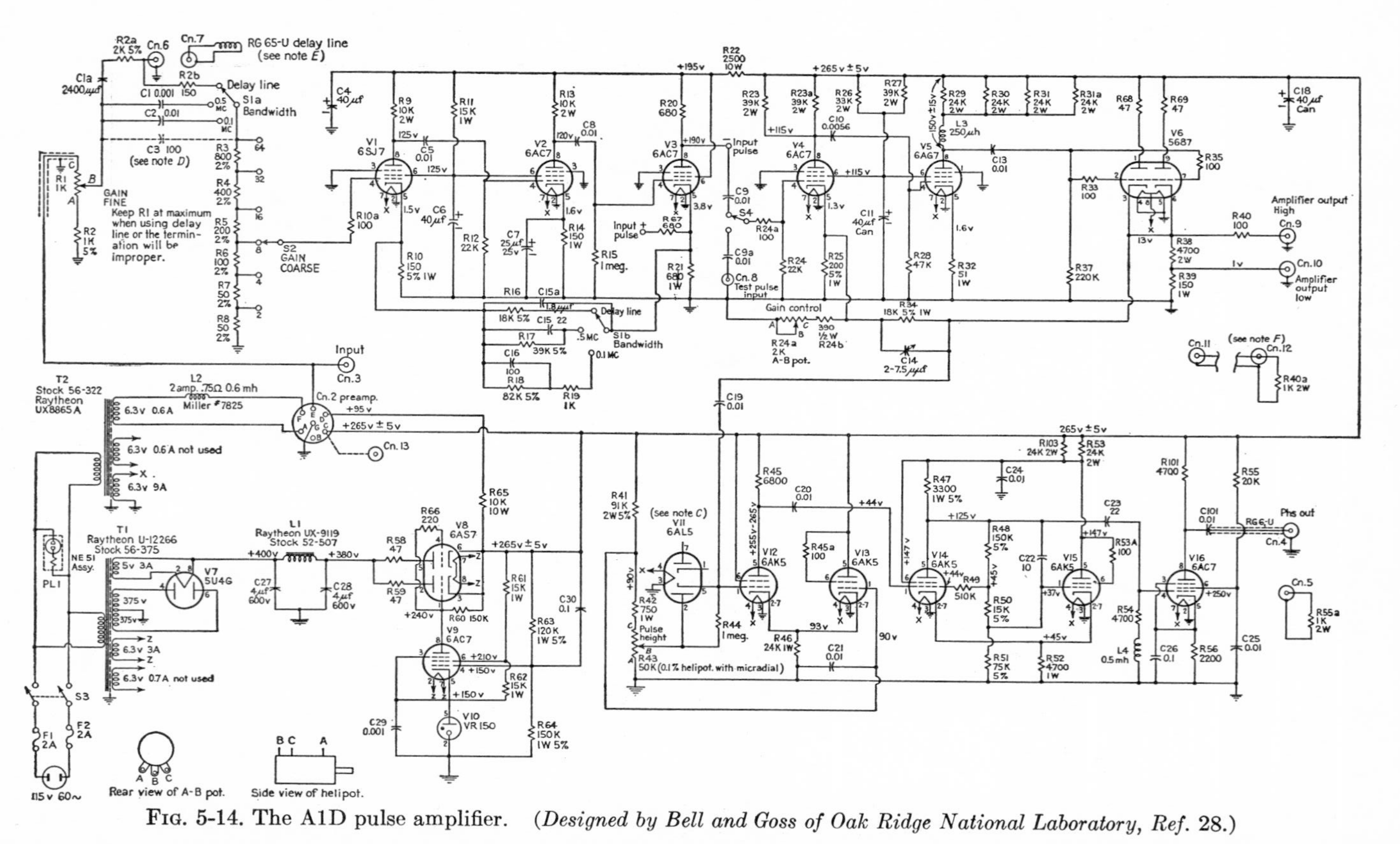

FIG. 5-14. The A1D pulse amplifier. (*Designed by Bell and Goss of Oak Ridge National Laboratory, Ref. 28.*)

B, the potential at the anode of the diode D_b is considerably lower than the potential of the anode of diode D_a. The quiescent cathode potential of the two diodes is arranged to be slightly higher than either of the anodes so that both diodes are normally cut off. A sudden drop of the correct magnitude in the diode cathode potential will now send a surge of current through D_a but will leave D_b unaffected. This negative pulse passes through the cross-coupling capacitor connected between the anode of A and the grid of B. If the capacitance is large enough, tube B will be momentarily driven toward cutoff. The consequent rise in the anode

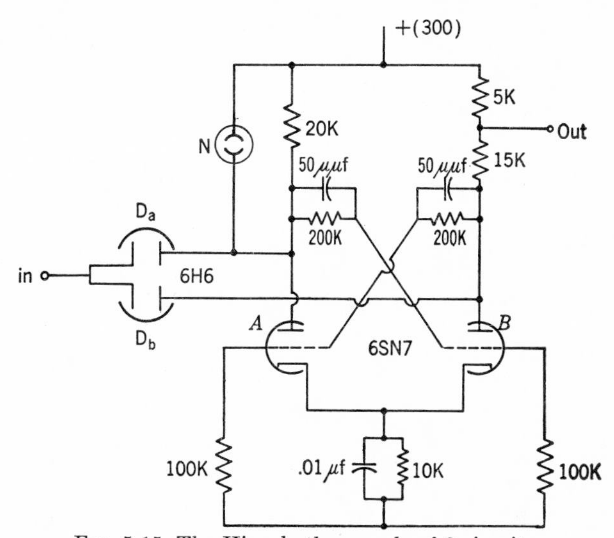

FIG. 5-15. The Higenbotham scale-of-2 circuit.

potential of tube B passes as a positive pulse through the cross-coupling capacitor to the grid of tube A. This drives the grid of tube A momentarily positive, causing it to go into the conducting state. The drop in the anode potential of tube A as it becomes conducting reinforces the action of the original negative pulse upon tube B. Accordingly, the net response of the entire circuit to a single negative pulse is to transfer the state of conduction from tube B to tube A. The action of flipping over takes a finite time, which may run from about 25 μsec to as little as 1 μsec, depending upon the stray capacitances and other circuit components. In the identical fashion the next negative pulse transfers the state of conduction back to tube B. The output point in the plate circuit of tube B moves positive whenever B becomes nonconducting and negative when B becomes conducting. A second flip-flop circuit, which responds only to negative pulses, therefore responds only to one pulse for every two pulses sent to the first flip-flop circuit.

The condition of a flip-flop circuit may be made visible by a neon tube, designated by N, which glows whenever tube A is conducting. Such neon tubes provide interpolating lights which are quite essential to the accurate use of the scaler. For example, in a series of three flip-flop circuits arranged to provide a scale of 8, the mechanical counter registers every eighth pulse fed to the scaler. The number of counts stored in the scaler is indicated by the states of the three neon tubes. In Fig. 5-16 we illustrate the conditions corresponding to various numbers of stored counts.

For convenience of reading, decade scalers are often used. A scale-of-16 unit may be changed to a scale-of-10 unit by a circuit arrangement which in effect introduces 6 false counts for every 10 real counts. A single output pulse from such a section thus represents 10 input pulses.

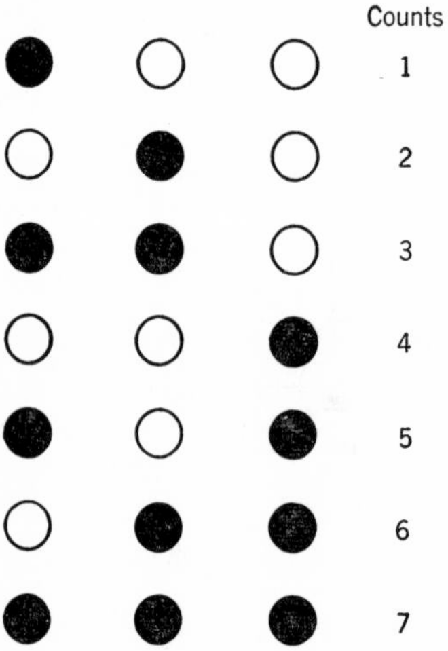

FIG. 5-16. Readings of the interpolating lights of a scale-of-8 counter.

For many applications, particularly in connection with the monitoring of relatively constant sources of radiation, an instrument which measures the counting rate directly is more convenient than a counting system based upon a scaler, a counter, and a clock. Instruments for measuring counting rates directly usually contain a circuit which transforms all pulses into square pulses of equal size and duration. These square pulses act to transfer equal increments of charge to a capacitor which leaks through a high resistance. The average potential across the capacitor is then proportional to, and a measure of, the average counting rate.

A variety of circuits may be used to establish the coincidence of pulses from independent detectors. The Rossi[29] coincidence circuit consists of two sharp-cutoff pentodes connected in the manner shown in Fig. 5-17*a*. Both tubes are normally in a conducting state. A negative pulse applied to either grid will drive that tube to cutoff. The effect of a negative pulse is thus equivalent to the opening of a switch in the equivalent network shown in Fig. 5-17*b* (r is the plate resistance of the tubes). The voltage at the output is

When both tubes are conducting,

$$V_o = V_s \frac{r/2}{R + r/2} \approx \frac{r}{2R} V_s \qquad (5\text{-}10)$$

When one tube is cut off,

$$V_o' = V_s \frac{r}{R + r} \approx \frac{r}{R} V_s \tag{5-11}$$

When both tubes are cut off,

$$V_o'' = V_s \tag{5-12}$$

Accordingly the voltage change which passes through the output capacitor is proportional to either

$$V_o' - V_o = \frac{r}{2R} V_s \tag{5-13}$$

or

$$V_o'' - V_o = V_s \left(1 - \frac{r}{2R}\right) \approx V_s \tag{5-14}$$

Because of the large difference between these signals, the simplest form of discriminator (see below) will detect the difference between the output

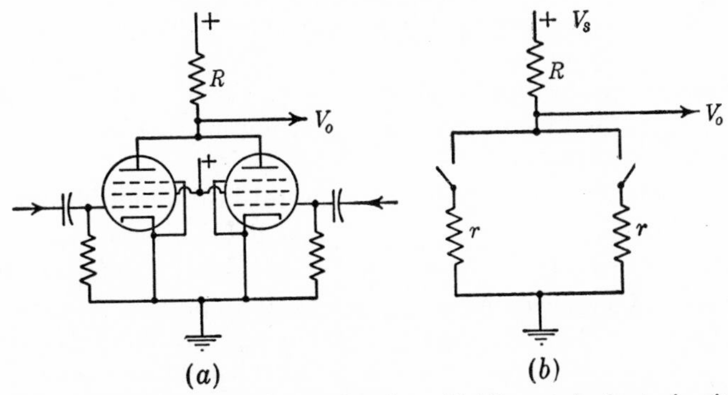

FIG. 5-17. (a) The Rossi coincidence circuit. (b) The equivalent circuit ($R \gg r$).

connected with a single pulse or the output connected with two coincident pulses. The coincidence-resolving time of such a circuit is determined both by the width of the input pulses and by the time constant of the circuit for a single pulse. This time constant, given by

$$T_s \approx Cr \tag{5-15}$$

is of the order of 0.2 μsec for typical conditions ($R \approx 0.2$ megohm, $r \approx 10{,}000$ ohms, and $C \approx 20$ $\mu\mu$f).

A modification of the Rossi coincidence circuit in which a common cathode resistance is used is capable of a shorter single-pulse rise time. However, larger pulses are needed for this cathode-follower type of coincidence circuit. Coincidence arrangements based upon the rectifying action of germanium crystals have been used successfully to obtain extremely short resolving times.

Delayed-coincidence arrangements are frequently used for measuring the time interval between pairs of generically related pulses, such as the pulses which result from a single particle passing through two widely separated counters, or the pulses arising from two particles which are emitted in a radioactive cascade. To detect a delayed coincidence, the first pulse must be converted into an artificial pulse which has various controllable delay times relative to the initiating pulse. The delay time is adjusted until the maximum number of coincidences are recorded between the artificial pulses and the second pulses. The delay time then gives the time interval between pairs of pulses. A variety of methods are available [24] for producing an artificial pulse with variable delay time.

For pulses spaced very close together (≤ 10 μsec) more direct methods are necessary for measuring the time interval between events. One such method is based upon the measurement of the voltage drop of a capacitor which discharges through a known resistance between the first and second pulses.

Multiple-coincidence arrangements measuring triple and higher coincidences utilize three or more tubes with either a common plate resistance or a common cathode resistance. The largest change in output voltage occurs when all tubes cut off simultaneously. This voltage change can be readily distinguished from single pulses or lower-order coincidences by a simple voltage discriminator.

The detection of anticoincidences is useful in differential analyzers as well as in many other instruments. The Rossi circuit can readily be adapted for this purpose. A phase inverter is used to convert the signal from the anticoincidence detector into a positive pulse. The corresponding input tube is biased to be nonconducting in the quiescent state. Obviously the largest output signal is obtained when a negative pulse reaches the regular input but no pulse reaches the anticoincidence input. A simple discriminator may be used to reject coincidences and pass only anticoincidences to the counter.

The object of most investigations with proportional counters is to obtain a pulse-height spectrum showing the number of pulses per unit pulse-height interval as a function of the pulse height. To this end one of three basic types of pulse analyzers may be employed. The simplest type contains a discriminator which transmits to the scaler only pulses which exceed a previously set height and rejects those which are lower. The observer sets the discriminator in succession for various heights and notes the corresponding counting rates. This distribution is called an integral bias curve. A typical example is shown in Fig. 5-18. The integral distribution may be differentiated numerically to obtain the counting rate per unit pulse-height interval vs. pulse height. An example of this distribution is shown in Fig. 5-19.

In integral pulse analyzers the borderline pulse height must be sharply defined and controllable over the range of pulse heights of interest. A variety of methods are available for such voltage discrimination. One simple method takes advantage of the characteristic of gas-filled triodes to fire at small, well-defined grid voltages. An adjustable bias holds the quiescent grid potential at large negative values, which are easily measured with a potentiometer. Positive pulses fed to a grid through a coupling capacitor fire the triode if they exceed the sum of the large negative bias and the small grid potential at which the tube fires. Because of their slow recovery time, gas-filled triodes are not used for high counting rates.

A vacuum diode which passes current only when the anode voltage is greater than the cathode voltage may also be used as a discriminator. The portion of a negative pulse to the cathode which exceeds the negative

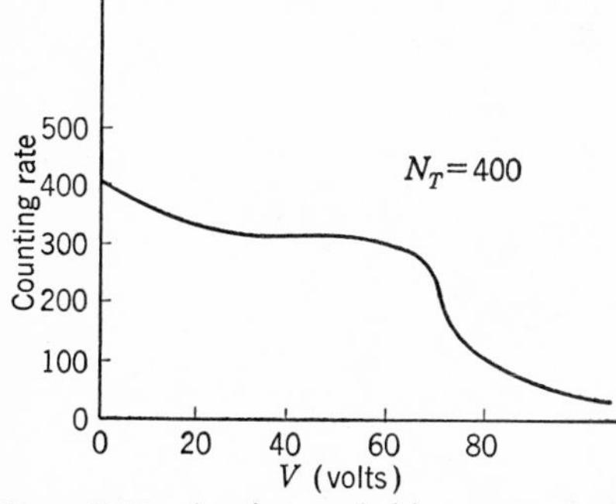

Fig. 5-18. An integral bias curve. A plot of the number of pulses during a given interval whose amplitudes are greater than the pulse height V, as a function of V. (*From Van Rennes, Ref.* 27.)

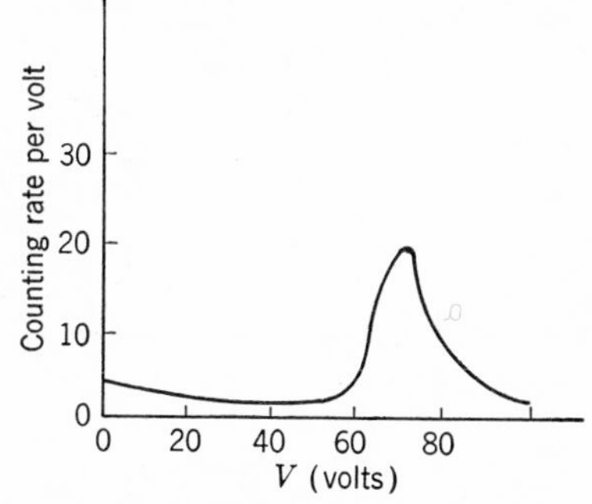

Fig. 5-19. Pulse-amplitude distribution. A plot of the number of pulses per volt as a function of the pulse height. (*From Van Rennes, Ref.* 27.)

anode bias is amplified to drive a counter. Sharp-cutoff triodes and multielectrode tubes which incorporate amplification with discrimination are also frequently used. While capable of high counting rates, vacuum discriminators have the disadvantage that their output depends upon the amount by which the pulse height exceeds the discriminator bias. If the balance is very small, the amplified pulse may not be sufficient to trip the counter. Accordingly the circuitry beyond the discriminator actually shares in the "judging" process with respect to marginal pulses.

The Schmitt trigger circuit (see Fig. 5-20) is one of several which have been devised to concentrate the discriminating process in a single carefully regulated element. Pulses which trip the circuit pass on to give an output which is essentially independent of the input. The action of this circuit is roughly as follows: Tube A is normally maintained at cutoff by a large preset negative bias, whereas tube B is normally conducting. A large positive pulse which renders tube A conducting causes the anode potential of A to drop and the common cathode potential of A and B to rise momentarily. The negative pulse fed from the plate of tube A to the grid of tube B drives tube B rapidly to cutoff. The plate potential of tube B, which is the take-off for the output of the discriminator, then rises abruptly to the supply potential. On its way down, the input pulse induces a detriggering, since the return of tube A to nonconduction sends out a positive pulse which causes tube B to return to the conducting state. The triggering action of the Schmitt circuit may be ascribed to a regenerative condition which exists when the biases on the two grids are about equal. The circuit could then exist in either of two stable states and could readily oscillate between the two states. In actual use, however, a

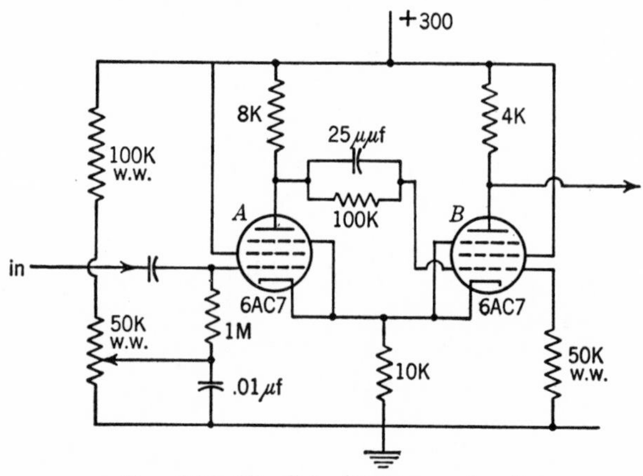

FIG. 5-20. The Schmitt trigger circuit.

natural hysteresis effect occurs, which delays the detriggering slightly and forestalls these oscillations.

Because the process of computing the pulse-height spectrum from the integral bias curve entails the subtraction of pairs of large, almost-equal numbers, the differences are subject to rather large statistical uncertainties. These uncertainties can be reduced considerably by using a differential arrangement which responds only to the pulses which fall within a preset energy interval. The spectrum is obtained directly by scanning the entire energy range in small steps and dividing each counting rate by the energy interval. In these so-called single-channel analyzers the input pulse is sampled by two pulse discriminators, one defining the lower boundary of the energy window and a second defining the upper boundary. The triggered pulses from the two discriminators are fed to an anticoincidence arrangement, which transmits an output pulse only when the lower discriminator is triggered and the upper discriminator is not triggered. Great care must be taken to fix precisely the bias difference between the two discriminators in a single-channel differential analyzer. In a typical case this bias difference is of the order of 1 volt, so that a relative shift of only 10 mv will cause an error of 1 per cent in the energy window.

The use of an integral bias analyzer or a single-channel analyzer to obtain a pulse-height spectrum is a time-consuming operation. If, as is often the case, the activity of the source changes appreciably during the scanning of the pulse-height spectrum, then the observed spectrum is not a true representation of the actual spectrum. Corrections can be made for the changes of the activity of the source when these changes occur slowly. However, for rapidly changing source activities this is not practical. This difficulty may be circumvented by using a multichannel

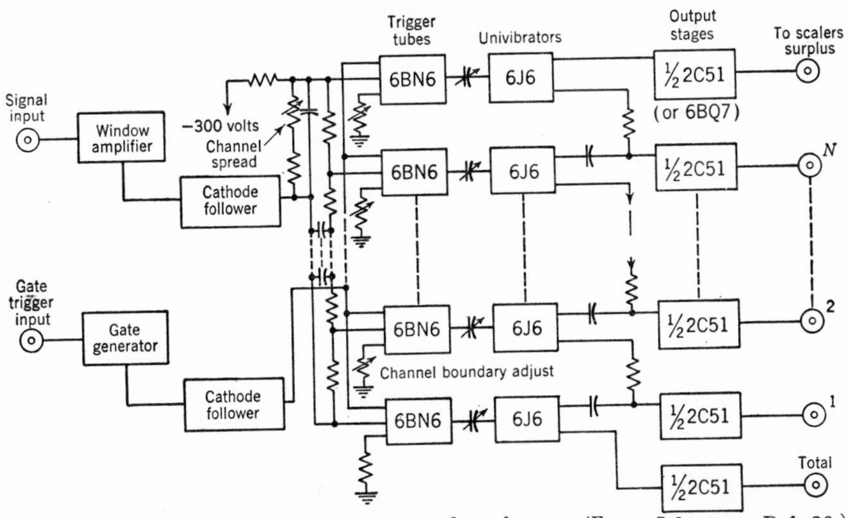

FIG. 5-21. Block diagram of a multichannel analyzer. (*From Johnstone, Ref.* 30.)

analyzer designed to count simultaneously the pulses which fall within many preset energy intervals. Strictly electronic multichannel analyzers are usually quite elaborate and involve a cascade of level-defining discriminators as well as the auxiliary circuitry required to translate the level-crossing information into counts in the appropriate channels. In Fig. 5-21 we show a block diagram of a recently designed electronic multichannel analyzer which, relative to earlier electronic analyzers, is economical in the use of tubes, has good stability in channel widths (~2 per cent), and is versatile in its application.

A number of multichannel analyzers are based upon electromechanical or electrooptical arrangements. In one simple electromechanical device for low counting rates ($\lesssim 5$ sec^{-1}), each voltage pulse is translated into a mechanical pulse by means of an electromagnetic driver similar in construction to the voice coil of a speaker. Small steel balls propelled by the driver undergo trajectories which depend upon the size of the initial impulse. An array of transparent tubes catches the balls, accumulates them, and displays them in a histogramlike pattern.

The cathode-ray oscilloscope is used as the basic element in several simple types of multichannel analyzers. In one arrangement an electronic circuit amplifies the pulse and deflects the trace rapidly to a vertical position which is a measure of the pulse height. A pulse stretcher then produces a horizontal trace whose length and intensity are independent of the height of the pulse. A time-exposed photograph presents the pulse-height spectrum as a series of horizontal lines, the intensities of which are approximately proportional to the pulse counts. Standard optical densitometer methods may be used to convert the density of a trace into a pulse count. In a method due to Maeder,[(31)] the oscilloscope screen is photographed through a so-called gray wedge, whose optical transmission varies uniformly along the horizontal axis. The locus of points on the photograph with equal densities of exposure then corresponds directly to a graph with the pulse height as the ordinate against pulse count as the abscissa. Bernstein, Chase, and Schardt[(32)] have recently developed this technique to the point that a simple electrooptical system is equivalent to a 50-channel analyzer with a counting-rate accuracy of 5 per cent.

Another successful variant of a cathode-oscilloscope system utilizes a series of anodes across the screen of the cathode-ray tube.[(33)] Each anode corresponds to a given pulse-height interval and is connected through an amplifier to a mechanical register. The cathode-ray current is controlled to flow only at the peak of the pulse. Thus every pulse is classified according to pulse height and counted. Another recent system[(72)] uses a 35-mm film record of proportional voltage pulses on a cathode-ray oscilloscope. In conjunction with an automatic electromechanical scanner this system is equivalent to a 100-channel analyzer. It can handle pulse rates up to 20,000 per second. A new type of pulse-height analyzer has been constructed recently[(73)] in which pulse amplitude is converted to time duration. Taking advantage of well-developed electronic methods of time measurement, it achieves a resolution, linearity, and stability accurate to within one per cent and is equivalent to a 250-channel analyzer. A number of other arrangements utilizing the cathode-ray tube have been developed. For a description of these as well as a discussion of their relative merits we refer the reader to the review article of Van Rennes.[(27)]

5-6. Photographic and Nuclear Emulsions.[(34,35)] An emulsion consisting of silver halide crystals mixed with gelatin and other materials can be employed to detect and at the same time permanently record the trajectory of ionizing particles which pass through it. The ionizing particles

When only a segment of a track is recorded in an emulsion, the residual range, *i.e.*, the missing segment of track, can be inferred from the approximate relationship

$$\frac{dn}{dx} = n'K'z^{2n'}m^{1-n'}R^{n'-1} \tag{5-19}$$

The sum of the observed and residual ranges in conjunction with Eq. (5-17) may be used for energy determination. When the range from a given short segment of track can be measured, Eq. (5-19) in conjunction with the grain density may be used to identify the particle.

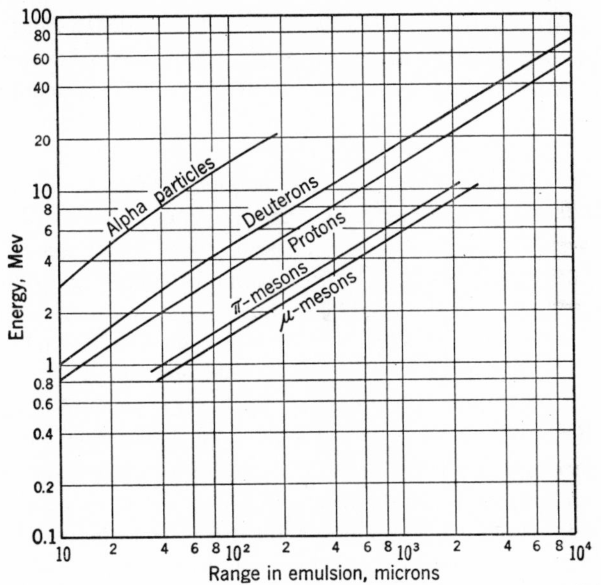

FIG. 5-22. Range vs. energy for various particles in nuclear emulsions. (*From Beiser, Ref.* 34.)

The fact that charged particles moving through an emulsion undergo frequent small deflections whose magnitudes depend upon the mass, charge, and energy of the particle is exploited in one method of identifying particles and measuring their energies. The method is based upon an experimental determination of the mean deflection angle between the tangents to successive short portions of a long track. A theoretical analysis has related this quantity to the energy, mass, and charge of the particle; the atomic number and density of the medium; and to an experimentally adjusted parameter.

A combination of a magnetic analyzer and the nuclear-emulsion technique has been used;[40,41] this method is based upon a determination of the deflection of a charged particle in an air gap between two nuclear plates. If the identity of the particle is known, this deflection can be used to determine the momentum. If the magnetic curvature and the total range are known, the mass of the particle can be established.

Emulsions impregnated with radioactive materials have proved quite useful in the study of alpha decay. Emulsions impregnated with special target materials are used for the study of nuclear reactions and for the detection or energy measurement of neutrons and gamma rays.

The sensitivity and the thickness of emulsions are unfortunately affected by temperature, humidity, age before development, and the conditions maintained during the development process. Consequently great pains must be taken to standardize the application and processing of nuclear plates so that corrections may be made to compensate for shrinkage or desensitization. Additional difficulties arise because track analysis is a very tedious process, which frequently is accompanied by subjective errors. Nevertheless, because of its economy, simplicity, compactness, and light weight, the nuclear-emulsion technique has become a very important one for many types of work. These advantages are particularly great in cosmic-ray investigations, and many important discoveries in this field have been made with the aid of nuclear emulsions.

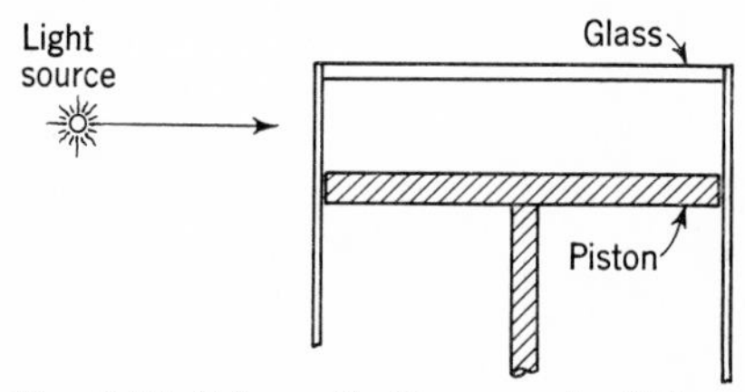

FIG. 5-23. Schematic diagram of a Wilson cloud chamber.

5-7. The Cloud Chamber.[42] The cloud chamber is an instrument in which the track of ions left in the wake of a charged particle passing through the chamber is rendered visible as a track of droplets, similar to the droplets which exist in a cloud. In the form due to Wilson[43] (see Fig. 5-23), which has played a historic role in nuclear physics, a sudden expansion of the cloud-chamber volume is employed to achieve the condition for droplet formation.

It is a well-known principle that an adiabatic expansion of the volume occupied by a noncondensible gas (such as air) will result in a decrease of temperature. If before the expansion the noncondensible gas is saturated with a condensible vapor (such as water), then a state of supersaturation will exist immediately following the expansion. The excess amount of moisture will tend to condense upon ions which exist in the gas. If conditions for the growth of moisture droplets are suitable, a charged particle which passes through the chamber shortly before an expansion will give rise after the expansion to a visible track of droplets. The degree of supersaturation after the expansion, which may be defined as the ratio of the actual density of vapor to the saturation density, is the main determinant governing the growth of droplets about ions. The supersaturation ratio in a cloud chamber depends upon the nature of the noncondensible gas, the nature of the vapor, the initial temperature, the pressure in the chamber, and the expansion ratio. The supersaturation ratio is given approximately by

$$S = \frac{P_1}{P_2}\left(\frac{1}{1+\epsilon}\right)^{\gamma} \tag{5-20}$$

where $1 + \epsilon$ is the expansion ratio, P_1 and P_2 are the saturation pressures for the initial and final temperatures of the chamber, and γ is the ratio of the specific heats of the gaseous mixture. Theoretical and experimental studies of drop formation indicate that, to obtain good tracks using a particular vapor, a critical supersaturation ratio is required; this is given approximately by

$$\ln S_c = k\left(\frac{\mathcal{O}}{T}\right)^{\frac{3}{2}} \frac{M}{\rho} \tag{5-21}$$

where $\mathcal{O}$ is the surface tension of the drop, T is the absolute temperature, M is the molecular weight of the fluid, ρ is the density of the fluid, and k is a constant (~ 0.5 when $\mathcal{O}$ is in dynes per centimeter and ρ in grams per cubic centimeter). Certain mixtures of liquids require a lower supersaturation ratio than the pure liquids. For example, a mixture of 60 per cent alcohol and 40 per cent water has a critical supersaturation ratio of 1.7, whereas water has 4.8 and alcohol 2.3.

In all experimental arrangements employing cloud chambers, photographs are taken of the tracks to provide a permanent record which may be studied at a later time. Early cloud chambers were triggered periodically so that it was a matter of chance as to whether an interesting track would be found on a photograph. To increase the yield of such photographs, most recent chambers incorporate Geiger counters on each side, and the expansion is triggered only when the Geiger counters are discharged simultaneously. For the study of artificially produced particles an electronic circuit coupled to the accelerator is usually employed; this circuit triggers the chamber in time to record a burst of particles. However, the fact that the expansion cloud chamber requires a period of the order of minutes to recover after each expansion imposes a serious limitation on such arrangements.

A continuously sensitive cloud chamber in which supersaturation is achieved by vapor diffusion has recently been developed[44] to a point that it has become a practical instrument for the study of nuclear-particle tracks. In downward-diffusion chambers a vertical temperature gradient is maintained by the use of a hot top plate and a cold bottom plate, and a vapor-density gradient is maintained by placing a source of vapor in the region of the hot plate. In upward-diffusion chambers the hot plate is on bottom. Because the saturation vapor pressure is an exponential function of temperature, it is possible with an attainable vapor flux to achieve a steady condition of supersaturation in a region of the chamber between the top and the bottom. The degree of supersaturation attainable and the proportion of the chamber volume which is supersaturated depend upon the temperatures, pressures, and vapor substances used. Some advantages which recommend the diffusion-type cloud chamber, apart from its continuous sensitivity, are (1) quick (~15 sec) reestablishment of equilibrium after a charged particle has passed through and (2) greater freedom from convection and turbulence. The instrument is particularly useful for the study of the mechanism of droplet formation. In Fig. 5-24 we show a diffusion cloud chamber.

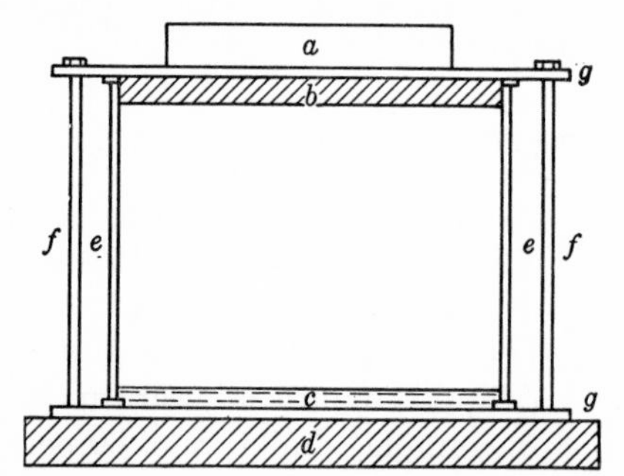

FIG. 5-24. Downward-diffusion chamber: *a*, resistance heater; *b*, vapor source of ½-in.-thick felt faced with velvet; *c*, pool of alcohol; *d*, dry ice; *e*, 10-in.-diameter glass cylinder; *f*, clamping studs; *g*, top and bottom plates of ⅛-in. copper. (*From Nielsen, Needels, and Weddle, Ref.* 44.)

In Fig. 5-25 we show an instrument developed by Cohen, called the cloud ion chamber, which combines the function of particle detection with the function of track registration. This instrument takes advantage of the large difference in mobility between electrons and positive ions. The rapid motion of the electrons leads to a signal which triggers the cloud-chamber expansion so that condensation occurs about the positive ions before they have moved substantially.

Cloud-chamber analysis shares many of the tedious features of nuclear-emulsion work, since the data used in investigations with cloud chambers are similar to the data employed in nuclear-emulsion work. The number of droplets per unit length of track, the total length of track, the total number of droplets, and the angles between tracks associated with nuclear events are the measured data which may be interpreted to determine the energy of particles or to identify particles. The curvature of a track in a cloud chamber placed in a magnetic field indicates the momentum of the particle and the sign of its charge. In this respect cloud chambers are superior to nuclear emulsions, since magnetic fields can readily be obtained which are strong enough to cause a measurable deflection within a cloud chamber, whereas they have not been obtained sufficiently strong to cause deflection within a single nuclear emulsion.

5-8. Neutron Detection. Since neutrons are uncharged, they do not interact appreciably with electrons, and hence they do not generate the types of signals which are the basis of detectors of charged particles and photons. Neutrons do, however, interact with nuclei, and many interactions yield moving charged particles or photons. Accordingly neutrons may be detected indirectly by the signals generated by these secondary particles.

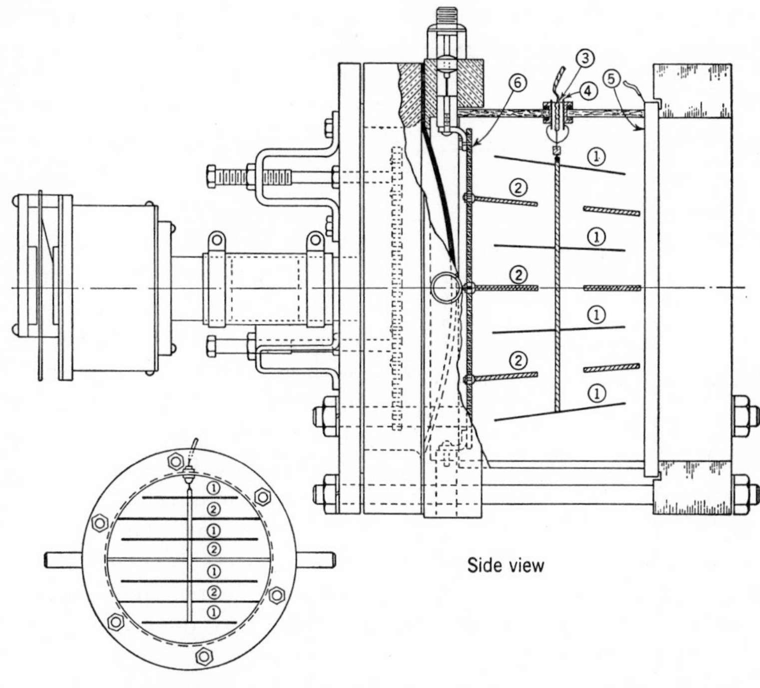

FIG. 5-25. Cross-sectional view of cloud ion chamber. (*From Cohen, Ref.* 45.)

The nuclear reactions which have been used for slow-neutron detection are

$$n + \mathrm{Li}^6 \rightarrow t + \alpha \tag{5-22}$$
$$n + \mathrm{B}^{10} \rightarrow \alpha + \mathrm{Li}^7 \tag{5-23}$$
$$n + \mathrm{N}^{14} \rightarrow p + \mathrm{C}^{14} \tag{5-24}$$
$$n + \mathrm{Cd}^{113} \rightarrow \mathrm{Cd}^{114} + \gamma \tag{5-25}$$

In addition, the fission of U^{235} induced by neutron bombardment yields highly ionizing charged products, so that this reaction is used for slow-neutron detection.

The property of neutrons of activating certain substances to beta and gamma radioactivity is often employed to measure neutron fluxes when the neutron energy is fixed. Thus the number of counts per second caused by an activated foil which, after a standard delay time, is placed in a standard position next to a beta counter is a measure of the original neutron flux that activated the foil. Indium foils are frequently used for this purpose.

Fast-neutron detectors are most often based upon the detection of the knock-on protons produced when neutrons impinge upon a hydrogenous material. In addition the following reactions are useful for fast-neutron detection:

$$n + B^{10} \rightarrow 2\alpha + t \tag{5-26}$$

$$n + B^{11} \rightarrow \alpha + Li^8 \tag{5-27}$$

where Li^8 decays very rapidly in the following steps:

$$Li^8 \xrightarrow{\beta^-} Be^8 \rightarrow 2\alpha \tag{5-27a}$$

The fission of U^{235} by fast neutrons also is used in some detecting instruments.

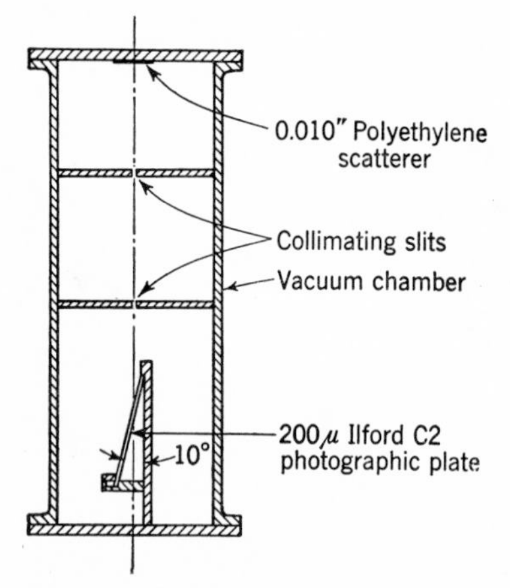

Fig. 5-26. Source-detector geometry for neutron-energy-spectrum determinations. (*From Allred, Phillips, Rosen, and Tallmadge, Ref.* 48.)

Numerous arrangements are used which combine suitable target materials with detectors of the secondary particles produced by neutrons. Ionization chambers that have been used incorporate a BF_3 gas filling or are lined with boron or uranium compounds. These chambers may be used as proportional counters in the low-energy region, since the reaction yield for a fixed neutron flux depends sensitively upon the neutron energy.

Scintillation detectors have also been successfully employed as indirect neutron detectors. A recent example[46] of such a detector consists of a molded Lucite cylinder, impregnated with ZnS grains, which is used in conjunction with a photomultiplier tube. In this case the Lucite serves as the hydrogenous material and the light guide. This detector is particularly useful for detecting neutrons even when an intense gamma-ray background exists, and efficiencies as high as a few per cent are realized. Another recent example[74] utilizes paraffin and ZnS and attains an efficiency of about 4 per cent. Scintillation counters are frequently used to detect the gamma rays after the capture of neutrons in a cadmium mass. The use of a crystal of LiI to serve both as the phosphor and as the source of target material based upon the $Li^6(n,\alpha)t$ reaction [Eq. (5-22)] appears quite promising.[47]

Nuclear emulsions loaded with all the target materials in the reactions listed above have also been used for neutron detection. The emulsion itself is a rich source of hydrogen for the detection of fast neutrons by knocks on protons. In one rather reliable arrangement a nuclear emulsion is exposed on edge to the neutron source, and the range and angle of the protons ejected within the emulsion are measured. In a second arrangement (see Fig. 5-26) a hydrogenous substance is placed outside the emulsion, and the geometry is chosen so that only recoil protons at a certain angle (generally the head-on protons) are recorded. The latter method allows greater accuracy than the former. The $B^{10}(n,2\alpha)t$ reaction in B^{10}-loaded emulsions is readily detected by the three-pronged star which results. The ranges of the two alpha particles and the triton lead directly to the neutron energy. The $B^{11}(n,\alpha)Li^8$ reaction is easily identifiable by a track in the emulsion which looks like a hammer. The handle corresponds to the initially emitted alpha particle, and the head corresponds to the two alpha particles which follow from the decay of Li^8 [Eq. (5-27*a*)].

Ordinary photographic emulsions having a layer of a Li^6 or B^{10} compound and a layer of a phosphor have been used by Kallman[(49)] in a three-step detection technique. The neutron induces a reaction, which yields a charged particle. The charged particle excites the phosphor, which emits photons. The photons then activate the AgBr grains in the emulsion, which become visible after development.

The determination of neutron energies in the high-energy range presents considerable difficulties. However, the fact that neutron-induced reactions have well-defined threshold energies is exploited in some measurements. Nuclear reactions in which neutrons are captured and protons are released have thresholds in the 0.5- to 2-Mev range. The neutron fission reactions of uranium and thorium have convenient thresholds in the 4- to 6-Mev range. For higher energies (6 to 18 Mev), reactions in which one neutron is captured and two neutrons are released are good threshold indicators. Threshold reactions are particularly useful for neutron detection when the gamma-ray background is large, since in these cases gamma rays rarely produce the same secondary effects as neutrons.

5-9. Range and Energy Loss of Charged Nuclear Particles in Matter. The determination of the energy of charged nuclear particles by means of cloud chambers, nuclear emulsions, crystal counters, scintillation counters, and ionization chambers is mostly based upon the measurement of the range of the particle or the measurement of the distance rate of energy loss in an absorbing medium. The range in an absorbing material associated with a collimated beam of monoenergetic charged particles may be established in various ways. For example, a counting device may be used to determine the number of particles which are transmitted when various thicknesses of an absorber are interposed in the beam. For a typical case the ratio P of the number present at various distances to the number present without the absorber at three different energies appears as shown schematically in Fig. 5-27a. Such curves are known as integral distribution curves. If every particle with a given energy traveled an identical distance in the absorber, the curve for this energy would appear as the vertical dashed line in Fig. 5-27a. The fact that identical particles with identical energies may penetrate to slightly different distances is indicative of the statistical nature of the stopping process and is referred to as "straggling." Despite the phenomenon of straggling we may identify characteristic range parameters with the integral curve corresponding to a given energy of a particle in an absorber. The mean range $\bar{R}$ is defined as the distance at which the integral range

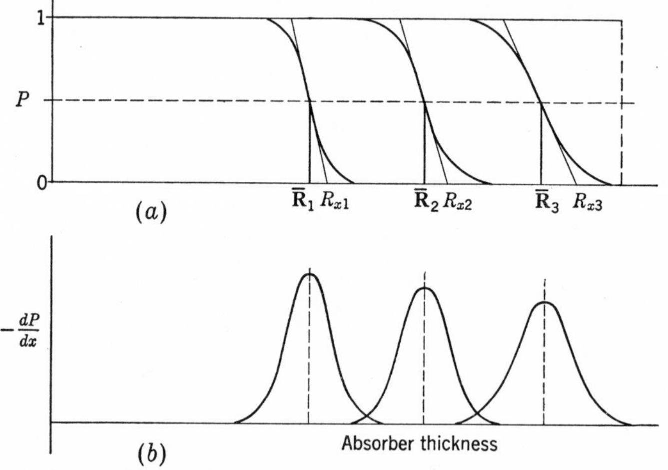

Fig. 5-27. (a) Integral range distribution curves. (b) Differential range distribution curves.

curve falls to $\frac{1}{2}$. The extrapolated range R_x is defined as the distance at which the tangent to the curve at $P(x) = \frac{1}{2}$ strikes the x axis.

The slope of the integral range distribution for an initially homogeneous source of particles has the form shown in Fig. 5-27b. Such curves, which are referred to as differential range distributions, may be represented rather well by the Gaussian function

$$-\frac{dP}{dx} = \frac{1}{\sigma(2\pi)^{\frac{1}{2}}} \exp\left[-\frac{(x - \bar{R})^2}{2\sigma^2}\right] \tag{5-28}$$

where σ is the standard deviation, which characterizes the extent of straggling. Using this equation, it can be shown that

$$R_x - \bar{R} = -\frac{P}{dP/dx} = \sqrt{\frac{\pi}{2}}\,\sigma \tag{5-29}$$

so that the two ranges are in close agreement when σ is small. Various means are available for finding the differential range distribution directly. For example, the relative number of tracks in a cloud chamber or nuclear emulsion which fall into various intervals of length may be plotted against the mean length for the interval. The relative number of particles which penetrate to the nth layer but not to the $(n + 1)$th layer of a series of detector-absorbers may be plotted against the average thickness penetrated. The curves so obtained may be represented quite well by Eq. (5-28).

The mean range of a particle in an absorbing medium is a function of the initial energy, the mass, and the charge of the particle and of the atomic number and the physical state of the absorber. This last factor enters primarily through the number of atoms per unit volume of the absorber, which is given by

$$\eta = \rho \frac{N_A}{A} \tag{5-30}$$

where N_A is Avogadro's number and ρ and A are the density and mass number of the absorber. We may therefore write

$$\bar{R} = \bar{R}(T_0,a,z,Z,\rho,A) \tag{5-31}$$

where a and z refer to the particle and A and Z to the absorber.

The intensity of a beam of charged particles remains practically constant until the absorber thickness becomes comparable with the mean range, where it changes rather abruptly; whereas the energy of the particles decreases continuously with the thickness of the absorber. This rate of loss of energy of a charged particle may be characterized by a function $-dT/dx$, the so-called *stopping power*, which depends upon the instantaneous energy of the particle, the mass and charge of the particle, the atomic number of the absorber, and the number of atoms per unit volume of the absorber. We may therefore write

$$-\frac{dT}{dx} = f(T,z,a,Z,\rho,A) \tag{5-32}$$

For a given incident particle and a given absorber, the $\bar{R}$ vs. T_0 relation and the $-dT/dx$ vs. T relation are connected by

$$\bar{R}(T_0) = \int_0^{\bar{R}(T_0)} dx = \int_{T_0}^{0} \frac{dx}{dT}\, dT = \int_0^{T_0} \left(-\frac{dT}{dx}\right)^{-1} dT \tag{5-33}$$

Accordingly, if $-dT/dx$ vs. T is known, the $\bar{R}$ vs. T_0 relation may be obtained, using the last form above, by numerical or mechanical integration. Conversely, if $\bar{R}(T_0)$ is known, we may find $-dT/dx$ vs. T by differentiation; *i.e.*, we use

$$\frac{d\bar{R}}{dT_0} = -\left(\frac{dT}{dx}\right)^{-1}_{T=T_0} \tag{5-34}$$

The rate of loss of energy of a particle in an absorbing medium may be determined in various ways. In air we may count the droplets per unit length of path in a cloud chamber or use a shallow ionization chamber to measure the number of ion pairs per unit path length and use the fact that the energy necessary to produce an ion pair is approximately constant (~35 ev) over a large range of energies. As we have previously indicated, the number of developed grains per unit length in a nuclear emulsion depends upon the rate of energy loss. However, the relation between these two quantities in this case is quite complicated [see Eq. (5-16)]. In a scintillation counter the number of photons produced in a layer of material is a measure of the energy loss. In principle the rate of energy loss in thin layers of any absorber may be determined in various ways, using magnetic or electrostatic analyzers to measure the energy before and after thin absorbers are placed in the beam. Such measurements have been carried out over a limited range of energies only recently.[50,51] Accordingly the experimental $-dT/dx$ curve for a given particle and a given absorber is usually obtained by differentiating the $\bar{R}(T_0)$ curve. The $\bar{R}$ and $-dT/dx$ functions have been the subject of considerable theoretical study and experimental investigation. These relationships have practical applications not only to shielding calculations and to energy measurement but also to the application of corrections for energy loss in thick targets. They are particularly important in high-energy work, where electric and magnetic analyzers become inaccurate.

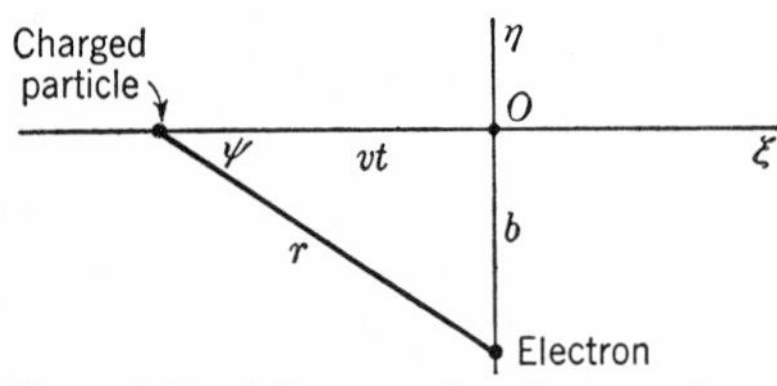

FIG. 5-28. Microscopic picture of an encounter of a massive charged particle with an electron.

In view of these applications we shall digress briefly to present a semiclassical theory, due to Bohr,[52] which gives an insight as to the nature of the stopping process. For exhaustive quantitative discussions of this subject we refer the reader to the recent works of Bethe and Ashkin[53] and Taylor.[54]

5-10. Semiclassical Theory of Stopping. The semiclassical theory of the stopping of charged nuclear particles in matter is based upon the following assumptions: (1) Charged nuclear particles travel in straight paths through the absorber. (2) They expend their energy by ionizing and exciting the atoms which they encounter in this path. (3) The velocity of the massive charged particle is so large compared to electronic velocities in atoms that we may regard the electrons as stationary during the time of "collision." (4) The velocity of the charged nuclear particle is nonrelativistic.

In Fig. 5-28 we indicate a microscopic picture of an encounter of the charged nuclear particle, having the charge ze and the mass am_p, with an atomic electron in an absorber of atomic number Z, mass number A, and density ρ. The coordinate axes ξ, η, and ζ are so chosen that the line of motion of the nuclear particle and the initial position of the electron form the $\xi\eta$ plane, and the time scale is such that $t = 0$ represents the instant at which the nuclear particle reaches the origin indicated in this figure. We define the distance b indicated in the figure as the impact parameter.

Let us now tentatively make the following two additional assumptions, which we shall later examine more carefully: (5) The electron is essentially free during the time of the encounter. (6) The net ξ component of impulse imparted to the electron vanishes. We may expect this last assumption to be approximately satisfied, since the ξ component of impulse imparted from $t = -\infty$ to $t = 0$ will tend to cancel the ξ component of impulse imparted from $t = 0$ to $t = \infty$. Of course, the η component of the impulse does not vanish but is given by

$$p_\eta = \int_{-\infty}^{\infty} f_\eta \, dt = \int_{-\infty}^{\infty} \frac{ze^2}{r^2} \sin \psi \, dt \tag{5-35}$$

To evaluate this integral, we transform to the variable ψ (see Fig. 5-28) with limits 0 and π and make use of the relationships

$$r = \frac{b}{\sin \psi} \tag{5-36}$$

$$-vt = b \cot \psi \tag{5-37}$$

$$dt = \frac{b}{v} \csc^2 \psi \, d\psi \tag{5-38}$$

Substituting Eqs. (5-36) and (5-38) into Eq. (5-35) and integrating, we find

$$p_\eta = \frac{2ze^2}{bv} \tag{5-39}$$

Consequently the total energy imparted to a single electron at a distance b from the line of motion is

$$T_e = \frac{p_\eta^2}{2m_e} = \frac{2z^2e^4}{m_e b^2 v^2} \tag{5-40}$$

In Fig. 5-29 we show a magnified macroscopic picture of the situation, showing a cylindrical shell of thickness db, length dx, and average radius b. In view of the above derivation and the cylindrical symmetry we would expect that all the electrons in this cylindrical shell will receive an energy given by Eq. (5-40). Consequently the loss of energy of the original charged particles in a distance dx due to the electrons in this shell may be obtained by multiplying the T_e given by Eq. (5-40) by the volume of the shell ($2\pi b \, db \, dx$) and the number of electrons per unit volume ($Z\rho N_A/A$). The rate of loss of energy due to electrons lying in a thick cylindrical region bounded by an upper impact parameter b_u and a lower impact parameter b_l is therefore

$$-\frac{dT}{dx} = \frac{4\pi z^2 e^4 N_A \rho Z}{m_e v^2 A} \int_{b_l}^{b_u} \frac{db}{b} = \frac{4\pi z^2 e^4 N_A \rho Z}{m_e v^2 A} B_e \qquad (5\text{-}41)$$

where by definition

$$B_e = \ln \frac{b_u}{b_l} \qquad (5\text{-}42)$$

From the form of our expression for B_e, which we shall call the electronic stopping power, it is obviously inadmissible to allow b_u to go to infinity or b_l to go to zero. It is thus necessary to examine our assumptions more

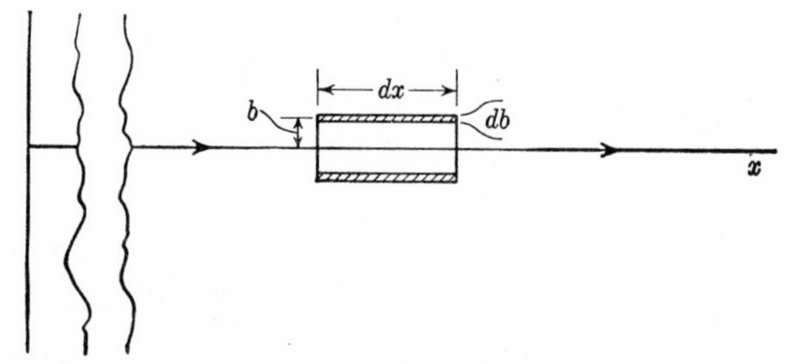

FIG. 5-29. Magnified macroscopic picture showing cylindrical shell formed by a small range of impact parameters and a small length.

carefully to see whether we may place reasonable limits on the impact parameter.

Assumption 6 is obviously violated in the event of a head-on collision ($b = 0$), since such a collision would result in the electron acquiring a velocity $2v$ in the ξ direction and hence the energy

$$T_e = \tfrac{1}{2} m_e (2v)^2 = 2 m_e v^2 \qquad (5\text{-}43)$$

This energy, of course, is the greatest possible energy the electron could acquire in a single collision, which is in contradiction with Eq. (5-40), which implies that the electron acquires an infinite energy when $b = 0$. If we equate the values of T_e given by Eqs. (5-40) and (5-43), we obtain immediately

$$b_l = \frac{ze^2}{m_e v^2} \qquad (5\text{-}44)$$

We might hope that, by using this as a lower limit, we can compensate for the error associated with our assumption that p_ξ vanishes.

We may set an upper limit for the impact parameter by questioning the validity of assumption 5. We know that the electrons in an absorber are normally bound to atoms. We also know that an electron in its ground atomic state cannot absorb an arbitrarily small quantity of energy. Instead each electron in an atom has a minimum excitation energy which it can accept. This is the energy needed to raise it to the first unoccupied atomic state. Let us denote by $\bar{I}$ the average minimum excitation energy for all electrons in an atom. Using $\bar{I}$ in conjunction with Eq. (5-40), we may set the upper limit

$$b_u = \frac{ze^2}{v}\left(\frac{2}{m_e\bar{I}}\right)^{\frac{1}{2}} \tag{5-45}$$

Equation (5-45) together with Eqs. (5-44) and (5-42) may be used to obtain a crude estimate of the electronic stopping power. More rigorous quantum-mechanical treatments[53,55,56] actually give the result

$$B_e = \ln \frac{2m_e v^2}{\bar{I}} \tag{5-46}$$

which differs by a factor of 2 from what we would obtain using the semi-classical theory and our crude assumptions as to the limits on the impact parameter. Even Eq. (5-46) is only an approximation, and corrections must be made in various energy ranges for physical effects discussed below.

At very low energies (~0.1 Mev) a charged nuclear particle in passing through matter will tend to capture and lose electrons. Consequently the effective charge of this particle is less than its true charge, and the energy loss does not increase as v decreases as much as Eq. (5-41) suggests. A quantitative expression for this effect has not yet been formulated. At moderately low energies (~1 Mev) another correction that must be made is due to the fact that inner electrons of atoms, because of their rapid motion and because of their shielding by the outer electrons, are not so effective in absorbing energy as might be anticipated on the basis of Eq. (5-46). Quantitative expressions have been formulated for this correction.[53,54] At higher energies (~25 Mev) a relativistic correction given by

$$B_r = -\ln\left(1 - \frac{v^2}{c^2}\right) - \frac{v^2}{c^2} \tag{5-47}$$

becomes appreciable and must be introduced. At extremely high energies (~1 Bev) two additional effects become important. One is a physical effect connected with Cerenkov radiation, which depends upon the density of the absorbing material and is due to the local dielectric polarization of the absorber by the incident charged particle. The second physical effect is a loss of energy by the particle in passing through an absorber due to the emission of continuous radiation which is known as *Bremsstrahlung* (brake radiation). Since these effects are not important in the energy range of interest in nuclear physics, we shall not go into them further.

The value of $\bar{I}$ which should be used in Eq. (5-46) has been the subject of considerable theoretical study.[55,56] Except for the cases of hydrogen and helium the theoretical problem is an extremely difficult one. However, several semiempirical evaluations of $\bar{I}$ have been made. For pure elements the simple relation

$$\bar{I} = CZ \tag{5-48}$$

proposed by Bloch,[57] with the constant $C = 11.5$ ev for light elements[58] and $C = 8.8$ ev for heavy elements,[53] leads to stopping powers which are in good agreement with those obtained by experiment. For mixtures of elements it is necessary to regard both Z in Eq. (5-41) and $\bar{I}$ in Eq. (5-46) as adjustable constants if one wishes to fit the experimental data. In fact this same device can be used to compensate for the fact that the inner electrons of atoms in heavy absorbers do not fully contribute to the slowing down of charged particles.

To determine the range of a particle in an absorbing medium, we may integrate the $-dT/dx$ function. Using Eqs. (5-33), (5-41), and (5-46) together with

$$dT = am_p v\, dv \tag{5-49}$$

we may write

$$\bar{R} = \frac{a}{z^2} \frac{m_p m_e}{4\pi e^4 N_A} \frac{A}{\rho Z} \mathbf{I} \tag{5-50}$$

where

$$\mathbf{I} = \mathbf{I}(v_0, Z) = \int_0^{v_0} \frac{v^3\, dv}{\ln\,(2m_e v^2/\bar{I})} \tag{5-51}$$

Since $\mathbf{I}$ depends upon the atomic number of the absorber logarithmically, it is a very slowly varying function of Z. Consequently the effect of the absorber would be expected to manifest itself mostly through the factor $A/\rho Z$. For the substances available in nature, $A \approx 2Z$; hence the dependence upon atomic number almost cancels out, and the main influence of the absorber in determining the range of charged particles is due to its density ρ. Because of this we often make use of a "range" defined by the combination

$$\bar{\mathbf{R}} = \rho \bar{R} \tag{5-52}$$

which is usually expressed in the units milligrams per square centimeter. In view of the insensitivity of $\bar{\mathbf{R}}$ to the atomic number of the absorber, a known $\bar{\mathbf{R}}$ curve for a given substance might for practical applications be used for all substances which have approximately the same atomic weight or number.

For a given initial velocity v_0 and a given absorbing material the influence of parameters which characterize the charged incident particle manifests itself through the combination a/z^2. Accordingly we would expect the ranges of a proton, a deuteron, a triton, a He^3 particle, and an alpha particle having the same initial velocity to be proportional to 1, 2, 3, $\frac{3}{4}$, and 1, respectively.

For a given initial energy T_0, the particle parameters also enter through the upper limit of the integral in Eq. (5-51) which is

$$v_0 = \left(\frac{2T_0}{m_p a}\right)^{\frac{1}{2}} \tag{5-53}$$

If we ignored the logarithmic term in the denominator of the integrand, the integral would be equal to $v_0^4/4$, or $T_0^2/m_p^2 a^2$. The influence of the particle parameters upon range would then be through the combination

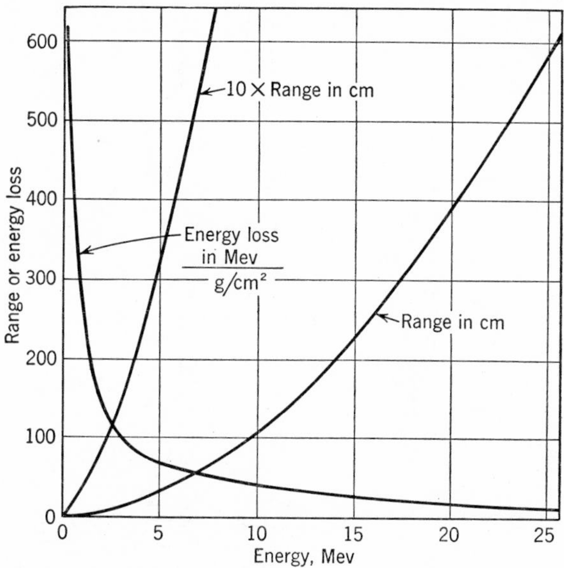

FIG. 5-30. Range vs. energy and energy loss vs. energy for protons in air at 15°C and 760 mm. (*Data taken from Bethe and Ashkin, Ref.* 53.)

$1/z^2 a$. Accordingly we would expect the ranges of a proton, a deuteron, a triton, a He^3 particle, and an alpha particle having the same initial energy to be proportional to 1, $\frac{1}{2}$, $\frac{1}{3}$, $\frac{1}{12}$, and $\frac{1}{16}$, respectively. The presence of the logarithmic term, of course, somewhat reduces the sensitivity of $\bar{R}$ to v_0. For a given absorber we may fit the experimental range-velocity curves quite well with the equation

$$\bar{R} = c \frac{a}{z^2} v_0^{n(v_0)} \tag{5-54}$$

where $n(v_0)$ varies from about 1.5 at low velocities to about 4 at high velocities.

The stopping powers of air and aluminum have been the subjects of the greatest amount of experimental investigation, and much of the application of the theory of the passage of charged particles through matter is to the transformation of the experimental range-energy curves for air or aluminum to range-energy curves for other materials. Details of these procedures and accurate graphs are given in several works to which the reader is referred.(1,53,59–61) In Fig. 5-30 we give the rate of energy loss and the range for 0- to 25-Mev protons in air. In Fig. 5-31 we indicate the specific energy loss for various particles in air over a wide range of energies.

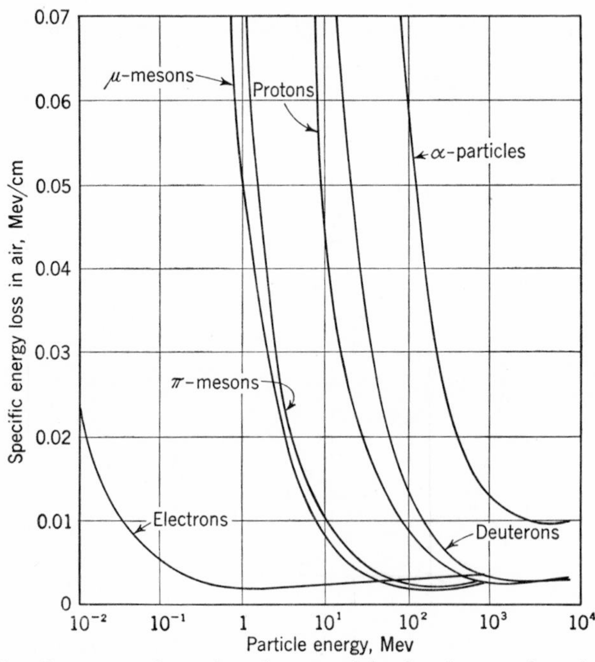

FIG. 5-31. Specific energy loss of various particles in air as a function of energy. (*From Beiser, Ref.* 34.)

5-11. Range and Energy Loss of Electrons. Most of the qualitative aspects of the previous discussion of the passage of charged nuclear particles through matter are also applicable to the passage of electrons in matter. However, there are several quantitative differences which must be taken into account if range measurements are to be used as the basis for estimating energies of electrons. Because the incident electrons have the same mass as the atomic electrons, they frequently give up substantial portions of their energy to individual atomic electrons. This fact is revealed clearly in cloud-chamber photographs and nuclear emulsions by the irregularity and waviness of electron tracks. In absorption studies this fact manifests itself in the large straggling associated with the integral and differential range curves. A typical integral distribution curve for initially monoenergetic electrons has the characteristic form shown in Fig. 5-32. It has become customary to characterize the range of monoenergetic electrons in an absorber by the point R_p at which the linear portion of the $P(x)$ curve meets the background. The more ambiguous point at which the absorption curve runs into the background is known as the maximum range.

A very interesting and important feature of beta-ray spectroscopy, which was discovered quite early in the development of nuclear physics, is the fact that beta particles emitted by most radioactive substances have a continuous range of energies from zero to a maximum. The maximum is referred to as the end-point energy of the beta spectrum, and it is a characteristic quantity associated with the particular radioactive

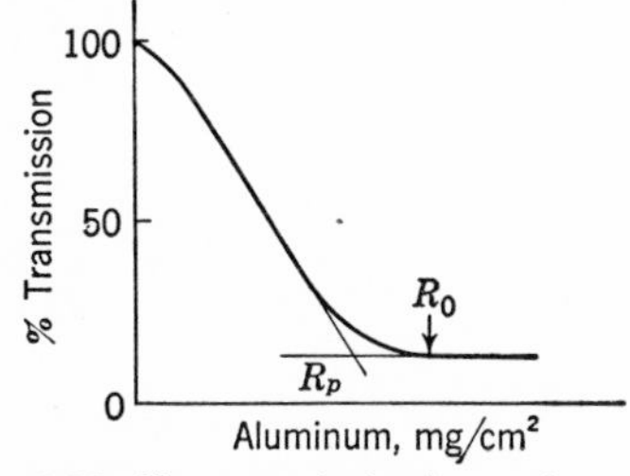

FIG. 5-32. Characteristic absorption curve of homogeneous electrons in aluminum. The point where extension of the linear portion of the curve meets the background is called the practical range R_p. The maximum range R_0 is the point where the absorption curve runs into the background. (*From Katz and Penfold, Ref.* 62.)

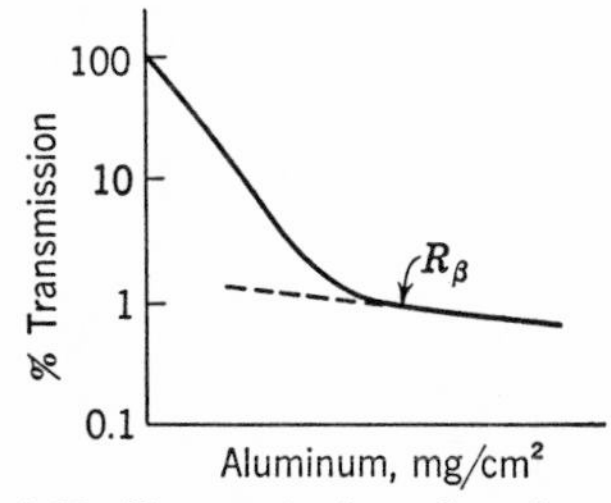

FIG. 5-33. Per cent of nuclear beta rays transmitted by various thicknesses of aluminum absorber. The background is the result of cosmic rays, natural radioactivity, and Compton electrons from gamma rays, when present. The point at which the absorption curve meets the background is called the range R_β of the betas. (*From Katz and Penfold, Ref.* 62.)

substance. We shall discuss the significance of these continuous distributions and these end-point energies in later chapters. For the moment we wish merely to consider the nature of the transmission curve for beta rays in an absorber. In Fig. 5-33 we show the percentage of nuclear beta rays transmitted as a function of the thickness of aluminum, using a logarithmic scale for $P(x)$. This curve has a much longer tail and does not have the linear region of the transmission curve for monoenergetic particles. In consequence, the problem of assigning a quantity R_β which will uniquely characterize the range of β particles in matter is more difficult than the problem of assigning a range to monoenergetic electrons. Various methods have been proposed for doing this, and we refer the reader to the comprehensive review article of Katz and Penfold[62] for a description of these methods. For our purposes here we shall refer to R_β roughly as the point at which the absorption curve meets the background when the transmission is plotted on a logarithmic scale. As might be expected, for a given absorber, R_β is related primarily to the end-point energy of the beta spectrum.

Numerous experimental studies have been made with aluminum absorbers to establish the variation of R_p with the initial energy of monoenergetic electrons and the variation of R_β with the end-point energy of the beta particles. Feather[63] has suggested for both purposes the equation

$$R = AT - B \tag{5-55}$$

where A and B are constants to be adjusted for different energy ranges.

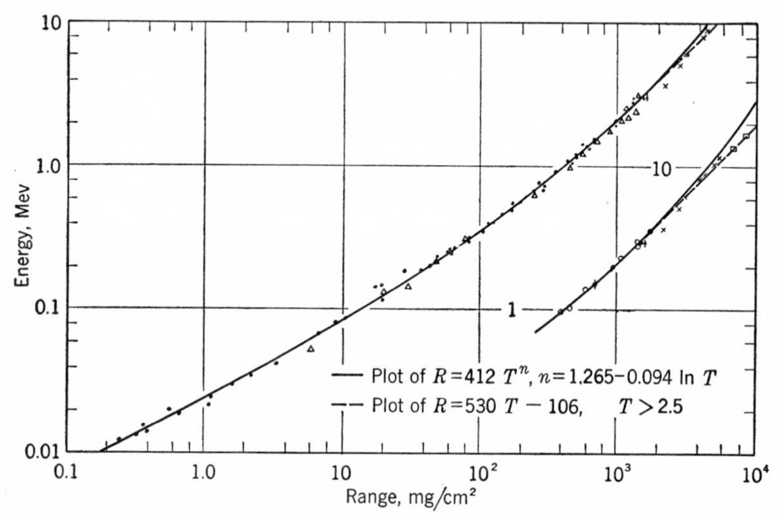

FIG. 5-34. Range-energy curve. The sources of the experimental points are listed in Ref. 62. The solid line represents Eq. (5-56) and is a good fit below 2.5 Mev. The dashed line represents Eq. (5-57) and is a good fit above 2.5 Mev. (*From Katz and Penfold, Ref.* 62.)

Katz and Penfold propose

$$R = 412T^{1.265-0.094 \ln T} \qquad T < 2.5 \text{ Mev} \tag{5-56}$$
$$= 530T - 106 \qquad T > 2.5 \text{ Mev} \tag{5-57}$$

where R is in milligrams per square centimeter and T is in Mev. An examination of Fig. 5-34 shows that these relationships fit the data very well. Thus, using these relationships in conjunction with simple absorption measurements, it is possible to establish the energy of monoenergetic electrons or the end-point energy of a beta spectrum with an accuracy to within a few per cent.

The theory of the ratio of loss of electron energy due to ionization and radiation is quite similar to the corresponding theory for charged nuclear particles, except that relativistic effects and *Bremsstrahlung* set in at much lower energies. According to relativistic quantum electrodynamics the energy loss due to excitation and ionization is [64]

$$-\frac{dT}{dx} = \frac{2\pi e^4 \eta Z}{m_e v^2}\left[\ln \frac{(T + m_e c^2)^3}{m_e c^2(1 - v^2/c^2)\bar{I}^2} - \frac{v^2}{c^2}\right] \tag{5-58}$$

The theory indicates that an electron and a proton having the same velocity lose about the same energy per unit length of path. However, if the electron and the proton have the same energy, the proton loses much more energy. As the energy increases from low values, the rate of energy loss tends to decrease rapidly up to about 1 Mev, where the rate of loss is almost constant for a large range of energies. The rate then increases very slightly with energy as the energy becomes very high.

The energy loss of an electron due to radiation becomes increasingly important at very high energies. In fact, for energies of the order of 100 Mev, practically all the energy loss is due to *Bremsstrahlung.*[65] The radiation losses for charged nuclear particles and mesons do not become important until energies measured in many Bev are reached.

Practically all our discussions concerning the penetration of high-energy electrons and charged nuclear particles are also applicable to positrons and mesons. In these cases, however, we must consider the additional losses due to the annihilation and decay of these unstable particles. We refer the reader to works on fundamental-particle physics for discussions of these losses.

It would appear to be appropriate at this juncture to discuss the penetration of gamma rays in matter. However, for the sake of efficiency, we shall postpone this discussion until the end of Chap. 7. By then the reader will have been introduced to several concepts which are needed for the description of the penetration of gamma rays.

PROBLEMS

5-1. The inside diameter of the cathode of a Geiger counter filled with argon is 2.00 cm, and the diameter of the central wire is 0.020 cm. The mean free path of electrons at the pressure of the filling is 10^{-2} cm. Calculate the potential fall in one mean-free electron path at the cathode and at the central wire. Calculate the distance from the central wire at which the energy gained in one mean-free path is equal to the ionization potential of argon (15.7 volts). Assume the counter is operating at 1000 volts.

5-2. Approximately how many ion pairs are formed in the stopping of a 7-Mev alpha particle in air? What is the magnitude (in electrostatic units and in coulombs) of the charge obtained if all the positive ions are collected without secondary ionization or recombination?

5-3. Verify Eqs. (5-29) and (5-39).

5-4. What thicknesses of air, aluminum, silver, and lead (in centimeters and in milligrams per square centimeter) will reduce the energy of a 5-Mev proton and a 5-Mev alpha particle by 1 kev?

***5-5.** Using Eqs. (5-41), (5-46), and (5-48), find the range, in milligrams per square centimeter, of protons in standard air at 5, 10, 15, 20, and 25 Mev. How do these results compare with those given in Fig. 5-30?

***5-6.** Convert Fig. 5-30 into a curve of range vs. velocity for protons in air and then infer $\mathbf{I}(v_0, Z)$ for air.

***5-7.** Ignoring anomalous effects at small energies, use the result of Prob. 5-6 to obtain an approximate range-energy relation for alpha particles in air.

†5-8. Prepare a bibliography of articles appearing in the literature since 1952 on (*a*) multichannel analyzers, (*b*) new detection methods for charged particles, (*c*) range and energy loss of particles in matter, (*d*) nuclear-emulsion techniques, (*e*) scintillating-counter techniques, and (*f*) methods of neutron detection and energy measurement.

REFERENCES

1. Bleuler, E., and G. J. Goldsmith: "Experimental Nucleonics," Rinehart & Company, Inc., New York, 1952.
2. Halliday, D.: "Introductory Nuclear Physics," John Wiley & Sons, Inc., New York, 1950.
3. Rossi, B., and H. Staub: "Ionization Chambers and Counters," *National Nuclear Energy Series*, Div. V, Vol. 2, McGraw-Hill Book Company, Inc., New York, 1949.
4. Wilkinson, D. H.: "Ionization Chambers and Counters," Cambridge University Press, New York, 1950.
5. Currans, S. C. and S. D. Cragg: "Counting Tubes: Theory and Applications," Academic Press, Inc., New York, 1949.
6. Staub, H.: *Exptl. Nuclear Phys.*, **1,** 1 (1953).
7. Jordan, W. H.: *Ann. Rev. Nuclear Sci.*, **1,** 207 (1952).
8. Stever, G.: *Phys. Rev.*, **61,** 38 (1942).
9. H. Kallman: *Phys. Rev.*, **75,** 629 (1949).
10. Jordan, W. H., and P. R. Bell: *Nucleonics*, **5**(4), 30 (1949).
11. Garlic, G. F. J.: *Prog. Nuclear Phys.*, **2,** 51 (1952).
12. Strickler, T. D., and W. G. Wadey: *Rev. Sci. Instr.*, **24,** 13 (1953).
13. Taylor, C. J., W. K. Jentschke, M. E. Remley, F. S. Eby, and P. G. Kruger: *Phys. Rev.*, **84,** 1034 (1951).
14. Stoddart, H. F., and H. I. Gove: *Phys. Rev.*, **87,** 262 (1952).
15. Hofstadter, R.: *Proc. Inst. Radio Engrs.*, **38,** 726 (1950).
16. Cerenkov, P. A.: *Phys. Rev.*, **52,** 379 (1937).
17. Frank, I., and I. Tamm: *Compt. rend. acad. sci U.R.S.S.*, **14,** 109 (1937).
18. Sternheimer, R. M.: *Phys. Rev.*, **91,** 256 (1953).
19. Furry, W. H.: *Phys. Rev.*, **72,** 171 (1947).
20. Mathers, R. I.: *Phys. Rev.*, **84,** 181 (1951).
21. Chang, W. Y., and S. Rosenblum: *Phys. Rev.*, **67,** 222 (1945).
22. Eichholz, G. G.: *Nucleonics*, **10**(10), 46 (1952).
23. Madansky, L., and R. W. Pidd: *Rev. Sci. Instr.*, **21,** 407 (1950).
24. Elmore, W. C., and M. Sands: "Electronics: Experimental Techniques," *National Nuclear Energy Series*, Div. V, Vol. 1, McGraw-Hill Book Company, Inc., New York, 1949.
25. Elmore, W. C.: *Nucleonics*, **2**(2), 4 (1948); **2**(3), 16 (1948); **2**(4), 43 (1948); **2**(5), 50 (1948).
26. Scarrott, G. G.: *Prog. Nuclear Phys.*, **1,** 73 (1953).
27. Van Rennes, A. B.: *Nucleonics*, **10**(7), 20 (1952); **10**(8), 22 (1952); **10**(9), 32 (1952); **10**(10), 51 (1952).

28. Bell, P. R., and C. G. Goss: private communication, Oak Ridge National Laboratory.
29. Rossi, B.: *Nature,* **125,** 636 (1930).
30. Johnstone, C. W.: *Nucleonics,* **11**(1), 39 (1953).
31. Maeder, D.: *Helv. Phys. Acta,* **20,** 139 (1947).
32. Bernstein, W., R. L. Chase, and A. W. Schardt: *Rev. Sci. Instr.,* **24,** 137 (1953).
33. Glenn, W. E., Jr.: *Nucleonics,* **4**(6), 50 (1949).
34. Beiser, A.: *Revs. Mod. Phys.,* **24,** 273 (1952).
35. Rotblat, W.: *Progr. Nuclear Phys.,* **1,** 37 (1950).
36. James, T. H., and G. C. Higgins: "Fundamentals of Photographic Theory," John Wiley & Sons, Inc., New York, 1948.
37. Comrady, A. E., *et al.:* "Photography as a Scientific Implement," Blackie & Son, Ltd., Glasgow, 1924.
38. Morand, M., and L. Van Rossum: article *in* J. W. Mitchell (ed.), "Fundamental Mechanism of Photographic Sensitivity," p. 317, Butterworth & Co. (Publishers) Ltd., London, 1951.
39. Lattes, C. M. G., G. P. S. Occhialini, and C. F. Powell: *Proc. Phys. Soc. (London),* **61,** 173 (1948).
40. Powell, C. F., and S. Rosenblum: *Nature,* **161,** 473 (1948).
41. Barbour, I.: *Phys. Rev.,* **78,** 518 (1950).
42. Das Gupta, N. N., and S. K. Ghosh: *Revs. Mod. Phys.,* **18,** 225 (1946).
43. Wilson, C. T. R.: *Proc. Roy. Soc. (London),* **85,** 285 (1911).
44. Nielsen, C. E., C. E. Needels, and O. H. Weddle: *Rev. Sci. Instr.,* **22,** 673 (1951).
45. Cohen, M. J.: *Rev. Sci. Instr.,* **22,** 966 (1951).
46. Hornyak, W. F.: *Rev. Sci. Instr.,* **23,** 264 (1952).
47. Hofstadter, R., J. A. McIntyre, H. Roderick, and H. I. West: *Phys. Rev.,* **82,** 749 (1951).
48. Allred, J. C., A. W. Phillips, L. Rosen, and F. K. Tallmadge: *Rev. Sci. Instr.,* **21,** 225 (1950).
49. Kallman, H.: *Research (London),* **1,** 254 (1948).
50. Kahn, D.: *Phys. Rev.,* **90,** 503 (1953).
51. Weyl, P. K.: *Phys. Rev.,* **91,** 289 (1953).
52. Bohr, N.: *Phil. Mag.,* **25,** 10 (1913); **30,** 518 (1915).
53. Bethe, H. A., and J. Ashkin: *Exptl. Nuclear Phys.,* **1,** 166 (1953).
54. Taylor, A. E.: *Rept. Progr. Phys.,* **15,** 49 (1952).
55. Bethe, H. A.: *Z. Physik,* **76,** 293 (1932).
56. Bloch, F.: *Ann. Physik,* **16,** 285 (1933).
57. Bloch, F.: *Z. Physik,* **81,** 363 (1933).
58. Wilson, R. R.: *Phys. Rev.,* **60,** 749 (1941).
59. Livingston, M. S., and H. Bethe: *Revs. Mod. Phys.,* **9,** 269 (1937).
60. Siri, W. E., *et al.:* "Isotopic Tracers and Nuclear Radiations," McGraw-Hill Book Company, Inc., New York, 1949.
61. Bethe, H.: "Range and Energy Curves," *U.S. Atomic Energy Comm. Document,* Brookhaven National Laboratory, 1949.
62. Katz, L., and A. S. Penfold: *Revs. Mod. Phys.,* **24,** 30 (1952).
63. Feather, N.: *Proc. Cambridge Phil. Soc.,* **34,** 599 (1938).
64. Heitler, W.: "The Quantum Theory of Radiation," Oxford University Press, New York, 1947.
65. Heitler, W.: *ibid.,* p. 221.
66. West, D.: *Progr. Nuclear Phys.,* **3,** 18 (1953).
67. Swank, R. W.: *Nucleonics,* **12**(3), 14 (1954).

68. Linden, B. R.: *Nucleonics*, **12**(3), 20 (1954).
69. Champion, F. C.: *Progr. Nuclear Phys.*, **3,** 159 (1953).
70. Kantz, A., and R. Hofstadter: *Nucleonics*, **12**(3), 36 (1954).
71. Jelley, J. V.: *Progr. Nuclear Phys.*, **3,** 84 (1953).
72. Hunt, W. A., *et al.: Rev. Sci. Instr.*, **25,** 268 (1954).
73. Thomas, J. W., V. V. Verbinski, and W. E. Stephens: *Rev. Sci. Inst.*, **24,** 1017 (1953).
74. Emmerich, W. S.: *Rev. Sci. Instr.*, **25,** 69 (1954).

CHAPTER 6

RADIOACTIVITY

Observations of the natural radioactive decay of heavy nuclides were the earliest sources of direct information about internal nuclear processes. These heavy elements tend to decay spontaneously by the emission of alpha particles, beta particles, and gamma rays. The nuclear instruments and methods which have been developed during the past 30 years have enabled physicists to produce additional radioactive substances which undergo decay not only by the above-mentioned processes but also by the emission of positrons and by the capture of K-orbital electrons. Indirect evidence of a substantial nature also reveals the transitory existence of nuclides which decay by the emission of neutrons, protons, alpha particles, and other light nuclei (see Sec. 7-1).

This chapter will be devoted to the introduction of concepts which are used to characterize radioactive-decay processes and to a discussion of radioactive-decay phenomena. In discussions of a single radioactive-decay process we shall refer to the decaying nuclide as the parent and the nuclide which is formed after the emission of a particle or gamma ray as the daughter.

6-1. The Radioactive-decay Law. The rate at which a nuclear species decays may be characterized by a time constant known as the half-life $\tau_{\frac{1}{2}}$, which is defined as the time required for one-half the parent nuclides to decay. Innumerable measurements reveal that this time constant is independent of the number of parent atoms present. This time constant is a characteristic of the nucleus, so that in the main it is independent of the chemical or physical state of the atom. However, in decay phenomena such as K capture and internal conversion, the electronic environment of the nucleus has a significant role. Thus chemical or physical changes appreciably altering this environment influence the time constant somewhat.

Various techniques are available for the direct measurement of half-lives which fall within the range

$$10^{-10} \text{ sec} < \tau_{\frac{1}{2}} < 10^{23} \text{ sec} \qquad (1 \text{ year} = 3.15 \times 10^{7} \text{ sec}) \qquad (6\text{-}1)$$

We may also characterize the rate of disintegration of a radioactive substance by a decay constant λ, measured in a unit of reciprocal time, which represents the fractional rate of the disintegration. In mathematical terms the decay constant is defined by

$$\lambda = -\frac{1}{N}\frac{dN}{dt} \tag{6-2}$$

where N is the number of nuclides present at an arbitrary instant. When integrated, this leads to the decay law

$$N = N_0 \exp(-\lambda t) \tag{6-3}$$

where N_0 is the number of atoms at $t = 0$. By definition of the half-life

$$\frac{N(\tau_{\frac{1}{2}})}{N_0} = \frac{1}{2} = \exp(-\lambda\tau_{\frac{1}{2}}) \tag{6-4}$$

It follows therefore that

$$\tau_{\frac{1}{2}} = \frac{\ln 2}{\lambda} = \frac{0.6931}{\lambda} \tag{6-5}$$

Another time constant frequently used is the average lifetime $\bar{\tau}$, which is defined by

$$\bar{\tau} = \frac{1}{N_0}\int^{N_0} t(N)\, dN \tag{6-6}$$

Using the decay law, changing to the variable $x = N/N_0$, and using the value of a well-known definite integral, we find

$$\bar{\tau} = -\frac{1}{\lambda}\int_0^1 \ln x\, dx = \frac{1}{\lambda} \tag{6-7}$$

We see, therefore, that $\bar{\tau}$ is the time required for nuclei to decay to the fraction $1/e$ of the original number, *i.e.*,

$$\frac{N(\bar{\tau})}{N_0} = \exp(-\lambda\bar{\tau}) = \frac{1}{e} \tag{6-8}$$

6-2. Transformations in Radioactive Decay. The transformations in radioactive-decay processes will be represented by the general equation

$$X^* \rightarrow X + x \qquad (\tau_{\frac{1}{2}}) \tag{6-9}$$

where X^* and X represent the symbols or integral parameters which are needed to characterize completely the parent and daughter, respectively, and x represents the corresponding symbols or parameters for the ejected particle. This equation will be illustrated below by specific examples.

In the case of alpha decay it has been established by experiment that the daughter nucleus is always 4 units less in atomic mass and 2 units less in atomic number. This difference is accounted for by the fact that the ejected alpha particle has the mass number 4 and the charge number 2. In terms of the integral nuclear parameters we may therefore represent an alpha decay process by Eq. (6-9) with the daughter nuclide characterized by

$$A = A^* - 4 \qquad D = D^* \qquad N = N^* - 2 \qquad Z = Z^* - 2$$

and with (6-10)

$$x = \alpha$$

A well-known example is

$$_{88}\mathrm{Ra}^{226} \rightarrow {}_{86}\mathrm{Rn}^{222} + \alpha \qquad (1620 \text{ years}) \qquad (6\text{-}11)$$

In the case of β^- decay a neutron in the nucleus transforms into a proton by emitting an electron. The nuclear transformation may be represented by Eq. (6-9) with

$$A = A^* \qquad D = D^* - 2 \qquad N = N^* - 1 \qquad Z = Z^* + 1$$

and with (6-12)

$$x = \beta^-$$

An example is

$$_{90}\mathrm{Th}^{231} \rightarrow {}_{91}\mathrm{Pa}^{231} + \beta^- \qquad (25.5 \text{ hr}) \qquad (6\text{-}13)$$

In β^+ decay a proton transforms into a neutron by emitting a positron. The nuclear transformation may be represented by Eq. (6-9) with

$$A = A^* \qquad D = D^* + 2 \qquad N = N^* + 1 \qquad Z = Z^* - 1$$

and with (6-14)

$$x = \beta^+$$

An example of this transformation is

$$_{29}\mathrm{Cu}^{61} \rightarrow {}_{28}\mathrm{Ni}^{61} + \beta^+ \qquad (3.4 \text{ hr}) \qquad (6\text{-}15)$$

In the *K*-capture process a *K*-orbital electron is captured by the nucleus, and in consequence a proton is changed to a neutron. The integral nuclear parameters undergo the identical transformation given above for positron decay. An example of transformation by *K* capture is

$$_{57}\mathrm{La}^{135} + e^- \rightarrow {}_{56}\mathrm{Ba}^{135} \qquad (19 \text{ hr}) \qquad (6\text{-}16)$$

The fact that, in beta decay and in *K* capture, the nucleus emits or absorbs electrons or positrons must not be interpreted to mean that these particles may exist inside the nucleus. In view of the inadequacies of the electron-proton model, the present view is that the β particle is created or annihilated by the transformation of a neutron (proton) inside the nucleus to a proton (neutron). The process may be likened to the creation or absorption of a photon during a radiative transition by an atom.

In decay by gamma emission, the nucleus simply emits energy in the form of a gamma ray and does not change its integral parameters. Therefore Eq. (6-9) is satisfied with

$$A = A^* \qquad D = D^* \qquad N = N^* \qquad Z = Z^*$$

and with (6-17)

$$x = \gamma$$

A gamma-emitting nuclide which exists for a measurable half-life is said to be an isomer of the daughter nuclide. The type of relationship which exists between these two nuclides is called isomerism. An example of an isomeric transition is

$$_{38}\mathrm{Sr}^{87m} \rightarrow {}_{38}\mathrm{Sr}^{87} + \gamma \qquad (2.8 \text{ hr}) \tag{6-18}$$

where in accord with recent convention we have denoted the isomer by a superscript m.

Frequently the product of an alpha or beta decay process or a nuclear-bombardment process is formed in an excited state, and this nuclide subsequently undergoes gamma decay. The half-lives of such transitions are usually too small to be measured. In many instances of gamma decay an internally converted electron appears as the result of the nuclear transition.

Although experimental observations are not yet conclusive, certain nuclides are thought to undergo an energetically permissible process known as double beta decay. A possible example is

$$_{50}\mathrm{Sn}^{124} \rightarrow {}_{52}\mathrm{Te}^{124} + 2\beta^- \qquad (>6 \times 10^{15} \text{ years}) \tag{6-19}$$

6-3. Energetics of Beta and Gamma Radiation. In our discussion of the energetics of beta and gamma radiation we shall, for generality, consider transitions from an excited state W^* of the parent to an excited state W of the daughter. Specialization for transitions between ground states may be made simply by setting W^* or W or both equal to zero.

Gamma radiation and internal conversion are the simplest modes of decay of a system of nucleons in an excited state. The energy released in gamma decay appears as a gamma ray with the energy

$$E_\gamma = W^* - W \tag{6-20}$$

In this case, of course, both W^* and W are excited states of the same nuclide, so that our notation simply indicates that the former is the initial state, whereas the latter is the final state.

When the gamma ray is internally converted, the electron, which is usually from the K or L shell, carries away the kinetic energy

$$T = W^* - W - W_c = E_\gamma - W_c \tag{6-21}$$

where W_c is the critical energy of the atomic X-ray level. Since the low-lying nuclear levels and the atomic X-ray levels are discrete, the kinetic-energy spectrum of the internally converted electrons, as measured with a beta-ray spectrometer, is a discrete spectrum. The intensity of the conversion lines is usually expressed in terms of the internal-conversion coefficients

$$\alpha_K = \frac{N_K}{N_\gamma} \qquad \alpha_L = \frac{N_L}{N_\gamma} \qquad \text{etc.} \tag{6-22}$$

where N_γ, N_K, N_L, etc., are the number of observed γ rays, K electrons, L electrons, etc., in a chosen time interval.

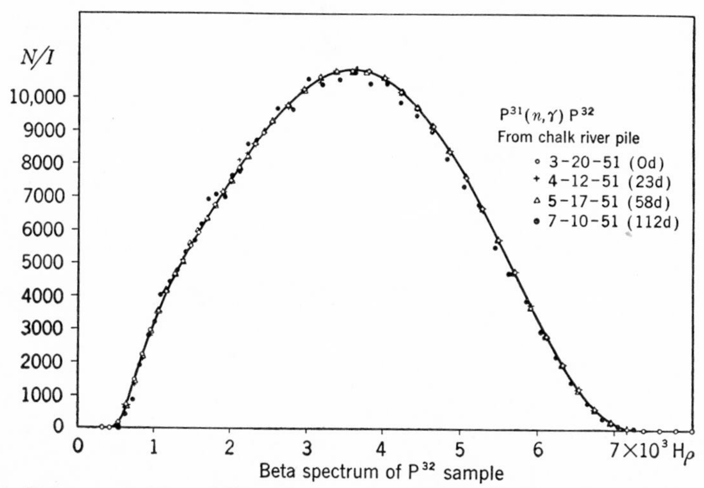

FIG. 6-1. Beta-ray spectra of P^{32} sample prepared by a $P^{31}(n,\gamma)P^{32}$ reaction. These four spectra were obtained over a period of 112 days. The spectra have been normalized at the maximum counting rates. The ordinates apply to the spectrum determined on Mar. 20, 1951. The distortion of the spectra at low energies is due to a thick source. The last spectrum was determined 127 days after the sample was removed from the pile. N is the number of counts per minute, and I is the current in the spectrometer coil. H is the magnetic field, and ρ is the radius of curvature. The end-point energy in this case is 1.704 ± 0.008 Mev. (*From Jensen, Nichols, Clement, and Pohm, Ref.* 2.)

The next simplest modes of decay are $\beta^\pm$ decay and K capture, which represent transitions between isobars. A strange feature of β^+ and β^- emission processes, which is revealed by studies with beta-ray spectrometers, is the continuous distribution of the kinetic energies of the emitted electrons or positrons. These energies vary from zero to a maximum which is called the end-point energy. In Fig. 6-1 we show a typical beta-ray spectrum. The continuous nature of this distribution seems to contradict the interpretation, which is supported by many experiments, that a nucleus may exist only in certain discrete energy states, and that it may therefore give off only a discrete quantity of energy in a transition from one state to another. To account for the continuous distributions in energy and at the same time to preserve conservation of energy, momentum, and angular momentum, Pauli in 1930 suggested that a neutral particle called the neutrino (η), having a negligible mass and a spin of $\frac{1}{2}$, is also emitted in β decay and carries away the remaining energy. We would expect that such a particle would be extremely difficult to detect, and this has indeed been the case. As yet, there has been no direct experimental verification of the existence of the neutrino, but the indirect evidence is very substantial. According to the neutrino hypothesis the fundamental processes in $\beta^{\pm}$ decay and K capture are

β^- decay:

$$n \rightarrow p + \beta^- + \eta \tag{6-23}$$

β^+ decay:

$$p \rightarrow n + \beta^+ + \eta \tag{6-24}$$

K capture:

$$p + e^- \rightarrow n + \eta \tag{6-25}$$

Applying the principle of conservation of energy to the β^- decay process, we obtain

$$M^* + W^* = M^+ + W + m_e + T_{\beta^-} + T_\eta \tag{6-26}$$

where M^+ is the mass of the positively ionized daughter and T_{β^-} and T_η denote the kinetic energies of the β^- particle and the neutrino, respectively. These kinetic energies must be determined using relativistic expressions. We have ignored in the above the atomic excitation energy, the recoil energy of the daughter, and the rest energy of the neutrino, since a simple analysis indicates that we may do so without exceeding experimental errors. Replacing the mass of the ionized daughter plus the mass of the beta particle by the mass of a neutral daughter atom, we may rewrite Eq. (6-26) as

$$M^* + W^* - W - M = T_{\beta^-} + T_\eta = T_{\beta^-,\max} \tag{6-27}$$

In arriving at the last form, we assume that, at the end point $T_{\beta^-,\max}$ of the beta spectrum, the neutrino carries away negligible energy.

The Q value of a β^- decay may be defined simply as the mass difference between the ground state of the parent and the ground state of the daughter. Accordingly for such a transition we have

$$Q = M^* - M = T_{\beta^-,\max} \tag{6-28}$$

The condition that the starred nuclide in its ground state be unstable with respect to β^- decay to the neighboring isobar that has $Z = Z^* + 1$ is

$$Q = M^* - M > 0 \tag{6-29}$$

If this condition is not fulfilled, the starred nucleus is stable with respect to β^- decay. Even if it is β^--stable, the starred nucleus may, nevertheless, undergo β^- decay providing it starts from an excited state and the expression on the left of Eq. (6-27) is positive.

Applying conservation of energy to β^+ decay and using the same assumptions as above, we find

$$M^* + W^* = M^- + W + m_e + T_{\beta^+} + T_\eta \tag{6-30}$$

where M^- is the mass of the negatively ionized daughter which is formed immediately following the decay. Since $M^- \simeq M + m_e$, we may rewrite Eq. (6-30) as

$$M^* + W^* - M - W - 2m_e = T_{\beta^+} + T_\eta = T_{\beta^+,\max} \tag{6-31}$$

The Q value of a β^+ decay, which is defined as the mass difference between the parent and the daughter, therefore is

$$Q = M^* - M = T_{\beta^+,\max} + 2m_e \tag{6-32}$$

The condition that the starred nucleus in its ground state be unstable with respect to β^+ decay to the isobar with $Z = Z^* - 1$ is

$$M^* - M - 2m_e > 0 \tag{6-33}$$

A nuclide which is stable with respect to β^+ decay may nevertheless undergo β^+ decay if it starts from an excited state and the left side of Eq. (6-31) is positive.

Applying conservation to the K-capture process, we obtain

$$M^* + W^* = M + W + W_K + T_\eta \tag{6-34}$$

The immediate product of K capture is a neutral atom with a missing K electron but with an extra valence electron. We include the X-ray excitation energy W_K associated with the daughter since it is appreciable for heavy elements. The Q value, or mass difference, in K capture is

$$Q = M^* - M = W_K + T_\eta \tag{6-35}$$

Since W_K is a discrete quantity, the neutrino can carry away only the remainder of the mass difference, which is also a discrete energy. K-capture processes can be detected by the X rays which are emitted when the daughter atoms fill the vacancies in the K shell. Because of their relatively low energies and because of the small intensities, these quanta are rather difficult to detect.

Another product of K capture is the Auger electrons emitted by some residual atoms in the course of their readjustment to a more stable state. This process may be viewed qualitatively as one in which the X ray emitted when an L electron jumps to fill the K-shell vacancy is captured by a second L electron, which is then ejected with the excess energy. Since the residual atom makes an over-all transition from the state with a single K vacancy to the state with two L vacancies, the excess kinetic energy of the Auger electron is approximately

$$T_e = W_K - 2W_L \tag{6-36}$$

To detect electrons with such small energies, the very thinnest windows must be used in the detection apparatus, or else the source must be mounted directly in the ionization chamber.

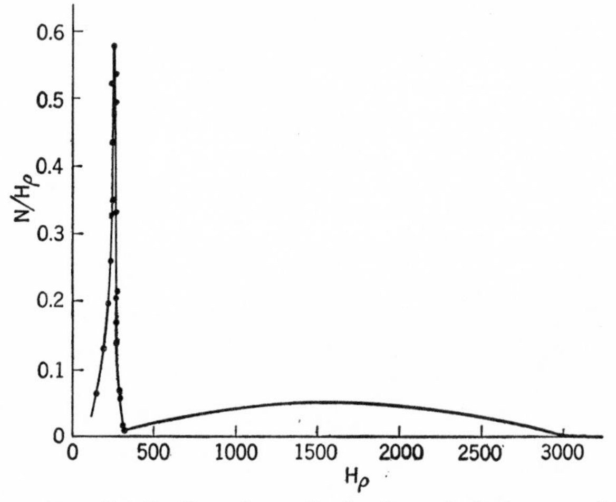

FIG. 6-2. Momentum distribution of negatively charged electrons emitted by radioactive Cu^{64}. The low-energy peak is a measure of the Auger electrons associated with K capture by this nucleus. The broader distribution is the spectrum of the negative beta particles emitted by the Cu^{64} nucleus. (*From Cook, Ref.* 3.)

In Fig. 6-2 we show the momentum spectrum of the electrons emitted by Cu^{64}, a radioactive nuclide which undergoes decay by β^- emission, β^+ emission, and K capture. The broader distribution is the β^- spectrum, whereas the large peak at low energies corresponds to the Auger electrons associated with K capture.

The condition that the starred nucleus in its ground state be unstable with respect to K capture is

$$Q = M^* - M > W_K \tag{6-37}$$

This condition is less stringent than the condition for β^+ instability, so that, if a nuclide is β^+-unstable, it will also be K-capture-unstable, although if it is K-capture-unstable, it need not be β^+-unstable. In the case of a nuclide which is β^+-unstable the ratio of the number of K-capture processes to β^+ emission is an important parameter which has been used to test the theory of positron decay.

The capture of L or M electrons is even more favorable from the energetic standpoint than the capture of K electrons. The appropriate energy equations may be obtained from Eqs. (6-34), (6-35), and (6-37) simply by replacing W_K by W_L or W_M. The probability of L or M capture is quite small, however, and only a few cases have been experimentally detected. The explanation for the rarity of L and M capture follows naturally when we consider the small probability for finding L and M electrons in the vicinity of the nucleus.

The acceleration of the electron toward the nucleus in the K-capture process may also result in the emission of gamma rays. The theory of this so-called "inner *Bremsstrahlung*" has been worked out for K capture by Morrison and Shiff.[24] The theory predicts a continuous distribution of gamma rays ranging in energy from zero to the maximum ($M^* - M - W_K$) available for the decay. Experimental confirmation of the theory in the case of the nuclide Fe^{55} has been made by Bradt *et al.*[25] and more recently in the case of A^{37} by Anderson *et al.*[26] The measurement of the shape and end point of this spectrum with scintillation spectrometers[27] has been used in several cases for obtaining mass differences and for studying the characteristics of these transitions.

6-4. Trends of Beta Stability and Beta Decay. Approximately 274 nuclides are known to exist[4,5] which are stable against all modes of radioactive decay. About 60 alpha emitters are known which are stable relative to beta decay. We classify these 334 nuclides into various nuclear types (E for even, O for odd) in the following table:

A	D	N	Z	Stable	α-unstable	Totals
O	O	O	E	55	16	71
O	O	E	O	50	8	58
E	E	O	O	4	0	4
E	E	E	E	165	36	201

Note that, although the odd mass numbers are almost equally divided between the (N-O, Z-E) and (N-E, Z-O) types, the even mass numbers show a marked preference for EE type. The exceptional OO types are $_1H^2$, $_3Li^6$, $_5B^{10}$, and $_7N^{14}$, the four lightest nuclides with odd atomic number.

We shall henceforth call a nuclide "beta-stable" if it exhibits no tendency to decay into another isobaric form by β^- or β^+ emission or K capture, even if the nuclide tends to undergo a more violent decay such as α emission or fission. If we locate the beta-stable nuclides on a two-dimensional equal-scale grid with the neutron number as the ordinate and the proton number as the abscissa, we will observe (see Fig. 6-3) that these nuclides lie along a rather narrow band. Apparently stability requires a delicate balance between the neutron number and the proton number. Another graphical representation of beta-stable nuclides employs a grid with A as the horizontal coordinate and D as the vertical coordinate (see Fig. 6-4). In view of the relations $A = N + Z$ and $D = N - Z$, the D and A axes make angles of 45° relative to the N and Z axes. On an equal-scale D-A plot, vertical lines join isobars, horizon-

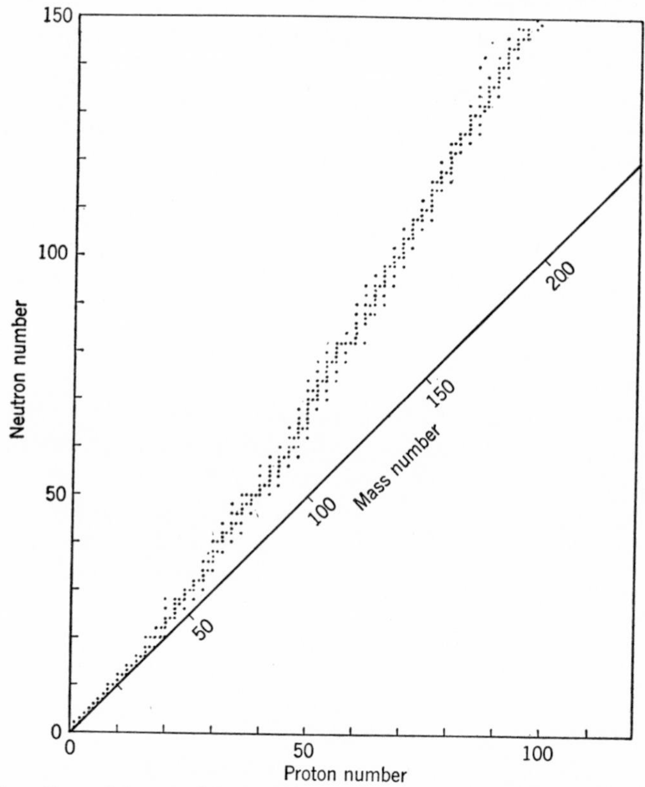

FIG. 6-3. Location of beta-stable nuclides on an N-Z coordinate system. The 45° line represents the locus of points for which $N = Z$. Values of A are indicated along this axis.

tal lines join isodiaspheres, 45° lines join isotopes, and 135° lines join isotones.

A curve $D_s(A)$ drawn through the center of density of the stable points on the D-A grid winds rather irregularly in certain regions. Nevertheless, this so-called "line of beta stability" has certain important general trends in that it starts at $A = 0$ quite close and parallel to the $D = 0$ axis and builds up gradually to about $D = 50$ for $A = 250$. In terms of N and Z this means that the stability condition changes gradually from $N = Z$ to about $N = Z + 50$.

A detailed analysis of the distribution of stable nuclei on such a plot reveals that, apart from two possible exceptions, all odd mass numbers have only one stable isobar. The two exceptional stable odd-mass isobaric doublets (Cd, In^{113}; Sb, Te^{123}) may be only apparent exceptions, since in each case the second isobar is relatively rare and may actually be unstable with respect to K capture but with a very long lifetime. Among even mass numbers there occur 70 cases of beta-stable isobaric doublets and four beta-stable isobaric triplets: Zr, Mo, Ru^{96}; Sn, Te, Xe^{124}; Te, Xe, Ba^{130}; and Xe, Ba, Ce^{136}. In cases of doublets and triplets, the atomic numbers of neighboring stable isobars always differ by 2 units.

If we also locate the known beta-unstable nuclides on a D-A plot, we shall note that, in general, nuclides above the line of stability decay by

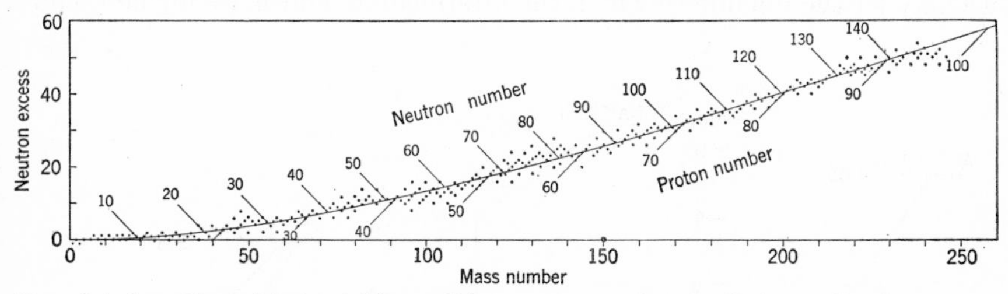

FIG. 6-4. Location of beta-stable nuclides on an equal-scale D-A coordinate system. On such a grid, vertical lines join isobars, horizontal lines join isodiaspheres, 45° lines join isotopes, and 135° lines join isotones. The smooth curve represents an empirical equation introduced in Chap. 8.

the emission of β^- particles, whereas nuclides below the line of stability decay by K capture or by the emission of β^+ particles. There are about 64 instances in which an unstable nuclide is bracketed above and below by beta-stable isobars, and in many of these instances the middle, unstable nuclide undergoes β^- decay, K capture, and positron decay. All of these nuclides are of the odd N-odd Z type.

Sargent[6] has pointed out that lifetimes and end-point kinetic energies in β decay are roughly correlated by an equation of the type

$$\log_{10} \tau_{\frac{1}{2}} = -C_1 \log_{10} T_{\max} + C_2 \tag{6-38}$$

where the constants must be adjusted to the experimental data. If we plot the experimental $\tau_{\frac{1}{2}}$ and $T_{\max}$ values on logarithmic graph paper, we shall find that the actual points scatter quite markedly from the best straight-line fit to the experimental data, so that the relationship is not very useful for quantitative work. We may, however, accept the qualitative conclusion that short beta lifetimes are usually associated with high decay energies. Accordingly, we may make rough estimates of decay energies on the basis of lifetime data, which are obtained more easily.

Although beta decay energies vary erratically, a few general trends may be noted. In connection with odd-mass nuclides let us introduce a new integral parameter n to denote the various isobars, letting $n = 0$ represent the beta-stable nuclide, $n = 1, 2, 3, \ldots$ denote successive neutron-rich isobars (negative-beta emitters), and $n = -1, -2, -3, \ldots$ denote successive proton-rich isobars (positive-beta emitters and K capturers). In general it appears that, for a given mass number, the greater the absolute value of n, the greater the energy of the decay. For n fixed (say, $n = 1$ or $n = -1$) there seems to exist a general tendency for beta decay energies to decrease as A increases.

In connection with even-mass isobars a difficulty arises in identifying an integer n with the nuclides, since in many instances two nuclides are stable. We can resolve this ambiguity in various ways. For example, we may let the nuclide to which the intermediate odd-mass nuclide tends

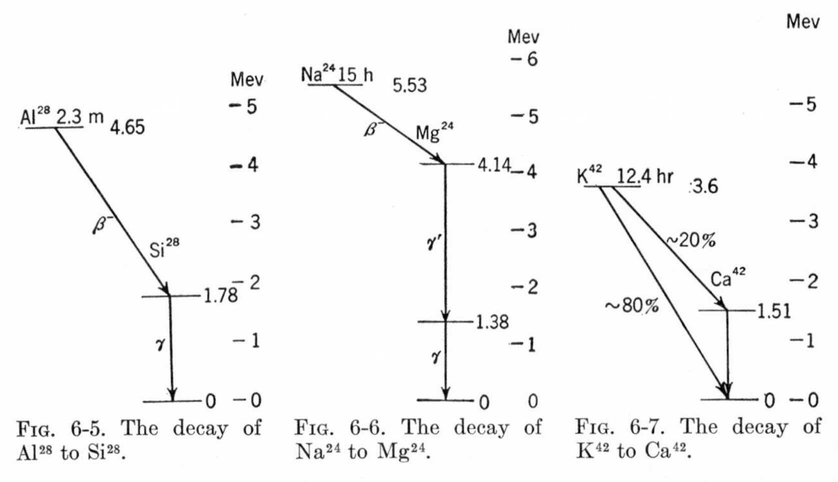

FIG. 6-5. The decay of Al^{28} to Si^{28}.

FIG. 6-6. The decay of Na^{24} to Mg^{24}.

FIG. 6-7. The decay of K^{42} to Ca^{42}.

to decay be the $n = 0$ nuclide. With such a rule we find again a general trend such that, for n fixed, the decay energy decreases with increasing A. However, for a fixed A but varying n, in addition to the tendency for the energy to increase with the absolute value of n, there exists a tendency for the decay from the odd-odd type of nuclide to be more energetic than the decay from the even-even type. These trends will be systematized in our discussion of the nuclear mass surface in Chap. 8.

6-5. Excited Nuclei in Beta and Gamma Decay.[5–9] The existence of excited states of nuclei is revealed in many instances of β decay and K capture. In fact, measurements of the energies and intensities of beta and gamma radiation as well as the coincidences and angular correlations between the radiated particles are major sources of information about the low-lying excited states of nuclei.

In Figs. 6-5 to 6-11 we show selected instances of energy levels which have been established by measurements of beta and gamma spectra.

The decay illustrated by the arrows in Fig. 6-5 gives rise to a simple beta spectrum and a simple gamma spectrum. The decay indicated on the energy-level diagram in Fig. 6-6 shows a simple beta spectrum and a complex gamma spectrum. The decay shown in Fig. 6-7 corresponds to a complex beta spectrum and a simple gamma spectrum. The branching ratios (see Sec. 6-11) are given on a percentage scale. The decay shown on the energy-level diagram in Fig. 6-8 gives rise to complex beta and gamma spectra. The levels shown in Fig. 6-9 give rise to compound spectra whose intensities depend upon the initial populations of the isomeric states of the parent. In Fig. 6-10 we show the levels associated with the branching decay of Cu^{64}. In Fig. 6-11 we show all the levels observed in the decay of isobars with $A = 125$.

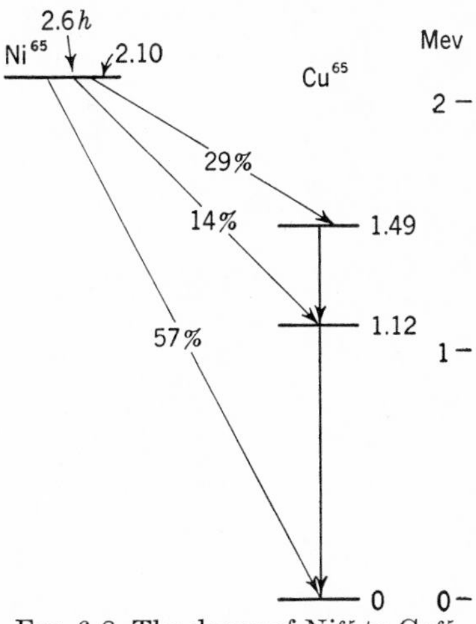

FIG. 6-8. The decay of Ni^{65} to Cu^{65}.

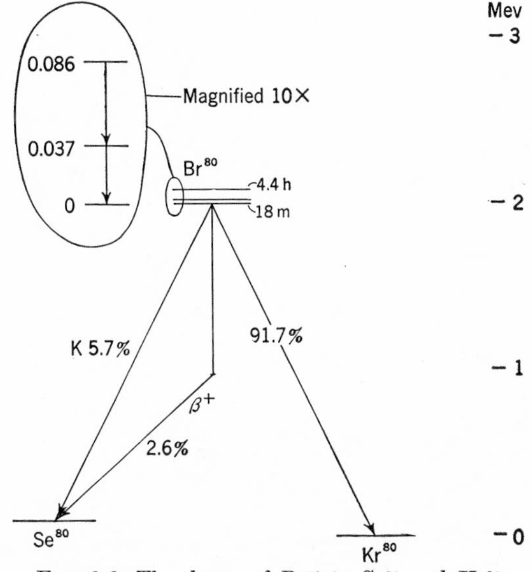

FIG. 6-9. The decay of Br^{80} to Se^{80} and Kr^{80}.

6-6. Energetics of Alpha Decay. The application of conservation of energy to decay by the emission of alpha particles leads to

$$M^* + W^* = M^{--} + W + m_{\text{He}}^{++} + T_\alpha + T_X \qquad (6\text{-}39)$$

where M^{--} is the mass of the doubly charged negative ion which is formed immediately following the emission of an alpha particle, m_{He}^{++} is the mass of the bare alpha particle, W is the excitation energy of the product nucleus (alpha particles themselves are not ejected in excited states), T_α

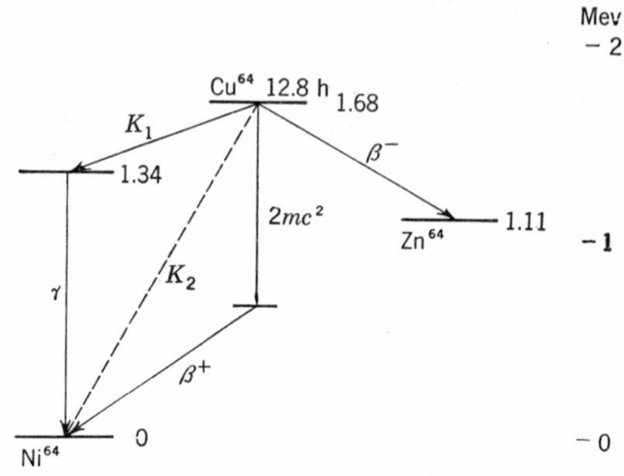

FIG. 6-10. The decay of Cu^{64} to Zn^{64} and Ni^{64}.

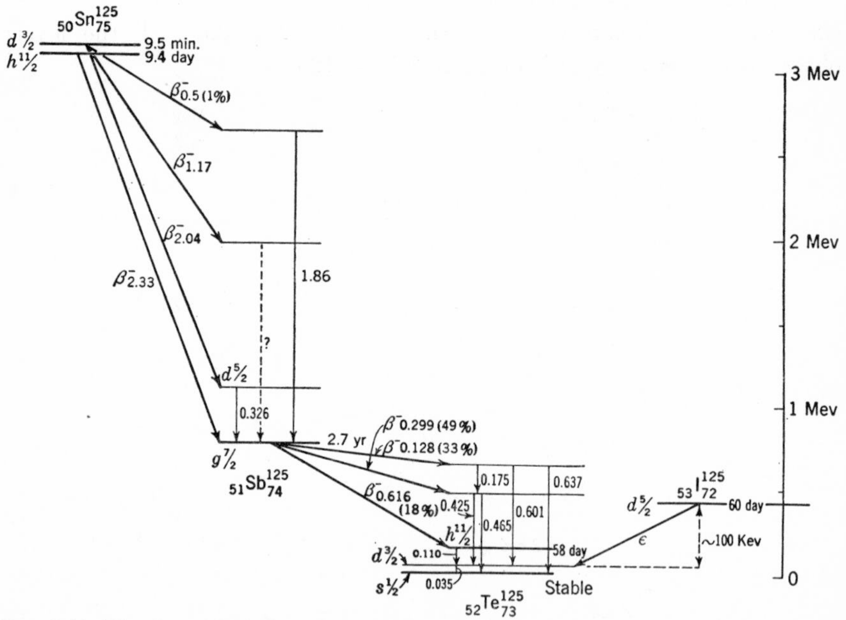

FIG. 6-11. The $A = 125$ isobars, showing observed decays and the associated energy levels. *(From Goldhaber and Hill, Ref. 8.)*

is the kinetic energy of the ejected alpha particle, and T_X is the kinetic energy of the recoil nucleus. Letting $T = T_X + T_\alpha$, $M^{--} = M + 2m_e$, and $m_{He}^{++} = m_{He} - 2m_e$, we may rewrite Eq. (6-39) as

$$M^* + W^* = M + W + m_{He} + T \tag{6-40}$$

or

$$Q + W^* - W = T \tag{6-41}$$

where we define the Q value, or disintegration energy, by

$$Q = M^* - M - m_{\mathrm{He}} \tag{6-42}$$

The recoil energy, which is significant in massive-particle emission, is difficult to measure directly. However, by applying the principle of conservation of momentum, we may express T in terms of the kinetic energy of the ejected particle. Since the derivation is applicable to the computation of the total kinetic energy associated with the emission of any light nuclear particle, we shall consider the general case.

Using nonrelativistic dynamics, we have

$$mv = MV \qquad \text{or} \qquad V = \frac{m}{M}v \tag{6-43}$$

where m and M are the masses and v and V are the velocities of the light and heavy nuclei, respectively. These velocities are along a straight line but are oppositely directed. Accordingly the total kinetic energy is

$$T = \frac{1}{2}mv^2 + \frac{1}{2}MV^2 = \frac{1}{2}mv^2\left(1 + \frac{m}{M}\right) = T_x\frac{M + m}{M} \tag{6-44}$$

where T_x is the kinetic energy of the small emitted particle. For most purposes it is sufficiently accurate to replace the masses by the mass numbers to obtain

$$T = T_x\frac{A + a}{A} \tag{6-45}$$

Returning to our consideration of alpha decay between ground states, we have

$$Q = T = T_\alpha\frac{A + 4}{A} = T_\alpha\frac{A^*}{A^* - 4} \tag{6-46}$$

This Q value must be positive if the starred nucleus is to be unstable relative to alpha-particle emission. Even if the Q value were negative, decay by alpha-particle emission can take place from an excited state, providing the left side of Eq. (6-41) is positive. Such instances occur as the final stage of many nuclear reactions (see Sec. 7–3).

An analysis of mass data indicates that alpha Q values [Eq. (6-42)] are usually positive for beta-stable nuclides with mass numbers greater than about 150. However, natural radioactivity with measurable lifetimes for the most part occurs when $A > 208$. In Fig. 6-12 we show the alpha-disintegration energies for the heavy nuclides plotted as a function of the mass number. The points corresponding to various isotopes are joined together by solid lines. We note that the alpha-disintegration energy decreases with A from $A = 212$ to $A = 238$. A sharp break in the alpha-disintegration energy occurs below $A = 212$, and a gradual rise appears to develop above $A = 238$.

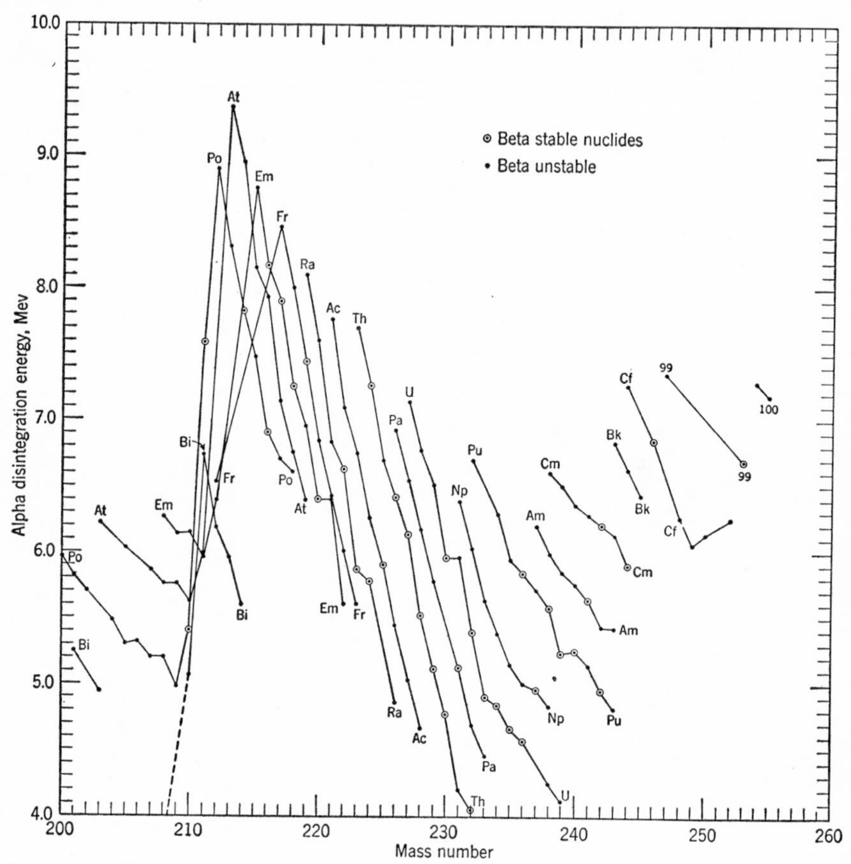

Fig. 6-12. Alpha energy vs. mass number for the heavy nuclides. (*After Perlman, Ghiorso, and Seaborg, Ref.* 10.)

6-7. The Coulomb Barrier. In Fig. 6-13 we indicate the energy relationships given by Eq. (6-40) for a system possessing the total energy $M^* + W^*$. We also indicate schematically on this diagram a hypothetical potential energy as it depends upon the distance between the daughter nucleus and the alpha particle. At long ranges the potential energy is simply the repulsive coulomb interaction energy

$$V_c = \frac{2Ze^2}{r} \tag{6-47}$$

However, when $r \leq R + r_\alpha$, where R is the radius of the daughter nuclide and r_α is the radius of the alpha particle, the potential changes drastically into a strictly nuclear attractive force. The exact nature of this force is still unknown. Assuming that the alpha particle and the daughter still are meaningful entities when $r < R + r_\alpha$, the energy difference between the ground-state mass of the parent and the effective potential energy between the alpha particle and the "virtual" daughter may be interpreted as the total kinetic energy of the alpha particle and the virtual daughter when they are bound together.

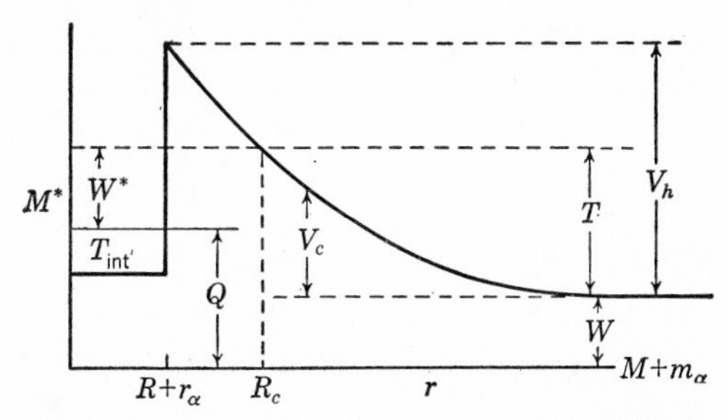

FIG. 6-13. Schematic diagram indicating the energy relationships in alpha decay and a hypothetical potential-energy function for the alpha particle and the daughter nucleus.

If we accept the expression $R = bA^{\frac{1}{3}}$ [Eq. (2-4)] as the radius of the daughter nucleus, we obtain

$$V_h = \frac{2Ze^2}{bA^{\frac{1}{3}} + r_\alpha} \tag{6-48}$$

as the approximate height of the coulomb potential barrier. Letting $b \approx r_\alpha = 1.5 \times 10^{-13}$ cm and inserting the Z and A values for a typical nuclide ($Z \approx 88$, $A \approx 225$), we find

$$V_h \approx 25 \text{ Mev} \tag{6-49}$$

The fact that this energy is much higher than the kinetic energies which are observed in natural alpha decay (4 to 8 Mev) is extremely puzzling if the decay process is considered from a classical viewpoint. Classically speaking, the alpha particle and the daughter could not separate unless the system had an energy at least as great as the height of the coulomb barrier. Furthermore, after the two particles separate, they should possess a total kinetic energy at least as great as the height of the coulomb barrier, since the coulomb potential energy would be converted to kinetic energy. However, these expectations are contradicted by the observed facts that products of the decay have kinetic energies which are far below the peak of the coulomb barrier. Apparently the alpha particle is capable of "tunneling" through the coulomb barrier, an intriguing property which we shall encounter again in later chapters.

The observed energy T may be used to compute the classical radius (see Fig. 6-13)

$$R_c = \frac{2Ze^2}{T} \tag{6-50}$$

which represents the closest distance between the alpha particle and the daughter allowed by classical theory.

6-8. Energy vs. Decay Constant in Alpha Decay. A correlation exists between the decay constant and the alpha kinetic energy such that large decay energies are usually associated with large decay constants (small half lives). A rather successful effort to express the correlation quantitatively was first made by Geiger and Nuttall[(11)] in 1911, who found an empirical relation between the alpha particles' range in air and the decay constant. This regularity may be converted into an equivalent relation between the decay constant and alpha energy by use of the range-energy curve for alpha particles in air. This equivalent Geiger-Nuttall law is

$$\log_{10} \lambda = c_1 \log_{10} T_\alpha + c_2 \tag{6-51}$$

where T_α is the kinetic energy of the alpha particle. The constants c_1 and c_2 may be evaluated quite readily by plotting the known pairs of λ and T_α values on log paper and fitting the best straight line to these points. It has been noted that an improvement in the fit of the data to Eq. (6-51) is obtained if c_2 is adjusted separately for various families.

Gamow[(12)] and Condon and Gurney,[(13)] using quantum mechanics, have derived a theoretical relationship which closely follows Eq. (6-51) over its range of application. The theoretical relation not only seems capable of a closer fit to the data but also affords an insight into the nature of the process. The theory treats the tunneling of an alpha particle through the coulomb barrier as the propagation of a wave through a region of rapidly varying index of refraction. The importance of the kinetic energy is perhaps apparent when we note that it determines the de Broglie wavelength [which is $h(2m_\alpha T)^{-\frac{1}{2}}$] of the outgoing waves at long distances. The theory leads to

$$\log_{10} \lambda = C - \frac{4\pi e^2 m_\alpha^{\frac{1}{2}}}{2^{\frac{1}{2}}\hbar \log_{10} e} \frac{ZT^{-\frac{1}{2}}}{[1 + (4/A)]^{\frac{1}{2}}} \tag{6-52}$$

where C is an almost constant quantity into which we have lumped a host of complicated effects which depend upon Z, A, R, T, the nuclear type, and the angular momenta of the parent and daughter nuclei. Since A varies over only a small range for the naturally radioactive species, we may with sufficient accuracy replace it by some average value (say 220). Inserting the natural constants into Eq. (6-52), we find, when T is expressed in Mev and λ in $\sec^{-1}$,

$$\log_{10} \lambda = C - 1.7037ZT^{-\frac{1}{2}} \tag{6-53}$$

In Fig. 6-14 we indicate the correlation of the experimental data for nuclides with even N and even Z with a curve based upon the Gamow-Condon-Gurney theory for which C is adjusted experimentally. Note that the agreement between theory and experiment is quite good, although small discrepancies are present. Discrepancies are greater when the theory is applied to odd-even, even-odd, or odd-odd nuclides,[14] although the theory stil gives the correct order of magnitude for the decay constant.

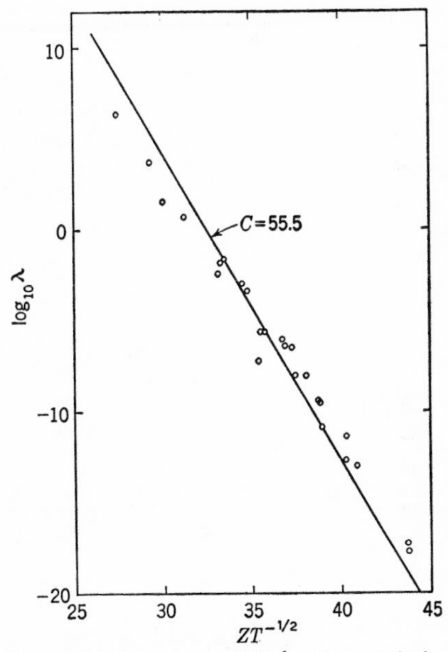

FIG. 6-14. $\log_{10} \lambda$ vs. $ZT^{-\frac{1}{2}}$, where λ is in $\sec^{-1}$ and T is in Mev. The straight line conforms to Eq. (6-53) with $C = 55.5$.

6-9. Excited Nuclei in Alpha Decay. In many cases of alpha decay the ejected particles have distinct groups of energies. Such an energy fine structure is to be expected if the transitions take place to excited states of the daughter. Whenever the energy of the subsequent γ radiation of the daughter nucleus has been measured, the energy balance within experimental error is just that to be expected from a simple system of levels and the formula

$$T_i = Q - W_i \tag{6-54}$$

where W_i is the ith level of the daughter nucleus. In Fig. 6-15 we indicate the system of levels of thorium C″, the alpha-particle energies, and the relative intensities.

A second instance involving alpha decay in which the excited states of nuclei are revealed is in the appearance of long-range alpha particles. The decay of a nucleus by β emission or K capture often leaves the product in an excited state. If the product is an alpha emitter having a very short lifetime, the additional excitation energy may be carried away in the alpha decay process rather than by γ emission. In such cases the alpha energy is

$$T_i = Q + W_i^* \tag{6-55}$$

where W_i^* is the ith level of the initial radioactive nucleus, and we consider only cases for which $W = 0$. In Fig. 6-16 we indicate the level scheme for radium C′ (Po^{214}), the alpha energies, and the relative intensities.

The relative intensities of the alpha-particle groups in the two phenomena just discussed provide direct experimental information concerning probabilities for transitions between various excited states of nuclei.

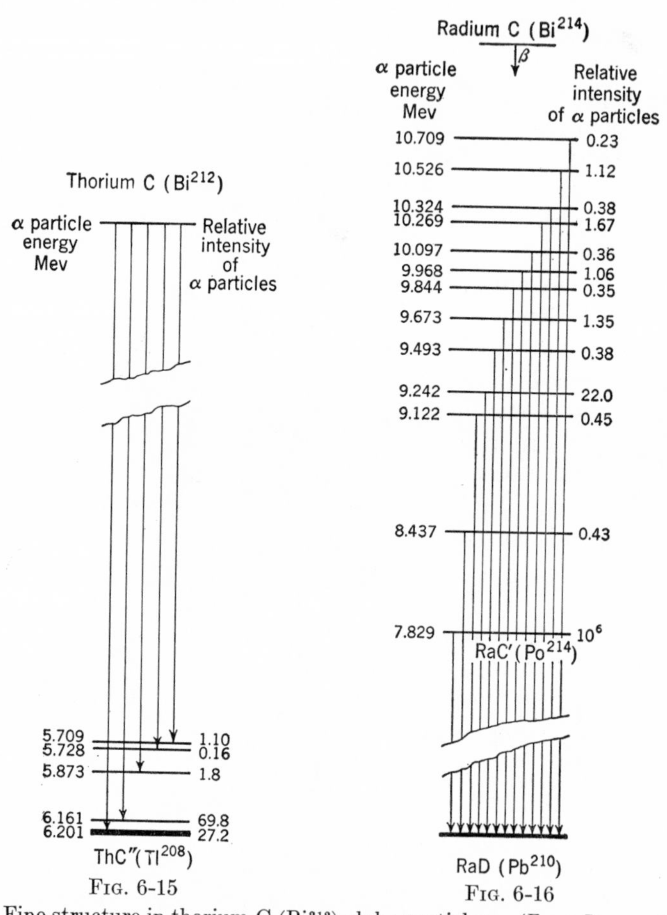

FIG. 6-15 FIG. 6-16

FIG. 6-15. Fine structure in thorium C (Bi^{212}) alpha particles. (*From Devons, Ref.* 15.)
FIG. 6-16. Long-range α particles from RaC′ (Po^{214}). (*From Devons, Ref.* 15.)

6-10. Activity. The activity of a sample is defined as the number of disintegrations per unit time. In the case of a single activity it is given by

$$A = \left| \frac{dN}{dt} \right| = \lambda N \tag{6-56}$$

The standard unit of activity is the curie, which today is defined as 3.7×10^{10} disintegrations/sec. In an earlier sense the curie applied only to the decay of radon (radon, Rn, is now frequently called emanation, Em); however, in the sense now accepted, the curie, the millicurie, and the microcurie are activity units for any radioactive substance. Recently a unit of activity called the rutherford has been introduced; it is defined as a disintegration rate of 10^6 disintegrations/sec. The name specific activity is applied to the disintegration rate per unit mass of radioactive substance.

Measurement of activities with the aid of counting devices may be used to determine the characteristic decay constant. For the case of a single activity we have, in view of Eq. (6-3),

$$A = \lambda N_0 \exp(-\lambda t) = A_0 \exp(-\lambda t) \tag{6-57}$$

Taking natural logarithms of both sides, we find

$$\ln A = \ln A_0 - \lambda t \tag{6-58}$$

Accordingly, the slope of a plot of the logarithm of the counting rate against time gives directly the constant λ. The intercept at $t = 0$ gives the initial activity A_0 multiplied by a factor which depends upon the geometry and the efficiency of the counting system. The procedure for evaluating λ is independent of the instant chosen for $t = 0$.

Quite often a radioactive sample contains two or more independent activities. If the corresponding disintegration rates differ appreciably, these decay rates may be determined by analytical or graphical methods. According to the decay law the total activity corresponding to a mixture of two independent activities is given by

$$A = A_1 + A_2 = A_{01} \exp(-\lambda_1 t) + A_{02} \exp(-\lambda_2 t) \tag{6-59}$$

Taking natural logarithms of both sides, we find

$$\ln A = \ln [A_{01} \exp(-\lambda_1 t) + A_{02} \exp(-\lambda_2 t)] \tag{6-60}$$

If $\lambda_1 \gg \lambda_2$, then after a time which is very long compared to $1/\lambda_1$, the first term in the brackets in Eq. (6-60) may be ignored, so that the activity is simply given by

$$\ln A \approx \ln A_{02} - \lambda_2 t \tag{6-61}$$

Accordingly the slope of the limiting straight line of $\ln A$ vs. t gives λ_2. If we extrapolate this limiting straight line to zero, we obtain A_{02}. Having identified A_{02} and λ_2, we can compute A_2 for all times. The simplest method for doing this is to take antilogarithms of the points of the straight line which represents $\ln A_2$. From these values we may compute the difference $A - A_2$. In view of Eq. (6-59) we find

$$\ln (A - A_2) = \ln A_{01} - \lambda_1 t \tag{6-62}$$

so that the logarithm of the differences between the total activity and the long-lived activity should be a straight line with the intercept ln A_{01} and the slope λ_1. If the actual curve is not quite a straight line, the constants A_{02} and λ_2 must be adjusted until the points corresponding to ln $(A - A_2)$ fall on a straight line.

When more than two independent activities are present, a similar analysis is used; the constants of the longest-lived activity are identified first, then the next longest, etc. In Fig. 6-17 we show a complex decay curve along with the curves which represent the individual activities.

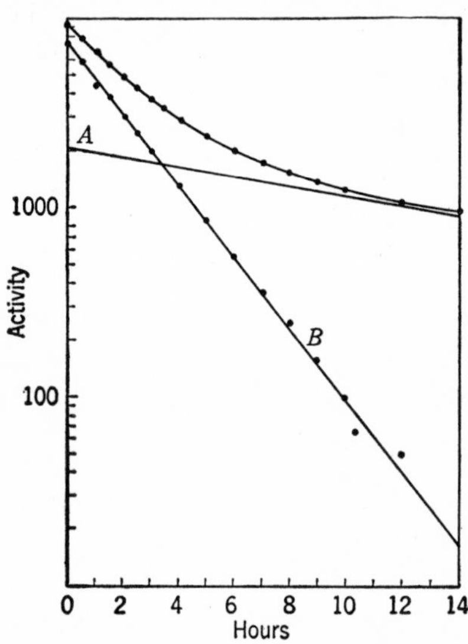

FIG. 6-17. Decay of bismuth daughter activities. A, 12-hr Bi^{203} and Bi^{204} activity; B, 95-min Bi^{202} activity. (*From Karraker and Templeton, Ref.* 16.)

6-11. Decay of Radioactive Chains. There exist in nature and there have been produced various chains of radioactive nuclei. These chains consist of an initial radioactive nuclide which decays through several radioactive nuclear types into a final stable product. Let us label by the letters $a, b, c, \ldots$ the parent, first-daughter, second-daughter, etc., substances. The rates of change of the numbers of nuclei of this set are

$$\frac{dN_a}{dt} = -\lambda_a N_a \tag{6-63}$$

$$\frac{dN_b}{dt} = \lambda_a N_a - \lambda_b N_b \tag{6-64}$$

$$\frac{dN_c}{dt} = \lambda_b N_b - \lambda_c N_c \tag{6-65}$$

where $N_a, N_b, N_c, \ldots$ are the numbers of nuclei of the parent, first daughter, second daughter, etc., at any instant of time. If we specify the initial conditions on these numbers, we can integrate each equation in turn. For example, let us consider the important case when only the parent substance is initially present, *i.e.*, when

$$N_a(0) = N_{a0} \qquad N_b(0) = 0 \qquad N_c(0) = 0 \qquad \ldots \tag{6-66}$$

Integration of Eqs. (6-63) to (6-65), etc., in turn gives

$$N_a(t) = N_{a0} \exp(-\lambda_a t) \tag{6-67}$$

$$N_b(t) = \lambda_a N_{a0} \left[\frac{\exp(-\lambda_a t)}{\lambda_b - \lambda_a} + \frac{\exp(-\lambda_b t)}{\lambda_a - \lambda_b} \right] \tag{6-68}$$

$$N_c(t) = \lambda_a \lambda_b N_{a0} \left[\frac{\exp(-\lambda_a t)}{(\lambda_b - \lambda_a)(\lambda_c - \lambda_a)} + \frac{\exp(-\lambda_b t)}{(\lambda_a - \lambda_b)(\lambda_c - \lambda_b)} + \frac{\exp(-\lambda_c t)}{(\lambda_a - \lambda_c)(\lambda_b - \lambda_c)} \right] \tag{6-69}$$

In the study of Eq. (6-68) the two extreme cases $\lambda_b \gg \lambda_a$ and $\lambda_a \gg \lambda_b$ are of particular interest. In the former case, *i.e.*, when the parent has a long lifetime compared with the daughter, the number of daughter nuclei after a time which is long compared to $1/\lambda_b$ will vary with time as indicated by (see Fig. 6-18*a*)

$$N_b = \frac{\lambda_a}{\lambda_b} N_{a0} \exp(-\lambda_a t) = \frac{\lambda_a}{\lambda_b} N_a \tag{6-70}$$

Thus we see that the number of daughter atoms is a fixed fraction of the parent. If the parent is so long-lived that the number present may be regarded as constant, we may also regard the number of daughter atoms as constant. This condition is known as secular equilibrium.

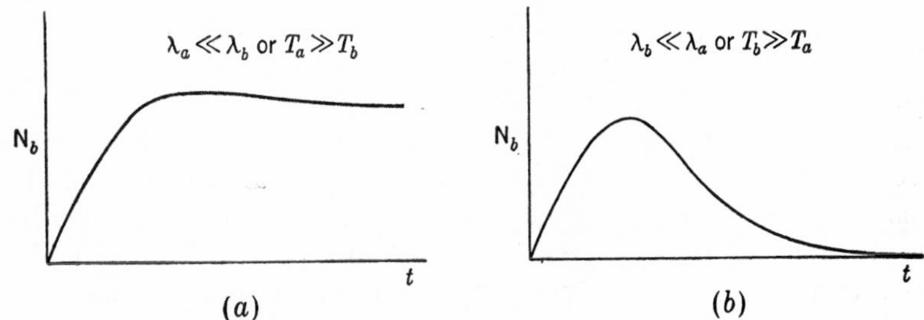

FIG. 6-18. Schematic diagram indicating number of daughter atoms as a function of time (*a*) for $\lambda_a \ll \lambda_b$ and (*b*) for $\lambda_b \ll \lambda_a$.

When the daughter is long-lived compared with the parent ($\lambda_a \gg \lambda_b$), the number of daughter atoms builds up rapidly. The number of daughter atoms existing after $t \gg 1/\lambda_a$ depends upon the decay rate of the daughter (see Fig. 6-18*b*) according to

$$N_b = N_{a0} \exp(-\lambda_b t) \tag{6-71}$$

The number of second-daughter nuclides present for various extreme relations between λ_a, λ_b, and λ_c may be determined by an investigation of Eq. (6-69). We must emphasize that Eqs. (6-67) to (6-69) all pertain to the initial conditions given by Eqs. (6-66). For other initial conditions the numbers of atoms existing at any instant may vary with time quite differently.

Sometimes members of a radioactive chain decay into two or more different types of nuclides, a phenomenon which is referred to as branching. For such cases the decay constant associated with the parent may be decomposed into partial decay constants λ_{ai}, which govern the fractional rate of decay to the different first daughters. We write

$$\lambda_a = \sum_i \lambda_{ai} = \lambda_a \sum_i \frac{\lambda_{ai}}{\lambda_a} = \lambda_a \sum_i r_{ai} \tag{6-72}$$

where $r_{ai} = \lambda_{ai}/\lambda_a$ is the so-called branching ratio. When branching occurs, the differential equation governing the decay must, of course, be modified accordingly.

The gross activity of a radioactive sample consisting of a generically related series is the sum of the activities of all the members of the series, *i.e.*,

$$A = A_a + \cdot \cdot \cdot + \cdot \cdot \cdot = \lambda_a N_a + \lambda_b N_b + \cdot \cdot \cdot \tag{6-73}$$

Accordingly the gross activity as a function of time can be obtained by substituting Eqs. (6-67) to (6-69) into Eq. (6-73). This gross activity will appear as a counting rate only if the detecting system is 100 per cent efficient for all the particles emitted in the decay, a condition which is rarely fulfilled. The function governing the counting rate can be obtained by multiplying each member of the right-hand side of Eq. (6-73) by the constants which depend upon the geometry of the system and the efficiency of the counter to the emitted particle.

6-12. Radioactive Chains and Spontaneous Fission. The heavy radioactive substances which are present in nature are all members of three chains whose existence must be attributed to the exceptionally long half-lives of three substances, Th^{232} (1.39×10^{10} years), U^{235} (7.1×10^8 years), and U^{238} (4.51×10^9 years). In our geological past there undoubtedly was present another radioactive chain whose longest-lived member was Np^{237} (2.2×10^6 years). The members of this chain have long ago decayed away to insignificant quantities.

In alpha, beta, and gamma decay, one never encounters a member of one chain which in the course of its decay switches over to another chain. The explanation is obvious, since alpha decay changes the mass number by 4, whereas beta and gamma decay have no effect upon the mass number. Accordingly the A value of any member of a radioactive chain may be characterized by one of the four expressions $4n$, $4n + 1$, $4n + 2$, and $4n + 3$, where the n's are integers ($\sim$50 to 60). The chains which contain Th^{232}, Np^{235}, U^{238}, and U^{237}, respectively, belong to these four general families.

By the methods of modern alchemy which we shall discuss in the next chapter, scientists have in recent years produced many collateral members of the four radioactive families. Besides radioisotopes of naturally occurring elements, eight transuranic elements have been produced [Np, Pu, Am, Cm, Bk, Cf, and the as yet unnamed elements 99 and 100 (see Refs. 21 to 23)]. In all probability many of these artificial radionuclides were present in nature during the early days of the universe. The fact they are not naturally present now is due to the fortuitous circumstance that we are here some 3 or 4 billion years after formation of the elements. Since the availability of these artificial radionuclides is rapidly

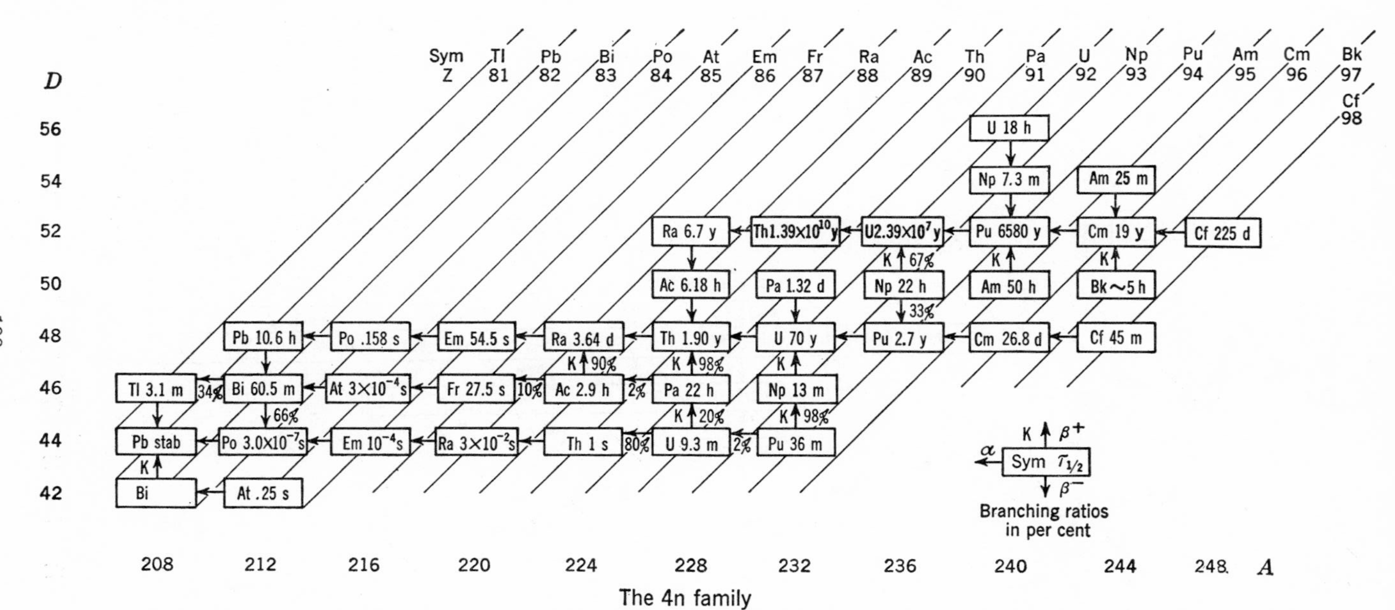

FIG. 6-19. Heavy members of the $4n$ radioactive family. (*Data from Hollander, Perlman, and Seaborg, Ref.* 5.)

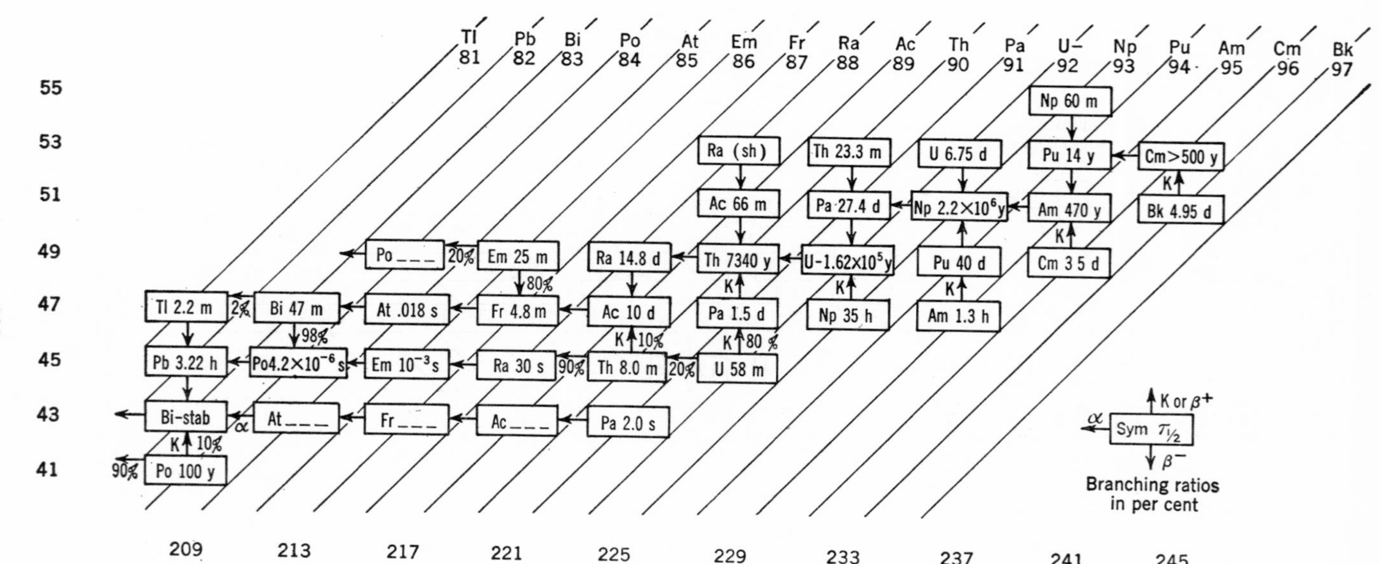

FIG. 6-20. Heavy members of the $4n + 1$ radioactive family. (*Data from Hollander, Perlman, and Seaborg, Ref.* 5.)

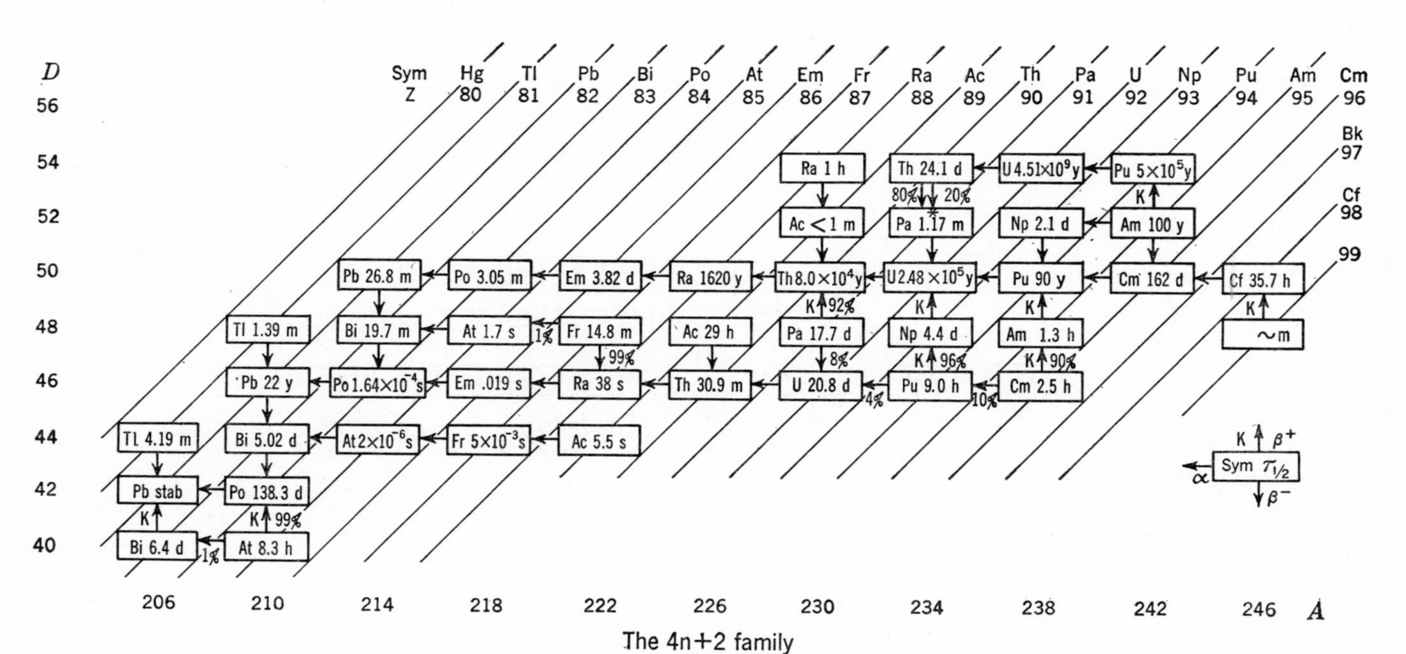

FIG. 6-21. Heavy members of the $4n + 2$ radioactive family. (*Data from Hollander, Perlman, and Seaborg, Ref.* 5.)

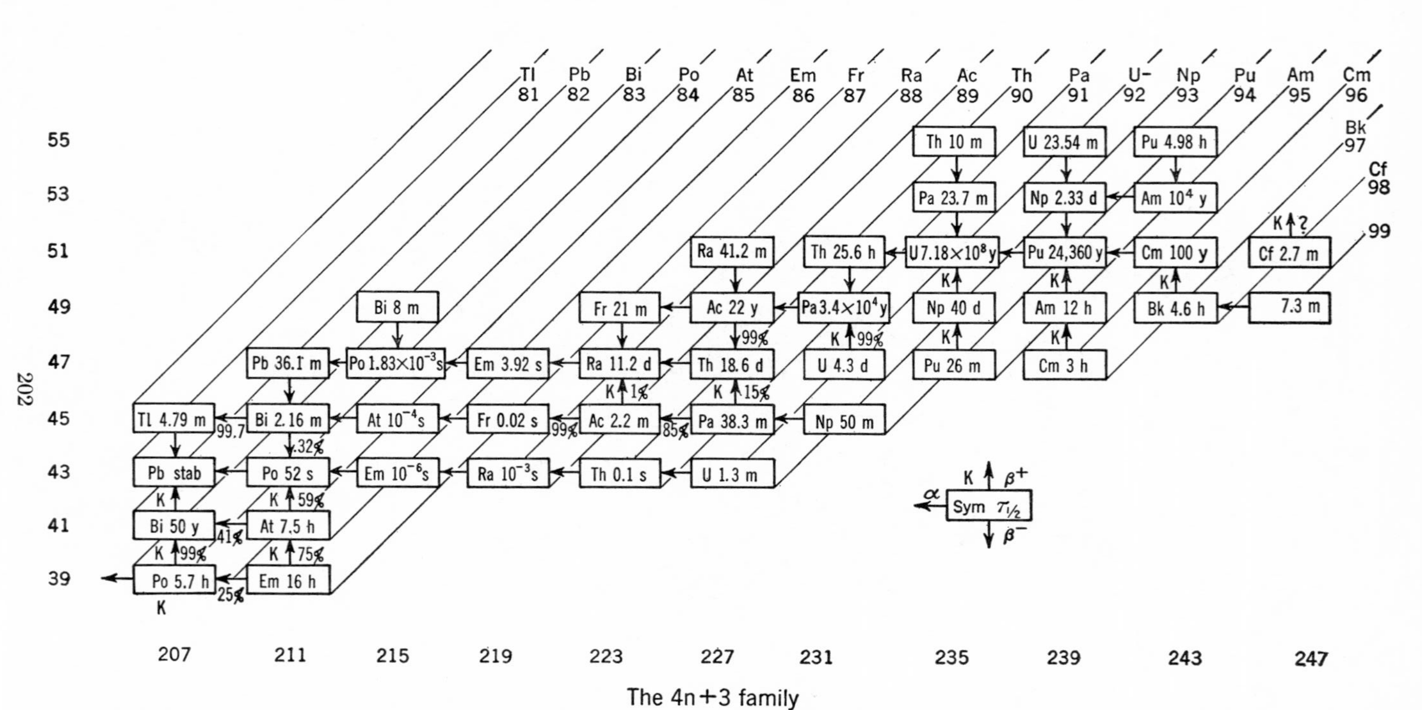

FIG. 6-22. Heavy members of the $4n + 3$ radioactive family. (*Data from Hollander, Perlman, and Seaborg, Ref.* 5.)

approaching that of some of the natural radionuclides, there is little point in treating them separately in a study of nuclear physics. In Figs. 6-19 to 6-22 we show the members of these radioactive families, along with their half-lives, as given in a recent table of isotopes compiled by Hollander, Perlman, and Seaborg.[5] The natural radioactive substances are those which lie along the chains of decay extending from Th^{232} to Pb^{208}, from U^{238} to Pb^{206}, and from U^{235} to Pb^{207}.

Shortly after the discovery of neutron-induced fission in 1939, Bohr and Wheeler[(17)] predicted the existence of a type of radioactive decay in which an unstable nucleus spontaneously breaks into two approximately equal fragments. The existence of this phenomenon, known as spontaneous fission, was verified experimentally in 1940, by Petrzhak and Flerov.[(18)] The results of measurements of spontaneous fission rates made at Los Alamos during World War II, which have recently been published,[(19)] indicate that these decay constants are extremely small compared to alpha decay constants. However, an extrapolation of the trend of spontaneous decay constants suggests that spontaneous-fission half-lives should be of the order of 1 sec or less for elements with $Z \approx 105$.[(20)] Accordingly it appears that we cannot continue much further in the construction of transuranic elements.

PROBLEMS

***6-1.** Fifty milligrams of radium in the form of $RaSO_4$ are sealed into a platinum container.

(*a*) How many milligrams of radon are present after the following times have elapsed: 1, 2, 3, 4, 5, 6, 7, 8, 9, 10 days; 5 years; 21 years; 1600 years?

(*b*) What substances and how many milligrams of each are present in the container after 1 day, 3 years, 21 years? (*Hint:* Use approximations which give results to 1 per cent.)

(*c*) What is the gamma activity of the material in the capsule after 1 day, 5 years, 21 years?

6-2. If a rock contains 1000 g of natural uranium, together with its decay products, how many grams of U^{235} and U^{238} were present 3 billion years ago (the earth is approximately 3 billion years old)? How many grams of each would be present 9 billion years hence if the rock were undisturbed?

6-3. If one starts with 1μg of 4.4-hr Br^{80m}, what quantities of 18-min Br^{80}, Se^{80}, and Kr^{80} are present after 1 min, 18 min, 4.4 hr, 4.4 days?

6-4. What is the kinetic energy of a Br^{80} nucleus after the emission of a 0.049-Mev gamma ray?

6-5. What is the kinetic energy of the residual nucleus after a decay of a P^{32} nucleus in which a maximum-energy beta particle is emitted?

6-6. What is the kinetic energy of the residual nucleus after a decay of U^{235} by alpha emission?

***6-7.** The following activities in counts per minute are recorded by a beta counter at $t = 0$ and after successive 1-min intervals: 900, 602, 409, 284, 205, 155, 121, 100, 84, 72, 65, 59, 54, 50, 47, 44, 41, 39. What half-lives are present, and what are the initial activities?

***6-8.** Observations of the decay of Th^{231} to Pa^{231} reveal β^- radiations of 302, 216, and 94 kev and γ radiations of 208, 167, 122, 85, 63, 59, and 22 kev. Find the simplest decay scheme which will account for these radiations. What other radiations might be expected from this decay scheme? How would the observation of coincidences assist in the verification of your decay scheme?

6-9. Trace out the principal links in the chains of decay starting from Cf^{248}, Cf^{246}, Cm^{245}, and 99^{247}. What similarities and differences exist in the sequences of alpha and beta decays in these four families?

REFERENCES

1. Segrè, E., and C. E. Wiegand: *Phys. Rev.*, **71**, 274 (1947).
2. Jensen, E. N., R. T. Nichols, J. Clement, and A. Pohm: *Phys. Rev.*, **86**, 115 (1952).
3. Cook, G. S.: *Am. J. Phys.*, **19**, 37 (1951).
4. "Chart of Nuclides," General Electric Company, Schenectady, N.Y., 1952.
5. Hollander, J. M., I. Perlman, and G. T. Seaborg: *Revs. Mod. Phys.*, **25**, 469 (1953).
6. Sargent, B. W.: *Proc. Roy. Soc. (London)*, **A139**, 659 (1933).
7. Mitchell, A. C. G.: *Revs. Mod. Phys.*, **22**, 36 (1950).
8. Goldhaber, M., and R. D. Hill: *Revs. Mod. Phys.*, **24**, 190 (1952).
9. "Nuclear Data," *Natl. Bur. Standards (U.S.) Misc. Publ.* 499, 1950.
10. Perlman, I., A. Ghiorso, and G. T. Seaborg: *Phys. Rev.*, **77**, 26 (1950).
11. Geiger, H., and J. M. Nuttall: *Phil. Mag.*, **22**, 613 (1911).
12. Gamow, G.: *Z. Physik*, **51**, 204 (1928).
13. Condon, E. U., and R. W. Gurney: *Nature*, **122**, 439 (1928).
14. Meinke, W. W., A. Ghiorso, and G. T. Seaborg: *Phys. Rev.*, **81**, 782 (1951).
15. Devons, S.: "Excited States of Nuclei," p. 34, Cambridge University Press, New York, 1949.
16. Karraker, D. K., and D. H. Templeton: *Phys. Rev.*, **81**, 515 (1951).
17. Bohr, N., and J. A. Wheeler: *Phys. Rev.*, **56**, 426 (1939).
18. Petrzhak, K. A., and G. N. Flerov: *Compt. rend. acad. sci. (U.R.S.S.)*, **28**, 500 (1940).
19. Segrè, E.: *Phys. Rev.*, **86**, 21 (1952).
20. Feather, N.: "Nuclear Stability Rules," Cambridge University Press, New York, 1935.
21. Ghiorso, A., *et al.: Phys. Rev.*, **93**, 257 (1954).
22. Thompson, S. G., *et al.: Phys. Rev.*, **93**, 908 (1954).
23. Fields, P. R., *et al.: Phys. Rev.*, **94**, 207 (1954).
24. Morrison, P., and L. I. Schiff: *Phys. Rev.*, **58**, 24 (1940).
25. Bradt, H., *et al.: Helv. Phys. Acta*, **19**, 222 (1946).
26. Anderson, C. E., G. W. Wheeler, and W. W. Watson: *Phys. Rev.*, **90**, 606 (1953).
27. Emmerich, W. S., S. E. Singer, and J. D. Kurbatov: *Phys. Rev.*, **94**, 113 (1954).

CHAPTER 7

NUCLEAR REACTIONS

The application of accelerators and precision instruments for controlling and measuring the energies of light nuclear particles is leading to a tremendous accumulation of data concerning the dynamic properties of nuclei. In this work an incident beam of light nuclear particles or gamma rays having known energies is projected against a known target substance. The ejected particles are identified; their energies at various angles are measured; and, whenever possible, the residual substances are identified. On the basis of such information it is possible in many cases to identify the detailed nuclear processes which occurred during the bombardment. Measurements of the number of incident particles per unit time, the number of ejected particles per unit time, and the angular distribution of ejected particles at various energies make it possible to assign certain functions, known as the cross section and the differential cross section, which are characteristic of the nuclei involved. These functions are thought to indicate the detailed nature of nuclear forces and the manner in which these forces act upon various groupings of nucleons. Nuclear physics will become a closed science when a theory is found which will enable physicists to predict the energies and cross sections for all possible nuclear processes. At this time we are very far from this goal.

The purpose of this chapter is to define certain dynamical properties of nuclei and to indicate how these properties may be inferred from bombardment experiments.

7-1. Types of Bombardment Processes. Bombardment processes may be divided into three catagories: (1) elastic scattering, (2) inelastic scattering, and (3) nuclear reactions. If the outgoing particles are the same as the incident particles and kinetic energy is conserved, we call the process elastic scattering. If the outgoing particles are the same as the incident particles but kinetic energy is lost, we refer to the process as inelastic scattering. If the outgoing particles are different from the incident particles, we refer to the process as a nuclear reaction. Of course, inelastic scattering and nuclear reactions provide the most detailed information about the internal structure and characteristics of nuclei, since these processes involve rearrangements of this internal structure.

The major conclusion which has been drawn from a great number of bombardment experiments in which the ejected and residual nuclei have been identified is that all the neutrons and protons involved are simply regrouped during the reaction. Experimental results permit the following statements: (1) As yet, no reaction has been observed whose interpretation requires the assumption that a proton or a neutron is annihilated or created. (2) No bombardment reaction has been directly observed whose interpretation requires the assumption that a proton transforms into a neutron or a neutron transforms into a proton. We leave to fundamental-particle physics the question whether protons or neutrons can be created or annihilated. Discussion of the second statement is somewhat academic, since a bombardment reaction in which a proton (neutron) is apparently converted into a neutron (proton) can be interpreted as a two-step process in which the neutrons and protons are first regrouped and then one of the products undergoes β decay. Therefore for the purposes of our discussion in nuclear physics we shall accept the conclusion that, in bombardment reactions involving moderate energies, neutrons and protons are conserved.

In 1936 Bohr[(1)] suggested that a nuclear-bombardment reaction may take place in two distinct steps: (1) the formation of a compound nucleus which exists for a time which is too short to be measured ($\gtrsim 10^{-17}$ sec) but which is long compared to the time it would take the incident particle to traverse the nuclear diameter ($\sim 10^{-21}$ sec), and (2) the decay of the compound nucleus in a manner which is energetically permissible and which is essentially independent of the capture process (*i.e.*, the compound nucleus in selecting a mode of decay forgets how it was formed). Indirect experimental evidence tends to confirm the existence of a compound nucleus for bombardment reactions at moderate energies. However, it remains to be determined at what energy nuclear collisions take on a nucleon-nucleon character. There are so many conveniences attendant to the compound-nucleus conception that we shall make considerable use of it in the discussions which follow. We recognize at the outset, however, that this picture of a nuclear reaction may still undergo modification.

Accordingly a great many bombardment reactions which have been investigated will be represented by an equation of the type

$$x + X \rightarrow X^* \rightarrow x' + X' \tag{7-1}$$

where x, X, X^*, x', and X' denote the incident, target, compound, ejected, and residual nuclei, respectively. In view of the conservation of protons and neutrons the following relations between the integral nuclear parameters must hold:

$$z + Z = Z^* = z' + Z' \tag{7-2}$$
$$n + N = N^* = n' + N' \tag{7-3}$$
$$a + A = A^* = a' + A' \tag{7-4}$$
$$d + D = D^* = d' + D' \tag{7-5}$$

Because of these relations a bombardment reaction is uniquely determined if we specify only the incident and ejected particle and the target atom. For example, the designation "$N^{14}(\alpha,p)$ reaction" can mean only the reaction

$${}_2He^4 + {}_7N^{14} \rightarrow ({}_9F^{18})^* \rightarrow {}_1H^1 + {}_8O^{17} \tag{7-6}$$

All the light nuclear particles (see Table 2-1) and photons have been used to induce nuclear reactions. However, with a few exceptions, only gamma rays, neutrons, protons, and alpha particles are ejected in bombardment reactions in the 0- to 10-Mev range. At moderately high bombardment energies (10 to 25 Mev) reactions have been noted in which two neutrons or a neutron and a proton are ejected.

While the nuclear reactions discussed above comprise the vast majority of reactions which have been studied thus far, several reactions have been observed which do not conform to the types discussed. For example, neutrons, gamma rays, and high-energy charged particles have been used to induce the fission of heavy nuclides. These reactions are highly exoergic ($Q \approx 150$ to 200 Mev), a fact which is related to the extra stability of the two medium-weight product nuclides. Apart from the practical applications of this reaction, it is interesting because of the large number of new radioactive nuclides which have been produced by fission.

Very-high-energy (100 to 400 Mev) gamma rays, neutrons, and charged particles have been observed to cause spallation,[(2)] a process in which many nucleons and small subgroups are ejected simultaneously. These reactions are also useful for the production of new radioactive nuclides.

The acceleration of particles heavier than He^4 has been accomplished in recent years, and the reactions induced by such particles are now being studied. Reactions induced by very-high-energy C^{12} particles have been used to produce transuranic elements [(3)] and to produce neutron-deficient nuclides. A host of unusual reactions and products have been found at Oak Ridge[(4)] by the bombardment of light nuclei with 25-Mev triply ionized nitrogen ions. The number of nuclear reactions which can occur seems almost boundless, since apparently there is a finite probability for almost any rearrangement process which satisfies the energy requirements.

At bombardment energies above 150 Mev the production of mesons becomes an important process.[(5)] A great number of interesting experiments have already been done in this new field of study, which has become a major subdivision of experimental physics. Since these experiments are primarily a part of field-particle physics, we shall not go into them in this book.

7-2. Q Values. The reaction energy, or Q value, of any reaction is defined as the difference between the total mass of the initial particles and the total mass of the products. Accordingly in a simple bombardment process we have

$$Q = M + m - M' - m' \tag{7-7}$$

where it is understood that mass and energy are equivalent in accord with the relation $E = Mc^2$. If Q is positive, the reaction is said to be exoergic. If Q is negative, the reaction is said to be endoergic. Neutral atomic masses are generally used for the calculation of the reaction energy despite the fact that the incident projectile does not have its extranuclear electrons. Since the products immediately formed as a result of the reaction also are lacking this same number of electrons, the mass associated with extra electrons belonging to the neutral atoms will automatically cancel in the expression for Q. As soon as the atomic masses are known to one or two more significant figures, corrections for changes in electronic binding energies may be necessary.

To illustrate the calculation of the reaction energy of a bombardment process, let us consider the data for the reaction given by Eq. (7-6). According to recent measurements the neutral atomic masses of the nuclides in this reaction are

$$\begin{array}{ll} M({}_7\text{N}^{14}) = 14.007515 & M({}_8\text{O}^{17}) = 17.004533 \\ M({}_2\text{He}^4) = \underline{\ \ 4.003873} & M({}_1\text{H}^1) = \underline{\ \ 1.008142} \end{array}$$

Thus

$$Q = 18.011388 \quad - \quad 18.012675 = -0.001287 \text{ MU}$$

The reaction above is endoergic with $Q = -1.198$ Mev. Consequently it cannot take place unless the incident particle has sufficient energy that the initial particles have 1.198 Mev kinetic energy in the coordinate system of the center of mass (see Sec. 7-3). The minimum energy of the incident particle needed for an endoergic reaction is known as the threshold energy. The reverse reaction $\text{O}^{17}(p,\alpha)$ is, of course, an exoergic reaction with $Q = 1.198$ Mev.

Considerable arithmetical convenience is attendant to the use of mass decrements for the calculation of reaction energies, since fewer significant figures are needed. In view of Eqs. (7-4) and (7-7) we see that

$$Q = \Delta + \delta - \Delta' - \delta' \tag{7-8}$$

where Δ, δ, Δ' and δ' are the mass decrements of the target, incident, residual, and ejected nuclides respectively. In our example we have (in mMU)

$$\Delta({}_7N^{14}) = 7.515 \qquad \Delta'({}_8O^{17}) = 4.533$$
$$\delta({}_2He^4) = \underline{3.873} \qquad \delta'({}_1H^1) = \underline{8.142}$$
$$11.388 \qquad\qquad 12.675$$

Consequently

$$Q = 11.388 - 12.675 = -1.287 = -1.198 \text{ Mev}$$

Although less convenient arithmetically, the use of nuclear energy data or binding-energy data for the calculation of reaction energies is sometimes best from the standpoint of interpreting the experimental data.

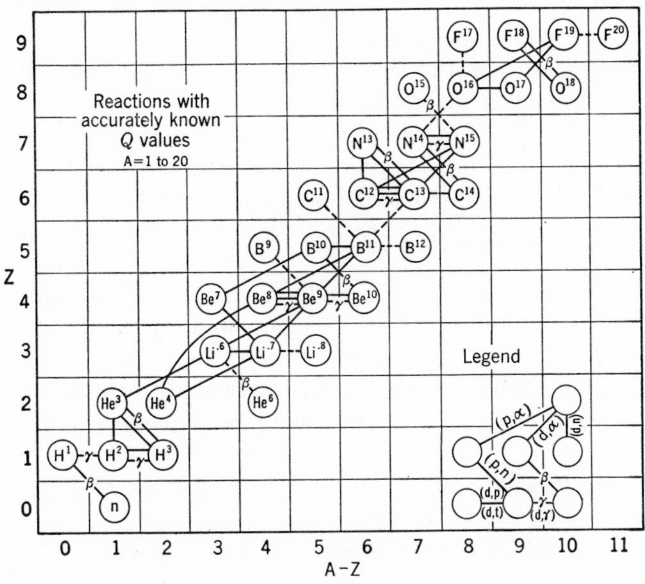

FIG. 7-1. The nuclear reactions having accurately known Q values at the present time are represented on this chart by lines connecting target nucleus and residual nucleus. *(From Li, Whaling, Fowler, and Lauritsen, Ref. 6.)*

Thus in view of Eqs. (2-69), (7-2), and (7-3) we have in bombardment reactions

$$\begin{aligned} Q = E + Zm_H + Nm_n + e + zm_H + nm_n \\ - (E' + Z'm_H + N'm_n + e' + z'm_H + n'm_n) \\ = E + e - E' - e' \end{aligned} \tag{7-9}$$

In terms of binding energies $B = -E$, which are always positive numbers,

$$Q = B' + b' - B - b \tag{7-10}$$

To illustrate the calculation with the use of the binding energies, we have in our example (in Mev)

$$B'({}_8O^{17}) = 131.700 \qquad B({}_7N^{14}) = 104.615$$
$$b'({}_1H^1) = 0.000 \qquad b({}_2He^4) = 28.283$$
$$Q = 131.700 - 132.898 = -1.198 \text{ Mev}$$

The experimental Q values of various reactions may be used for the precise determination of nuclear masses. It should be clear that the experimental Q value in conjunction with any three of the four parameters in Eqs. (7-7) to (7-10) leads to the value of the fourth parameter. During the past few years the careful measurement of the Q values of reactions involving light nuclei has made it possible to assign mass values to all known light atoms without recourse to any mass-spectroscopic data. This has been accomplished by the investigation of various reaction chains which link light nuclei to the standard O^{16} (see Fig. 7-1). Thus experimental Q values not only allow a valuable independent check on mass-spectroscopic measurements but also provide the only available method for measuring the masses of many of the unstable nuclides created during nuclear reactions.

Several simple relations existing between reaction energies and particle binding energies are worth noting. For example, using Eq. (2-77), the Q value of a reaction may be written in the form

$$Q = (M + m - M^*) - (M' + m' - M^*) = B_x(X^*) - B_{x'}(X^*) \quad (7\text{-}11)$$

A reaction, therefore, is exoergic (endoergic) if the initial particle is more strongly (less strongly) bound in the compound nucleus than the ejected particle is.

Particle binding energies are intimately related to the Q values of the (γ,x') or (x,γ) reactions. From the definition of particle binding energies we have

$$B_{x'}(X) = M' + m' - M = -Q[X(\gamma,x')X'] \quad (7\text{-}12)$$

Similarly

$$B_x(X') = M + m - M' = Q[X(x,\gamma)X'] \quad (7\text{-}13)$$

The Q value of a (γ,x') reaction is also the Q value of the decay process

$$X \rightarrow X' + x'$$

When a reaction leads to a beta-unstable residual, Eq. (7-8) may be replaced by

$$Q = \delta + \Delta - \delta' - \Delta'_{da} - Q_\beta \quad (7\text{-}14)$$

where Δ'_{da} is the mass decrement of the daughter of the residual nucleus and Q_β is the Q value of this decay. If the daughter is also unstable, Δ'_{da} may be replaced by the mass defect of its daughter plus the Q value of the second beta decay. In this way all Q values may be related to the mass decrements of beta-stable nuclides and the beta-decay Q values. A list of mass decrements of beta-stable nuclides and beta-decay Q values is contained in Appendix I. Beta-decay energies are given in the table of Hollander, Perlman, and Seaborg (Ref. 5, Chap. 6) and on the General Electric chart of the Nuclides (Ref. 4, Chap. 6).

Particle binding energies or Q values can often be related to the Q values of two or more reactions. Thus we may write

$$\begin{aligned} B_x(X') &= M + m - M' + m' - m' + m'' - m'' \\ &= M + m'' - M' - m' + m' + m - m'' \\ &= Q[X(x'',x')X'] + Q[x'(x,\gamma)x''] \\ &= Q[X(x'',x')X'] + B_x(x'') \end{aligned} \tag{7-15}$$

For example

$$\begin{aligned} B_n(X') &= Q[X(d,p)X'] + Q[p(n,\gamma)d] \\ &= Q[X(d,p)X'] + B_n(d) \end{aligned} \tag{7-16}$$

7-3. Energetics of Reactions. The analysis of the dynamical nuclear energies involved in reactions is most conveniently carried out if we make

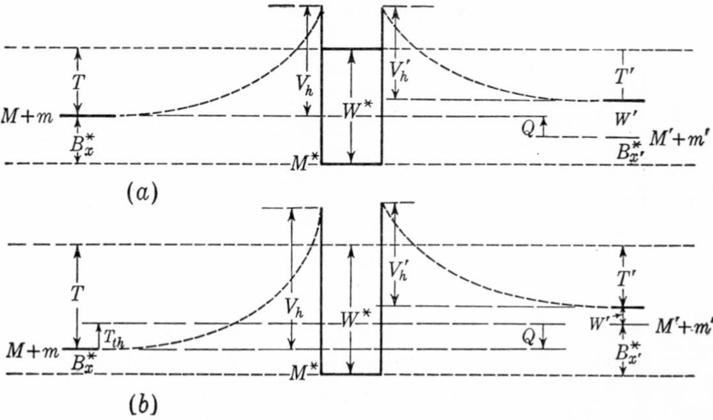

FIG. 7-2. Energy relationships in (a) an exoergic reaction, (b) an endoergic reaction.

use of the center-of-mass coordinate system. At the conclusion of the analysis we may convert to the laboratory coordinate system to relate the quantities in the equations to the experimental observations. In the center-of-mass system the conservation-of-energy principle for a nuclear reaction yields (all quantities are in identical energy or mass units)

$$M + m + T = M^* + W^* = M' + m' + T' + W' \tag{7-17}$$

where T is the total kinetic energy of the incident and target particles, T' is the total kinetic energy of the ejected and residual particles, and W^* and W' are the excitation energies of the compound and residual nucleus (x, x', and X are in their ground states in almost all experimental situations). If we subtract M^* from all terms, we get

$$B_x(X^*) + T = W^* = B_{x'}(X^*) + T' + W' \tag{7-18}$$

We indicate in Fig. 7-2a the energy relationships given by Eq. (7-18) as well as the Q value for an exoergic reaction. In Fig. 7-2b we indicate these relationships for an endoergic reaction. We also show schematically on these diagrams the coulomb barrier between the incident and target nucleus and the coulomb barrier between the ejected particle and product nucleus. The heights of these barriers are given approximately by

$$V_h = \frac{zZe^2}{bA^{\frac{1}{3}} + r_x} \tag{7-19}$$

and

$$V'_h = \frac{z'Z'e^2}{bA'^{\frac{1}{3}} + r_{x'}} \tag{7-20}$$

where r_x and $r_{x'}$ are the radii of the incident and ejected particles. These energy barriers against the inward or outward penetration of charged particles run from about 5 to 30 Mev for alpha particles and He^3, and from 2.5 to 15 Mev for protons, deuterons, and tritons.

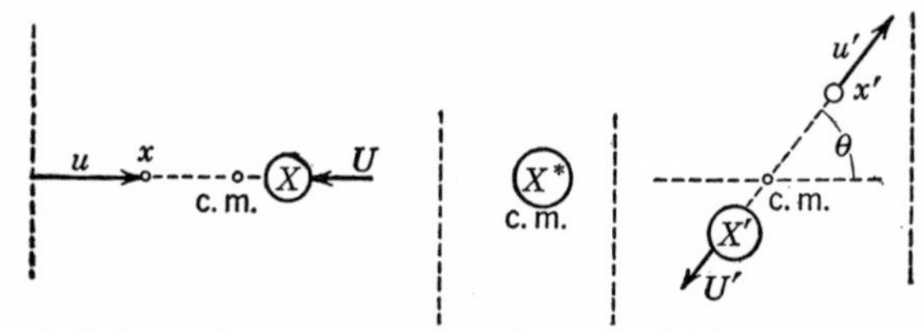

FIG. 7-3. Diagram showing the three stages of a nuclear reaction as viewed in the center-of-mass system.

In view of these barriers we might expect that nuclear processes induced by charged particles could not take place unless the kinetic energies of the charged particles are greater than the heights of these barriers. However, experiments indicate that here also particles may "tunnel" through potential barriers.

According to Eqs. (7-7) and (7-17) the Q value of a reaction is given by

$$Q = -T + T' + W' \tag{7-21}$$

which may be written as

$$Q' = Q - W' = T' - T \tag{7-22}$$

where Q' will be called the experimental Q value. To obtain the experimental Q value, we must therefore determine the total kinetic energies of the initial and final particles in the center-of-mass system.

These quantities may be related to the kinetic energies T_x and $T_{x'}$ of the incident and ejected particles in the laboratory system. Let us denote the magnitude, in the center-of-mass system, of the velocities of the incident, target, ejected, and residual nuclei by the letters u, U, u', and U', respectively (see Fig. 7-3). Using nonrelativistic dynamics and accepting the fact that the total momentum in the center-of-mass system vanishes, we have

$$mu = MU \tag{7-23}$$

and

$$m'u' = M'U' \tag{7-24}$$

Consequently we find

$$T = \frac{1}{2}mu^2 + \frac{1}{2}MU^2 = \frac{1}{2}mu^2\left(1 + \frac{m}{M}\right) \tag{7-25}$$

and

$$T' = \frac{1}{2}m'u'^2 + \frac{1}{2}M'U'^2 = \frac{1}{2}m'u'^2\left(1 + \frac{m'}{M'}\right) \tag{7-26}$$

Having eliminated the velocities of the target and residual nuclei, we must now express u and u' in terms of the velocities v and v' of the incident and ejected particle in the laboratory system, or in terms of

$$T_x = \tfrac{1}{2}mv^2 \tag{7-27}$$

and

$$T_{x'} = \tfrac{1}{2}m'v'^2 \tag{7-28}$$

the corresponding kinetic energies in the laboratory system. Ignoring the thermal motion of the target nucleus, we may accept the laboratory system as fixed to X. The center-of-mass coordinate system, which is fixed to X^*, therefore moves to the right with the velocity U. The Galilean law of addition of velocities thus gives

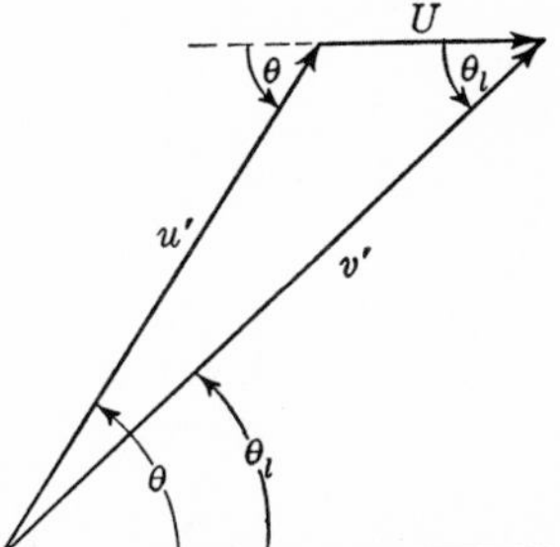

FIG. 7-4. Diagram showing the angular relationships between the velocity vectors involved in a nuclear reaction.

$$u = v - U \tag{7-29}$$

Using this in conjunction with Eq. (7-23), we readily find that

$$u = \frac{M}{M + m}v \tag{7-30}$$

and

$$U = \frac{m}{M + m}v \tag{7-31}$$

Using Eq. (7-30) with Eq. (7-25), we obtain finally

$$T = \frac{mM}{M + m}\frac{v^2}{2} = \frac{1}{2}m_r v^2 = \frac{T_x}{1 + (m/M)} = \frac{T_x}{1 + (a/A)} \tag{7-32}$$

where the last form is an approximation obtained by replacing the masses by the mass numbers.

The elimination of u' requires a vector subtraction of velocities. In Fig. 7-4 we indicate the relation between the velocity vectors and the angles θ and θ_l of the ejected particle in the center-of-mass system and the laboratory system, respectively. The law of cosines gives

$$u'^2 = v'^2 + U^2 - 2v'U \cos \theta_l \tag{7-33}$$

Using Eqs. (7-26), (7-28), (7-31), and (7-33), we find for the total kinetic energy of the ejected and residual nucleus in the center-of-mass system

$$T' = T_{x'}\left(1 + \frac{m'}{M'}\right) + T_x \frac{m'm}{M'} \frac{M' + m'}{(M + m)^2} - \frac{2(mT_x m'T_{x'})^{\frac{1}{2}}}{M'} \frac{M' + m'}{M + m} \cos \theta_l \tag{7-34}$$

or

$$T' = T_{x'}\left(1 + \frac{a'}{A'}\right) + \frac{aa'}{(A + a)A'} T_x - \frac{2(aa'T_xT_{x'})^{\frac{1}{2}}}{A'} \cos \theta_l \tag{7-35}$$

where the last form is a good approximation obtained by replacing the masses by the mass numbers and by using Eq. (7-4). By combining Eqs. (7-22), (7-32), and either (7-34) or (7-35), we obtain the experimental Q value $Q' = Q - W'$ in terms of the kinetic energies of the incident and ejected particles and the angle of the ejected particle with respect to the beam, all relative to the laboratory system. In the case using the approximation (7-35), we obtain

$$Q' = T_{x'}\left(1 + \frac{a'}{A'}\right) - T_x\left(1 - \frac{a}{A'}\right) - \frac{2(aa'T_xT_{x'})^{\frac{1}{2}}}{A'} \cos \theta_l \tag{7-36}$$

In recent precision work these kinetic energies are determined by the use of electrostatic or magnetic analyzers. When a thick target is used, corrections must be made for the loss of energy in penetrating the target material.

The Q value of an endoergic reaction is sometimes determined by measuring the kinetic energy of the incident particle which is needed to barely induce this reaction. This threshold is found by extrapolating the curve of yield vs. T_x to zero. Let us examine Eq. (7-21) for the case when W' is zero and for an initial T well above threshold. As we decrease T_x or T, obviously T' also decreases. At the threshold, T' is zero, and consequently

$$Q = -T_{th} = -\frac{T_{x,th}}{1 + (a/A)} \tag{7-37}$$

The inverse of Eq. (7-36) is sometimes applied to the problem of securing particles with precisely defined kinetic energies either when the energies are outside the range of the accelerator or, as in the case of neutrons, when the particle cannot be accelerated. Assuming that the Q value of a reaction is known (let $W' = 0$), we can solve Eq. (7-36) to obtain the kinetic energy of the ejected particle at any angle in the laboratory system and for any incident energy. The result is

$$T_{x'} = \left\{ \frac{(aa'T_x)^{\frac{1}{2}}}{A + a} \cos \theta_l \pm \left[\left(\frac{A' - a}{A + a} + \frac{aa'}{(A + a)^2} \cos^2 \theta_l \right) T_x + \frac{A'}{A + a} Q \right]^{\frac{1}{2}} \right\}^2 \tag{7-38}$$

Accordingly we may vary the kinetic energy $T_{x'}$ by varying T_x or by selecting particles ejected at various angles.

7-4. Excited States in Nuclear Reactions. Two excitation energies, W^* referring to the compound nucleus and W' referring to the residual nucleus, have appeared in our discussion of the energetics of nuclear reactions. We might expect, therefore, to use the data obtained in nuclear reactions to infer information about nuclear energy levels. The fact that experimental Q values depend upon W' is utilized in the most precise method for finding the low-lying energy states of nuclei. Thus in many reactions induced by monoergic incident particles, the ejected particles are found to have a discrete spectrum of kinetic energies. Using the equations developed in the preceding section, we may assign an experimental Q value (Q_i') to each kinetic-energy group. The largest Q value almost always corresponds to the reaction which leaves the product in the ground state, and consequently it gives the Q of the reaction. From the set of Q values or kinetic energies we may therefore compute the energy levels of the product by

$$W_i' = Q - Q_i' = Q + T - T_i' \tag{7-39}$$

In Fig. 7-5 we show the proton groups which have been observed in the $Al^{27}(d,p)Al^{28}$ reaction, and in Fig. 7-6 we give the energy levels of Al^{28} which are calculated from these groups.

According to Eq. (7-18) the excitation energy of the compound nucleus may take any of a continuous range of values from $B_x(X^*)$ upward depending upon T, which is controlled by the experimenter [Eq. (7-32)]. In Table 7-1 we indicate approximate values of B_x in Mev for the light

TABLE 7-1. APPROXIMATE BINDING ENERGIES OF LIGHT NUCLEAR PARTICLES (IN MEV)

A^*	n	p	d	t	χ	α
25	9.8	9.0	16.5	20.0	20.0	9.2
100	8.4	7.5	13.7	15.8	15.8	3.6
200	6.5	5.7	10 0	10.3	10.2	−3.8

nuclear particles in light, medium, and heavy nuclides. These rough estimates are based upon empirical considerations which we shall discuss

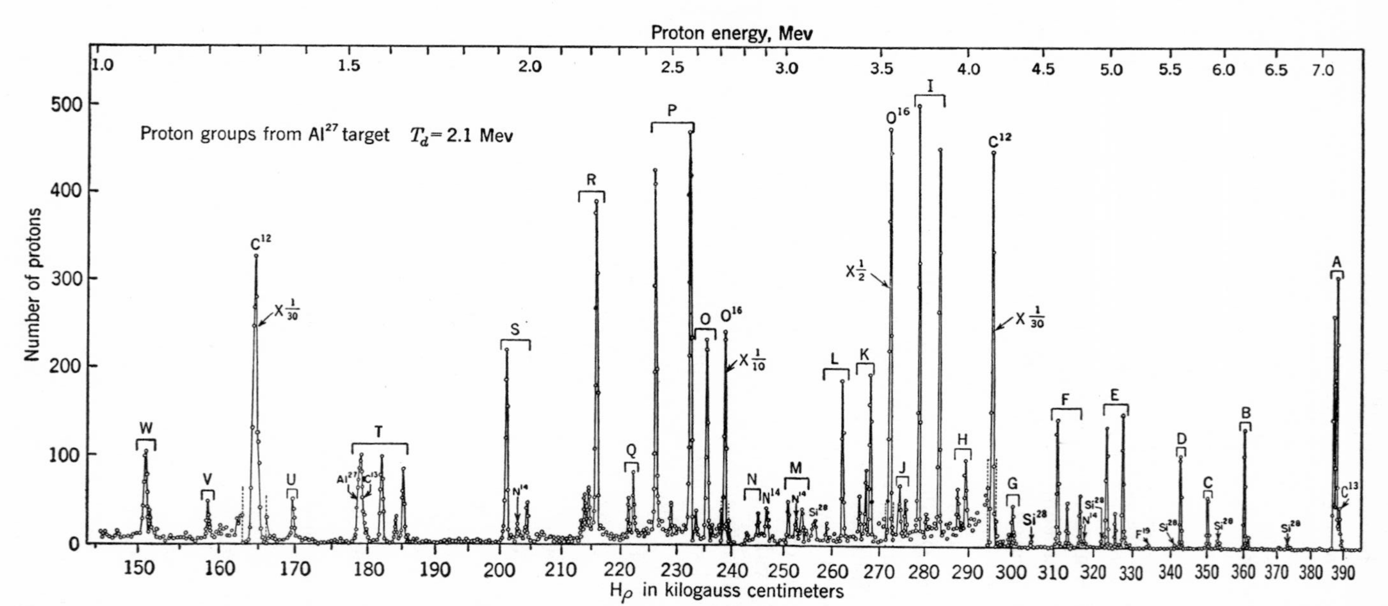

FIG. 7-5. Proton groups at 90° from the $Al^{27}(d,p)Al^{28}$ reaction as observed by Enge, Buechner, and Sperduto (Ref. 7) using 2.1-Mev deuterons obtained from the original Van de Graaff accelerator. A magnetic analyzer was used for the measurement of proton energies. Proton groups from reactions with other nuclei in the target are identified on the figure.

in Chap. 8. It should be apparent that, with the exception of excitation by alpha-particle capture in heavy nuclides, the compound nucleus formed in the first step of a reaction always has a large excitation energy. The characteristic energy levels W_i^* of the compound nucleus which lie above $B_x(X^*)$ are revealed by the resonances in the relative yield of the reaction for a fixed incident flux. These are noted at critical values of the incident-particle kinetic energy (T_x) when the energy spread of the incident beam is small. The critical laboratory kinetic energies (T_{xi}) correspond to critical total kinetic energies (T_i) in the center-of-mass system which satisfy

$$\frac{T_{xi}}{1 + (m/M)} = T_i = W_i^* - B_x(X^*) \qquad (7\text{-}40)$$

In Fig. 7-7 we show a yield curve for the $C^{13}(p,n)N^{13}$ reaction which shows a resonance structure associated with the levels of N^{14} above $B_p(N^{14}) = 7.542$ Mev.

As a single comprehensive illustration of our discussion of excited states in nuclear reactions, let us consider all the bombardment reactions which will yield information concerning the excited states of ${}_7N^{14}$. In Table 7-2 we list the incident and target nuclides which produce ${}_7N^{14}$ as a compound nucleus and the binding energies of the various incident particles in ${}_7N^{14}$. In Table 7-3 we list the neutron-, proton-, and alpha-yielding reactions which lead to ${}_7N^{14}$ as the residual nucleus, together with the Q values of these reactions. In the reactions represented in Tables 7-2 and 7-3 we may dismiss all those for which the target nuclide is radioactive with a short half-life, since these cannot serve as a target in a practical experiment.

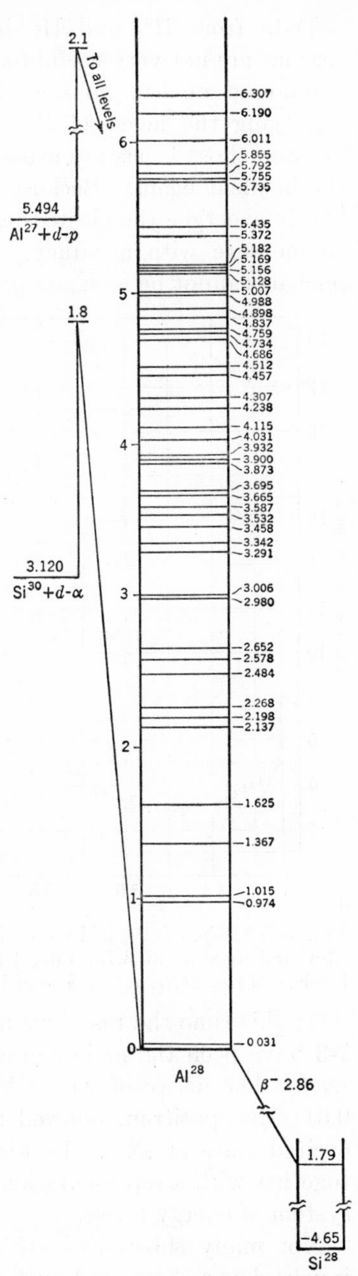

FIG. 7-6. Energy levels of Al^{28} inferred from proton groups in Fig. 7-5. (*From Enge, Buechner, and Sperduto, Ref.* 7.)

Data from H^3- and He^3-induced reactions are sparse and for two reasons are not very useful for energy-level work. H^3 and He^3 bring the compound nucleus to such high states of excitation that resonances signifying the levels of the compound nucleus are difficult to detect because those levels are usually spaced closer than the energy spread of the incident beam. Because H^3- and He^3-induced reactions are usually highly exoergic, the ejected-particle energies are large and hence difficult to measure with accuracy, so that the energy levels of the residual nucleus cannot be assigned precisely.

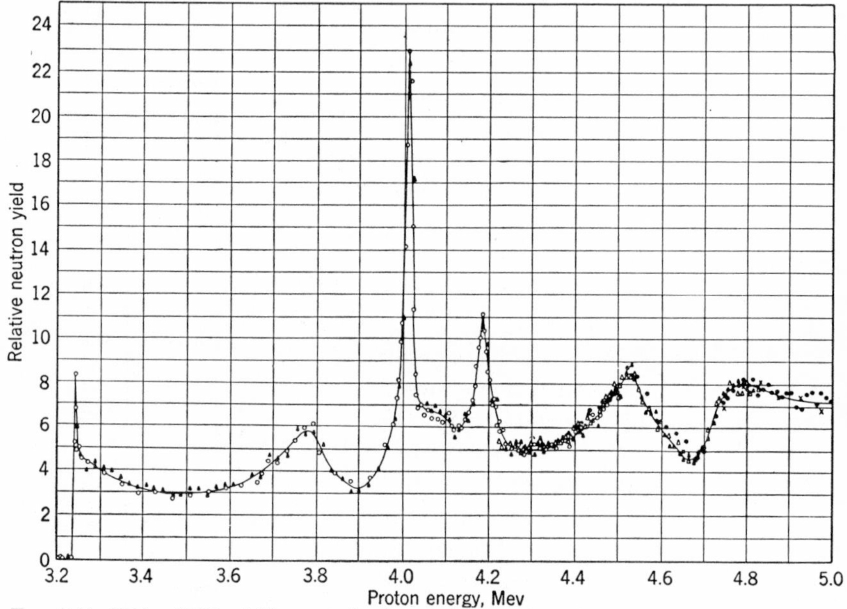

FIG. 7-7. $C^{13}(p,n)N^{13}$ yield curve in forward direction showing threshold at 3.236 Mev and maxima at 3.78, 4.01, 4.10, 4.18, 4.52, and 4.8 Mev corresponding to N^{14} levels. (*From Bair, Kington, and Willard, Ref.* 8.)

At this time the reactions marked with daggers (†) in Tables 7-2 and 7-3 have been the main source of data concerning the excited states of $_7N^{14}$. The decay of $_8O^{14}$, which proceeds by the emission of a (1.8 ± 0.01)-Mev positron followed by a 2.3-Mev γ ray, indicates a 2.3-Mev excited state of $_7N^{14}$. In Fig. 7-8 we show the known levels of $_7N^{14}$, together with a representation of the reaction data which has led to this system of energy levels.

Not many substances are as fortunately situated as $_7N^{14}$ in being involved as a compound nucleus or a residual nucleus in so many observable nuclear reactions. A variety of considerations restrict the usefulness of particular nuclear reactions in energy-level studies. To study the levels of the compound nucleus, we must be able to determine the incident-particle kinetic energies with considerable accuracy, and we must be able to measure variations in the yield of the outgoing particle or the quantity of residual nuclides formed. To study the levels of residual nuclei, we must be able to measure precisely the kinetic energies of both the incident and ejected particles. In this latter connection gamma- and neutron-yielding reactions and highly exoergic reactions have only limited usefulness.

TABLE 7-2. INCIDENT AND TARGET NUCLIDES WHICH PRODUCE $_7N^{14}$ AS COMPOUND NUCLEUS

Incident	n	p†	d†	t	χ	α†
Target	$_7N^{13}$	$_6C^{13}$	$_6C^{12}$	$_6C^{11}$	$_5B^{11}$	$_5B^{10}$
$B_x(_7N^{14})$, Mev	10.545	7.542	10.264	22.718	20.720	11.613
Activity of target	10 m β^+	Stable	Stable	20 m β^+	Stable	Stable

TABLE 7-3. REACTIONS WHICH LEAD TO $_7N^{14}$ AS THE RESIDUAL

Reaction	$_7N^{14}(n,n)$	$_6C^{14}(p,n)$	$_6C^{13}(d,n)$†	$_6C^{12}(t,n)$	$_5B^{12}(\chi,n)$	$_5B^{11}(\alpha,n)$†
Q, Mev	0	−0.627	5.317	4.007	17.359	0.1538
Activity of target	Stable	5580 y	Stable	Stable	0.027 s β^-	Stable
Reaction	$_8O^{14}(n,p)$	$_7N^{14}(p,p)$†	$_7N^{13}(d,p)$	$_7N^{12}(t,p)$	$_6C^{12}(\chi,p)$	$_6C^{11}(\alpha,p)$
Q, Mev	....	0	8.320	....	4.771	2.916
Activity of target	76 s β^+	Stable	10 m β^+	0.013 s β^+	Stable	20 m β^+
Reaction	$_9F^{17}(n,\alpha)$	$_8O^{17}(p,\alpha)$	$_8O^{16}(d,\alpha)$†	$_8O^{15}(t,\alpha)$	$_7N^{15}(\chi,\alpha)$	$_7N^{14}(\alpha,\alpha)$†
Q, Mev	4.729	1.198	3.116	12.456	9.732	0
Activity of target	70 s β^+	Stable	Stable	2.1 m β^+	Stable	Stable

† Reactions marked with dagger have been the main source of data on excited states of $_7N^{14}$.

In principle, the most direct method of measuring the energy levels by bombardment reactions is to use gamma rays for the incident particle. In this case $B_x(X^*) = 0$, and the initial and compound nuclei are the same. Presumably, the low-lying levels associated with a target material might be explored by scanning the yield of the (γ,γ') reaction as a function of the incident gamma-ray energy or by measuring the ejected gamma-ray groups. However such observations are rendered exceedingly difficult by our inability to produce highly monochromatic gamma rays or to measure the energies of highly monochromatic gamma rays and by the fact that the strong gamma-ray interactions with atomic electrons generally mask the nuclear interactions. Recent successful attempts [25–27] in this direction using several ingenious techniques have been confined to the study of a few isolated low-lying levels.

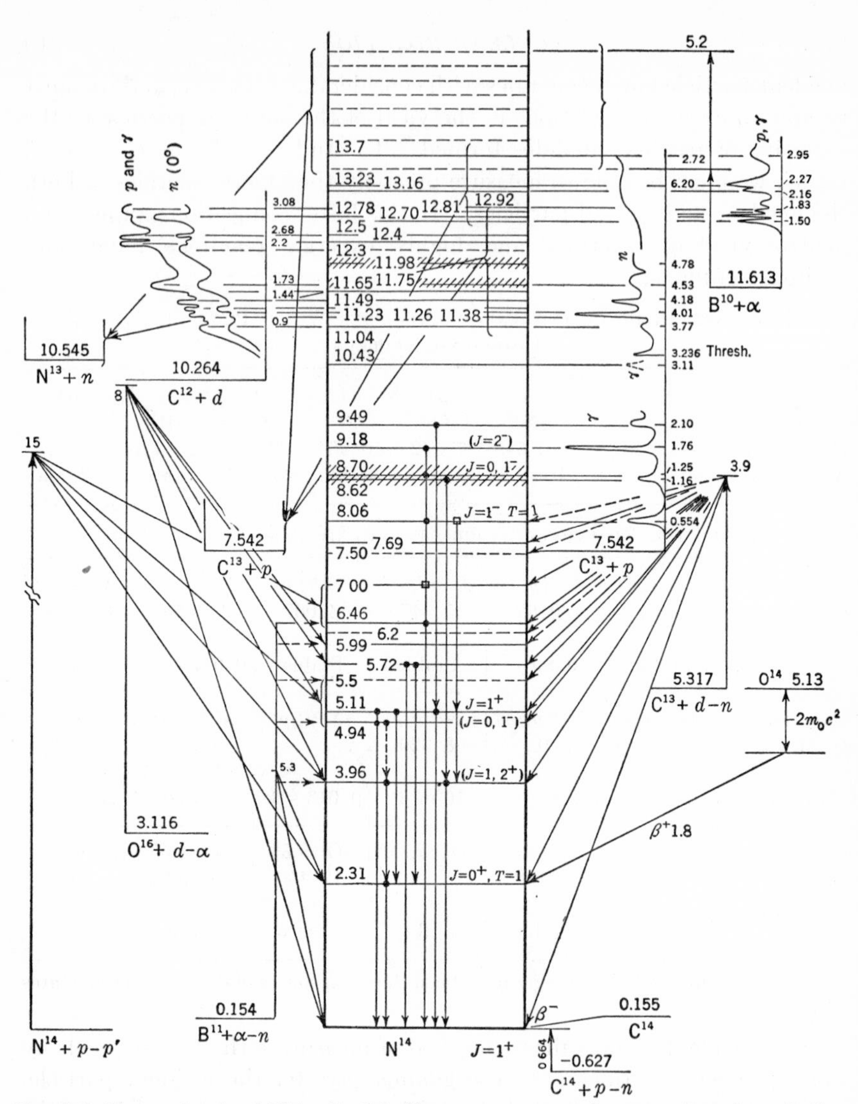

FIG. 7-8. Energy levels of N^{14}. In this diagram, energy values are plotted vertically in Mev, based on the ground state as zero. Uncertain levels or transitions are indicated by dashed lines; levels which are known to be particularly broad are cross-hatched. For reactions in which N^{14} is the compound nucleus, thin-target excitation functions are shown schematically (where known), with the yield plotted horizontally and the bombarding energy vertically. Bombarding energies are indicated in laboratory coordinates and plotted to scale in center-of-mass coordinates. Values of total angular momentum J and parity (see Chap. 12) which appear to be reasonably well established are indicated on the levels; less certain assignments are enclosed in parentheses. Excited states of the residual nuclei involved in these reactions have generally not been shown; where transitions to such excited states are known to occur, a brace has been used to suggest reference to another diagram.

For reactions in which the present nucleus occurs as a residual product, excitation functions have not been shown; a vertical arrow with a number indicating some bombarding energy—usually the highest—at which the reaction has been studied, is used instead. (*From Ajzenberg and Lauritsen, Ref.* 9.)

Closely related to the excitation of nuclear energy levels by gamma rays is the recently discovered phenomenon[28,29] of electric excitation of nuclear levels by charged nuclear particles. This is an inelastic scattering process induced by protons, alpha particles, etc., which may be interpreted roughly as one in which the electric pulse caused by the passage of a charged nuclear particle induces a transition of the target nucleus from its ground state to low-lying excited states. The gamma rays emitted in the return to the ground state then give directly the energy levels of the target nucleus. More detailed theoretical explanations of the coulomb excitation process have been given[30,31]. These suggest that the direction of the gamma-ray quanta is correlated with the direction of the incident particles and the scattering angle of the exciting projectile. This technique promises to be a useful one for determining the energies of low-lying levels and for classifying these states.[32]

The high-lying levels of target nuclei might be explored by noting the yields in reactions of the (γ,x) type, where x is the proton, neutron, or alpha particle. These reactions are possible when the gamma-ray energies go above the (γ,x) thresholds, which roughly conform to the values indicated in Table 7-1 [see Eq. (7-18)]. Here again, the lack of continuously variable monoergic sources of gamma rays has hindered such work. Despite this, scientists at the University of Saskatchewan[10] and the National Bureau of Standards[11] have recently succeeded in detecting such sharp resonances with betatron gamma rays. Certain broad resonances at higher gamma-ray energies have been noted in (γ,n) and (γ,p) reactions, but their interpretation is quite different from that given in this discussion (see Sec. 13-15).

7-5. Nuclear-reaction Cross Sections. The relative yield of ejected particles for a given incident flux is influenced by certain external factors such as the physical form of the target material and the target thickness. It is therefore desirable to define concepts which are independent of these external factors and are a measure of the tendency of a nucleus to undergo nuclear reactions. For this purpose it is useful to define the total cross section of nuclides as the effective area presented by the nucleus to the beam. Essentially we assign to each nucleus an equivalent fictitious disk, whose face is perpendicular to the beam and whose area is such that the total number of particles which would fall on the fictitious disk if the incident particles maintained their original trajectories is equal to the total number actually removed from the beam as a result of nuclear collisions (see Fig. 7-9).

The number of scatterers presented to a beam by a thin target is

$$N_s = \frac{N_A \rho S \, \Delta x}{M} \tag{7-41}$$

where N_A is Avogadro's number, S the area of the beam, Δx the thickness, ρ the density, and M the gram-atomic weight of the target material. Defining the beam intensity I as the number of particles crossing a unit area per unit time, we make the fundamental assumption that the change of intensity due to the thin layer is related to the original intensity simply as the effective area presented by all the scatterers is to the total area of the beam. Accordingly we take as the definition of the total cross section σ of a single nucleus

$$\frac{\Delta I}{I} = \frac{-\sigma N_s}{S} = \frac{-\sigma N_A \rho}{M} \Delta x = -\sigma \eta \, \Delta x = -\mu \, \Delta x \tag{7-42}$$

where η is the number of target nuclei per unit volume. The product $\mu = \sigma\eta$ is called the linear absorption coefficient. The product $\rho \, \Delta x$

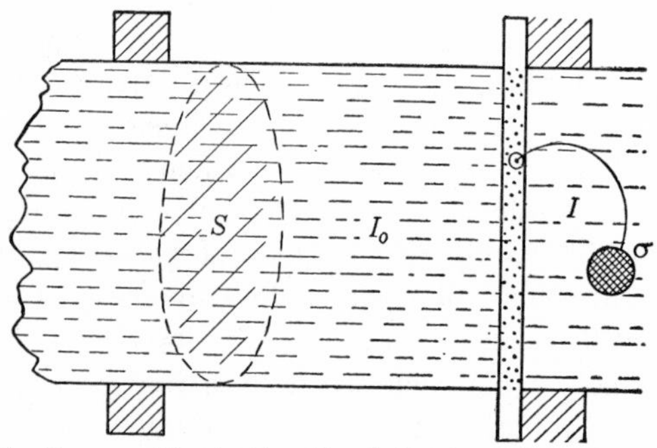

FIG. 7-9. Schematic diagram illustrating the definition of total cross section in terms of the reduction of intensity caused by a thin target. Insert shows schematically a microscopic view of the effective disk presented by an atom.

measured in milligrams per square centimeter is sometimes called the "thickness" of the target. A convenient unit for nuclear cross sections is 10^{-24} cm^2, which is called a barn.

In principle, to obtain an experimental cross section for particles of a given energy, it is necessary to measure only the fractional change in the intensity of a monoenergetic beam caused by a thin layer of known thickness. We use a thin layer to minimize the error due to the overlapping of the "shadows" caused by different scatterers (*i.e.*, to ensure that each incident particle participates in no more than one nuclear collision) and also to minimize the loss of energy of the incident particles in the target. This last consideration is particularly important when the incident particles are charged. Since the change in intensity in a thin target is small, it is often more convenient to measure the loss in intensity by noting the number of nuclear processes occurring per unit time which result in the removal of a particle from the beam. For example, if the removal of one particle from the beam results in the ejection or scattering of the same or another particle at an arbitrary angle with respect to the beam, we may count the number of particles which are scattered or ejected at various angles with respect to the beam and then integrate the distribution. By so doing, we obtain directly $n = -S\,\Delta I$, the total number of particles per unit time removed from the beam. In terms of the total number of scattered or ejected particles the total cross section is given by

$$\sigma = \frac{n}{IN_s} \tag{7-43}$$

If several independent processes occur which can be experimentally distinguished by the nature or energy of the scattered or ejected particles, we may decompose the total cross section into partial cross sections for the various processes. Accordingly we set

$$\sigma = \sigma_1 + \sigma_2 + \cdots = \sum_i \sigma_i \tag{7-44}$$

where the partial cross section for the ith process is

$$\sigma_i = \frac{n_i}{IN_s} \tag{7-45}$$

and n_i is the number of processes or particles of the ith type per unit time.

Experiments indicate that the transmission of neutrons or gamma rays through moderately thick layers of target material obeys quite well a relation which may be deduced immediately if we assume that only single-collision processes take place. It follows from this assumption that the energy of the particles in the beam at any depth x in the material is constant. Treating σ, therefore, as a constant, letting ΔI be a differential, and letting I_0 be equal to the intensity at $x = 0$, we may integrate Eq. (7-42) to obtain

$$I = I_0 \exp(-\sigma\eta x) = I_0 \exp(-\mu x) \tag{7-46}$$

The measurement of the ratio between the intensity transmitted through a known thickness of target material and the original intensity, in conjunction with a determination of η, thus leads to a value for the total cross section. Most measurements of cross sections for neutrons and gamma rays make use of thick targets and are based upon Eq. (7-46).

In order to derive accurate cross sections from the intensity data obtained in such measurements, considerable care must be taken to establish the energy homogeneity of the source, the purity of the absorber, and the efficiency of the detector. Furthermore careful design of the geometry of the apparatus is necessary to minimize the unwanted scattered particles which enter the detector or to make it possible to correct for these particles. In Fig. 7-10 we indicate the arrangement used in

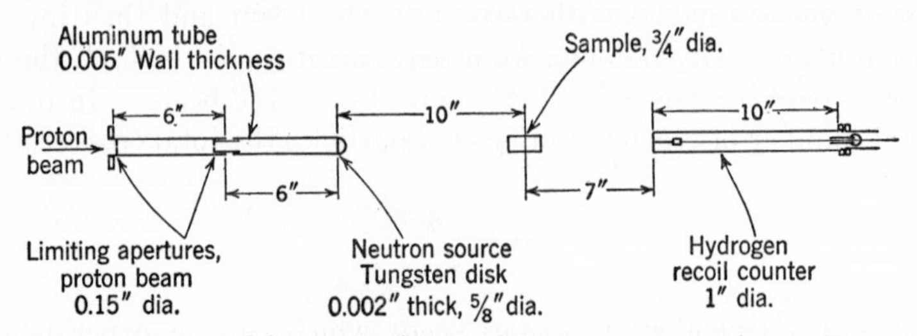

FIG. 7-10. Apparatus used for measuring total neutron cross sections. The counting rate of the detector on the left is measured with and without the scatterer. (*From Barschall, Ref.* 12.)

many neutron-absorption experiments to determine total neutron cross sections. In Fig. 7-11 we indicate a schematic view of the apparatus and collimating system used by Davisson and Evans for the measurement of total gamma cross sections. In this latter case, lead shields and collimators assist materially in reducing the background radiation.

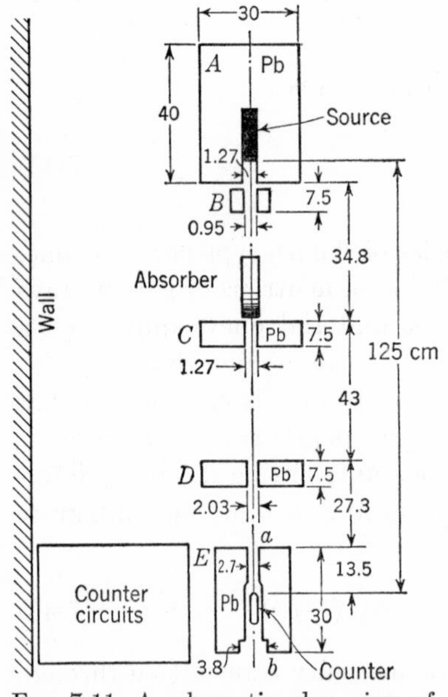

FIG. 7-11. A schematic plan view of a very satisfactory apparatus and collimating system for the measurement of total absorption coefficients. All dimensions are shown in centimeters. (*From Davisson and Evans, Ref.* 13.)

Experimental data are now available[14,15] giving the relationship of neutron cross section vs. energy for various substances for the kinetic-energy range from 0.001 ev to around 20 Mev. The low-energy-neutron data (0.001 to 100 ev) have been obtained by using time-of-flight methods and crystal spectrometers. The data for medium-fast neutrons (10 kev to 3 Mev) have been obtained using neutrons from the $Li^7(p,n)Be^7$, the $C^{12}(d,n)N^{13}$, and the $D(d,n)He^3$ reactions where the incident deuterons or protons are accelerated by an electrostatic generator. By carefully regulating the incident beam, by using a thin target, and by limiting the angle subtended by the target, it has proved practical to limit the energy spread of the neutron beam in this region to as low as 1 kev. To avoid sacrificing intensity, however, a greater energy spread is usually used. The data on very fast neutrons (10 to 20 Mev) have been obtained using neutrons from the $T(p,n)He^3$ and $T(d,n)He^4$ reactions. The energies of the neutrons obtainable from these five reactions at 0° and 180° for various values of the incident-particle energy are shown in Fig. 7-12.

The experimental neutron-cross-section data indicate that there are large fluctuations in the relationships of neutron cross section vs. energy, particularly in the low-energy region and for lighter nuclides. In Fig. 7-13 we give the neutron cross sections for sulfur, which show these large

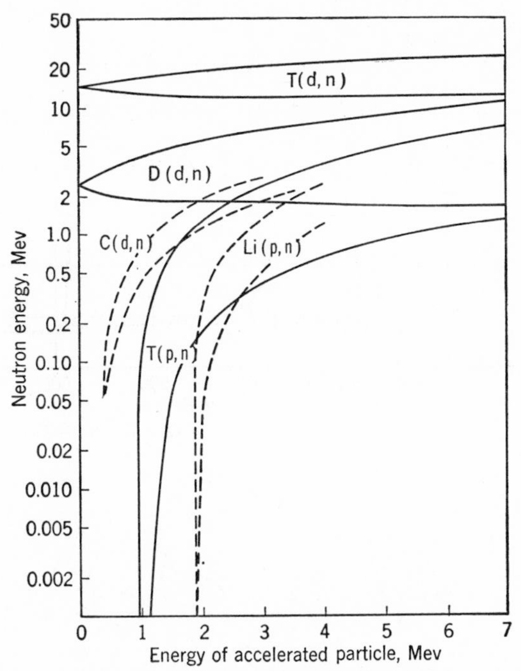

FIG. 7-12. Range of neutron energies obtainable from various sources. The upper and lower curves for each case are for neutrons emitted at 0° and 180° respectively in the laboratory system. (*From Hanson, Taschek, and Williams, Ref.* 16.)

fluctuations or resonances. Certain general statements can be made concerning the spacing of these rapid fluctuations in the neutron cross section of typical nuclides. The resonances in light nuclides ($A < 50$) and in certain special heavy nuclides such as Bi, Pb, and Sn are few and widely spaced in the region below 1 Mev. The spacing, however, decreases very rapidly with increasing A, and for $A > 65$ the spacing is so small that the current data indicate only a continuous variation of cross section with energy. We have already indicated that these resonances are associated with the excited states of the compound nucleus which are formed by neutron capture.

Apart from the resonances there appear to exist certain regularities in total neutron cross sections. These regularities are illustrated in Fig.

7-14. In this figure the nuclear cross sections are given in terms of nuclear areas, which are computed from $R = 1.45A^{\frac{1}{3}} \times 10^{-13}$ cm. The $\sigma(T,A)$ surface reveals that neighboring nuclides show similar variations with energy, but that the shape of the sectional curves changes gradually

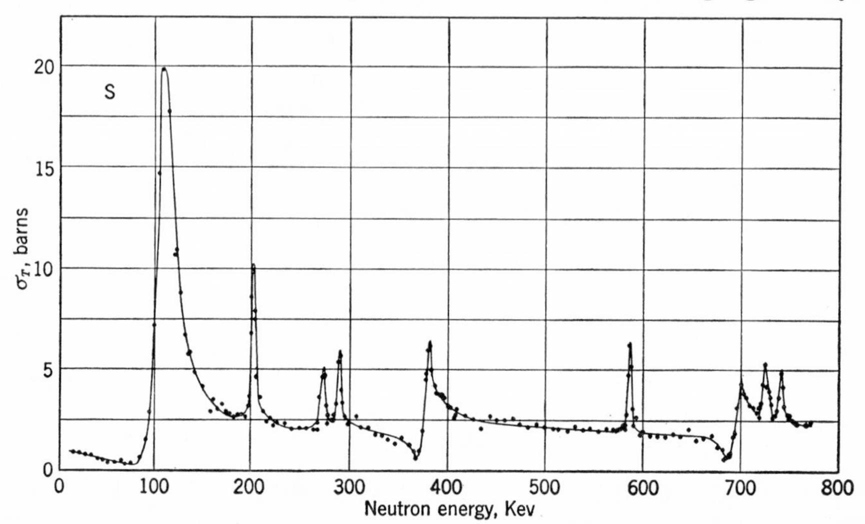

FIG. 7-13. Neutron cross sections of S^{32}. (*From Peterson, Barschall, and Bockelman, Ref.* 17.)

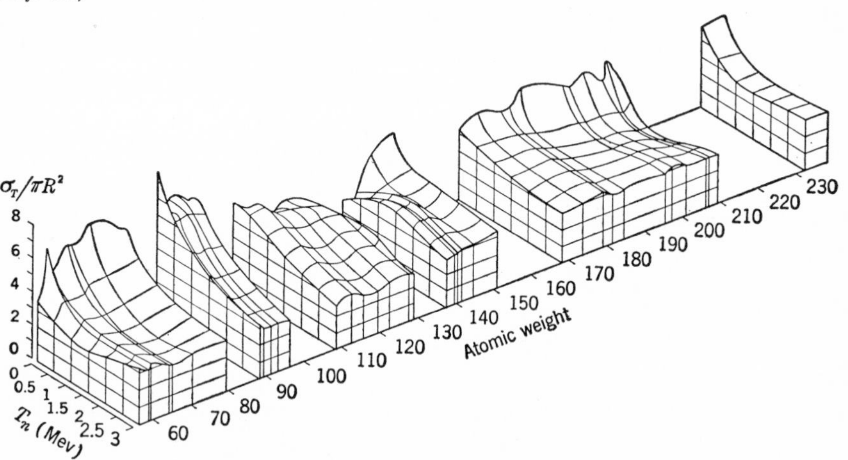

FIG. 7-14. Total neutron cross sections of elements heavier than Mn as a function of neutron energy. The surface is based on measurements for the atomic weights at which straight vertical lines appear in the figure. (*From Barschall, Ref.* 18.)

with A so that nuclides differing greatly in A have cross-section curves which differ quite markedly. An interesting feature of this surface is the fact that the peak cross section, which occurs at low energies for light elements, tends to shift to higher energies for the heavy elements.

As a result of interactions with atomic electrons, charged particles in passing through matter lose energy; hence precise cross-section measurements for protons, deuterons, alpha particles, etc., must be made with relatively thin targets and must be based upon the detection of ejected or scattered particles rather than the minute intensity change upon transmission through the target. Accordingly, the experiment leads directly to the partial cross sections rather than the total cross section.

When the residual nucleus of a reaction induced by charged particles is radioactive, the convenient method of stacked foils is available for measuring the cross section as a function of the energy of the incident particles. In this method the absorber is an assembly of thin layers of a particular type of target material. After exposure to the beam these layers are disassembled, and the disintegration rates of the various layers are determined by means of counters which are sensitive to the disintegration products of the radioactive residuals (usually beta particles). The energy of the incident charged particles available at any layer may be inferred from the range-energy relation for the absorber and the incident particle. The intensity available at each layer may be assumed to be approximately constant as long as the total target thickness is small compared to the mean range of the particles in the target material. It can be shown on the basis of the laws of radioactivity that the relative activities or disintegration rates at a given time after the bombardment are proportional to the original numbers of radioactive products formed in each layer during the bombardment. Since the intensity is the same for each layer, the activities, when plotted against the corresponding energies, give directly the relative cross sections as a function of energy. With careful calibration of the various components in these experiments, it is possible to obtain absolute cross sections by this method as well. If several chemically separable types of radioactive residuals are produced, partial cross sections for the different processes can also be established.

7-6. Differential Cross Section per Unit Solid Angle. Most experiments designed to establish partial cross sections are based upon the measurement of the intensity distribution of ejected or scattered particles from thin targets as a function of the angles θ_l and φ_l (see Fig. 7-15). This distribution may be characterized by a function $\sigma_l(\theta_l,\varphi_l)$, known as the differential cross section per unit solid angle, which is defined by

$$\sigma_l(\theta_l,\varphi_l)\,\Delta\Omega_l = \frac{\Delta n}{IN_s} \tag{7-47}$$

where

$$\Delta\Omega_l = \sin\theta_l\,\Delta\theta_l\,\Delta\varphi_l \tag{7-48}$$

is an element of solid angle and Δn is here the number of ejected or scattered particles per unit time which go into $\Delta\Omega_l$. The solid-angle interval $\Delta\Omega_l$, which is determined by the sensitive area of detector and the distance of the detector (see Fig. 7-15) from the target according to

$$\Delta\Omega_l = \frac{\text{area of window}}{R^2} \tag{7-49}$$

must be small enough so that the change in $\sigma_l(\theta_l,\varphi_l)$ is small over the range of angles subtended by the detector window. Not only is the differential cross section per unit solid angle a useful intermediate concept in the experimental determination of partial cross sections, but in addition it has a direct physical significance in nuclear physics which is becoming more

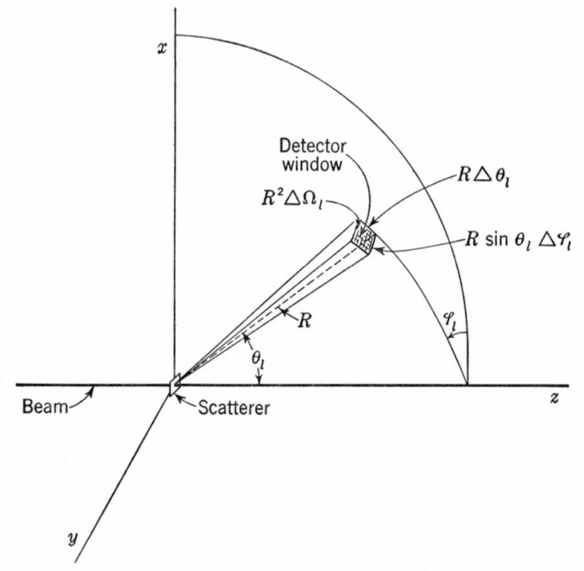

Fig. 7-15. Macroscopic picture of scattering arrangement as viewed in the laboratory system.

and more important as nuclear physics develops. This importance stems from the sensitivity of $\sigma_l(\theta_l,\varphi_l)$ to the nature of nuclear forces. Thus the agreement between experimental and theoretical differential cross sections per unit solid angle for all energies and all nuclei would provide a very convincing "proof" of the theory which yields the theoretical function. In Fig. 7-16 we show a recently published set of differential cross sections. In conjunction with the total cross sections in Fig. 7-14 these results have played an important role as a test for theories of neutron scattering.

The theoretical analysis of collision phenomena is greatly simplified if we use the center-of-mass coordinate system. In this system the total energy of the system, apart from the constant initial rest energy, is the total kinetic energy of the incident particle and the scatterer. In view of Eq. (7-32) we may express this energy as

$$T = \frac{1}{2} m_r v^2 = \frac{p^2}{2m_r} \tag{7-50}$$

where

$$m_r = \frac{Mm}{M + m} \tag{7-51}$$

and by definition

$$p = m_r v \tag{7-52}$$

In effect we have transformed our two-body problem into an equivalent one-body problem in which the center of mass serves as an infinitely

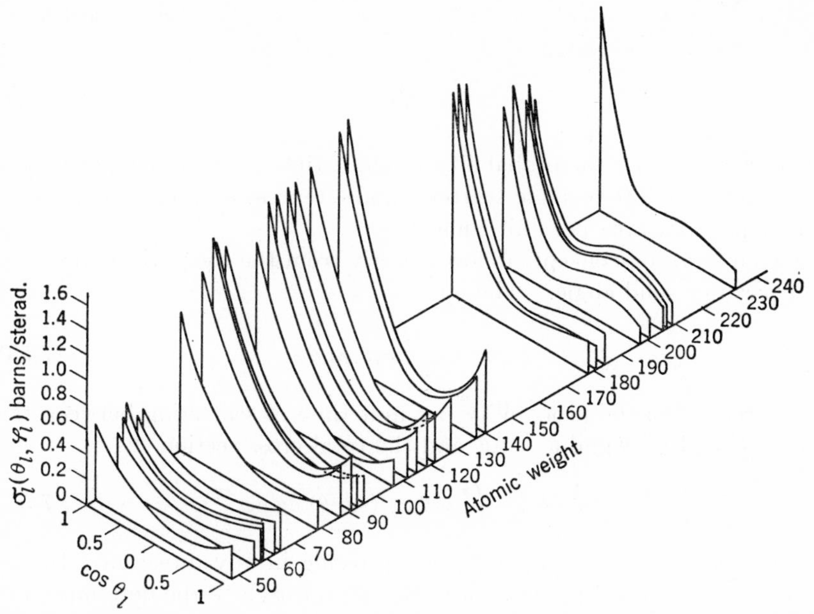

Fig. 7-16. Differential cross section for elastic scattering of 1-Mev neutrons as a function of the cosine of the scattering angle and of atomic weight. (*From Walt and Barschall, Ref.* 24.)

heavy scatterer and the incident particle has the mass m_r and velocity v. If the ejected particle is different from the incident particle or has a different energy (*i.e.*, if a nuclear reaction or inelastic scattering occurs), the final system is equivalent to an infinitely heavy scatterer and a particle with the mass

$$m'_r = \frac{m'M'}{M' + m'} \tag{7-53}$$

and with the kinetic energy

$$T' = \frac{1}{2} m'_r v'^2 = \frac{p'^2}{2m'_r} \tag{7-54}$$

where T' is obtained from Eq. (7-21).

In view of the independence of the different scatterers the ratio $\Delta n/N_s$ in Eq. (7-47) is simply the number of particles per unit time scattered by a single scatterer into the solid angle $\Delta\Omega_l$. Thus in the theoretical derivation of the differential cross section we may pretend that there is only one scatterer in the beam. In order to define a theoretical concept which corresponds to the experimental quantity defined by Eq. (7-47), we must use the basic connection between statistics and probability. According to this connection, when dealing with ratios of large numbers of particles, we may replace numbers of particles by probabilities for a single particle, or numbers per unit time by probabilities per unit time. Consequently we may accept for the basic definition of the theoretical cross section in the center-of-mass system

$$\sigma(\theta,\varphi)\,\Delta\Omega = \frac{w}{\mathcal{I}} \tag{7-55}$$

where w represents the probability per unit time for scattering or transition into $\Delta\Omega$ due to a single scatterer and $\mathcal{I}$ represents the incident probability per unit area per unit time.

Two integrated concepts follow directly from the theoretical cross section per unit solid angle. These are

$$\sigma(\theta) = \int_0^{2\pi} \sigma(\theta,\varphi)\,d\varphi \tag{7-56}$$

which relates to the probability per unit time of scattering between the cones defined by θ and $\theta + \Delta\theta$, and the total cross section

$$\sigma = \int_0^{2\pi}\int_0^{\pi} \sigma(\theta,\varphi)\,(\sin\theta)\,d\theta\,d\varphi \tag{7-57}$$

which relates to the probability of scattering in any direction. In the next section we shall present the classical approach to the determination of elastic-scattering cross sections and the determination of capture cross sections. Our purposes are to illustrate some of the concepts used in the discussion of cross sections and at the same time to furnish a reference from which to view the actual observations and the quantum-mechanical discussion which will be given in Chap. 13.

7-7. Classical Determination of Cross Sections. In the classical treatment we assume that one particle is incident per unit area per unit time, so that we may set $\mathcal{I} = 1$. The probability per unit time w may then be equated to an area, in a plane containing the scatterer which is perpendicular to the beam; all particles whose paths, if undeviated, would intersect this area will be scattered into $\Delta\Omega$. In Fig. 7-17 we indicate a differential area which is subtended by the impact parameters b and $b + \Delta b$ and the radii at the angles ϕ and $\phi + \Delta\phi$. If we can show that all particles whose initial lines of motion intersect this area will go into

angular momentum is conserved. Since energy is also conserved, it is necessary that the final velocity and the outgoing impact parameter be equal to the initial velocity and impact parameter, respectively. Conservation of angular momentum also leads to the relation

$$m_r v_d d = m_r v b \tag{7-64}$$

or

$$v_d = \frac{vb}{d} \tag{7-65}$$

where v_d is the velocity of the particle at D. Conservation of energy implies immediately that

$$\frac{1}{2} m_r v_d^2 + \frac{Zze^2}{d} = \frac{1}{2} m_r v^2 \tag{7-66}$$

Using Eq. (7-64) and dividing through by $m_r v^2/2$, we obtain

$$\frac{b^2}{d^2} + \frac{2k}{d} = 1 \tag{7-67}$$

where

$$k = \frac{Zze^2}{m_r v^2} = \frac{Zze^2}{2T} \tag{7-68}$$

Equation (7-67) may be rewritten in the form

$$d^2 - 2kd - b^2 = 0 \tag{7-69}$$

which leads to

$$d = k + (b^2 + k^2)^{\frac{1}{2}} \tag{7-70}$$

The properties of a hyperbola are such that the triangles OAB and ACD in the figure are identical. Thus the length AB is equal to a. Since

$$c = (b^2 + a^2)^{\frac{1}{2}} \tag{7-71}$$

and since

$$d = a + c = a + (b^2 + a^2)^{\frac{1}{2}} \tag{7-72}$$

we may, in view of Eq. (7-70), infer that

$$k = a \tag{7-73}$$

From the figure we may finally conclude that

$$b = a \cot \frac{\theta}{2} = \frac{Zze^2}{2T} \cot \frac{\theta}{2} \tag{7-74}$$

Accordingly the differential cross section per unit solid angle is

$$\begin{aligned} \sigma(\theta,\varphi) &= \left(\frac{Zze^2}{2T}\right)^2 \frac{\cot \frac{1}{2}\theta \csc^2 \frac{1}{2}\theta}{2 \sin \theta} \\ &= \left(\frac{Zze^2}{4T}\right)^2 \csc^4 \frac{\theta}{2} \end{aligned} \tag{7-75}$$

where we have used Eq. (7-62). This is the well-known result of Rutherford. The experimental verification of this distribution for alpha-particle scattering played an important part in the establishment of the electron-nucleus model of the atom. The observations of deviations from this distribution at high energies and at large angles provided the earliest measure of the nuclear radius.

Upon integration we find that the total cross section corresponding to the above differential cross section is infinite. This infinity suggests that a nucleus effectively presents an infinite area to charged particles. However, this integrated result is not physically significant, since nuclei are actually surrounded by electrons, which screen the coulomb field of the nucleus whenever the charged particle passes at a distance greater than the atomic radius. Thus the high singularity in the differential cross section at $\theta = 0$ does not really exist, and in consequence the total cross section is finite. For the case of low-energy particles the total cross sections are of the order of atomic dimensions.

Let us next consider a hypothetical situation in which two classical particles coalesce when they come in contact. The effective area for such a process might be used to characterize the probability for the formation of a compound nucleus. When the incident particle is neutral, it will be captured whenever the impact parameter is less than $R + r_x$. Equation (7-63) thus represents a classical expression which might be used for the neutron-capture cross section (see Chap. 9). When the incident particle bears the charge ze, the relative motion in the center-of-mass system corresponds to the hyperbolic orbit of the Rutherford scattering case, providing that the distance of closest approach d exceeds $R + r_x$. We may assign a capture cross section for this case by calculating the critical impact parameter b_c which would result in the incident particle just grazing the target (*i.e.*, the case for which $d = R + r_x$). It follows immediately from Eqs. (7-67) and (7-68) that the classical capture cross section in this case is

$$\sigma = \pi b_c^2 = \pi(R + r_x)^2 \left[1 - \frac{Zze^2}{(R + r_x)T}\right] \tag{7-76}$$

This result implies that the capture cross section is finite whenever $T > Zze^2/(R + r_x)$ but that it vanishes whenever $T < Zze^2/(R + r_x)$. Accordingly, Eq. (7-76) confirms our earlier statement that according to classical physics a reaction should not proceed unless the kinetic energy exceeds the coulomb barrier. As we have pointed out, this prohibition is violated by experiment; hence a more realistic description is needed. Such a description will be discussed in Chap. 13.

7-8. Transformation to Laboratory System. Let us assume that a theoretical analysis yields finally the differential and total cross sections in the center-of-mass system. If the time interval of the experiment is fixed, the differential cross section may be defined as the number of particles sent into $\Delta\Omega$ by a single scatterer divided by the number of incident particles per unit area. Since the area of the beam is unchanged and since these numbers are unchanged, the differential and total cross sections are therefore unaffected by the transformation from the center-of-mass system to the laboratory system. However, since the angles of the scattered particles differ in these two systems, the angular transformation alters the differential cross sections per unit solid angle. It is apparent from the triangle in Fig. 7-4 that

$$\tan \theta_l = \frac{u' \sin \theta}{u'(\cos \theta) + U} = \frac{\sin \theta}{(\cos \theta) + \gamma} \qquad \text{and} \qquad \varphi_l = \varphi \tag{7-77}$$

where $\gamma = U/u'$. This ratio can be evaluated in terms of the reaction and excitation energies by using Eqs. (7-31), (7-26), and (7-21). It follows after some algebra that

$$\gamma = \left(\frac{M' + m'}{M + m} \frac{mm'}{MM'} \frac{T}{Q - W' + T}\right)^{\frac{1}{2}} \approx \left(\frac{aa'}{AA'} \frac{T}{Q - W' + T}\right)^{\frac{1}{2}} \tag{7-78}$$

When elastic scattering occurs, γ is simply $m/M \approx a/A$.

Using the fact that the differential cross section is unaltered by the motion of the coordinate system, *i.e.*, that

$$\sigma_l(\theta_l,\varphi_l)\, d\Omega_l = \sigma(\theta,\varphi)\, d\Omega \tag{7-79}$$

where $d\Omega_l$ and $d\Omega$ are the corresponding solid angles, we obtain immediately

$$\frac{\sigma(\theta,\varphi)}{\sigma_l(\theta_l,\varphi_l)} = \frac{\sin \theta_l}{\sin \theta} \frac{d\theta_l}{d\theta} \tag{7-80}$$

To evaluate the factor on the right, let us consider the triangle in Fig. 7-20*a* which is obtained from the similar triangle in Fig. 7-4 by dividing each side by u'. It is apparent from this triangle that

$$\cos \theta_l = \frac{\gamma + \cos \theta}{(1 + \gamma^2 + 2\gamma \cos \theta)^{\frac{1}{2}}} \tag{7-81}$$

Differentiating both sides with respect to θ and dividing the result by $\sin \theta$, we obtain

$$\frac{\sin \theta_l\, d\theta_l}{\sin \theta\, d\theta} = \frac{1 + \gamma \cos \theta}{(1 + \gamma^2 + 2\gamma \cos \theta)^{\frac{3}{2}}} \tag{7-82}$$

When γ is very small ($M \gg m$ for elastic scattering), the differential cross sections per unit solid angle are related by the equation

$$\begin{aligned} \sigma_l(\theta_l,\varphi_l) &= \sigma(\theta,\varphi)(1 + 2\gamma \cos \theta) \\ &= \sigma(\theta_l + \gamma \sin \theta_l,\, \varphi_l)(1 + 2\gamma \cos \theta_l - 2\gamma^2 \sin^2 \theta_l) \end{aligned} \tag{7-83}$$

Thus, even if $\sigma(\theta,\varphi)$ is independent of the angles, as in the case of the collision of elastic spheres, nevertheless $\sigma_l(\theta_l,\varphi_l)$ will vary slightly with the angle θ_l.

An interesting special case occurs when $\gamma = 1$. This case is realized in the important problem of proton-proton scattering and approximately in that of neutron-proton scattering. It can be shown in this case from Eq. (7-77) that $\theta = 2\theta_l$, a relation which is obvious from the fact that the basic triangle (Fig. 7-20*b*) is now an isosceles triangle. The relation

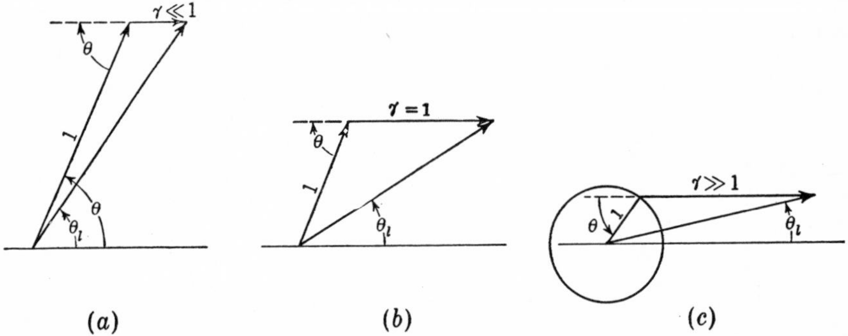

FIG. 7-20. Diagrams illustrating relation between angles in center-of-mass and laboratory coordinate systems (*a*) when $\gamma \ll 1$, (*b*) when $\gamma = 1$, and (*c*) when $\gamma \gg 1$.

between the differential cross sections per unit solid angle is now

$$\begin{aligned}\sigma_l(\theta_l,\varphi_l) &= \sigma(\theta,\varphi)2^{\frac{3}{2}}(1 + \cos\theta)^{\frac{1}{2}} \\ &= 4\sigma(\theta,\varphi)\cos\tfrac{1}{2}\theta \\ &= 4\sigma(2\theta_l,\varphi_l)\cos\theta_l \end{aligned} \tag{7-84}$$

If $\sigma(\theta,\varphi)$ is a constant c, we have

$$\sigma_l(\theta_l,\varphi_l) = 4c\cos\theta_l \tag{7-85}$$

a result which is known as the cosine law.

The case for which $\gamma \gg 1$ is interesting in that the angles of scattering in the laboratory system are restricted. Thus using the diagram for this case (Fig. 7-20*c*), it readily follows that

$$-\text{arc sin}\,\frac{1}{\gamma} \leq \theta_l \leq \text{arc sin}\,\frac{1}{\gamma} \tag{7-86}$$

7-9. Absorption of Gamma Rays. The study of the scattering and absorption of gamma rays belongs primarily to quantum electrodynamics, which is more closely related to fundamental-particle physics than to nuclear physics. However, the nuclear physicist has considerable interest in the results of this study because approximate estimates of the energy of gamma rays resulting from nuclear reactions and radioactive decay can be made by means of absorption measurements and because the design of radiation shields and the solution of radiation-dosage problems depend upon an understanding of the process of absorption. Since the subject also provides several simple illustrations of some of the concepts which we have introduced in this chapter, we shall digress to summarize briefly the important results in this field.

We have indicated that the variation of intensity of monenergetic gamma rays with the thickness of an absorber conforms to the exponential law [Eq. (7-46)]. The total cross section σ must here be identified with the entire atom since the atomic electrons and the nuclear coulomb field play major parts in the absorption of gamma rays. In the gamma-ray energy range of interest to nuclear physics ($\sim$0.1 Mev to 25 Mev) the principal processes which contribute to the total cross section are the photoelectric effect, the Compton effect, and pair production. The photoelectric effect is an inelastic process comparable in some respects to a nuclear reaction, in that the incident particle (gamma ray) is absorbed and another particle (usually a K-shell electron) is ejected, leaving the atom in an excited state. The Compton effect is a type of elastic scattering process, in which the incident gamma ray imparts energy and momentum to an atomic electron, and consequently the scattered photon appears with less energy and momentum (hence a longer wavelength). In the pair-production process, which can occur only when the gamma ray has an energy greater than $2m_ec^2$, the gamma ray, in interacting with the coulomb field of the nucleus, is converted into an electron-positron pair. The excess energy over the threshold energy appears as the kinetic energy of the two particles.

Each of the above three processes results in the removal of gamma rays from a beam; consequently they contribute additively to the experimentally measured total absorption coefficients. In view of this we may decompose the total cross sections into three partial cross sections; *i.e.*, we let

$$\sigma = \sigma_f + \sigma_c + \sigma_p \tag{7-87}$$

where σ_f, σ_c, and σ_p refer to the cross sections for the photoelectric effect, the Compton effect, and pair production, respectively. We may also identify partial cross sections with various photonuclear processes. However, these cross sections are quite small compared to the cross sections discussed above, so that we shall not consider them here (see Chap. 13).

Roughly speaking, for any element the Compton cross section is the largest component in the important region of energies from about 0.5 to 5 Mev, and it decreases slowly as the energy increases. At lower energies the photoelectric cross section predominates, but it falls off rapidly with increasing energy. At very high energies the pair-production cross section predominates, and it increases slowly with energy. The total absorption cross section consequently has a minimum at some intermediate energy. This fact is illustrated in Fig. 7-21, in which we show the experimental mass absorption coefficients in square centimeters per gram as a function of the gamma-ray energy in Mev for various metals. For example, we note that aluminum, copper, and lead are most transparent at about 20, 8, and 2 Mev, respectively. The mass absorption coefficient is defined as

$$\mu_m = \frac{\sigma\eta}{\rho} = \frac{\sigma N_A}{A} \tag{7-88}$$

and is usually used when thickness is expressed as ρx. We note from the experimental results that between 0.5 and 5 Mev the mass absorption coefficient is quite insensitive to the atomic number of the substance.

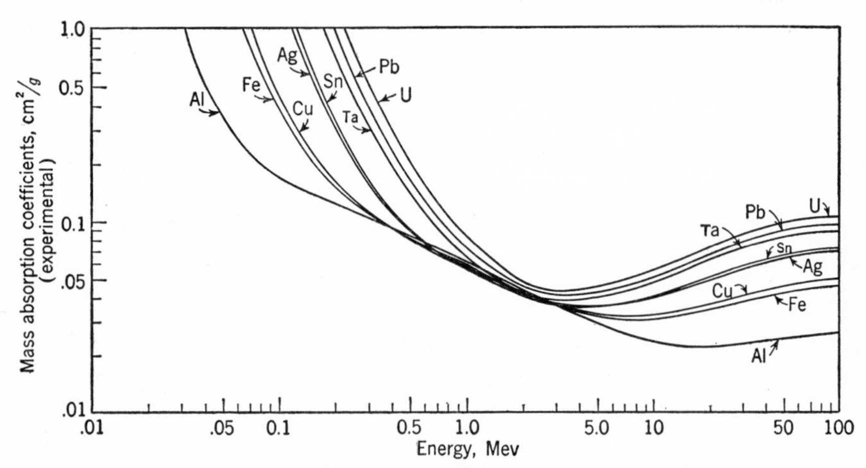

FIG. 7-21. Experimental mass absorption coefficients, in square centimeters per gram, vs. gamma-ray energy for various substances. (*From Snyder and Powell, Ref.* 19.)

The results of theoretical studies based upon quantum electrodynamics[20] and the Dirac theory of the electron indicate that between 0.1 and 25 Mev the total cross section may be placed approximately in the form

$$\sigma = \sigma_e[Z^5\alpha^4 f_f(\zeta,Z) + Zf_c(\zeta) + Z^2\alpha f_p(\zeta,Z)] \tag{7-89}$$

where

$$\sigma_e = \frac{8\pi e^2}{3m_e c^2} = 0.6652 \times 10^{-24}\ \text{cm}^2 \tag{7-90}$$

$$\alpha = \frac{e^2}{\hbar c} = \frac{1}{137.04} \tag{7-91}$$

$$\zeta = \frac{E_\gamma}{m_e c^2} = \frac{h\nu}{m_e c^2} = \frac{\hbar c k}{m_e c^2} \tag{7-92}$$

The constant σ_e is called the classical electron cross section. The dimensionless function $f_c(\zeta)$ depends upon the gamma-ray energy alone, whereas the dimensionless functions $f_f(\zeta,Z)$ and $f_p(\zeta,Z)$ depend primarily upon ζ but have a slight dependence upon Z. In Fig. 7-22 we indicate the general nature of these functions. Analytical representations of these functions are given by Heitler[20] and by Davisson and Evans.[13] Using such representations, we may construct theoretical curves of

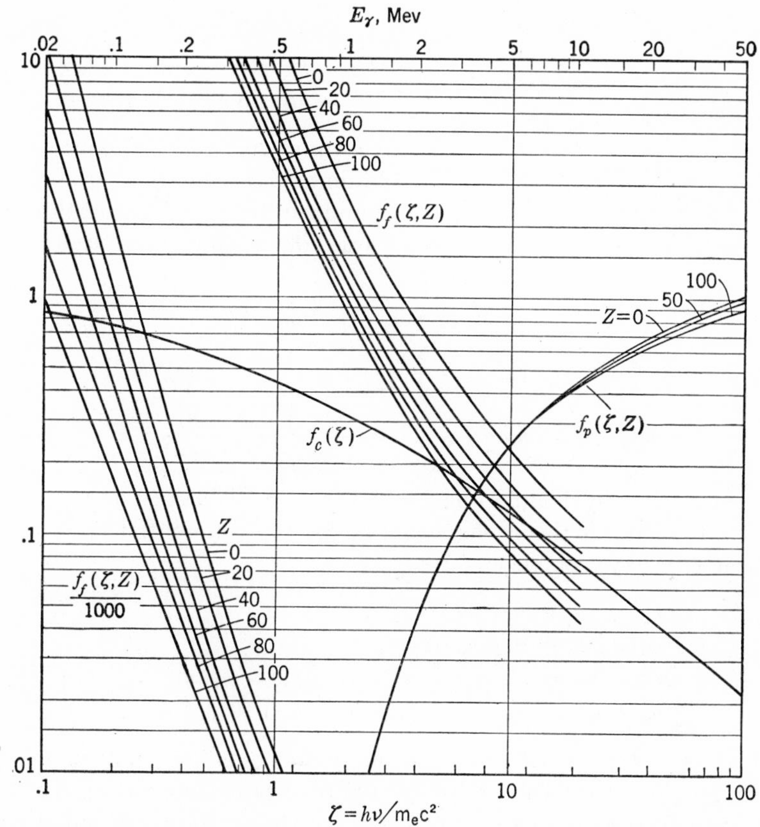

FIG. 7-22. The functions $f_f(\zeta,Z)$, $f_c(\zeta)$, and $f_p(\zeta,Z)$. [*$f_f(\zeta,Z)$ interpolated from data in Davisson and Evans, Ref.* 13; $f_c(\zeta)$ and $f_p(\zeta,Z)$ *from Heitler, Ref.* 20.]

absorption coefficient vs. energy for any elementary or complex substance.

In view of Eq. (7-88) and the fact that the atomic cross sections for the Compton effect depend explicitly upon Z, which is approximately proportional to A, we can readily account for the fact that mass absorption coefficients are almost the same as we go from element to element in the energy region in which the Compton effect predominates.

7-10. Differential Cross Sections for Gamma-ray Absorption. For the Compton effect we may assign a differential cross section which characterizes either the distribution of the scattered photons or the knock on electrons. These distributions are not independent, because the angles of scattering of the photon and electron are directly related (see Fig. 7-23). To obtain the relations, we use the principles of conservation of energy and momentum. These immediately lead to

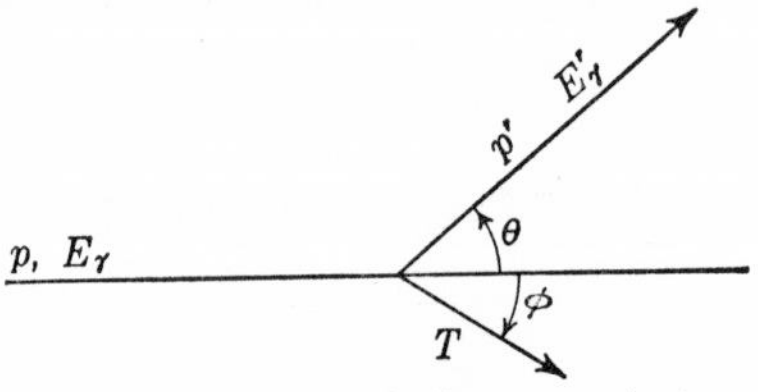

$$\hbar ck = \hbar ck' + m_e c^2(\gamma - 1) \tag{7-93}$$

$$\hbar k = \hbar k' \cos\theta + m_e v\gamma \cos\phi \tag{7-94}$$

$$0 = \hbar k' \sin\theta - m_e v\gamma \sin\phi \tag{7-95}$$

FIG. 7-23. Angles of photon and electron in Compton scattering.

We may solve these equations to obtain any three of the variables k', θ, ϕ, and v in terms of the fourth. Taking θ as this independent variable, a series of algebraic steps leads to

$$k' = \frac{k}{1 + \zeta(1 - \cos\theta)} \tag{7-96}$$

$$\tan\phi = \frac{\cot\frac{1}{2}\theta}{1 + \zeta} \tag{7-97}$$

$$T = m_e c^2(\gamma - 1) = \frac{\hbar k\zeta(1 - \cos\theta)}{1 + \zeta(1 - \cos\theta)} \tag{7-98}$$

For unpolarized incident radiation, Klein and Nishina[21] on the basis of the Dirac electron theory have found for the differential cross section for scattering by a single electron

$$\sigma_c(\theta,\varphi) = \frac{3\sigma_e}{16\pi} \frac{1 + \cos^2\theta}{[1 + \zeta(1 - \cos\theta)]^3} \left\{1 + \frac{\zeta^2(1 - \cos\theta)^2}{(1 + \cos^2\theta)[1 + \zeta(1 - \cos\theta)]}\right\} \tag{7-99}$$

The atomic differential cross section is obtained by multiplying Eq. (7-99) by Z, and the total cross section follows by integrating the result over the entire solid angle. In the case of the scattering of radiation by an atom, we may regard as identical the center-of-mass and the laboratory systems. In Fig. 7-24 we show the distributions characterized by Eq. (7-99). In the limit as ζ approaches 0 (*i.e.*, as the wavelengths become very long), Eq. (7-99) reduces to the well-known classical result of Thomson

$$\sigma_{cl}(\theta,\varphi) = \frac{3\sigma_e}{16\pi}(1 + \cos^2\theta) \tag{7-100}$$

the subscript *cl* denoting classical.

In the case of the photoelectric effect a differential cross section may be assigned to characterize the distribution of the ejected electrons.

When the incident gamma ray is polarized in the $\varphi = 0$ plane and has an energy well above the critical K-shell energy and when the electrons are ejected with nonrelativistic velocities, then the atomic differential cross section for photoelectrons is approximately

$$\sigma_f(\theta,\varphi) = \frac{3\sigma_e}{8\pi} Z^5\alpha^4 \left(\frac{1}{\zeta}\right)^{\frac{7}{2}} \frac{4\sqrt{2}\sin^2\theta\cos^2\varphi}{[1-(v/c)\cos\theta]^4} \tag{7-101}$$

Integration over the entire solid angle gives the atomic photoelectric cross section. Equation (7-101) is actually only a crude approximation,

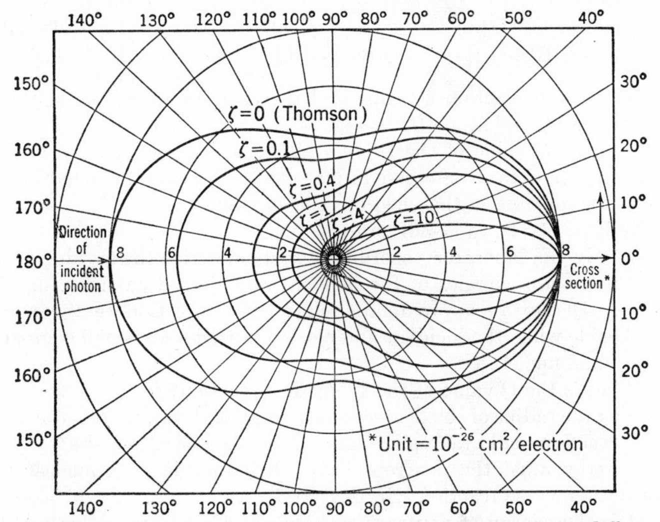

FIG. 7-24. Compton effect. Polar-coordinate representation of the differential cross section per unit solid angle for the number of photons scattered at the angle θ. (*From Davisson and Evans, Ref.* 13.)

and the results are substantially changed when consideration is given to the relativistic effects and the effect of proximity to a K edge (see Davisson and Evans[13]).

The differential cross sections characterizing the electron and positron distributions in pair production are complicated and will not be reproduced here. Because the gamma-ray energy in excess of the threshold energy may be divided in various ways between the electron and positron, we may define a concept which is a measure of the probability for the creation of a positron in a specific energy interval between T and $T + dT$ with the electron going into the corresponding energy interval permitted by conservation of energy. The atomic pair-production cross section follows when this cross section is integrated over all possible positron energies.

Because of its great practical importance in shielding and dosage problems, the entire subject of gamma-ray absorption has been investigated anew in recent years in an effort to eliminate large inconsistencies which existed in the earlier literature. We refer the reader to several review articles[13,19,22,23] which summarize this recent work and present the quantitative details.

PROBLEMS

7-1. The Q value of the $He^4(d,p)$ reaction is -3.22 Mev. What is the mass of the product?

***7-2.** Verify the formula (Ref. 6)

$$\begin{aligned}16\Delta(H^1) = &-9Q[n(\beta^-)H] + 10Q[H^1(n,\gamma)H^2] + 5[2\Delta(H^2) - \Delta(He^4)] \\ &- Q[O^{16}(d,\alpha)N^{14}] + Q[C^{14}(\beta^-)N^{14}] + Q[C^{13}(d,p)C^{14}] - Q[C^{13}(d,\alpha)B^{11}] \\ &- Q[B^{11}(d,\alpha)Be^9] - Q[Be^9(p,\alpha)Li^6] - Q[Li^6(p,\alpha)He^3] + Q[H^2(d,n)He^3]\end{aligned}$$

7-3. Determine the reaction Q value and the excitation energies of the first five states of Al^{28} from the values of $H\rho$ in Fig. 7-5.

7-4. What is the Q value of the $C^{13}(p,n)N^{13}$ reaction (see Fig. 7-7)? How large an error does the use of mass numbers in place of masses cause? What energy levels correspond to the maxima in the yield of this reaction?

7-5. Verify Eqs. (7-34), to (7-36) and (7-38).

***7-6.** Using only the laboratory coordinate system, derive the Q value of a reaction in terms of the kinetic energies of the incident and ejected particles for the special case $\theta_l = 90°$. Derive an approximate relativistic correction to the above result which is applicable when the incident and ejected particles are small compared to the target and residual nuclei.

7-7. (*a*) What is the Q value of the $D(d,n)He^3$ reaction?

(*b*) Assuming the radius of the deuteron to be 2×10^{-13} cm, what is the least energy at which this reaction could take place, according to classical physics?

(*c*) What energy must the neutrons have when they leave a nuclear reactor to barely induce the reverse reaction ${}_2He^3(n,d){}_1H^2$?

7-8. What is the energy of neutrons emitted at 45° and at 135° as a result of the bombardment of a Li^7 target by 1-Mev and 2-Mev protons? The Q of the $Li(p,n)$ reaction is -1.645 Mev.

7-9. What thickness of sulfur ($\rho = 2.00$) will reduce a neutron-beam intensity to 50 per cent at 111 kev and at 250 kev?

***7-10.** If the differential cross section per unit solid angle in the center-of-mass coordinate system corresponds to $\sigma(\theta,\varphi) = a^2(1 + \alpha \cos \theta)$, what is the total cross section in the laboratory system? Plot the differential cross section per unit solid angle in the laboratory system when $a^2 = 10^{-24}$ cm, $\alpha = 0.1$, and (*a*) $\gamma = 0.5$, (*b*) $\gamma = 1$, and (*c*) $\gamma = 2$.

7-11. How must Eq. (7-75) be modified when the incident particle and scatterer are identical so that the scattered particle is indistinguishable from the recoil particle?

7-12. Use Fig. 7-22 to determine approximately the mass absorption coefficient of platinum for gamma rays at 0.1, 1, 5, and 10 Mev.

REFERENCES

1. Bohr, N.: *Nature,* **137,** 344 (1936).
2. Templeton, D. H.: *Ann. Rev. Nuclear Sci.,* **2,** 93 (1953).
3. Hollander, J. M.: *U.S. Atomic Energy Comm. Document UCRL* 1396, 1951.

4. Reynolds, H. L., D. W. Scott, and A. Zucker: *Proc. Natl. Acad. Sci. U.S.*, in press.
5. Marshak, R. E.: "Meson Physics," McGraw-Hill Book Company, Inc., New York, 1952.
6. Li, C. W., W. Whaling, W. A. Fowler, and C. C. Lauritsen: *Phys. Rev.*, **83**, 512 (1951).
7. Enge, H. A., W. W. Buechner, and A. Sperduto: *Phys. Rev.*, **88**, 963 (1952).
8. Bair, J. K., J. D. Kingston, and H. B. Willard: *Phys. Rev.*, **90**, 575 (1953).
9. Ajzenberg, F., and T. Lauritsen: *Revs. Mod. Phys.*, **24**, 324 (1952).
10. Katz, L.: American Physical Society meeting, Washington, May, 1953.
11. Koch, H. W., and R. S. Foote: *Phys. Rev.*, **91**, 455 (1953).
12. Barschall, H. H.: *Am. J. Phys.*, **8**, 538 (1950).
13. Davisson, C. M., and R. D. Evans: *Revs. Mod. Phys.*, **24**, 79 (1952).
14. Adair, R. K.: *Revs. Mod. Phys.*, **22**, 249 (1950).
15. Atomic Energy Commission Neutron Cross Section Advisory Group: *U.S. Atomic Energy Comm. Document AECU* 2040, 1952.
16. Hanson, A. O., R. F. Taschek, and J. H. Williams: *Revs. Mod. Phys.*, **21**, 4 (1949).
17. Peterson, R. E., H. H. Barschall, and C. K. Bockelman: *Phys. Rev.*, **79**, 593 (1950).
18. Barschall, H. H.: *Phys. Rev.*, **86**, 431 (1952).
19. Snyder, W. S., and J. L. Powell: *U.S. Atomic Energy Comm. Document AECD* 2739, 1950.
20. Heitler, W.: "The Quantum Theory of Radiation," Oxford University Press, New York, 1947.
21. Klein, O., and Y. Nishina: *Z. Physik*, **52**, 853 (1929).
22. Bethe, H. A., and J. Ashkin: *Exptl. Nuclear Phys.*, **1**, 304 (1953).
23. White, G. R.: *Natl. Bur. Standards (U.S.) Rept.* 1003, 1952.
24. Walt, M., and H. H. Barschall: *Phys. Rev.*, **93**, 1062 (1954).
25. Ilakovac, K., and P. B. Moon: *Phys. Rev.*, **93**, 254 (1954).
26. Metzer, F. R., and W. B. Todd: *Bull. Am. Phys. Soc.*, **29**, 39 (1954).
27. Harbottle, G.: *Nucleonics*, **12**(4), 64, (1954).
28. Huus, T., and C. Zupancic: *Klg. Danske Videnskab. Selskab, Mat.-fys. Medd.*, **28**(1) (1953).
29. McClelland, C., and C. Goodman: *Phys. Rev.*, **91**, 760 (1953).
30. Ter-Martirosyan, K. A.: *J. Exptl. Theoret. Phys. (U.S.S.R.)*, **22**, 284 (1952).
31. Alder, K., and A. Winther: *Phys. Rev.*, **91**, 1578 (1953).
32. Goldburg, W. I., S. A. Cox, and R. M. Williamson: *Bull. Am. Phys. Soc.*, **29**, 40 (1954).

CHAPTER 8

SYSTEMATICS AND TENDENCIES OF NUCLEI

In our discussion of the trends of beta stability and instability we noted that the location of the stable and unstable nuclides on a D-A grid gives a revealing picture of nuclear systematics and tendencies. A much more complete picture may be given by introducing a third coordinate perpendicular to the D and A axes which represents a mass or energy parameter such as Δ, f, E, or ϵ. Although the energy parameters have greater theoretical importance, we shall here make use of the mass decrement as the additional coordinate in order to adhere more closely to the experimental data. This chapter will be devoted largely to a discussion of the facts revealed by such a representation of nuclear data.

8-1. The Mass Surface. The function $\Delta(A,D)$ in a space with Δ, D, and A as coordinates constitutes a surface which we shall frequently refer to as the mass surface (since $\Delta = M - A$ immediately implies M). The graphical representation of $\Delta(A,D)$ on a two-dimensional surface may be accomplished by the use of contour lines which connect the points of equal values. We must be careful to remember, however, that these lines, unlike those on ordinary contour maps, have physical significance only at the integral D and A or N and Z points.

According to the available mass data, mass decrements mainly depend upon the value of A, that is,

$$\Delta(A,D) \approx \Delta_m(A) \tag{8-1}$$

where, as we shall justify later, the subscript m denotes minimum. One may readily verify the truth of this statement by scanning a table of experimental mass decrements. To show the general nature of $\Delta_m(A)$, we have plotted in Fig. 8-1 the decrements of beta-stable nuclides. The points show rather simple trends which are represented quite well by the smooth curve shown in this figure (see Sec. 8-2). Note, however, that in some regions the nuclear masses show local trends which depart from the general trend represented by the smooth curve. These local trends have been given considerable study in recent years in connection with theories of complex nuclei which incorporate the shell-structure concepts of atomic theory. We shall postpone consideration of these "shell-structure" irregularities until Sec. 8-7.

Since mass number is the most important variable upon which nuclear masses depend, we may best study the smaller dependence of mass upon the neutron excess by examining the relative masses of isobars. For this purpose let us use the experimental facts at our disposal to infer the nature of a section of the $\Delta(A,D)$ surface which corresponds to a constant

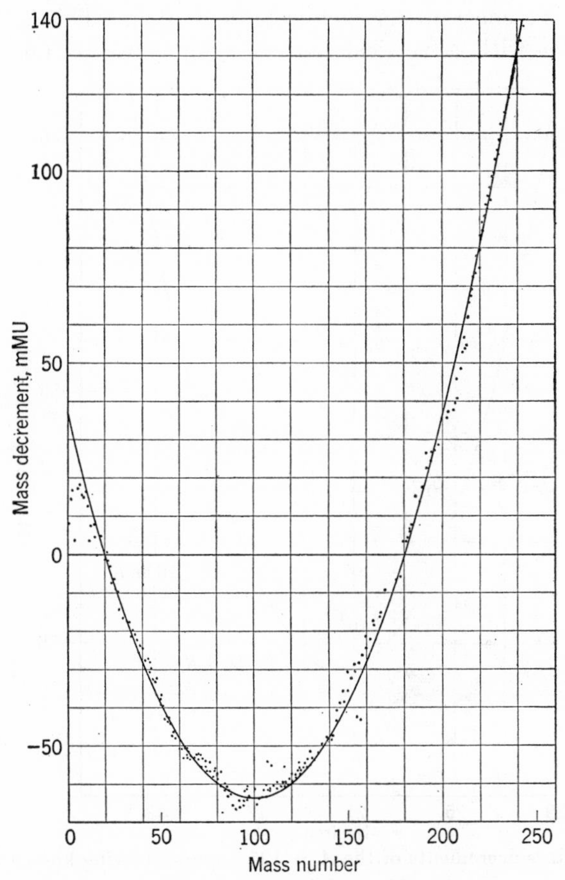

FIG. 8-1. Mass decrements of beta-stable nuclides. The smooth curve corresponds to Eq. (8-7).

value for A. From the fact that beta-unstable odd-mass nuclei tend to decay to a single stable isobar, we may reasonably suppose that an isobaric section has a minimum point whose coordinate is denoted by $D_m(A)$, which lies close to the point for the beta-stable nuclide. Since only a few accurate experimental points are available for the determination of the shape of isobaric-section curves and since these are quite close to the minimum point $D_m(A)$, it is natural to represent these curves by the simplest function which has a minimum point and which can be adjusted to the known data. We shall therefore accept the widely made assumption that the mass corrections for the isobaric points away from the minimum have the quadratic form

$$\Delta_q = [D - D_m(A)]^2 J(A) \tag{8-2}$$

where $J(A)$ is a constant for each isobaric section. This is the equation of a parabola with a vertical axis of symmetry. $D_m(A)$ locates the

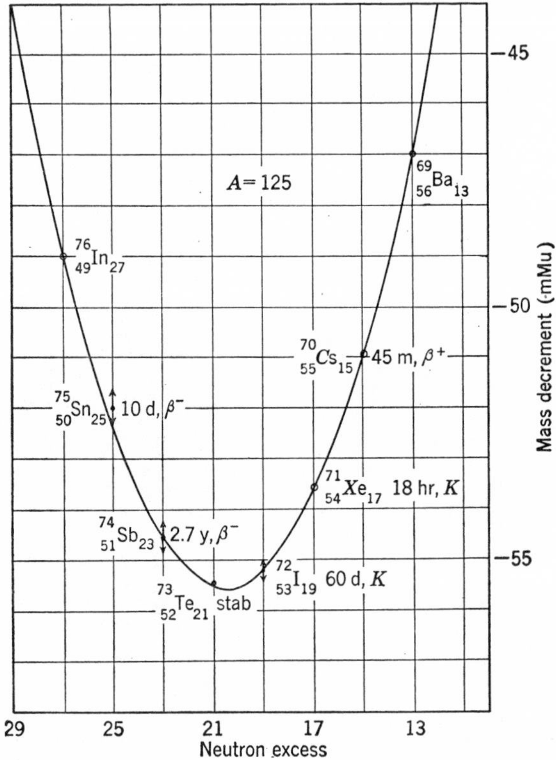

FIG. 8-2. Mass decrements of the $A = 125$ isobars, showing known activities.

neutron excess for the vertex, and $J(A)$ determines the breadth of this parabola.

In Fig. 8-2 we show the isobaric section corresponding to mass number 125, indicating the N, Z, and D numbers, in that order, for each physical point. Te(73, 52, 21), the stable isobar, is positioned at −55.4 mMU, a mass decrement assigned by Halsted[(1)] with an uncertainty of ±0.3 mMU. Sb(74, 51, 23), which is a 2.7-year β^- emitter, Sn(75, 50, 25), which is a 10-day β^- emitter, and I(72, 53, 19), which is a 60-day K-active nuclide, are positioned at points relative to Te which have been determined from decay energies.[(2)] The approximate relative uncertainties of these points are indicated by arrows. The mass decrements of Xe(71, 54, 17), an 18-hr *K*-active nuclide, of Cs(70, 55, 15), a 45-min β^+ emitter, and of the remaining as yet undetected isobars are not known; hence they are positioned along a hypothetical parabola which passes close to the experimental points. While the good fit of the parabola may be fortuitous, nevertheless it is clear that the parabolic assumption accounts for the rule as to how the nature of the activity varies with neutron excess and also for the rule regarding the variation of decay constant with the deviation of the neutron excess from the neutron excess for the stable nuclide (see Sec. 6-4). The rule regarding the variation of the decay energy with mass number suggests that $J(A)$ increases (*i.e.*, parabola sections grow steeper) as A decreases.

The beta systematics of even-mass nuclides suggests that the even-A isobaric sections have a more complicated form than the odd-mass sections. Fortunately the data on even-mass nuclides are more abundant, so that explorations of the nature of these isobaric sections are feasible. In Fig. 8-3 we indicate the isobaric sections corresponding to mass number 124, with Sn, Sb, Te, I, and Xe positioned at the experimental mass decrements.[1] In this case Te(72, 52, 20) and Xe(70, 54, 16) nuclides are definitely stable. Sn(74, 50, 24) is observed to be stable, although it may be unstable against double beta decay with a half-life greater than 10^{16} years. The other isobars have the following properties: Sb(73, 51, 22) is known to be β^--active ($\tau_{\frac{1}{2}} = 60$ days), and it may also undergo *K* capture; and I(71, 53, 18) is β^+- and *K*-capture-active ($\tau_{\frac{1}{2}} = 4$ days). The activities of the remaining nuclides are not known, but they probably conform with expectations on the basis of the two curves shown in Fig. 8-3.

These curves are drawn to fit an assumption that the OO nuclides and EE nuclides lie along two identical parabolas with the OO curve lying directly above the EE curve. These special assumptions, which are made in the interests of simplicity, are adequate for explaining beta systematics (see Sec. 6-4). In particular these curves account for the rule that stable even-A nuclides are almost always the EE type, for the rule that the atomic numbers of stable isobaric doublets differ by 2 units, and for the general trend of the variation of lifetime with nuclear type and with the deviation of the neutron excess from the stable neutron excess.

We have thus far concluded that the experimental nuclear mass surface actually consists of three mass surfaces corresponding to the odd-mass surface and the OO and EE even-mass surfaces. The relationship between the odd-mass surface and the two even-mass surfaces can be established in a variety of ways. One of the more practical ways is to examine the relative masses of a series of isotopes of an element with even Z and a series of isotopes of an adjacent element with odd Z. Such studies reveal that for the even-Z isotopes the points corresponding to the isotopes with even N lie on a curve which lies below the curve joining the isotopes with odd N. In the series of odd-Z isotopes the curve corresponding to the isotopes with even N also lies below the curve corresponding to the isotopes with odd N. We may therefore conclude that

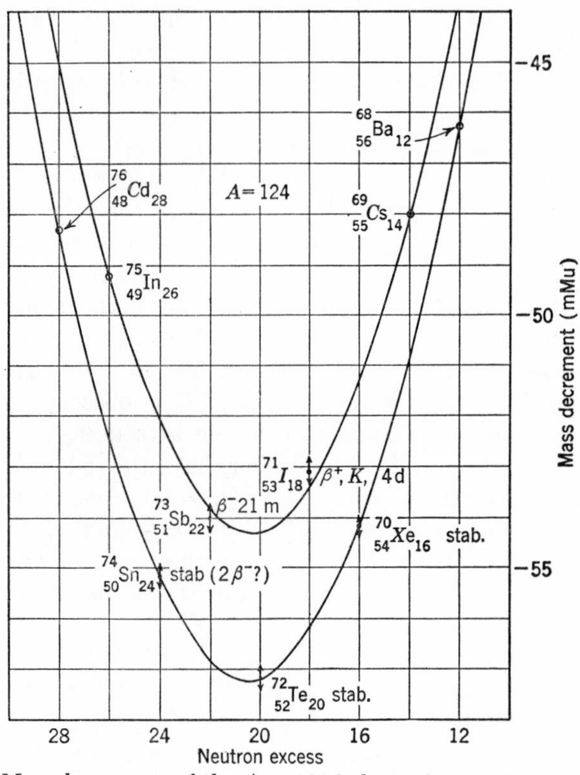

FIG. 8-3. Mass decrements of the $A = 124$ isobars, showing known activities.

the OO surface lies above the OE-EO, which lies above the EE surface. Estimates of these separations suggest that the OE-EO surface is approximately centered between the OO surface and the EE surface.

To avoid dealing with three nuclear surfaces, it is convenient to use the intermediate odd-mass surface for all nuclei, but to rectify the OO and EE points to this surface by some correction factor. Quite generally, we might expect the points on the EE and OO surfaces to deviate from the odd-mass surface by correction factors which are functions of N and Z or of D and A. Approximate rectification can be obtained, however, by using a correction which depends only upon A and upon the number of outermost pairs of neutrons or protons. Such a correction may be expressed in the form

$$\Delta_p = \mathfrak{d}H(A) \tag{8-3}$$

where

$$\begin{aligned} \mathfrak{d} &= 1 \text{ for OO-type nuclides (no pairs)} \\ &= 0 \text{ for OE- or EO-type nuclides (one pair)} \\ &= -1 \text{ for EE-type nuclides (two pairs)} \end{aligned} \tag{8-4}$$

and $H(A)$ is a function of A alone. This correction will be referred to as the pairing correction.

We must point out here too that this is a very special assumption, which is not actually borne out in detail by the quantitative evidence now available. However, in the main Eq. (8-3) may be made, by an appro-

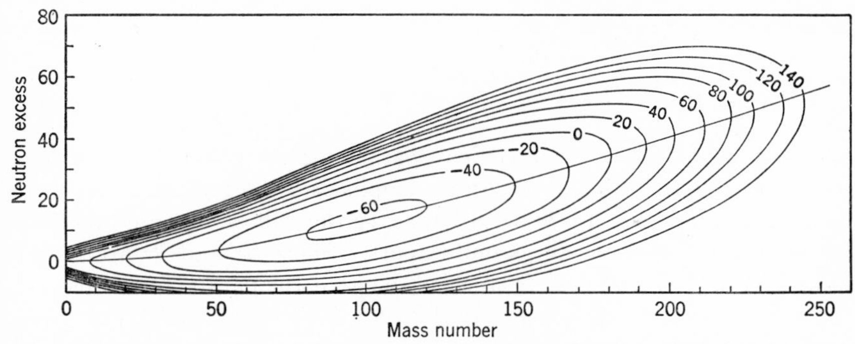

FIG. 8-4. Schematic diagram of nuclear energy surface when discontinuities are ignored. The contour lines correspond to equal values of the mass decrement.

priate choice of H, to account for numerous qualitative observations concerning odd-even effects and beta systematics.

Ignoring the discontinuities associated with nuclear type and the irregularities which may be identified with shell structure, we can now piece together a picture of a smooth, approximate nuclear mass surface which conforms closely to the central experimental surface. The surface has the general shape of a long narrow valley the bottom of which goes from $\Delta \approx 20$ mMU at $A \approx 10$ downward to $\Delta \approx -65$ mMU at $A \approx 100$ and then upward gradually to $\Delta \approx 155$ mMU at $A \approx 250$. At the same time the valley curves gently from $D \approx 0$ at $A \approx 10$ toward positive D values with $D \approx 13$ at $A \approx 100$ and $D \approx 55$ at $A \approx 250$. The sides of the valley are much steeper at the entrance (small A) than at the end ($A \approx 250$). In Fig. 8-4 we schematically represent this surface by means of contour lines.

8-2. The Empirical Mass Surface. Our discussion has indicated that mass decrements may be approximately represented by the equation

$$\Delta(A,D) = \Delta_m(A) + \mathfrak{d}H(A) + \theta^2 J(A) \tag{8-5}$$

where by definition

$$\theta = D - D_m(A) \tag{8-6}$$

It should be clear that the four functions of the single variable A—$\Delta_m(A)$, $D_m(A)$, $H(A)$, and $J(A)$— completely characterize the approximate mass surface. These key functions thus give the basic information necessary for the approximate computation of all nuclear energy parameters such as masses, packing fractions, binding energies, and reaction energies.

We shall now introduce a set of key functions which have been inferred[3–6] from a survey of the experimental data and from considerations of simplicity. These functions, which are quite useful for $A > 10$, are

$$\Delta_m{}^e(A) = 0.01(A - 100)^2 - 64 = 100(\mathbf{A} - 1)^2 - 64 \quad \text{mMU} \tag{8-7}$$

$$D_m{}^e(A) = \frac{0.4A^2}{A + 200} = \frac{40\mathbf{A}^2}{\mathbf{A} + 2} \tag{8-8}$$

$$J^e(A) = 25A^{-1} = (4\mathbf{A})^{-1} \quad \text{mMU} \tag{8-9}$$

$$H^e(A) = 10A^{-\frac{1}{2}} = \mathbf{A}^{-\frac{1}{2}} \quad \text{mMU} \tag{8-10}$$

where $\mathbf{A} = A/100$ is a convenient parameter for some computations $(0.1 < \mathbf{A} < 2.5)$. The superscript e emphasizes the fact that these are empirical functions. In Table 8-1 we give the values of these functions for mass numbers spaced 10 units apart. Since H^e and J^e are of the order of 1 mMU, it is clear from this table that the parabolic and pairing terms are only small corrections to the main mass term. With Eqs. (8-5) and (8-6) these functions characterize an empirical mass surface which appears to be quite close to the present experimental surface, except in the highly irregular regions (see Fig. 8-1). Without question, the departures of actual masses from the empirical masses may be reduced by using more complex key functions or by modifying slightly the round empirical constants used above. However, any improvements of this nature will be relatively small compared to the intrinsic irregular departures of the experimental masses from values computed with the empirical functions. We might note that the actual D values of the minima obtained by fitting parabolas to the experimental mass decrements of isobars deviate in an irregular fashion from any *smooth* function of A which fits the center of density of these minimum points. Since these irregular deviations are sometimes of the same order of magnitude as the computed values of θ [Eqs. (8-6) and (8-8)], the parabolic-correction term often loses its significance. Fortunately, in many applications of the mass surface this parabolic correction is quite small, so that even crude estimates of its effect are useful.

Accepting the limitations noted above, let us consider what general aspects of nuclear energies can be learned from the empirical mass surface.

TABLE 8-1. EMPIRICAL FUNCTIONS

A	mMU						mMU	
	$\Delta_m{}^e(A)$	$H^e(A)$	$J^e(A)$	$D_m{}^e(A)$	$N_m{}^e(A)$	$Z_m{}^e(A)$	$B_n{}^e(A)$	$B_p{}^e(A)$
10	17.000	3.162	2.500	0.190	5.095	4.905	10.792	9.952
20	0.000	2.236	1.250	0.727	10.364	9.636	10.592	9.752
30	−15.000	1.826	0.833	1.565	15.782	14.218	10.392	9.552
40	−28.000	1.581	0.625	2.667	21.334	18.666	10.192	9.352
50	−39.000	1.414	0.500	4.000	27.000	23.000	9.992	9.152
60	−48.000	1.291	0.417	5.538	32.769	27.231	9.792	8.952
70	−55.000	1.195	0.357	7.259	38.630	31.370	9.592	8.752
80	−60.000	1.118	0.312	9.143	44.572	35.428	9.392	8.552
90	−63.000	1.054	0.278	11.172	50.586	39.414	9.192	8.352
100	−64.000	1.000	0.250	13.333	56.666	43.334	8.992	8.152
110	−63.000	0.953	0.227	15.613	62.806	47.194	8.792	7.952
120	−60.000	0.913	0.208	18.000	69.000	51.000	8.592	7.752
130	−55.000	0.877	0.192	20.485	75.242	54.758	8.392	7.552
140	−48.000	0.845	0.179	23.059	81.530	58.470	8.192	7.352
150	−39.000	0.816	0.167	25.714	87.857	62.143	7.992	7.152
160	−28.000	0.791	0.156	28.444	94.222	65.778	7.792	6.952
170	−15.000	0.767	0.147	31.243	100.622	69.378	7.592	6.752
180	−0.000	0.745	0.139	34.105	107.052	72.948	7.392	6.552
190	17.000	0.725	0.132	37.026	113.513	76.487	7.192	6.352
200	36.000	0.707	0.125	40.000	120.000	80.000	6.992	6.152
210	57.000	0.690	0.119	43.024	126.512	83.488	6.792	5.952
220	80.000	0.674	0.114	46.095	133.048	86.952	6.592	5.752
230	105.000	0.659	0.109	49.209	139.604	90.396	6.392	5.552
240	132.000	0.645	0.104	52.364	146.182	93.818	6.192	5.352
250	161.000	0.632	0.100	55.555	152.778	97.222	5.992	5.152

The empirical $\Delta^e(D,A)$ function leads immediately to the empirical mass

$$M^e = A + 10^3\Delta^e(D,A) \qquad \text{MU} \tag{8-11}$$

the empirical packing fraction (see Fig. 2-6)

$$f^e = \frac{\Delta_e(D,A)}{A} \qquad \text{mMU} \tag{8-12}$$

the empirical nuclear energy [see Eq. (2-73)]

$$E^e = \Delta^e(D,A) - \tfrac{1}{2}A(\Delta_n + \Delta_H) - \tfrac{1}{2}D(\Delta_n - \Delta_H) \tag{8-13}$$

and the empirical nuclear energy per particle

$$\epsilon^e = \frac{E^e}{A} \tag{8-14}$$

Since $-\frac{1}{2}A(\Delta_n + \Delta_H)$ is the dominant component of the nuclear energy, the actual nuclear energy and nuclear energy per particle are represented quite accurately (on a percentage basis) by the empirical expressions.

We may obtain quite useful estimates of nuclear Q values by using our approximate mass surface. Since such energies usually involve the differences between two points which are quite close together on the mass surface, the erratic fluctuations of the actual masses are usually accentuated. Accordingly we must expect the difference between the actual Q value and the empirical Q value to be quite large in some cases.

Let us consider a bombardment reaction symbolically given by the transformation

$$x(a,d) + X(A,D) \rightarrow X'(A',D') + x'(a',d') \tag{8-15}$$

Using the empirical-surface functions for $\Delta(A,D)$ and $\Delta'(A',D')$ but the experimental mass decrements for the incident and ejected particles, we may write [see Eq. (7-8)]

$$Q^e = Q_m + Q_p + Q_q \tag{8-16}$$

where

$$Q_m = \delta - \delta' + \Delta_m{}^e(A) - \Delta_m{}^e(A') \tag{8-17}$$

$$Q_p = \mathfrak{d}H(A) - \mathfrak{d}'H(A') \approx (\mathfrak{d} - \mathfrak{d}')H(A) \tag{8-18}$$

$$Q_q = \theta^2 J(A) - \theta'^2 J(A') \approx (\theta^2 - \theta'^2)J(A) \tag{8-19}$$

Using Eq. (8-7) and $A' = A + (a - a')$, we find by simple algebra

$$Q_m = \delta - \delta' + 2(a - a') - \frac{(a - a')^2}{100} - 2(a - a')\frac{A}{100} \quad \text{mMU} \tag{8-20}$$

The fact that $Q_m(A)$, which is the dominant term in most bombardment reactions, is a simple linear function of A for each type of reaction is a great convenience in applications of the empirical mass surface. The simpler expressions to the right of Eqs. (8-18) and (8-19) are usually adequate for the computation of the smaller terms Q_p and Q_q. In fact, for many purposes Q_p and Q_q may be ignored altogether. In Tables 8-2*a* and 8-2*b* we tabulate the functions Q_m for all interesting bombardment reactions. For most applications of these tables, the entries may be rounded off to the nearest mMU or Mev. Three decimal places are listed because of the possible usefulness of these tables in residual analysis.

Table 8-3 has in each space in the body of the table the coefficient $\mathfrak{d} - \mathfrak{d}'$ for Q_p, the pairing term, for various types of initial nuclei and for any combination of captured and released particles listed for that space. The calculation of Q_q, the parabolic correction, which is the most tedious, may in part be facilitated by the use of the equation

$$\theta' - \theta = d - d' - (a - a')\frac{dD_m{}^e}{dA} \tag{8-21}$$

TABLE 8-2*a*. Q_m VALUES IN MMU
(c = captured; r = released)

r \ c	γ	n	p	d	t	χ	α
γ	0	$10.972 - a$	$10.132 - a$	$18.695 - b$	$22.907 - c$	$22.887 - c$	$11.713 - d$
n	$-10.992 + a$	0	-0.840	$7.743 - a$	$11.975 - b$	$11.955 - b$	$0.801 - c$
p	$-10.152 + a$	0.840	0	$8.583 - a$	$12.815 - b$	$12.795 - b$	$1.641 - c$
d	$-18.775 + b$	$-7.763 + a$	$-8.603 + a$	0.000	$4.252 - a$	$4.232 - a$	$-6.902 - b$
t	$-23.087 + c$	$-12.055 + b$	$+12.895 + b$	$-4.272 + a$	0	-0.020	$-11.134 - a$
χ	$-23.067 + c$	$-12.035 + b$	$-12.875 + b$	$-4.252 + a$	0.020	0	$-11.114 - a$
α	$-12.033 + d$	$-0.981 + c$	$-1.821 + c$	$6.822 + b$	$11.114 + a$	$11.094 + a$	0
np	$-21.164 + b$	$-10.152 + a$	$-10.992 + a$	-2.389	$1.863 - a$	$1.843 - a$	$-9.291 - b$
nn	$-22.044 + b$	$-10.992 + a$	$-11.832 + a$	-3.229	$1.023 - a$	$1.003 - a$	$-10.131 - b$
pp	$-20.324 + b$	$-9.312 + a$	$-10.152 + a$	-1.549	$2.703 - a$	$2.683 - a$	$-8.451 - b$

$a = 2\mathbf{A} = 0.02A \qquad c = 6\mathbf{A} = 0.06A$
$b = 4\mathbf{A} = 0.04A \qquad d = 8\mathbf{A} = 0.08A$

TABLE 8-2*b*. Q_m VALUES IN MEV

r \ c	γ	n	p	d	t	χ	α
γ	0	$10.216 - a$	$9.454 - a$	$17.407 - b$	$21.329 - c$	$21.311 - c$	$10.906 - d$
n	$-10.235 + a$	0	-0.782	$7.210 - a$	$11.150 - b$	$11.132 - b$	$0.746 - c$
p	$-9.453 + a$	0.782	0	$7.992 - a$	$11.932 - b$	$11.914 - b$	$1.528 - c$
d	$-17.482 + a$	$-7.228 + a$	$-8.010 + a$	0	$3.959 - a$	$3.941 - a$	$-6.427 - b$
t	$-21.497 + c$	$-11.225 + b$	$-12.007 + b$	$-3.978 + a$	0	-0.019	$-10.367 - a$
χ	$-21.478 + c$	$-11.206 + b$	$-11.988 + b$	$-3.959 + a$	0.019	0	$-10.349 - a$
α	$-11.204 + d$	$-0.913 + c$	$-1.696 + c$	$6.352 + b$	$10.348 + a$	$10.330 + a$	0
np	$-19.706 + b$	$-9.453 + a$	$-10.235 + a$	-2.224	$1.735 - a$	$1.716 - a$	$-8.652 - b$
nn	$-20.489 + b$	$-10.235 + a$	$-11.017 + a$	-3.007	$0.953 - a$	$0.934 - a$	$-9.434 - b$
pp	$-18.924 + b$	$-8.671 + a$	$-9.453 + a$	-1.442	$2.517 - a$	$2.498 - a$	$-7.870 - b$

$a = 1.862\mathbf{A} = 0.01862A \qquad c = 5.587\mathbf{A} = 0.05587A$
$b = 3.725\mathbf{A} = 0.03725A \qquad d = 7.449\mathbf{A} = 0.07449A$

TABLE 8-3. $\mathfrak{d} - \mathfrak{d}'$ FOR EE, OO, OE, AND EO INITIAL NUCLIDES

r \ c	γ, α	n, χ	p, t	d
γ, nn, pp, α	0, 0, 0, 0	−1, +1, +1, −1	−1, +1, −1, +1	−2, +2, 0, 0
n, χ	−1, +1, +1, −1	0, 0, 0, 0	−2, +2, 0, 0	−1, +1, −1, +1
p, t	−1, +1, −1, +1	−2, +2, 0, 0	0, 0, 0, 0	−1, +1, +1, −1
d, np	−2, +2, 0, 0	−1, +1, −1, +1	−1, +1, +1, −1	0, 0, 0, 0

where

$$\frac{dD_m{}^e}{dA} = 0.4\,\frac{(A + 400)A}{(A + 200)^2} = 0.4\,\frac{(\mathbf{A} + 4)\mathbf{A}}{(\mathbf{A} + 2)^2} \tag{8-22}$$

is a function which has very limited variation (see Fig. 8-5). In Table 8-4 we give the functions for the change in θ occasioned by various nuclear reactions.

8-3. Q Values and Particle Binding Energies. Ignoring the parabolic and pairing corrections, we may obtain from Table 8-2 a qualitative survey of nuclear-reaction energies. Some noteworthy points are the marked exoergic nature of (d,γ), (d,n), (d,p), and (d,α) reactions, as well

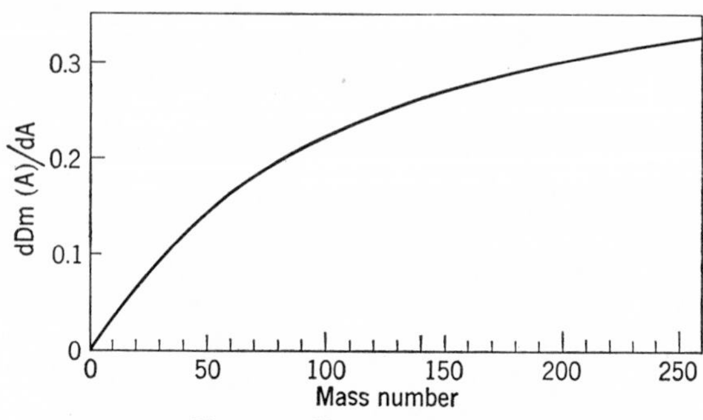

FIG. 8-5. Slope of $D_m{}^e(A)$.

as the corresponding triton- and He^3-induced reactions. The opposite reactions are, of course, markedly endoergic. The (p,α) and (n,α) reactions also tend to be exoergic except for light nuclei. We note also that reactions in which two neutrons or a neutron and a proton are ejected are generally endoergic.

TABLE 8-4. $\theta' - \theta$ VALUES

$$D' = \frac{dD_m{}^e}{dA}$$

r \ c	γ	n	p	d	t	χ	α
α	0	$1 - D'$	$-1 - D'$	$-2D'$	$1 - 3D'$	$-1 - 3D'$	$-4D'$
n	$-1 + D'$	0	-2	$-1 - D'$	$-2D'$	$-2 - 2D'$	$-1 - 3D'$
p	$1 + D'$	2	0	$1 - D'$	$2 - 2D'$	$-2D'$	$1 - 3D'$
d	$2D'$	$1 + D'$	$-1 + D'$	0	$1 - D'$	$-1 - D'$	$-2D'$
t	$-1 + 3D'$	$2D'$	$-2 + 2D'$	$-1 + D'$	0	-2	$-1 - D'$
χ	$1 + 3D'$	$2 + 2D'$	$2D'$	$1 + D'$	2	0	$1 - D'$
α	$4D'$	$1 + 3D'$	$-1 + 3D'$	$2D'$	$1 + D'$	$-1 + D'$	0
np	$2D'$	$1 + D'$	$-1 + D'$	0	$1 - D'$	$-1 - D'$	$-2D'$
nn	$-2 + 2D'$	$-1 + D'$	$-3 + D'$	-2	$-1 - D'$	$-3 - D'$	$-2 - 2D'$
pp	$2 + 2D'$	$3 + D'$	$1 + D'$	2	$3 - D'$	$1 - D'$	$2 - 2D'$

The Q values of (γ,x) reactions give immediately the binding energy of the ejected particle in the initial nucleus [see Eq. (7-12)] by simply reversing the sign, *i.e.*,

$$B_x(X) = -Q[X(\gamma,x)X'] \tag{8-23}$$

If we scan the values of the main term for (γ,x) reactions given in the first column of Table 8-2, we observe that with the exception of the

α particle, the Q_m values are always negative, and hence particle binding energies are always positive. The high stability of the alpha particle accounts for the fact that alpha-particle binding energies become negative for heavy nuclides. We may obtain an approximate estimate of the critical mass number corresponding to zero alpha-particle binding by equating to zero

$$Q_\alpha(A) = -12.033 + 8\mathbf{A} = -B_\alpha(A) \tag{8-24}$$

We find $A \approx 150$ to be the critical mass number. Thus, roughly speaking, beta-stable nuclei above this mass number are unstable against alpha decay, and those below this value are stable.

Although this calculation, in approximate agreement with results from experimental masses, indicates that alpha instability sets in for medium-weight nuclei, the observations of natural alpha activity appear to set a higher limiting value of A, in the neighborhood of $A = 208$. The apparent contradiction resolves itself when consideration is given to the lifetimes of alpha decay. With a few exceptions, nuclides with mass numbers between 150 and 208, although energetically capable of alpha decay, have lifetimes which are too long to be measured.

Alpha decay processes do not change the nuclear type; hence the empirical alpha decay energy is independent of the pairing correction. In the heavy-nuclide region the parabolic-breadth factor $J(A)$ is quite small, so that the empirical parabolic correction is also relatively small. Accordingly, we might expect Eq. (8-24) to provide a fair representation for alpha decay energies. If, as a typical example, we let $A = 225$, we find $Q = 5.97$ mMU $= 5.56$ Mev, a result which compares fairly well with experimental Q values in this region. However, Eq. (8-24) suggests that alpha decay energies tend to increase slightly above 225 and decrease slightly below 225, whereas the experimental values tend to vary in the reverse fashion. These differences may be accounted for by giving attention to shell irregularities in the nuclear mass surface (see Sec. 8-5).

The predominant term in the empirical expression for neutron binding energies is

$$B_n(A) = 10.992 - 2\mathbf{A}\ (\text{mMU}) = 10.235 - 1.862\mathbf{A}\ (\text{Mev}) \tag{8-25}$$

which provides a reasonably good over-all representation of neutron binding energies. This fact is illustrated in Fig. 8-6, in which we plot, for beta-stable nuclides, the neutron binding residuals

$$R_n = B_n^x - B_n(A) \tag{8-26}$$

vs. the neutron number. B_n^x here denotes the neutron binding energy computed from experimental data. We observe that, whereas $B_n(A)$ varies from about 11 to 6 mMU, the neutron-binding-energy residuals have a relatively small variation and fluctuate about zero. Certain regularities in these fluctuations may be noted by carefully examining Fig. 8-6. These will be discussed in Sec. 8-5.

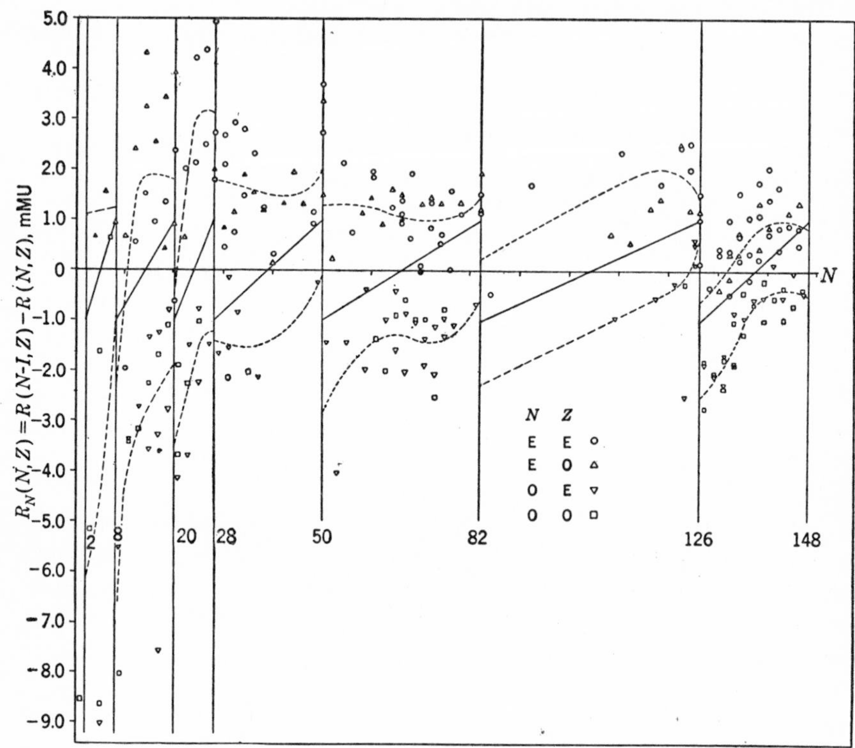

FIG. 8-6. The residual neutron binding energy vs. neutron number. The points are designated as to type, *i.e.*, as to the evenness or oddness of the number of neutrons or protons. Note the over-all scatter of points above and below the horizontal axis, with even-N nuclides tending to lie above and odd-N nuclides tending to lie below. (*From Green and Edwards, Ref.* 6.)

The principal term in the empirical proton binding energies is given by

$$B_p(A) = 10.152 - 2\mathbf{A}\ (\text{mMU}) = 9.453 - 1.862\mathbf{A}\ (\text{Mev}) \qquad (8\text{-}27)$$

which ranges 0.84 mMU below $B_n(A)$. We may define the proton-binding-energy residual in an analogous way by letting

$$R_p = B_p^x - B_p(A) \qquad (8\text{-}28)$$

In Fig. 8-7 we show the residuals for beta-stable nuclides plotted as a function of the proton number. Again we note that, except in the very-light-nuclide region, these residuals are relatively small and tend to fluctuate about zero in a manner which suggests certain regularities.

8-4. Beta Systematics. Certain general statements may be made concerning the energetic effects in nuclear reactions which can be identified with the smaller terms Q_p and Q_q. The pairing correction to Q values is negative whenever the residual nuclide has a greater degree of oddness than the target nuclide and positive when the residual nuclide

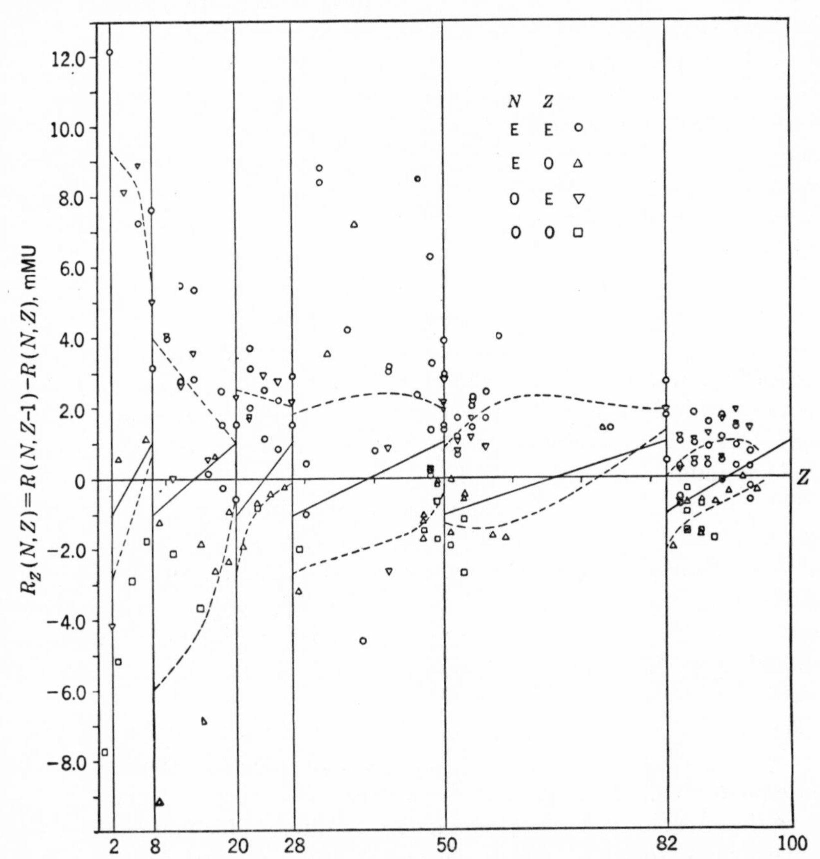

FIG. 8-7. The residual-proton-binding energy vs. proton number. The points are designated as to the type, *i.e.*, as to the evenness or oddness of the number of neutrons and protons. Note the over-all scatter of points above and below the horizontal axis, with even-Z nuclides tending to lie above and odd-Z nuclides tending to lie below. (*From Green and Edwards, Ref.* 6.)

has a greater degree of evenness than the target nuclide. The pairing correction, of course, is greater for light nuclides than for heavy nuclides.

Since most target nuclides are stable, generally the coordinate θ which characterizes the initial nuclide is small. As we shall point out, this is particularly true if the target nuclide has odd mass number. Accordingly most nuclear reactions result in an increase in the absolute magnitude of the θ coordinate; *i.e.*, the final nuclide is usually farther away from the valley than the initial nuclide. In consequence the parabolic correction to nuclear Q values is usually negative. This correction is relatively unimportant for heavy-nuclide reactions, although it is quite large for reactions involving light nuclides.

The pairing and parabolic corrections have an important influence upon the beta stability of the residual nuclide in nuclear reactions. If the product nuclide is an OE- or EO-type nuclide, it will almost certainly be β^--unstable if $\theta' \gg 1$ and will be K-capture- or β^+-unstable if $\theta' \ll -1$. If we accept the assumption that $\theta \approx 0$ for the target, Table 8-4 can be used to predict the instability or stability of odd-mass residuals. Whenever $\Delta\theta$ is comparable to or greater than 1, the residual nuclei will tend to decay by negative-beta emission. When $\Delta\theta$ is strongly negative, the residual nucleus will tend to decay by positron emission or K capture. Whenever $\Delta\theta \approx 0$, the residual nucleus tends to be stable. Letting $dD_m{}^e/dA \approx 0.25$, we would expect from Table 8-4 that the following reactions will often leave β^--active residuals: (γ,p), (γ,d), (n,γ), (n,p), (n,d), (d,p), and (d,α). We would expect the following reactions to leave residuals which tend to decay by positron emission or K capture: (p,γ), (p,n), (d,γ), (d,n), (α,γ), and (α,n); and the following reactions to leave stable residuals: (p,α), (t,γ), and (d,p).

The pairing correction has a large influence whenever the residual is an even-mass nuclide. If it is an OO-type nuclide, it will almost certainly be beta-unstable, tending to β^- activity for the reactions in the first group listed above, to K-capture and β^+ activity for the second group, and probably to all three types of activity for the third group. When the residual is an EE type, it is less likely to be beta-active, unless the θ' coordinate is really large in absolute value.

The study of beta-decay energetics presents the best opportunity for a detailed exploration of Q_p and Q_q, since A is unchanged in beta decay and consequently Q_m vanishes. In beta decay the neutron excess D and hence the coordinate θ always change by 2 units. This fact enables us to derive simple formulas which account for the general trends of beta decay energies. Considering first odd-mass isobars, let us tentatively accept the assumptions that the pairing correction vanishes and that the isobaric sections are parabolas given by Eq. (8-2). These assumptions immediately imply that the limiting θ values for the stable odd isobars are ± 1, since, if θ lies outside these limits, a change of 2 units as required in β decay or K capture will reduce the absolute value of Δ_q and hence the mass.

Let us denote by D_0 the neutron excess of the isobar closest to $D_m(A)$. If our assumptions are correct, this isobar should be the stable isobar. Let D_1, D_2, . . . denote the neutron excesses of the neighboring neutron-rich isobars and D_{-1}, D_{-2}, . . . the neighboring neutron-deficient isobars. It follows readily that the corresponding θ values are given by

$$\theta_i = D_i - D_m(A) = D_0 + 2i - D_m(A) = 2i + \theta_0 \qquad (8\text{-}29)$$

where i is an integer which labels the successive isobars and where

$$\theta_0 = D_0 - D_m(A) \qquad (8\text{-}30)$$

is a quantity which takes on values more or less at random between ± 1. We can now write the parabolic mass correction as

$$\Delta_q = J\theta_i^2 = (i + \tfrac{1}{2}\theta_0)^2 4J = (i + \tfrac{1}{2}\theta_0)^2 \mathbf{A}^{-1} \qquad (8\text{-}31)$$

where in the last form we use our empirical width function from Eq. (8-9). For an assumed $D_m(A)$ such as Eq. (8-8) we can compute θ_0 for any odd A by taking the differences between $D_m(A)$ and the nearest odd integer. Unfortunately, our empirical $D_m(A)$ function and the corresponding semiempirical functions (see Chap. 9) are not so good that complete significance can be attached to these small differences. An analysis of experimental data indicates that the true line of beta stability meanders rather irregularly. This meandering is revealed clearly if we locate the θ coordinates of the odd-mass stable nuclides in relation to our $D_m^e(A)$ (see Fig. 8-8). The light solid curves in Fig. 8-8 join isodiaspheres. The jagged line, which joins the centers of the stable limits of the isodiaspheres, is probably a fairly good representation of the position of the true line of beta stability in relation to our empirical one. The fact that the jagged line tends to fluctuate about our empirical line of beta stability is indicative of the accuracy of our $D_m^e(A)$ as a representation of the line of beta stability. The solid curve represents an improved estimate of the line of beta stability in which local irregularities are smoothed out. In view of the irregularities and uncertainties in the line of beta stability we must at the moment treat θ_0 as intrinsically uncertain to the extent of about ± 1. With these limitations in mind, let us accept Eq. (8-31) and proceed to the analysis of beta decay energies based upon it. In β^- decay, i decreases by 1 unit. Since $M^* - M = J(\theta_i + 2)^2 - J\theta_i^2$, it follows by simple algebra that the mass difference is

$$M^* - M = (1 + 2i + \theta_0)4J = (1 + 2i + \theta_0)\mathbf{A}^{-1} \qquad (8\text{-}32)$$

where i is now the integer, usually zero or positive, which characterizes the daughter. On the other hand the mass difference which is involved in β^+ decay and K capture is given by

$$M^* - M = (1 - 2i - \theta_0)4J = (1 - 2i - \theta_0)\mathbf{A}^{-1} \qquad (8\text{-}33)$$

where i is the integer, usually zero or negative, which characterizes the daughter. For decay to the stable isobar, which is the type usually observed, $i = 0$; hence we have

$$M^* - M = (1 \pm \theta_0)4J = (1 \pm \theta_0)\mathbf{A}^{-1} \tag{8-34}$$

where the upper sign is for β^- decay and the lower sign is for β^+ decay or K capture. Letting $\theta_0 \approx 0$, we see that $\mathbf{A}^{-1}$ provides an indication of the order of magnitude of these mass differences. The mass differences in decay to beta-stable odd isobars, however, might be expected to vary from zero to twice the value of $\mathbf{A}^{-1}$, depending upon the value of θ_0.

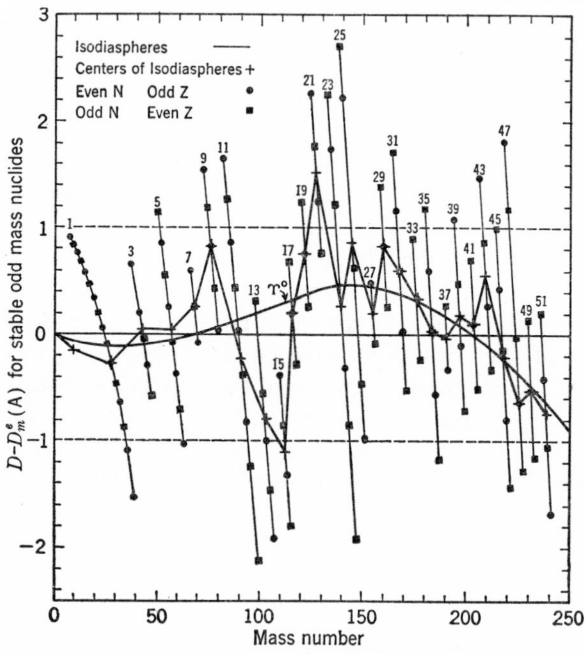

FIG. 8-8. $\theta = D - D_m^e(A)$ vs. mass number for beta-stable odd-A nuclides. $\Upsilon°$ locates an improved smooth representation of the line of beta stability relative to the base line, which corresponds to the empirical function $D_m^e(A)$. (*From Green and Engler, Ref.* 5.)

These numbers may be used for estimating β^- decay energies and K-capture energies since 1 Mev $\approx$ 1 mMU. However, we must subtract $2m_e$ ($\sim$1 Mev) to estimate the kinetic energies in β^+ decay. This last consideration suggests, in agreement with experimental observations, that heavy, neutron-deficient, odd-A isobars cannot undergo β^+ decay unless they are two or more steps from the beta-stable isobar.

For even-mass isobars we must include the pairing correction. When this is done, the complete mass difference is given by

$$\begin{aligned} M^* - M &= \pm 2H(A) + [1 \pm (2i + \theta_0)]4J(A) \\ &= \pm 2\mathbf{A}^{-\frac{1}{2}} + [1 \pm (2i + \theta_0)]\mathbf{A}^{-1} \end{aligned} \tag{8-35}$$

where in the last form we use our empirical H and J functions. The first upper and lower signs correspond to an initial nuclide of the odd-odd type and the even-even type, respectively, and the second set of signs have the same meaning as indicated previously. The pairing term is dominant for the decay of heavy even-A isobars which lie near the valley. The parabolic term, however, dominates for nuclides which are several steps away from the zero isobar or for light nuclides. We have already noted that the pairing correction accounts for the numerous instances of stable pairs of EE-type isobars. The expected limiting θ values of beta-stable EE-type isobars can readily be obtained from Eq. (8-35) by using the lower sign in the first term, letting $\theta = 2i + \theta_0$, and setting the mass difference equal to zero. The observed limits conform roughly to the expression so obtained. It is interesting, although perhaps fortuitous, that our empirical functions predict that (1,1), (3,3), (5,5), and (7,7) OO isobars will be β^-- and β^+-stable, since for these very light nuclides the unfavorable pairing correction is smaller than the favorable parabolic effect.

Since the Q values of beta decay are usually small compared to Q values of bombardment reactions, the inherent irregularities of the nuclear mass surface associated with shell effects are more important in beta-decay energetics. Indeed, in some cases, shell effects and other irregularities account for the greatest part of the beta decay energy. We shall, therefore, give some attention to these surface irregularities.

8-5. "Magic Numbers." For many years it has been recognized that certain values of Z or N are "magic," in that they are particularly favored in nature from the standpoint of the stability and abundance of nuclides which have these proton and neutron numbers. For example, there are 10 beta-stable isotopes with $Z = 50$, whereas the average number of beta-stable isotopes for even-Z elements is less than 6. As another example, there are seven beta-stable isotones which have $N = 82$, whereas the average number of beta-stable isotones for even N is less than four. By counting the number of beta-stable isotopes or isotones for each value of N and Z[7] it is possible to draw certain qualitative conclusions concerning which values are favored.

The irregularities in the distribution of unstable nuclides, as well as the values of N and Z which are missing from stable species, also provide evidence for magic numbers, since nearby nuclides can transform to an anomalously stable nuclide by beta decay or alpha decay. In confirmation of the notion of favored values of Z and N, precise Q-value data, beta decay energies, and mass data indicate that certain nuclides possess masses which are significantly lower than the masses predicted on the basis of a smooth surface. Additional evidence for "magic" numbers is also revealed in the variation with N of (n,γ) cross sections as well as in the variation with Z of the quadrupole moments of nuclei. The general conclusion reached by most investigators after examination of the above evidence is that the Z or N numbers 2, 8, 20, 28, 50, 82, and 126 play a role in nuclear physics somewhat analogous to that played in atomic physics by the numbers 2, 10, 18, 36, 54, and 86, which are the Z values of the noble gases. The evidence suggests that several other N and Z values are magic but apparently have somewhat smaller stability anomalies associated with them. These numbers are sometimes referred to as semimagic or minor magic numbers. At this time there is no universal agreement as to which are the minor magic numbers.

The most convincing and quantitative evidence now available concerning favored, or magic, numbers comes from the data on nuclear masses, Q values, and beta decay energies. The analysis of the discontinuities in the experimental mass surface is greatly facilitated if Eq. (8-7) is used as a reference surface and the study is confined to mass residuals. These may be defined by

$$R(N,Z) = \Delta - \Delta_m^e(A) \tag{8-36}$$

where Δ is the experimental mass defect for the nuclide (N,Z). Corresponding to these mass residuals, we may define for every nuclear reaction the Q-value residuals

$$R_Q = Q - Q_m(A) \tag{8-37}$$

where Q is the experimental ground-to-ground-state reaction energy and $Q_m(A)$ is the function given in Table 8-2 for each particular reaction. It follows immediately from Eqs. (8-37), (7-8), and (8-17) that

$$R_Q = R(N,Z) - R(N',Z') \tag{8-38}$$

We see that the residual Q values are related only to the masses (or mass residuals) of the target and product nuclides and not to the very light particles involved in the reaction. In this respect the residual-Q-value data have the same significance as beta decay Q values, since

$$Q_{\beta^-} = M(N^-,Z^-) - M(N,Z) = R(N^-,Z^-) - R(N,Z) \tag{8-39}$$

and

$$Q_{\beta^+} = M(N^+,Z^+) - M(N,Z) = R(N^+,Z^+) - R(N,Z) \tag{8-40}$$

By referring the mass decrements and Q values to $\Delta_m^e(A)$ and $Q_m(A)$ instead of to our complete empirical functions, the tasks of computing residuals and decomposing and identifying the parts of residuals with physical effects are greatly simplified. At the same time we still retain the advantages of having reference functions which are close to the experimental values.

In Fig. 8-9 we show the experimental mass residuals for beta-stable nuclides. The open circles here denote odd-A nuclides, whereas the closed circles denote even-A nuclides. For the purposes of this discussion we may ignore the curved lines and the crosses on this figure (see Sec. 9-7). We note that the experimental residuals tend to fluctuate

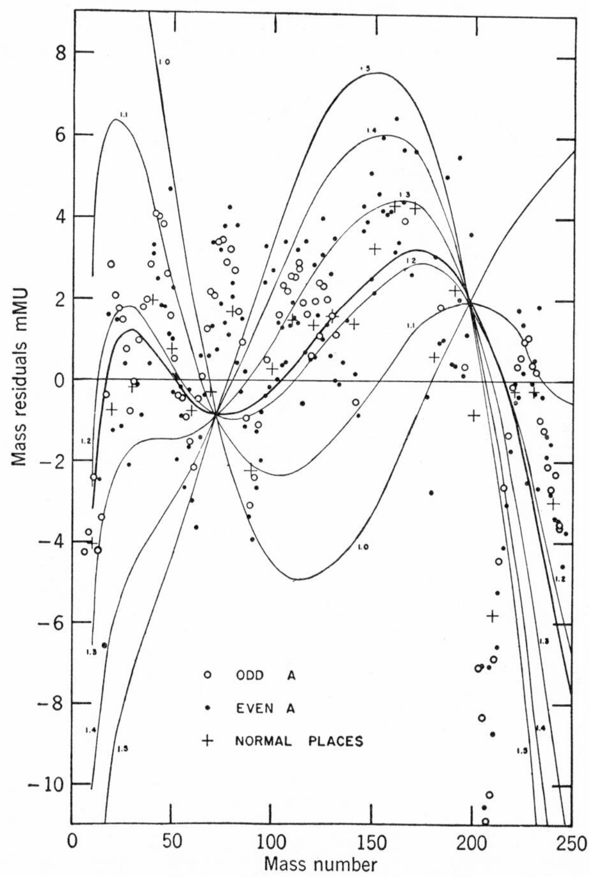

Fig. 8-9. The closed and open circles represent the mass residual of beta-stable nuclides relative to the values computed on the basis of Eq. (8-7). The significance of the crosses and the curved lines will be discussed in Sec. 9-7.

about the zero axis rather erratically. The standard deviation of the experimental points from the reference line is about 2.4 mMU. This is less than 1 per cent of the total variation (see Table 8-1, second column) of the mass decrements themselves. Accordingly we may conclude that our simple reference function Eq. (8-7) fits the experimental data quite well.

Perhaps the most outstanding feature of the mass residuals shown on Fig. 8-9 is the "short-wavelength" oscillations which occur in certain regions. We shall see (Sec. 8-7) that these may be interpreted as the effects of shell structure in nuclei analogous to the shell structure which occurs in atoms.

Since we have not introduced pairing and parabolic terms, the mass residuals, of course, reflect these two effects also. These effects show up mainly in the local scattering of the mass residuals. For odd-A values the θ coordinates of beta-stable nuclides should be between $+1$ and -1. Hence we would expect to see local deviations from the valley of the mass surface varying from about 0 to $25A^{-1}$. For $A > 10$ these variations are relatively small compared to the shell-structure oscillations. The scatter of even-A points, all but four of which are of the EE type, is expected to be larger, since the pairing correction permits stable EE nuclides to take on larger values of θ. This expectation is borne out by the data shown in Fig. 8-9. One might expect to see more clearly the trends of the shell effects as well as any other systematic deviations if the residuals were corrected for the pairing and parabolic effects. Unfortunately the precise functions $H(A)$, $D_m(A)$, and $J(A)$ which best characterize the pairing and parabolic effects are still uncertain. The difficulty lies with the fact that pairing anomalies and shell-structure anomalies cause large changes in the calculated position of the line of beta stability and in the calculated parabolic width. Since these anomalies are not yet known well enough to compensate for their effect, we cannot assign the best $H(A)$, $D_m(A)$, and $J(A)$ functions as yet.

8-6. Pairing Anomalies. Physically the pairing effect has been identified with a stabilizing interaction associated with the pairing of the last neutrons and/or protons. Were other things equal, EE-type nuclides would be expected to be the most stable nuclides, since they have two outermost pairs. OE- and EO-type nuclides, which both have only one outermost pair, are expected to be less stable, and the OO type should be the least. Coryell and Suess[8] in recent discussions use the EE surface as the reference surface and allow for the possible separation of the OE and EO surfaces. They denote the additional energy associated with the unpaired neutron in an OE-type nuclide by the letter ν, and the additional energy associated with the unpaired proton in an EO-type nuclide by the letter π. Assuming these energies to be additive, they denote the additional energy associated with an OO-type nuclide by $\pi + \nu$. To allow for the possibility of an interaction between the last proton and last neutron, we shall denote the additional pairing energy of an OO nuclide by the symbol τ. Since the function H which we previously introduced represented one-half the separation of the EE and OO surfaces, we may set

$$H = \tfrac{1}{2}\tau = \tfrac{1}{2}(\pi + \nu) \tag{8-41}$$

where the latter form is true only if the additivity assumption is correct. If we retain the convention of referring all nuclides to a surface halfway between the EE and OO surfaces, then the departures of the OE and EO surfaces from this intermediate surface are

$$\Delta_\nu = \nu - \tfrac{1}{2}\tau = \tfrac{1}{2}(\nu - \pi) \tag{8-42}$$

and

$$\Delta_\pi = \pi - \tfrac{1}{2}\tau = \tfrac{1}{2}(\pi - \nu) \tag{8-43}$$

respectively, where again the last two forms correspond to the additivity assumption.

A number of techniques have been employed to evaluate pairing anomalies.[9-12] A recent study[6] indicates that, apart from a few exceptional cases, the additivity assumption is approximately correct. No simple representation of π-ν differences has yet been found. The differences appear to run of the order of ± 0.4 Mev, switching abruptly in magnitude and sign at the magic numbers.

In connection with their study, Green and Edwards[6] have examined the relative merits of three functions which have been used to characterize the over-all trend of the pairing correction. These are Eq. (8-10) and two functions[13,14]

$$H(A) = \frac{36}{A^{\frac{3}{4}}} \qquad \text{mMU} \tag{8-44}$$

and

$$H(A) = \frac{140}{A} \qquad \text{mMU} \tag{8-45}$$

They conclude that of these three functions Eq. (8-10) leads to the best over-all variation with A but that a somewhat larger constant (12 instead of 10) would improve the agreement in magnitudes. However, they call attention to a theoretical treatment of shell effects[15] which suggests that pairing corrections are not really representable by any simple function of A, N, or Z.

8-7. Shell-stabilizing Correction. In addition to the effects discussed thus far, current ideas about nuclear structure suggest that we may identify a shell-stabilizing mass term which has minima at magic and semimagic N and Z numbers. It has been difficult to estimate this mass term, because the accurate data now available are confined to such a small region of the mass surface, and because it is difficult to apportion the parts of the mass residual to the separate physical effects which may account for them. An analysis of the residual proton and neutron binding energies after the pairing and parabolic corrections have been considered suggests that, to represent the shell-stabilizing term, the nuclear mass surface should be broken up into various regions which lie between planes defined by the major magic proton numbers and the major magic neutron numbers. Let us use the subscript i to denote a region of the mass surface lying between the upper magic neutron number N_u and the lower magic neutron number N_l and the subscript j to denote a region of the mass surface lying between the magic proton numbers Z_u and Z_l. The present available evidence does not contradict the simple assumption that within a given zone the shell correction has the restricted form

$$S_{ij}(N,Z) = -\alpha_i(N - N_i)^2 - \alpha_j(Z - Z_j)^2 + k_{ij} \tag{8-46}$$

where α_i, α_j, N_i, Z_j, and k_{ij} are constants which must be adjusted for each region. This shell function has the shape of an inverted cup with the peak value at (N_i,Z_j), a point which usually lies within the ij zone. S_{ij} takes on its minimal values along the boundaries of the zone and has the greatest absolute minimum at the corners of the zone (*i.e.*, at the doubly magic nuclides).

If we accept Eq. (8-46) for the shell-stabilizing term, it readily follows that, when the target and final nuclide lie in the same zone, a shell correction for the Q value of an $X(x,x')$ reaction arises which is given by

$$Q_S = 2\alpha_i(n - n')\left[N - \left(N_i - \frac{n - n'}{2}\right)\right] + 2\alpha_j(z - z')\left[Z - \left(Z_i - \frac{z - z'}{2}\right)\right] \tag{8-47}$$

This formula is quite tractable and immediately suggests a procedure for evaluating the constants, α_i, N_i, α_j, and N_j. Since $z - z' = 0$ and $n - n' = -1$, the shell contribution to the residual neutron binding energies is

$$-Q_S = B_{nS} = 2\alpha_i[N - (N_i - \tfrac{1}{2})] \tag{8-48}$$

By fitting straight-line segments to the residuals between various magic numbers after the other effects have been allowed for, we can evaluate α_i and N_i. The fact that these straight-line segments slope upward signifies that, as the shell is filled up, each neutron is more tightly bound. This is in harmony with expectations based upon the atomic model, since we recall that the energy necessary to remove an electron from an almost closed shell is greater than the energy necessary to remove it from an almost open shell.

The shell contribution to the residual proton binding energies is given by

$$-Q_S = B_{pS} = 2\alpha_j[Z - (Z_j - \tfrac{1}{2})] \tag{8-49}$$

an expression which is useful for the evaluation of α_j and Z_j. Estimates of α_i, α_j, N_i, and Z_j based upon recent data on proton and neutron binding energies are given in a paper by Green and Edwards.[6] Rather than using an extensive set of empirical constants, we can obtain qualitative estimates of shell effects by using the constants (all in mMU)

$$\bar{\alpha}_i = \frac{1}{N_u - N_l} \tag{8-50}$$

$$\bar{\alpha}_j = \frac{1}{Z_u - Z_l} \tag{8-51}$$

$$\bar{N}_i = \frac{N_u + N_l}{2} \tag{8-52}$$

$$\bar{Z}_j = \frac{Z_u + Z_l}{2} \tag{8-53}$$

These constants correspond to the straight-line segments shown in Figs. 8-7 and 8-8. In using these constants, we are exploiting the latitude now available to us by virtue of the uncertainties in the existing data. Essentially we are representing the shell-structure function by the expression

$$S_{ij}(N,Z) = -\frac{1}{N_u - N_l}\left(N - \frac{N_u + N_l}{2}\right)^2 - \frac{1}{Z_u + Z_l}\left(Z - \frac{Z_u + Z_l}{2}\right)^2 + k_{ij} \tag{8-54}$$

This expression, which, of course, must be treated only as a first approximation, has the distinct advantage of requiring only one empirical constant (k_{ij}) for each zone, other than the magic numbers themselves. Estimates of k_{ij} are given in Table 8-5.

TABLE 8-5. ESTIMATED k_{ij} IN mMU

i, j	2,2	3,2	3,3	4,3	4,4	5,4
k_{ij}	−2.5	2.5	3.0	7.0	3.5	2.5
i, j	5,5	6,5	6,6	7,6	8,7	
k_{ij}	5.5	6.5	8.0	3.5	1.5	

When added to our empirical mass surface the shell-structure term represented by Eq. (8-54) accounts rather well for the observed departures from the general trends of beta stability, nuclear masses, and nuclear Q values. In Fig. 8-10 we give the location of the minima of isobaric sections which have been computed using a recent collection of beta decay energies (circles) and a recent set of mass values (squares). The upper coordinate scale represents the values of Z, which, according to our empirical line of beta stability, correspond to the values of A represented by the central scale, *i.e.*,

$$Z_m^e(A) = \tfrac{1}{2}[A - D_m^e(A)] \tag{8-55}$$

The lower coordinate scale represents the corresponding values of N, *i.e.*,

$$N_m^e(A) = \frac{1}{2}[A + D_m^e(A)] \tag{8-56}$$

It will be noted that, in the neighborhood of magic Z numbers, the experimental vertex points move abruptly upward in relation to our smooth line of beta stability, whereas, in the neighborhood of the magic N numbers, they move abruptly downward. This behavior of the actual line of beta stability has a simple qualitative explanation. Whenever

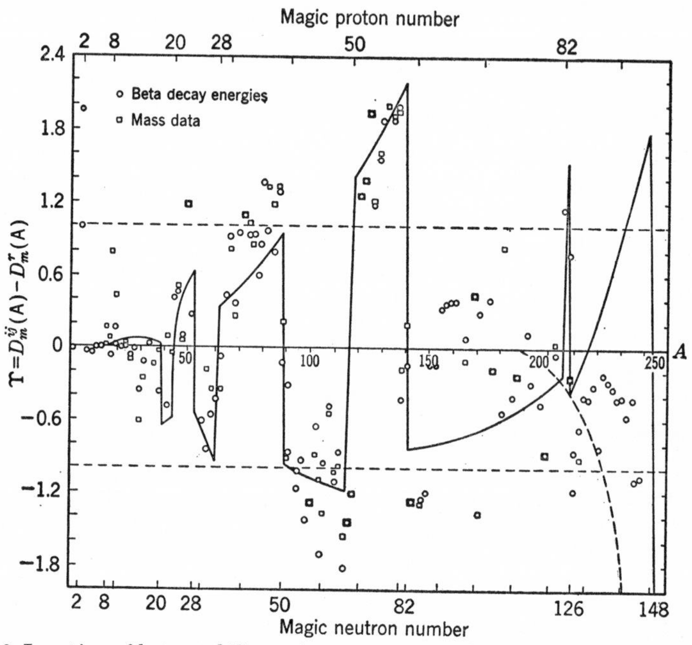

Fig. 8-10. Location of beta-stability point vs. mass numbers. The circles and squares indicate the points computed on the basis of experimental data. The solid line represents the line of stability computed on the basis of our shell correction and our smooth reference line of beta stability. The dashed line indicates the change in the smooth base line apparently needed in the very heavy regions. (*From Green and Edwards, Ref:* 6.)

the smooth line of beta stability comes in a region of a given magic number which we shall denote by N^*, the least-mass line will tend to deflect so as to seek N^*. In relation to any smooth, steadily increasing $D_m(A)$ function, the least-mass line will thus drift toward the neutron-rich region before it reaches $A^* = A_m(N^*)$. It will then run along the magic N number,[16] reaching into the neutron-deficient region after $A^* = A_m(N^*)$ and breaking away finally toward the smooth line of beta stability when the parabolic correction becomes dominant. The opposite behavior is expected when $Z_m(A)$ approaches a magic Z value.

The solid curve in Fig. 8-10 represents the location of the line of beta stability computed on the basis of our simplified shell correction. It is clear that the predicted line does fluctuate in accord with experimental observations. The agreement would be improved even further if, in the very heavy region, $D_m^e(A)$ were taken as the dashed curve indicated in Fig. 8-10.

In Fig. 8-11 we show a comparison between the experimental residuals for all beta-stable nuclides and the residuals computed with our shell-

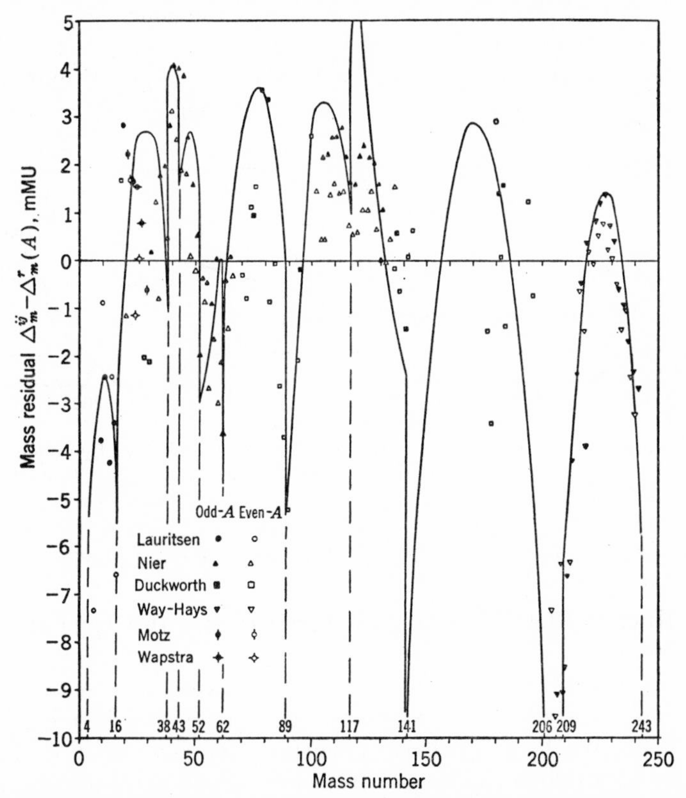

FIG. 8-11. The mass residuals vs. mass number for beta-stable nuclides. The solid symbols represent odd-A nuclides and the open symbols even-A nuclides. The discontinuous curve represents the mass residuals for the beta-stable points of a surface which incorporates our smooth reference functions and our reference shell-stabilizing term. (Sources of data are given in Ref. 6.)

stabilizing term. The computed curve fits well in several regions and shows the breaks at A values where they are experimentally observed. The deviations in some regions suggest, however, that the simplified shell correction can be improved upon. The experimental points in Figs. 8-10 and 8-11 do not indicate any marked effects which may be identified with semimagic numbers. The neglect of such numbers in Eqs. (8-46) and (8-54) therefore appears to be justified.

Perhaps the most significant observation to which we are led from our approximate representation of the shell effect is the large variation of masses which can be identified with a shell-stabilizing term. The fact that, in most regions where accurate mass values are available, the line of beta stability cuts the corners of shell zones has tended to obscure this feature of the experimental mass surface. Only in the heavy region do we meet a situation where we can gauge the true range of the shell correction from the doubly magic corner to the peak of the zone. In Fig. 8-12 we indicate how our reference line of beta stability (which is a fairly good one) crosses with respect to zones defined by magic N and magic Z numbers. We may conclude, therefore, that shell effects greatly distort

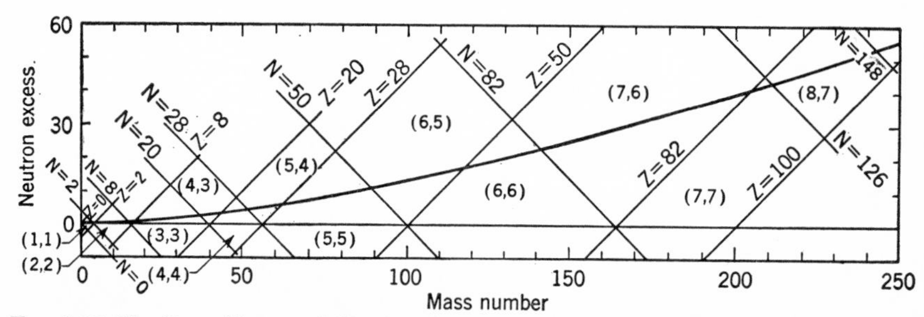

FIG. 8-12. The line of beta stability in relationship to zones defined by magic numbers. The numbers in parentheses are the indices of the zone (i,j). *(From Green and Edwards, Ref.* 6.)

the masses of beta-stable nuclides from what they would be in the absence of shell effects.

8-8. Nuclear Characteristics and Tendencies. In Chaps. 2, 6, and 7 and in the previous sections of this chapter we have attempted to organize the experimental data of nuclear physics, particularly as they concern the ground states of nuclei, in such a way as to reveal the regularities of these data. We have, perhaps, gone far enough so that it would be profitable to attempt to abstract from our survey the main characteristics and tendencies of nuclei and nuclear forces which have important physical significance. In the subsections below we shall label these characteristics and tendencies and summarize the evidence supporting the conclusion embodied in these labels.

Nuclear Energies Saturate. To organize the actual experimental data, we have concentrated our attention on the mass decrements (Aston's mass defects). However, the nuclear energies have far greater physical meaning in nuclear physics, since they represent the true mass deficiencies of bound systems of nuclei. If we ignore the pairing, parabolic, and shell corrections, we find, using Eqs. (8-12), (8-13), (8-7), and (8-8), that the nuclear energy per particle is given approximately by

$$\epsilon_m{}^e(A) = -\left(\frac{\Delta_n + \Delta_H}{2} + 2\right) + \frac{36}{A} + \frac{A}{100} - \frac{0.4A}{A + 200}\,\frac{\Delta_n - \Delta_H}{2} \qquad \text{mMU} \qquad (8\text{-}57)$$

This function, which percentagewise is quite accurate, even for nuclides somewhat removed from the line of stability, varies only slightly with A (see Fig. 8-13), so that roughly speaking we may say that all nuclides except the lightest have approximately the same nuclear energy per particle. In contrast with this saturation of nuclear energies, atomic energies per particle vary markedly with the number of particles. According

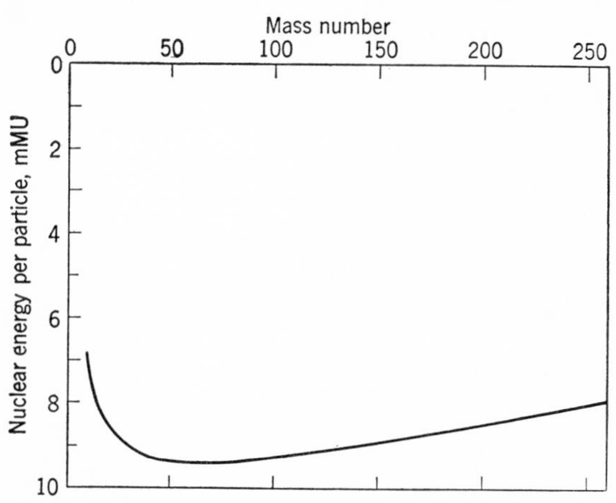

FIG. 8-13. The trend of the nuclear energy per particle.

to the Thomas-Fermi theory the atomic energy per electron is given approximately by[17]

$$\epsilon_a \approx -20Z^{\frac{4}{3}} \qquad \text{ev} \qquad (8\text{-}58)$$

Nuclear Matter Is Incompressible and Dense. The experimental relationship $R \propto A^{\frac{1}{3}}$, or $V \propto A$, also has a simple physical significance. We would expect these relationships to correspond to a collection of incompressible spheres packed together in the smallest possible volume (*e.g.*, an elastic bag of marbles). We shall refer to this property as the incompressibility of nucleons. It is sometimes referred to as the saturation of nuclear densities.

Apart from relatively small irregularities associated with electronic shell structure, atomic radii do not vary appreciably from 1.5 A. Accordingly the density of electronic matter is given roughly by

$$\rho_e \approx 0.6 \times 10^{-4}Z \qquad \text{g/cm}^3 \qquad (8\text{-}59)$$

Recalling [Eq. (2-7)] that nuclear densities are approximately equal to 10^{14} g/cm^3, we see that nuclear matter is about 10^{16} to 10^{18} times as dense as electronic matter. In view of this tremendous difference in densities one might wonder whether any natural laws can simultaneously apply both to electrons and nuclei.

Nuclear Forces Are Strong. The energy necessary to remove the last proton or neutron in nuclei is of the order of 6 to 10 Mev. This contrasts greatly with the ionization energy of neutral atoms, which runs of the order of 5 to 25 ev. Thus we see that within nuclear ranges ($\sim 10^{-13}$ cm) nuclear energies are much greater than atomic energies are at atomic ranges ($\sim 10^{-8}$ cm). We might legitimately inquire about the ratio of nuclear energies at nuclear distances with respect to coulombic energies at nuclear distances. The answer again is that the nuclear energies are larger, although, of course, the ratio of energies is smaller. Order-of-magnitude estimates worth keeping in mind for the nuclear, electrostatic, and gravitational potential energies of two protons at a distance of 2×10^{-13} cm are

$$V_n \approx 30 \text{ Mev} \qquad V_e \approx 0.7 \text{ Mev} \qquad V_g \approx 10^{-37} \text{ Mev}$$

V_e and V_g were computed with the assumptions that the known expressions for the electrostatic and gravitational potentials still hold. The nuclear potential energy is a guess based upon theoretical studies of the deuteron. We may conclude, therefore, that nuclear forces are very strong forces.

Nuclear Forces Have Short Range. Accepting the experimental facts concerning the incompressibility of nuclear matter, we can explain the saturation of nuclear energies if we assume that the strong attractive forces which hold a nucleus together have a range which is short, or comparable to the diameter of nucleons. Each nucleus would then interact with or bind only its immediate neighbors, and the number of bonds per particle, and therefore the binding energy per particle, would be constant. If, on the contrary, nuclear forces had a long range, as the coulomb forces have, each particle would interact with every other particle in the nucleus, and the energy per particle would tend to increase with the number of particles. Additional and more direct experimental evidence for the short-range nature of nuclear forces has come from the analysis of the results of scattering experiments (see Chap. 13).

Nuclear Forces Turn Repulsive at Very Short Ranges. The incompressibility of nuclear matter requires that nuclear forces effectively turn into strong repulsive forces when the distance between nucleons is small compared to nuclear diameters. Such an effective repulsion may arise in a variety of ways. It may be that the proper nuclear forces are ordinary static forces similar to electrostatic and gravitational forces, which actually turn repulsive at short ranges. Theoretical studies, however, do not favor this hypothesis. In the study of molecular bonds we encounter effective forces between atoms which have properties similar to those needed to explain incompressibility. The fact that these molecular forces effectively turn repulsive at short ranges is a quantum-mechanical effect connected with the phenomenon of resonance or electron exchange. For this reason serious consideration has been given to the possibility that nuclear forces may also be of an exchange nature.

Nuclear Forces Are Charge-symmetric. The assumption that the proper nuclear forces between nuclear particles are not directly dependent upon the character of the nucleon, *i.e.*, upon whether it is a neutron or proton, has been widely made and seems to be a reasonably good approximation. Many different investigations make it possible to estimate the proper nuclear forces which exist between charged particles apart from the coulombic interaction. We shall indicate below that the fact that the EO and OE points almost lie on a single surface suggests that the proper nuclear forces are independent of charge character. The most direct experimental test of the charge-symmetry hypothesis comes from the results of proton-proton and neutron-proton scattering experiments. Since the effect of the coulomb forces in a proton-proton scattering can be theoretically calculated, the deviations from strictly coulomb scattering may be attributed to the proper nuclear forces. An analysis of the experiments in the 0- to 10-Mev region indicates that for comparable states the proton-proton nuclear force is just about the same as the force involved in neutron-proton scattering, where the coulombic force is absent. An indirect dependence upon the charge character of the nucleon is thought to exist because nucleons obey a generalized exclusion principle. This would be similar to the apparent spin-spin dependence of the forces between electrons which arises indirectly as a result of the ordinary exclusion principle.

The fact that neutrons and protons transform into one another has prompted the view that both particles are different states of a single entity, called a nucleon. We may speak of a nucleon in the n state or a nucleon in the p state in the same way as we speak of an electron in a spin $\frac{1}{2}$ state or an electron in a spin $-\frac{1}{2}$ state. The analogy between the two charge states of a nucleon and the two allowed spin states of a spin $\frac{1}{2}$ particle has been used quite extensively in the theoretical literatures. This analogy makes it possible to treat a nucleus as an assembly of identical particles in the same way that we treated the electrons in an atom as an assembly of identical particles. In the nuclear case we must, however, introduce an additional degree of freedom to specify the character of the nucleon, that is, n or p. The name isobaric spin (formerly called isotopic spin) has been applied to this degree of freedom.

Neutrons and Protons Tend To Pair. The experimentally established relationship between EE, OO, and odd-mass points can readily be explained by assuming that paired neutrons or paired protons have a greater binding energy per particle than unpaired neutrons or protons. The additional stability of paired particles is expected for spin $\frac{1}{2}$ particles when certain simple types of interactions exist between nucleons. In the EE type both the last neutron and the last proton are paired. In the OE (or EO) type the last proton (neutron) is paired. The fact that the OE and EO points almost lie on the same surface, along with the approximate equality of the energy interval between the three effective surfaces, suggests that the proper nuclear forces are independent of the charge character (isobaric spin) of the nucleons. One might expect the OE type to be slightly higher in energy then the EO type because in the former case the last pair has a coulomb interaction. This expectation is confirmed in the case of pairs of isobaric nuclides with neutron and proton numbers $(Z_1 + 1, Z_1)$ and $(Z_1, Z_1 + 1)$—*e.g.*, ${}_1{}^2H^3$ and ${}_2{}^1He^3$. For these "mirror" nuclides the observed energy differences agree rather well with the energies calculated assuming an additional coulomb interaction. However, in most other cases this coulomb energy effect is relatively small compared to the intrinsic π-ν differences which we have noted in Sec. 8-6.

Nuclear Energies Tend To Quantize. According to current nuclear theory the mass effects which we identified with shell structure in Secs. 8-5 to 8-7 are indicative of a tendency of nucleons to take on only discrete energies. Electrons have this tendency to a high degree, and to a good approximation we may view a complex atom as a collection of electrons, each occupying an available discrete energy state of a single electron in a modified coulomb field. This model of the atom is successful because the attractive central coulomb interactions between the electrons and the nucleus are much greater than the repulsive coulomb interactions between electrons. In the nucleus, however, there is no dominant central field to which every nucleon is bound, and the interaction between particles is quite strong. Accordingly the independent-particle model, which is the basis of the quantum-mechanical treatment of the atom, would hardly seem applicable to the nucleus, and the very notion of quantum states would seem untenable. To accept this surmise would, however, be premature. Recent theoretical studies indicate that the independent-particle model and the central-field approximation can account for much of the evidence concerning magic numbers (see Chap. 11).

8-9. Excited States of Nuclei. In this chapter we have made considerable use of the mass surface as a means of organizing the mass data concerning the ground states of nuclides. In Chaps. 6 and 7 we discussed the evidence that indicates that nuclides also have characteristic excited states. These excited states manifest themselves in alpha, beta, and gamma decay and in nuclear reactions. Data concerning the excited states of nuclides have been reported in many thousands of papers, and the rate of accumulation seems to be increasing very rapidly. Several collections of excited levels concerned with special portions of nuclear spectroscopy are now available.[2,18–22] We may gain some insight into the scope and complexity of nuclear spectroscopy if we consider the large amount of experimental and interpretive effort consumed in the study of the $_7N^{14}$ nuclide (Fig. 7-8), which is only one of approximately 1100 nuclides now known.

To extend the nuclear-mass-surface concept to include excited states of nuclides, we might (conceptually at least) make use of a three-dimensional plot which has vertical posts at each grid point of a D-A or N-Z coordinate system. Horizontal markers along the vertical posts would represent the ground and excited states of nuclides on a scale with the zero mass decrement defining the horizontal D-A or N-Z plane. Lines of different colors, each representing a particular transformation, would connect the initial and final nuclides. Such a master plot would contain the complete story of the characteristic levels of nuclei and their involvements in nuclear transformations.

Of course, it would be impossible to represent the information contained in such a plot on a two-dimensional surface. Essentially each energy-level diagram such as Fig. 7-8 represents one vertical post of our master plot together with the known connections linking that nucleus to other nuclei. It would take as many such diagrams as there are nuclides to be equivalent to our master three-dimensional plot. By representing on a single sheet of paper sets of levels corresponding to nuclides which are related in some way, we may greatly reduce the number of diagrams which will give us the equivalent of our three-dimensional master plot. For example, we might represent sections of our master plot, each section corresponding to a single value of N, or a single value of Z, or a single value of A. Since isobars are so closely related to each other and can transform to one another by β^- decay, β^+ decay, or K capture, it would seem that the most physically significant sections would be isobaric sections. In Fig. 6-11 we have shown the $A = 125$ isobaric section of our master plot, showing the locations of the known excited states as well as the known ground states, all in relation to the ground state of Te^{125}. For this case the only cross connections represented are those corresponding to isobaric transformations. With a few exceptions, such as (n,p) and $(d,2n)$ reactions, other transformations would connect to other isobaric sections. We note that for $A = 125$ only a few levels are known for each nuclide.

If we attempted to compile a complete set of isobaric sections or to construct a master model at the present time, we would find that there are vast gaps in our knowledge as to the positions of the excited states of nuclei. Many of these gaps are due to the unavailability of experimental techniques for the exploration of certain ranges of excited states. Other gaps exist simply because we have not yet done the experiments which will give the data concerning these regions. By virtue of the development of precision techniques in nuclear spectroscopy and the tremendous effort in this field we are now approaching the era when we can start to construct an accurate master plot containing most of the low-lying excited states of most of the known nuclides. But for the moment we must seek regularities in the vast confusion of the fragmentary data on energy levels of nuclides.

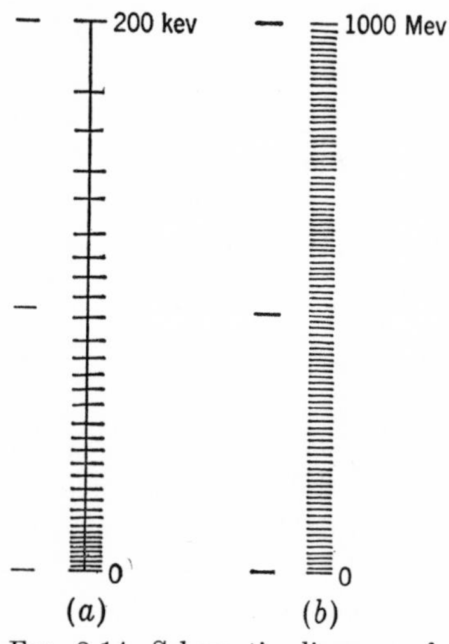

Fig. 8-14. Schematic diagram of positions of successive stripping levels for (*a*) a typical atom, (*b*) a typical nucleus.

In this connection it may prove instructive to compare certain features of atomic energy states with those of nuclear energy states. The energies required to remove the outermost particle (electron) in the atomic case are of the order of 5 to 25 ev, whereas in the nuclear case they are of the order of 5 to 15 Mev for neutrons and protons. The removal of an electron in an atom, of course, results in an ion of the same element, whereas the removal of a proton or neutron results in an essentially different nuclide. By virtue of the enhanced coulomb field acting on the outermost electron, successive ionization levels in the atomic case are spaced wider and wider apart, whereas in the nuclear case stripping levels are approximately equally spaced (5 to 15 Mev). We indicate in Fig. 8-14*a* a crude estimate of the atomic energy levels of a typical atom ($Z \approx 50$) corresponding to the successive ionization levels which result from the step-by-step stripping of the outer electrons. The last step ($\sim$33,000 ev) can be calculated by using the Bohr formula for a hydrogenic system. The disassembled system is about 200,000 ev above the ground static. In Fig. 8-14*b* we indicate crude estimates of the stripping levels of a typical nucleus ($A \approx 125$). The completely disassembled system is about 1000 Mev above the ground state. Thus there are two essential differences in the location of the energy points corresponding to the successive stripping of the last electron in the atom and the stripping of the last nucleon in the nucleus. In the first place, the orders of magnitudes of the energies involved differ by factors varying from 10^6 to 300. In the second place, ionization levels of atoms are unequally spaced, whereas stripping levels of nuclei are approximately equally spaced. The complete set of energy levels which may be identified with a single atom or a single nucleus is located within the ranges represented by these stripping levels. However, a diagram showing such complete sets would be so complicated as to be entirely inexplicable.

The states of greatest theoretical interest to the nuclear physicist as well as to the atomic physicist are the levels lying just above the ground state. These are of the order of 0 to 20 ev above the ground state in the atomic case and of the order of 0 to 20 Mev above the ground state in the nuclear case. Experiments indicate that the low-lying (<10 Mev) nuclear states are relatively fewer in number, broader, and more widely spaced (measured on a scale in Mev) than are the low-lying atomic levels (measured in ev). It has, in fact, been possible to study the detailed shape of individual nuclear levels (natural line widths), whereas it has proved very difficult to study the shapes of individual atomic levels. The highly excited states of nuclei ($>$ 10 Mev), however, are closely spaced and frequently overlap each other, so that only in special cases has it been possible to study the individual levels.

Various estimates have been proposed for the average distance between the excited states of nuclides. Wigner[23] on the basis of the review of Hornyak and Lauritsen[24] suggests that for light nuclei the average distance between levels is given by

$$D \approx 2 \exp\left(-\tfrac{1}{2}W^{\frac{1}{2}}\right) \tag{8-60}$$

where D and W are in Mev.

For medium and heavy nuclides a relation of the type[25]

$$D = C \exp\left(-\alpha W^{\frac{1}{2}}\right) \tag{8-61}$$

where C and α depend upon A and rather insensitively upon W, is suggested by a statistical treatment of the independent-particle and liquid-drop models (see Chaps. 9 and 11). The independent-particle model gives

$$C = 2\sqrt{2}\, A^{-\frac{1}{4}}\epsilon^{\frac{1}{4}}W^{\frac{3}{4}} \tag{8-62}$$

and

$$\alpha = -\pi\sqrt{\frac{A}{\epsilon}} \tag{8-63}$$

where $\epsilon = 21.4$. The liquid-drop model gives

$$C = 0.81W^{\frac{5}{7}}A^{\frac{1}{7}} \tag{8-64}$$

and

$$\alpha = 0.72A^{\frac{2}{7}}W^{\frac{1}{4}} \tag{8-65}$$

The present experimental evidence indicates that there are actually fewer low-lying levels and more high-lying levels than are indicated by these formulas.

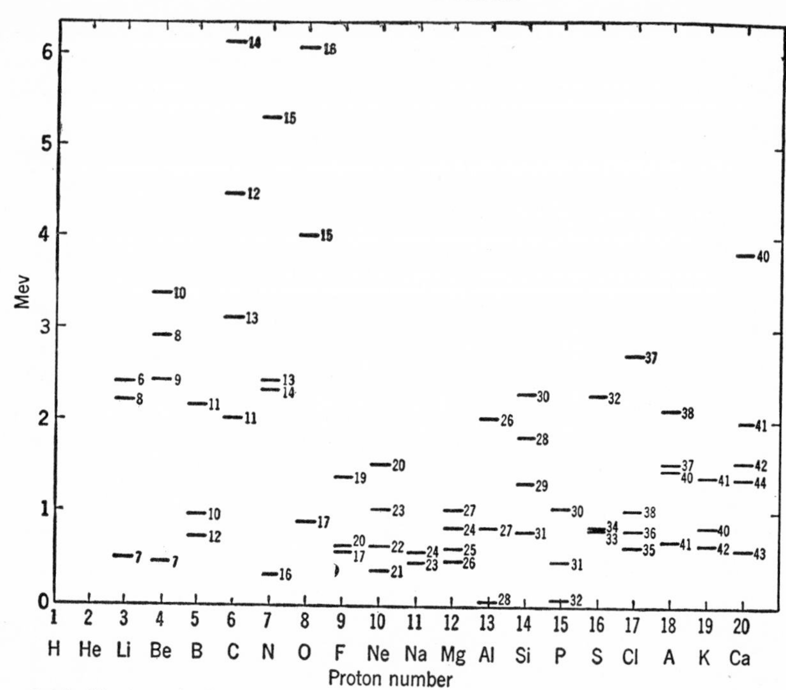

FIG. 8-15. First excited states, in Mev, vs. proton number up to $Z = 20$. Mass numbers of nuclei are given beside the level positions. (*From Pieper, Ref.* 28.)

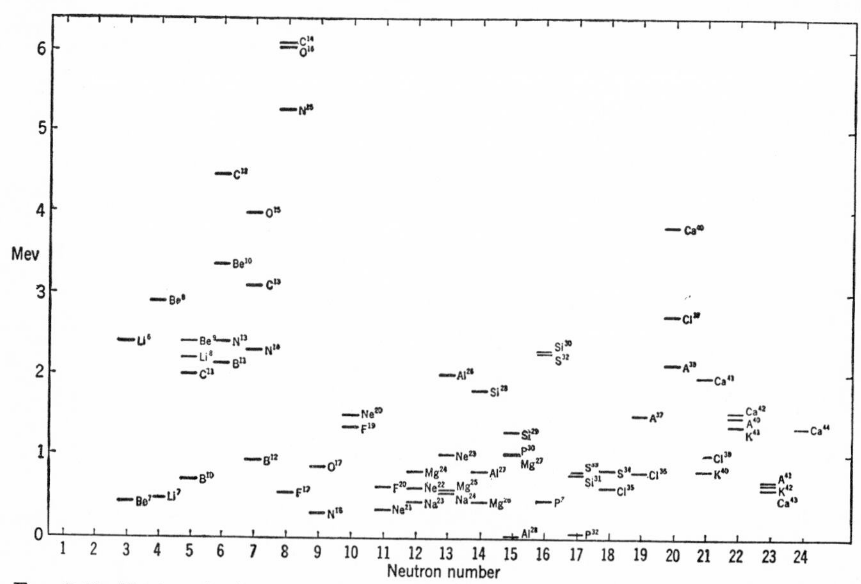

FIG. 8-16. First excited states, in Mev, vs. neutron number up to $N = 24$. (*From Pieper, Ref.* 28.)

Certain regularities have been noted[26–28] in the position of the low-lying levels of nuclei; these are closely related to the shell-structure regularities of the ground states of nuclei. Evidence for such shell effects is shown in Figs. 8-15 and 8-16, in which the energies of the first excited states of various nuclei are plotted against proton and neutron numbers. These plots indicate definite changes in the magnitude of the energies at the magic numbers 8 and 20. Pieper[28] has collected additional data in the neighborhood of $N = 28$, and here too he finds evidence for a closed shell. We shall return to a more detailed consideration of the significance of these shell effects in Chap. 11.

PROBLEMS

8-1. Plot the isobaric sections for $A = 25$, 133, and 239, each relative to a stable isobar. Assuming Eq. (8-2) is applicable, evaluate D_m and J for each of these cases.

8-2. Plot the isobaric sections for $A = 26$, 134, and 238. Assuming Eqs. (8-2) and (8-3) are applicable, evaluate J, H, and D_m for these nuclides.

8-3. Compute $\Delta_m(A)$, Δ_p, Δ_q, and $\Delta^e(A,D)$ for six beta-stable nuclides with known masses which are about equally spaced in A from 10 to 250. Compute $\Delta^x - \Delta^e(A,D)$ for these cases.

8-4. Using a parabolic correction, estimate the mass decrements of the nuclei Ti^{44}, Cr^{48}, and Fe^{52} on the basis of the experimental values $\Delta(Ca^{44}) = -30.76$ and $\Delta(Ti^{48}) = -36.82$ and $\Delta(Cr^{52}) = -42.92$ (all in mMU).

8-5. For a stable nuclide with $A > 25$ compute the empirical Q values for reactions induced by γ, n, p, d, t, χ, and α particles in which γ, n, p, α, and $2n$ are released. Whenever possible, compare these Q values with experimental Q values.

8-6. Approximately how many steps away from the beta-stable nuclide for $A = 50$, 100, 150, 200, and 250 must one go before the neutron and proton binding energies vanish?

8-7. What may be learned from a plot of the distance between the largest and smallest D values of EE-type beta-stable isobars as a function of A?

8-8. Compute the approximate shell correction for the masses in Prob. 8-3.

8-9. Compute the approximate shell correction to the Q values in Prob. 8-5.

***8-10.** Assuming a smooth surface characterized by Eq. (8-5) and a shell correction of the type given by Eq. (8-46), derive expressions for the minimum mass function, the line of beta stability, and the parabolic width which are applicable within a shell zone.

***8-11.** Using Eq. (8-2), show that in the neighborhood of the line of stability the mass difference between the odd-A atoms (A,N,Z,D) and $(A, N - 1, Z + 1, D - 2)$ varies approximately linearly with A, N, Z, or D when any one of the other three parameters is held constant. Show that the shell correction [Eq. (8-46)] contributes an additional strictly linear term to these mass differences. What do the slopes and intercepts of these lines give? What additional information may be obtained from the mass differences for even-A atoms?

REFERENCES

1. Halsted, R. E.: *Phys. Rev.*, **88**, 666 (1952).
2. Hollander, J. M., I. Perlman, and G. T. Seaborg: *Revs. Mod. Phys.*, **25**, 469 (1953).

3. This work and the related work described in Chap. 9 were carried out by the author with the aid of many students. The surveys and calculations of Bert A. Clanton, Julius Salacz-Dohnanyi, David F. Edwards, Nicholas A. Engler, Richard Gentry, Anna Hendren, Kiuck Lee, Nina J. Marucci, Robert B. Minogue, John S. Nader, Rosalind Oppenheim, Richard Oswald, and Kenneth L. Zankel were particularly helpful.
4. Green, A. E. S.: *Phys. Rev.*, **83,** 1248 (1951); **86,** 654 (1952).
5. Green, A. E. S., and N. A. Engler: *Phys. Rev.*, **91,** 40 (1953).
6. Green, A. E. S., and D. F. Edwards: *Phys. Rev.*, **91,** 46 (1953).
7. Flower, B. H.: *Progr. Nuclear Phys.*, **2,** 235 (1952).
8. Coryell, C. D., and H. E. Suess: *Phys. Rev.*, **26,** 609 (1952).
9. Glueckauf, E.: *Proc. Phys. Soc. (London)*, **61,** 21 (1948).
10. Suess, H. E.: *Phys. Rev.*, **81,** 1071 (1951).
11. Coryell, C. D.: *Ann. Rev. Nuclear Sci.*, **2,** 305 (1953).
12. Kohman, T. P.: *Phys. Rev.*, **85,** 530 (1952).
13. Fermi, E.: unpublished.
14. Glasstone, S.: "Sourcebook on Atomic Energy," D. Van Nostrand Company, Inc., New York, 1950.
15. Mayer, M. G.: *Phys. Rev.*, **78,** 22 (1950).
16. Kohman, T. P.: private communication.
17. Condon, E. U., and G. H. Shortley: "The Theory of Atomic Spectra," Cambridge University Press, New York, 1935.
18. "Nuclear Data," *Natl. Bur. Standards (U.S.) NBS Circular* 499 (1950).
19. Mitchell, A. C. G.: *Revs. Mod. Phys.*, **22,** 36 (1950).
20. Alburger, D. E., and E. M. Hafner: *Revs. Mod. Phys.*, **22,** 272 (1950).
21. Ajzenberg, F., and T. Lauritsen: *Revs. Mod. Phys.*, **24,** 321 (1952).
22. Goldhaber, M., and R. D. Hill: *Revs. Mod. Phys.*, **24,** 179 (1952).
23. Wigner, E.: *Am. J. Phys.*, **17,** 99 (1949).
24. Hornyak, W. F., and T. Lauritsen: *Revs. Mod. Phys.*, **20,** 191 (1948).
25. Devons, S.: "Excited States of Nuclei," p. 134, Cambridge University Press, New York, 1949.
26. Pollard, E. C.: *Nucleonics*, **2**(4), 1 (1948).
27. Scharff-Goldhaber, G.: *Phys. Rev.*, **87,** 218 (1952).
28. Pieper, G. F.: *Phys. Rev.*, **86,** 1299 (1952).

CHAPTER 9

LIQUID-DROP MODEL AND FISSION

In the preceding chapter we attempted to systematize the experimental data for ground states of nuclei by using an empirical mass surface which embodies the main regularities of nuclear masses. In the present chapter we shall discuss a theory which leads to a mass surface closely resembling our empirical mass surface. This so-called liquid-drop model has been investigated principally by Weiszäcker,[1] Bethe and Bacher[2] Bohr and Wheeler,[3] and Feenberg.[4] It has been exploited widely in nuclear physics as a basis for the prediction and interpretation of nuclear phenomena.

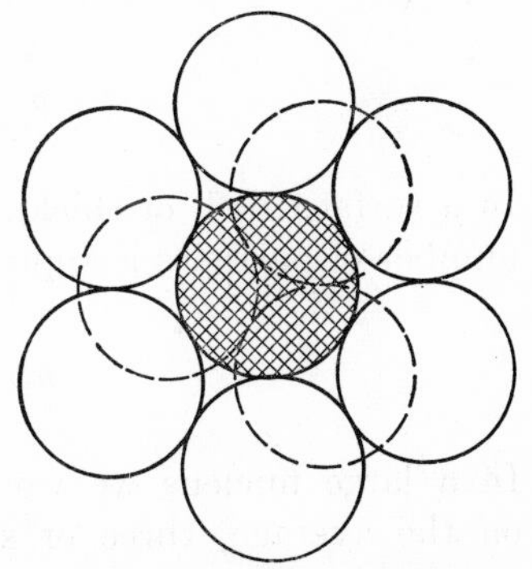

FIG. 9-1. Diagram indicating the 12 neighbors of a sphere (shaded) in closest packing arrangement. Three (dotted) are in contact above, and three (not shown) are in contact below.

The basic premise of the liquid-drop model of complex nuclei is that the number of nucleons in a typical nucleus is sufficiently large that the individuality of nucleons may be disregarded. While the treatment of such a system is most rigorously given by using the methods of quantum statistical mechanics, it is possible to arrive at three components of the expression for the energy of a complex nucleus by simple classical considerations. These components are the volume binding energy, the surface energy, and the coulomb energy. A fourth component known as the symmetry energy cannot be accounted for on classical grounds.

9-1. Volume Binding Energy. The fact that nuclear matter is almost incompressible, as is indicated by the equation $R = bA^{\frac{1}{3}}$, suggests that we treat a complex nucleus as a collection of a large number of rigid spheres held by charge-independent nuclear forces in a spherical closest packing arrangement. In view of the short-range character of the nuclear forces, we may assume that every interior nucleon has 12 bonds, one for each neighbor in contact with it (see Fig. 9-1). If each bonding energy is $-U$, then an energy of $-6U$ is identified with each interior nuclear particle (each bond energy belongs to two particles). Neglecting tentatively the fact that the nucleons on the surface do not have all 12 neighbors, we obtain as the approximate total nuclear energy

$$E_v = -6UA \tag{9-1}$$

We call this the volume energy, since it is simply proportional to the volume or the number of nucleons in the nucleus. This is the negative energy which holds the nucleus together. We might hope to assign a value to the constant U on the basis of a study of the deuteron problem, since the deuteron has only a single bond. Unfortunately assignments of U on this basis are not consistent with the experimental results for complex nuclei.

9-2. Surface Energy. Let us correct for the error introduced into our previous estimate by neglecting the fact that the surface nucleons do not actually possess 12 neighbors. The number of particles per unit volume in a sphere of radius R containing A nucleons is

$$\rho = \frac{A}{V} = \frac{3A}{4\pi R^3} = \frac{3}{4\pi b^3} \tag{9-2}$$

In a surface shell of thickness d equal to the diameter of a nucleon the number of particles is approximately

$$\delta A = \rho d 4\pi R^2 = \frac{3d}{b} A^{\frac{2}{3}} \tag{9-3}$$

In a large nucleus we would expect that each surface particle lacks, on the average, three or slightly more neighbors. The total volume energy should consequently be corrected by subtracting approximately $-3U\,\delta A/2$, since only half of the missing bonds should be identified with the surface particles. This correction, which is positive, may be regarded as the surface energy. Using Eq. (9-3), we find

$$E_s \approx \frac{4.5Ud}{b} A^{\frac{2}{3}} \tag{9-4}$$

Another way of arriving at such a dependence upon A is to assume that a nuclear surface tension exists of magnitude Θ (in ergs per square centimeter). The total surface energy associated with this surface tension is

$$E_s = 4\pi R^2 \Theta = 4\pi b^2 \Theta A^{\frac{2}{3}} \tag{9-5}$$

These two explanations are, of course, equivalent. We may view a collection of nucleons, held together by short-range forces, as having a tendency to maximize the number of nuclear bonds and thereby reach the most stable condition, or a tendency to minimize the number of missing nuclear bonds. In either case we would expect the surface area to tend to a minimum, *i.e.*, that the nucleus would take on a spherical shape. Such a tendency is characteristic of a fluid held together by surface tension.

9-3. Coulomb Energy. The fact that Z of the nucleons are protons, each of which carries a charge $+e$, leads to an additional positive energy correction. If we assume the protons are uniformly distributed within the nuclear sphere, we can readily compute the additional electrostatic coulomb energy by the use of Gauss's theorem in electrostatics. We treat the nucleus as a sphere of radius $R = bA^{\frac{1}{3}}$ having a charge $q = Ze$ and a uniform charge density

$$\rho_c = \frac{3q}{4\pi R^3} = \frac{3Ze}{4\pi b^3 A} \tag{9-6}$$

The electrostatic energy is simply the work done against electrostatic forces in assembling such a sphere. Let us suppose we have already assembled a sphere of radius r, and we wish to add on a shell of thickness dr which contains the charge

$$dq = \rho_c 4\pi r^2\, dr \tag{9-7}$$

Treating the entire charge of the sphere as concentrated at the center, we find that the work done in bringing dq from infinity to r is

$$dE_c = \rho_c \frac{4\pi r^3}{3} (\rho_c 4\pi r^2\, dr) \frac{1}{r} \tag{9-8}$$

Integrating this from 0 to R, we obtain

$$E_c = \frac{\rho_c{}^2 16\pi^2 R^5}{15} = \frac{3Q^2}{5R} = \frac{3Z^2e^2}{5bA^{\frac{1}{3}}} \tag{9-9}$$

One might arrive at the coulomb interaction by calculating the total interaction energy between pairs of protons which are distributed uniformly throughout a sphere of radius R. The result obtained is approximately the same as Eq. (9-9) with the principal exception that Z^2 is replaced by $Z(Z - 1)$.

The fact that this positive energy term increases rapidly with Z suggests that a collection of A nucleons may minimize its total energy by going to an all-neutron system, which it could do by β^+ decay or K capture. Nuclei in nature, however, do not show such a tendency; instead they seem to seek the division $Z = N = A/2$ for light nuclei and a somewhat lesser proportion of protons for heavy nuclei. Since the coulomb energy is relatively small for light nuclei, we might expect the fact that $Z \approx N$ for stable light nuclei to be indicative of the presence of a strictly nuclear force which has a minimum energy when

$$N = Z \qquad \text{or when} \qquad D = N - Z = 0$$

An energy term proportional to D^2 would of course have such a property. For heavier nuclei such an energy term together with the coulomb energy, which is a minimum when $Z = 0$, would lead to a compromise adjustment which would have $D = N - Z > 0$. This is in accord with observations of the trend of the line of beta stability. It is apparent that, to account for the trend, we must go beyond simple classical considerations and consider the nature of the strictly nuclear force.

9-4. Symmetry Energy. The best available evidence concerning low-lying nuclear quantum states supports the idea that nuclear forces are charge-symmetric. The evidence suggests that, were it not for the coulomb interaction between protons and the neutron-proton mass difference, the positions of neutron energy states and proton energy states would be identical. For simplicity of discussion let us consider a hypothetical system in which the masses of the neutron and proton are identical and no coulomb interaction exists between protons. Let the energy states be ordered by a number n which is equal to 1, 2, 3, . . . , with successive states corresponding to greater and greater energies, and let us consider only systems for which $A = 4n$. Since each state can accommodate four particles: a neutron with up spin (spin $\frac{1}{2}$), a neutron with down spin (spin $-\frac{1}{2}$), a proton with up spin, and a proton with down spin, we are led immediately to expect the division $N = Z = A/2 = 2n$, since this distribution would permit the total system to settle into the lowest energy state. Other distributions would of necessity require that some of the particles go into the $n + 1$, $n + 2$, . . . quantum states so that the entire system would then have more energy. This simple explanation for the tendency of nuclei to have $N = Z$ unfortunately breaks down when we consider what would be expected if several quantum states had the same energy on the basis of the strictly nuclear forces. Quantum states which have identical energy arise frequently in atomic physics and so might also be expected in nuclear physics. If, for example, we had nuclear energy degeneracy between the n, $n + 1$, $n + 2$, and $n + 3$ states, then it might be expected that the last four particles in an $A = 4n$ nucleus might distribute themselves in an effort to minimize the coulomb energy and the effect of the proton-neutron mass difference. If the neutron-proton mass difference could be ignored, then in an $A = 4n$ nucleus the last four particles might go into the neutron state of the n, $n + 1$, $n + 2$, and $n + 3$ states, producing a stable neutron-rich system.

In the $A = 4(n + 1)$ system the last 8 particles might go into the up- and down-spin neutron states, giving a highly neutron-rich system. The last 12 particles in the $A = 4(n + 2)$ system or the last 16 particles in the $A = 4(n + 3)$ system would then have to distribute themselves with 8 in neutron states and 4 in proton states or 8 in neutron states and

8 in proton states, respectively. While this argument is modified somewhat when we consider the neutron-proton mass difference, nevertheless we would expect the line of beta stability to have a very characteristic type of irregularity whenever we come to degenerate nuclear states. While irregularities in the line of beta stability have been noted, they do not conform to the characteristics to be expected by the simple picture given above. The actual evidence suggests that in the hypothetical system the tendency of nuclei to equal N and Z persists, despite degeneracy. This can be explained if we assume that the tendency to fill quantum states completely is much stronger than might be expected according to the simple interpretation given above.

Thus far, only a rather complex quantum-mechanical argument employing exchange forces seems capable of accounting for this strong tendency to equal N and Z. Qualitatively speaking, we have to introduce an exchange force which is attractive for all four particles in the same quantum state but is repulsive between identical particles (such as up-spin neutrons) in different states even if these states are degenerate. If forces of this nature were present, then the stablest hypothetical nuclear system containing A nucleons would be filled in sets of four with $N = Z = A/2$, since such a system would have the greatest number of attractive bonds and the least number of repulsive bonds. Other apportionments of A between N and Z would involve fewer attractive bonds and more repulsive bonds and in consequence would be less stable. The quantum-mechanical theory (see Chap. 11) suggests that the additional symmetry energy relative to an equally divided system is given by

$$E_{sym} = 6kUA\left(\frac{D}{A}\right)^2 \tag{9-10}$$

where k is a constant relating the strength of the exchange force to the strength of the ordinary force. One might also expect Eq. (9-10) on the basis of "dimensionality" and phenomenological considerations.

Besides this symmetry energy we might add a pairing energy term to represent the well-known tendency of nucleons to form pairs. However, we shall omit this term since we have nothing to add to the discussion of this term beyond what was given in the preceding chapter.

9-5. Semiempirical Mass Surface. Collecting the four energy terms discussed in the preceding sections, we obtain for the total interaction energy of a complex nucleus

$$E = -6UA + 4\pi b^2 \mathcal{O} A^{\frac{2}{3}} + \frac{3Z^2e^2}{5bA^{\frac{1}{3}}} + 6Uk\frac{D^2}{A} \tag{9-11}$$

A complete theory should give the values of the various constants in this equation, or at least relate them to one or two experimental constants. However, because we lack a true understanding of the basic nature of nuclear forces, it has not yet been possible to arrive at a theoretical set of constants which are consistent with the nuclear energy data. Instead it has been customary to accept the above functional dependence of E upon A, Z, and D, and to adjust the constants to fit the experimental nuclear energy data. Accordingly the nuclear energy is written in the form

$$E^w = -a_1 A + a_2 A^{\frac{2}{3}} + a_3 \frac{Z^2}{A^{\frac{1}{3}}} + \frac{a_4}{4}\frac{D^2}{A} \tag{9-12}$$

where the a's are adjustable constants and the equation is now treated as semiempirical. The superscript w stands for Weiszäcker,[1] who has been largely responsible for this equation.

Numerous sets of the constants have been proposed in the literature, each set following as a result of some adjustment procedure. To facilitate the detailed study of the effect of these constants on the semiempirical surface, let us express this equation in a form which will permit comparison with our empirical mass surface. The semiempirical mass decrement corresponding to the semiempirical energy is

$$\Delta^w(A,D) = A\,\frac{\Delta_n + \Delta_{\rm H}}{2} + D\,\frac{\Delta_n - \Delta_{\rm H}}{2} - a_1 A + a_2 A^{\frac{2}{3}} + \frac{a_3}{4}\frac{(A-D)^2}{A^{\frac{1}{3}}} + \frac{a_4}{4}\frac{D^2}{A} \tag{9-13}$$

To obtain the equation for the neutron excess at the minimum of the mass-decrement valley, let us set

$$\frac{\partial \Delta^w}{\partial D} = 0 = \frac{\Delta_n - \Delta_{\rm H}}{2} - \frac{2a_3}{4}\frac{A - D_m{}^w}{A^{\frac{1}{3}}} + \frac{2a_4}{4}\frac{D_m{}^w}{A} \tag{9-14}$$

Solving for $D_m{}^w$, we obtain

$$D_m{}^w = D_m{}^w(A) = \frac{a_3 A^{\frac{5}{3}} - (\Delta_n - \Delta_{\rm H})A}{a_4 + a_3 A^{\frac{2}{3}}} \tag{9-15}$$

Defining the coordinate θ^w for any nuclide by

$$\theta^w = D - D_m{}^w(A) \tag{9-16}$$

and substituting $D = D_m{}^w(A) + \theta^w$ into Eq. (9-13), we obtain after considerable cancellation

$$\Delta^w(A,D) = \Delta_m{}^w + J^w(D - D_m{}^w)^2 \tag{9-17}$$

where

$$\Delta_m{}^w = \Delta_m{}^w(A) = \left(\frac{3\Delta_n + \Delta_{\rm H}}{4} - a_1\right)A + \left(\frac{\Delta_n - \Delta_{\rm H}}{4} + \frac{a_4}{4}\right)D_m{}^w + a_2 A^{\frac{2}{3}} \tag{9-18}$$

$$J^w = J^w(A) = \frac{a_4 + a_3 A^{\frac{2}{3}}}{4A} \tag{9-19}$$

The key functions $\Delta_m^w(A)$, D_m^w, and $J^w(A)$ are expected to be quite close to the empirical functions which we defined in the preceding chapter. We may take advantage of these similarities to make a microscopic examination of the goodness of fit of the semiempirical surfaces corresponding to various sets of constants which have appeared in the literature.

9-6. Semiempirical Functions. In Table 9-1 we list various sets of semiempirical constants which have appeared in the literature, together with the neutron and hydrogen mass decrements which were originally used in conjunction with each set. The entries marked with a dagger refer to equations in which $Z(Z - 1)$ was used in the coulomb term.

TABLE 9-1. SETS OF EMPIRICAL CONSTANTS (IN MMU)

Symbol	Author	Ref.	Δ_n	Δ_H	a_1	a_2	a_3	a_4
I	Bethe-Bacher	2	8.450	8.070	14.885	14.176	0.623	83.770
II	Fermi	7	8.930	8.123	15.04	14.0	0.627	83.0
III	Mattauch-Flugge	8	8.945	8.131	15.74	16.5	0.647	88.24
IV	Feenberg†	4	8.920	8.130	15.035	14.069	0.627	77.755
V	Pryce	9	8.930	8.123	15.089	15.035	0.655	84.199
VI	Metropolis-Reitweiser	10	8.982	8.142	15.0825	14.0	0.627	82.970
VII	Fowler†	11	8.930	8.132	16.432	17.989	0.741	96.872
VIII	Green-Engler	5	8.982	8.142	16.720	18.500	0.750	100.00
IX	Green	31	8.982	8.142	16.918	19.120	0.763	101.78

† These authors use a coulomb energy proportional to $Z(Z - 1)$ instead of to Z^2.

Several procedures have been employed in arriving at these sets of constants. The most frequently used procedure has been to adjust a_3 and a_4 first, so that $D_m^w(A)$ matches as closely as possible the experimental line of beta stability. To see how well this has been accomplished, we show in Fig. 9-2 the deviations

$$\Upsilon^w = D_m^w(A) - D_m^e(A) \tag{9-20}$$

corresponding to the various sets. The superscript e, of course, identifies the empirical functions of Chap. 8. The solid circles are an estimate of the experimental line of beta stability which has been smoothed out to eliminate local fluctuations (see Fig. 8-8). The deviations appear quite large on this plot; however, when consideration is given to the fact that $D_m^e(A)$ varies from 0 to 55 (see Table 8-1), it becomes obvious that these semiempirical equations fit fairly well.

The fit of the line of beta stability is more sensitive to the ratio of a_3 to a_4 than it is to the actual values of these constants. Hence it is possible to have substantially different sets of constants which yield almost identical curves. Several efforts to evaluate a_3 directly have been based upon the study of mirror nuclides. Since these nuclides are pairs with identical A but with $D = \pm 1$, it follows from Eq. (9-13) that the mass difference is

$$M(1) - M(-1) = \Delta_n - \Delta_{\mathrm{H}} - a_3 A^{2/3} \tag{9-21}$$

Thus we may in principle use the experimental mass differences for mirror nuclei to evaluate a_3. Green and Engler[5] in their adjustment proceeded in the following manner: A pair of values of a_3 and a_4 was chosen which yielded a fairly satisfactory $D_m{}^w(A)$. Then a_1 and a_2 were adjusted

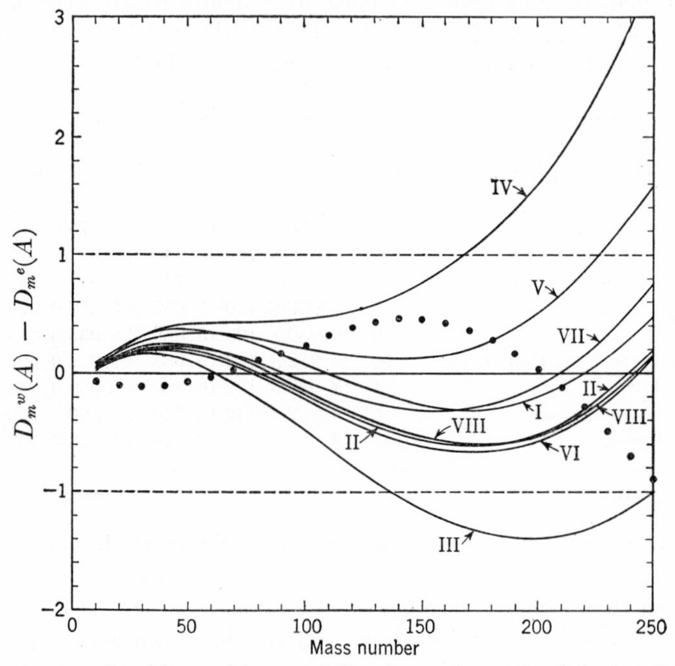

FIG. 9-2. Semiempirical lines of beta stability for various sets of semiempirical constants. The solid circles are taken from the smooth curve in Fig. 8-8. (*From Green and Engler, Ref.* 5.)

by an iterative procedure so that $\Delta_m{}^w$ matched as closely as possible the mass decrements of beta-stable nuclides. a_3 and a_4 were next changed by a constant factor to improve further the match of $\Delta_m{}^w(A)$ to the experimental data. Final small adjustments of a_1, a_2, a_3, and a_4 were then made to obtain best fits for both $D_m{}^w(A)$ and $\Delta_m{}^w(A)$. Since the semiempirical functions cannot be made to fit the experimental data exactly, the final adjustment of the semiempirical constants is associated with a small degree of arbitrariness. Figure 9-3 indicates the accuracy of the $\Delta_m{}^w(A)$ function corresponding to the set of constants arrived at in this way, as well as that of the functions corresponding to other constants which have appeared in the literature. In this figure we plot the residuals

$$R^w(A) = \Delta_m{}^w(A) - \Delta_m{}^e(A) \tag{9-22}$$

for the different sets of constants. The solid circles are an estimate of the experimental minimum of the mass-decrement surface which has been smoothed out to eliminate local irregularities.[6] Note that the deviations of some of the functions represented on this residual plot are quite substantial.

It is rather difficult to compare the function $J^w(A)$ with experiment because parabolic widths cannot be evaluated accurately with the data

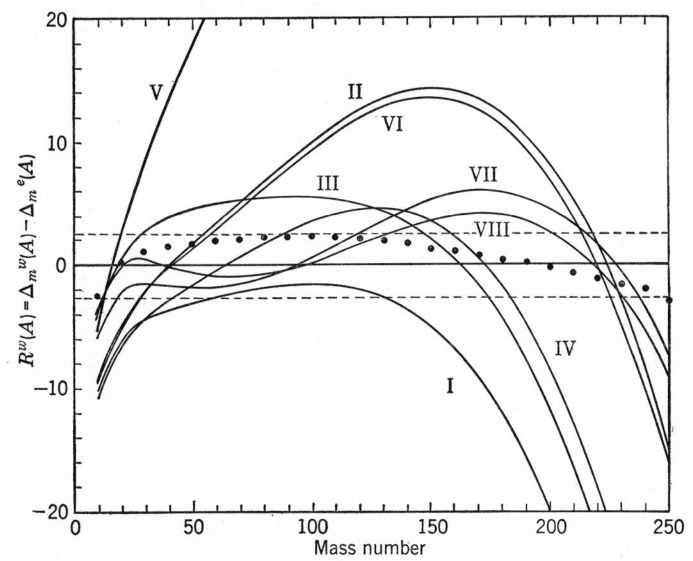

FIG. 9-3. Semiempirical residuals vs. mass number for various sets of semiempirical constants. (See references in Table 9-1.) I, Bethe and Bacher; II, Fermi; III, Mattauch and Flugge; IV, Feenberg; V, Pryce; VI, Metropolis and Reitweiser; VII, Fowler; VIII, Green and Engler. The small solid circles represent an estimated smooth residual from the experimental data. (*From Green and Engler, Ref.* 5.)

which are now available. If we define the ratio parameter r by

$$J(A) = rJ^e(A) = r25A^{-1} \qquad \text{mMU} \tag{9-23}$$

where $J(A)$ is the parabolic width determined from experimental data, then it can be readily shown that, for odd mass numbers,

$$r = [(\Delta^- - \Delta_s) + (\Delta^+ - \Delta_s)]A(200)^{-1} \tag{9-24}$$

where Δ^-, Δ^+, and Δ_s are the mass defects of the first β^--unstable isobar, the first β^+-unstable isobar, and the stable isobar, respectively. Accordingly experimental values for r can be determined only when two or more isobaric mass differences are known. Since we know two mass differences only for the heavy isobars and a few scattered light and medium-weight isobars, we cannot chart out the experimental r function at this time. The results now available are shown in Fig. 9-4, in which the experimental r values are represented by circles (mass data) and squares (beta-decay data). Also shown in this figure are the curves representing the theoretical ratios

$$r^w = \frac{J^w}{J^e} \tag{9-25}$$

We note that none of the analytical r's including our $r = 1$ has particular merit relative to the others. It is probable that the experimental pairing differences for odd-mass nuclides noted by Coryell and others have contributed to the scatter of the experimental r values seen in this figure.

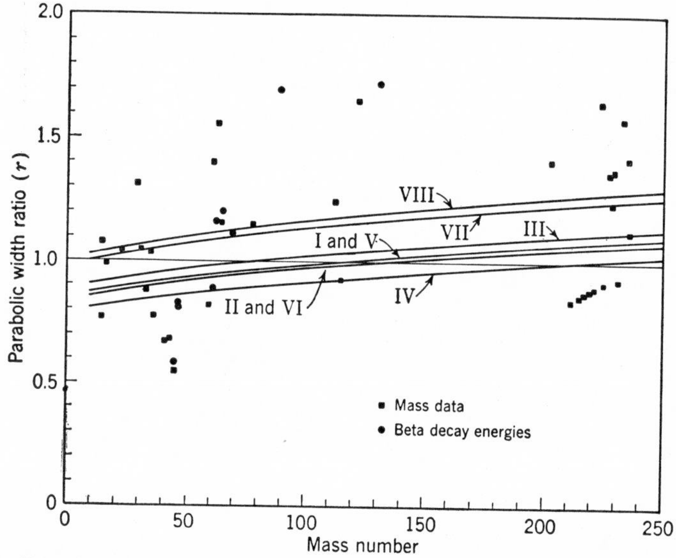

FIG. 9-4. Experimental and semiempirical parabolic-width ratios vs. mass number. The horizontal line $r = 1$ corresponds to our empirical parabolic-width function $J^e = 25/A$. (*From Green and Engler, Ref.* 5.)

9-7. Coulomb Radius Constant. An interesting by-product of the adjustment of semiempirical formulas to nuclear masses is the evaluation of the coulomb radius constant b. In view of the lack of understanding of nuclear forces, the significance of the nuclear-energy constants a_1, a_2, and a_3 is still obscure. However, if one assumes that the charge on the nucleus is uniform and accepts the formula $R = bA^{\frac{1}{3}}$, then, since $a_3 = 3e^2/5b$, the determination of a_3 gives the radius constant which characterizes the nuclear charge distribution. The standard procedure for evaluating a_3 has been to use the mass differences of mirror nuclides in conjunction with Eq. (9-21). These adjustments lead to $a_3 \approx 0.63$ mMU, which corresponds to $b \approx 1.48$ (in 10^{-13} cm). However, there are a number of reasons why we should suspect this determination of a_3 or b. In the first place, mirror nuclides have low atomic numbers, and this is certainly a region for which the liquid-drop model is not expected to be reliable. The validity of $R = bA^{\frac{1}{3}}$ is also in doubt for such light nuclei. In addition, certain nonclassical coulomb exchange effects[2] which are customarily neglected are quite appreciable in this region.

The adjustment procedure of Green and Engler ignored the mirror-nuclide data and instead concentrated on fitting mass defects and the line of beta stability over the entire range of A. The value $a_3 = 0.750$ arrived at in this study corresponds to a radius constant 1.237, which is substantially smaller than the older value. Independently of this work, recent studies of μ-mesonic X rays, electron scattering, and isotope shift also indicate a nuclear-radius constant in the neighborhood of 1.20.

In view of the importance of this question Green[31] has carried out a least-square analysis of the mass data directed at refining the coulomb radius constant and establishing the precision of the determination. The results of this recent study are shown in Fig. 8-9. Here the experimental residual data (circles and black dots) are shown in relation to semiempirical functions obtained by least squares. The crosses represent the centers of gravity of the mass-residual values located in twenty-four A intervals of ten units each, centered at $A = 10, 20, 30$, etc. The least-square adjustment was made to these so-called normal places. The heavy curved line represents the semiempirical function which minimizes the sum of the squares of the deviations. It corresponds to $b = 1.216$ and the energy constants of set IX in Table 9-1. The family of light curved lines represents the best fits attainable when the radius constant is fixed at the values indicated. From a close examination of this figure it should be clear that the heavy curve and the curve corresponding to $r_0 = 1.20$ are far superior to the remaining curves. A statistical calculation indicates that the heavy curve, when examined in relation to the normal places, is significantly better than the curve corresponding to $b = 1.20$. The root-mean-square deviation of the normal places from the heavy curve is 1.98 mMU.

Since much of the discussion in this chapter has been carried through with the analysis of small residuals, it is important to point out that the fundamental physical quantity of interest here, the nuclear energy, ranges from 0 to about -2000 mMU. The coulomb energy itself ranges from 0 to about 1200 mMU. The fact that the semiempirical equation together with four adjusted constants (one of which should be credited with the prediction of the line of beta stability) is capable of predicting these energies or the corresponding mass defects with a root-mean-square deviation of only 2 mMU would appear to indicate that the equation has considerable validity. It is satisfactory that the radius constant associated with the "best" fit agrees with the average radius constant obtained from μ-mesonic X-ray studies to within the small errors assigned to each value. The results of electron-scattering, isotope-shift studies as well as mirror-nuclide mass differences can also be interpreted using this radius constant. Since all of these phenomena depend upon the charge distribution of the nucleus, it would appear that the coulomb radius constant $b \approx 1.22$ is now fairly well established. We must, however, call attention to the fact that other substantially different radius constants are still being reported in the literature. Since these constants for the most part are determined from nuclear processes which sense the outer nucleons of a nucleus, it is not surprising that they lead to larger results. Nevertheless, it might be expected that, if the proton and neutron distributions were known, it should be possible to account for all these reported radii. However, we have not yet reached this level of understanding of the nucleus.

9-8. Difficulties with the Liquid-drop Model. Close examinations of Figs. 8-9 and 9-2 disclose that even the best semiempirical functions do not conform to the detailed trend of the experimental data. This apparently is a fundamental limitation of the semiempirical equation which cannot be corrected by an adjustment of constants. The major assumptions which have been examined in attempts to account for these discrepancies have been (1) the statistical assumptions, especially in connection with light nuclei, (2) the assumption of uniform charge density, (3) the incompressibility assumption, and (4) the assumption that shell effects are small and can be allowed for by simply smoothing out the observed irregularities. Clearly when the number of particles is of the order of 10 or less, we cannot accept the fundamental assumption of the liquid-drop model that the particles are many. To a large extent very light nuclei must be regarded as special individuals which may or may not have characteristics similar to their neighbors. Consequently, as we have pointed out earlier, it would be best not to attempt to adapt the liquid-drop model in its literal form to this region.

The assumption that charge is distributed uniformly throughout the nuclear volume also may be too stringent. Since protons repel each other, they would tend to concentrate on the outside of the sphere, and hence the charge density might be expected to be greater in the outer layers of the nucleus than in the center. On the other hand recent electron-scattering experiments (Refs. 21 and 22, Chap. 2) suggest that the charge distribution falls off as one goes to the outer layers. The presence of nuclear quadrupole moments indicates that charge distributions also vary with angle. The manner with which experimental quadrupole moments vary with N and Z defies explanation on the basis of a classical liquid-drop model.

The incompressibility assumptions must also be regarded with skepticism. A great variety of experiments support the general accuracy of the relationship $R = bA^{\frac{1}{3}}$ and hence also support the assumption of nuclear incompressibility. Nevertheless the experimental data can also be interpreted to allow for departures from constant density of the order of 10 or 20 per cent.

Several quantitative attempts have been made to relate the differences between the liquid-drop-model surface and the experimental surface to the nonuniform charge density and the compressibility of complex nuclei. To allow for these effects, the semiempirical constants have been permitted to vary somewhat with A. Recent studies, however, suggest that distortions of the nuclear mass surface due to shell effects are greater than had initially been thought to be the case. It now appears that some of the distortions which have been attributed to incompressibility or nonuniform charge density may actually be due to shell effects. However, the entire problem of apportioning the energies of complex nuclei to the component physical effects has yet to be resolved.

Assuming the semiempirical constants to be constant, we may develop an expression for the semiempirical Q value for any reaction by the procedure used in Chap. 8 for the empirical Q value. Unfortunately the algebraic expressions so obtained are quite complicated and difficult to apply. Because of this, most applications of the semiempirical equation as a reference equation for the study and interpretation of Q-value residuals have been made with the aid of compilations of semiempirical masses[10] which have been computed with the aid of large-scale machines. Since these compilations are not universally available, we might use for this same purpose the more convenient empirical functions, which are in many respects "averages" of the semiempirical functions. The main differences between the semiempirical Q values and the empirical Q values will be associated with the residual $R^w = \Delta_m{}^w(A) - \Delta_m{}^e(A)$. We see therefore that the anticipated differences in Q values are given approximately by

$$\Delta Q = (a - a')\frac{dR^w}{dA} = (a - a')\left[\frac{d\Delta_m{}^w(A)}{dA} - \frac{d\Delta_m{}^e(A)}{dA}\right] \tag{9-26}$$

The slope of the semiempirical function from (9-18) is

$$\frac{d\Delta_m{}^w}{dA} = \frac{3\Delta_n + \Delta_{\mathrm{H}}}{4} - a_1 + \left(\frac{\Delta_n - \Delta_{\mathrm{H}}}{4} + \frac{a_4}{4}\right)\frac{dD_m{}^w}{dA} + \frac{2a_2}{3A^{\frac{1}{3}}} \tag{9-27}$$

where

$$\frac{dD_m{}^w}{dA} = \frac{D_m{}^w}{A} + \frac{a_3}{6J^wA^{\frac{1}{3}}}\left(1 - \frac{D_m{}^w}{A}\right) \tag{9-28}$$

and the slope of the empirical function is

$$\frac{d\Delta_m{}^e}{dA} = 0.02(A - 100) \qquad \text{mMU} \tag{9-29}$$

The difference in the slopes represented in Eq. (9-26) for the semiempirical equation with the constants of Green and Engler is shown in Fig. 9-5. Since $a - a'$ is usually an integer less than 4, we see by examining the graph that the differences between the Q values based upon the principal term in the Weiszäcker equation and the Q values based upon the principal term in the empirical equation are relatively small in most regions. Accordingly we shall use the more convenient empirical functions for

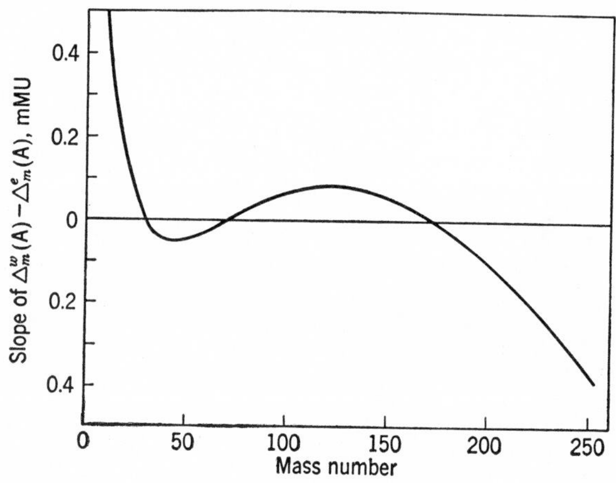

FIG. 9-5. Slope of the residual $\Delta_m{}^w(A) - \Delta_m{}^e(A)$ for the constants of Green and Engler.

some applications in conjunction with the liquid-drop model. By so doing, of course, we are compromising somewhat the theory of the liquid-drop model but not by much more than it has already been compromised by the use of adjusted, rather than theoretical, constants and by the use of constant, rather than variable, parameters.

9-9. Fission. The process of fission, which was discovered in 1939 by Hahn and Strassman,[(12)] is unique in that two approximately equal fragments are formed as the main products of the reaction. Such a division by a heavy element yields a reaction energy which is far greater than the reaction energy associated with any of the usual bombardment or decay reactions. Because $D_m(A)$, the line of beta stability, curves upward rapidly as A increases, the products of fission tend to have anomalously large neutron excesses, and in consequence the product nuclides tend to undergo several steps of beta decay. Since the masses of such neutron-rich nuclides have not been measured experimentally, we must use a semiempirical mass formula or our empirical mass formula to estimate the energy released in the fission process.

In binary fission we define the fission energy, using the usual symbols, by the equation

$$Q_f = M^* - M' - m' \tag{9-30}$$

where the asterisk denotes the nuclide which fissions and the primes denote the products of fission. For simplicity, let us study the case of fission into equal parts by a nucleus with even mass number. In terms of nuclear decrements the reaction energy in the symmetrical case is

$$Q_f = \Delta(A^*,D^*) - 2\Delta(\tfrac{1}{2}A^*,\tfrac{1}{2}D^*) \tag{9-31}$$

Let us assume that the initial nucleus has a neutron excess approximately equal to $D_m(A^*)$ (since we usually start with almost beta-stable nuclides). Using a smooth mass surface, the reaction energy becomes

$$Q_f = \Delta_m(A^*) - 2\Delta_m(\tfrac{1}{2}A^*) - 2J(\tfrac{1}{2}A^*)[\tfrac{1}{2}D^* - D_m(\tfrac{1}{2}A^*)]^2 \tag{9-32}$$

If we use the functions characterizing our empirical nuclear surface instead of those for the Weiszäcker surface, the results have a very simple form. Thus, using Eq. (8-7), we obtain for the principal component of the fission energy

$$\begin{aligned} Q_{fm} &= 0.01(A^* - 100)^2 - 64 - 2[0.01(\tfrac{1}{2}A^* - 100)^2 - 64] \\ &= 0.005A^{*2} - 36 = 50\mathbf{A}^{*2} - 36 \qquad \text{mMU} \end{aligned} \tag{9-33}$$

To illustrate the use of this result, we note that for U^{236}

$$Q_{fm} = 50(2.36)^2 - 36 = 242.5 \text{ mMU}$$

Equation (9-33) suggests that all nuclei with mass number above (below)

$$A^* = (7200)^{\frac{1}{2}} \approx 85$$

are unstable (stable) with respect to equal binary fission. This estimate of the borderline A value is modified by the negative parabolic term, which may be quite substantial, because the products of fission are far from the line of beta stability. The θ coordinate of a product of symmetrical fission is given approximately by

$$\theta' = \frac{1}{2} D_m(A^*) - D_m\left(\frac{1}{2} A^*\right) = \frac{100D_m(A^*)}{A^* + 400} \approx \frac{100D^*}{A^* + 400} = \frac{D^*}{\mathbf{A}^* + 4} \tag{9-34}$$

We note that, for the symmetrical fission of U^{236} ($A^* = 236$, $D^* = 52$), we have $\theta' = 8.2$. The large positive θ' values of the fission products of heavy nuclei suggest that they will tend to undergo about three or four steps of beta decay before reaching the stability line.

The parabolic component of the fission reaction energy, again using our empirical surface, is approximately

$$Q_{qf} = -2J\left(\frac{A^*}{2}\right)\theta'^2 = -\frac{100}{A^*}\left(\frac{100D^*}{A^* + 400}\right)^2 = -\frac{1}{\mathbf{A}^*}\left(\frac{D^*}{\mathbf{A}^* + 4}\right)^2 \tag{9-35}$$

For U^{236} this is -28.2 mMU, or -26.4 Mev.

Since the parabolic energy of the initial nuclide is negligible, one-half the magnitude of the above parabolic component can be identified with each of the nuclides formed in symmetrical fission. This is quite a substantial amount of energy, and in consequence we might conjecture that decay by neutron emission is also a possibility for the products of fission. This possibility may be readily investigated by calculating the neutron binding energy for a typical fission product, using the empirical equations developed in the preceding chapter. According to these equations the binding energy of the last neutron in a nucleus with coordinates A' and D' is given approximately by

$$B_n^e(A',D') = (10.972 - 2\mathbf{A}') - (\mathfrak{d}' - \mathfrak{d}'')\mathbf{A}'^{-\frac{1}{2}} - (\theta'^2 - \theta''^2)(4\mathbf{A}')^{-1} + B_{ns} \quad \text{mMU} \tag{9-36}$$

where $\theta' = D' - D_m(A')$ and θ'' and $\mathfrak{d}''$ refer to the nuclide which is formed when a neutron is pulled out of the (A',D') nuclide. When consideration is given to the slope of the line of beta stability, we find that, for a medium-weight nuclide, $\theta'' \approx \theta' - 0.75$. Consequently, when θ' is large, we can let

$$\theta''^2 \approx \theta'^2 - 2 \times 0.75\theta'$$

or

$$-(\theta'^2 - \theta''^2)(4\mathbf{A}')^{-1} \approx 1.5\theta'(4\mathbf{A}')^{-1} \tag{9-37}$$

For the symmetrical products of U^{236} $(A' = 118)$ this parabolic energy is equal to $(1.5 \times 8.2)/(4 \times 1.18) = 2.5$ mMU $= 2.3$ Mev. Considering the first and third terms in Eq. (9-36) but ignoring the pairing and shell energies, we find that the binding energy of the last neutron in a typical fission product is of the order of 6.0 mMU, or 5.6 Mev. Accordingly the medium-weight substances formed in fission cannot spontaneously emit neutrons unless they have an excitation energy greater than about 6 mMU. Since the nuclear fragments actually carry away an appreciable fraction of the fission energy as internal excitation energy, these fragments are actually energetically capable of emitting neutrons. These so-called "prompt" neutrons are emitted almost instantaneously ($\sim 10^{-12}$ sec) after the fission process. Experiment indicates that there are about two or three instantaneous neutrons emitted per fission.

The beta decay energies of fission products are large because in a β^- decay process the change in θ is -2, and hence the corresponding differences in the parabolic energies are large. Should a fission product decay by beta emission to a highly excited state of the daughter nucleus, the excitation energy of the daughter may be greater than its neutron binding energy, and a neutron may be ejected. The delayed neutrons which have been observed emanating from fission products are thought to arise in this manner.

9-10. Activation Energy. Although all nuclei having $A \geq 90$ are energetically unstable relative to decay by fission, nevertheless the probability for the spontaneous fission of naturally occurring heavy nuclei in their ground states is very small. For example, the half-life of U^{235} relative to spontaneous fission is about 10^{17} years. Apparently there exists a highly effective barrier against fission which holds any naturally occurring nucleus in a metastable state of equilibrium. The probability of penetrating this barrier is relatively small unless the nucleus has an excitation energy (W^*) which is almost equal to or greater than an activation energy (W^a), which represents the difference between the height of the barrier and the ground-state energy of the nucleus. In Fig. 9-6 we indicate the hypothetical potential energy of a nucleus as a function of the distance between the centers of two virtual or actual fission fragments. This figure indicates the physical significance of the statement that the original nucleus is in a metastable state of equilibrium.

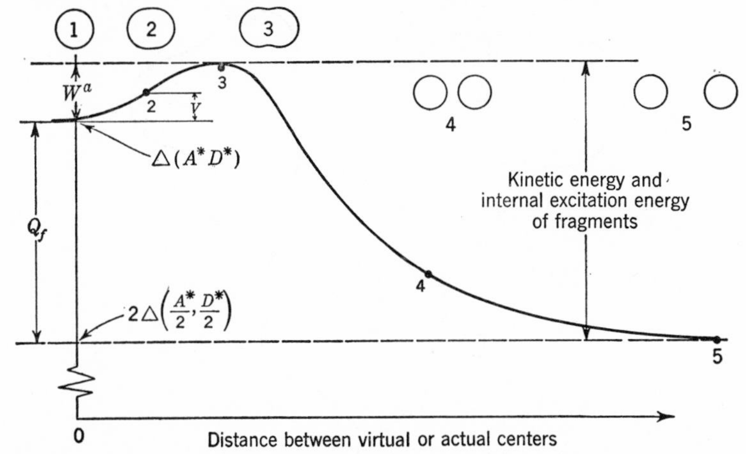

FIG. 9-6. Schematic diagram of the potential energy between two equal fission fragments.

The activation energy W^a by definition is the classical energy required to bring the nucleus to the condition of unstable equilibrium from which it will spontaneously dissociate into two parts. For very heavy naturally occurring nuclei ($A \sim 230$), activation energies are of the order of 4 to 6 Mev, that is, of the same order as the excitation energies acquired by a compound nucleus in the capture of slow or moderately fast neutrons. For medium-weight nuclei, activation energies are of the order of 50 Mev, which is very large compared to the excitation energy of the compound nucleus due to the capture of any light nuclear projectile. Thus from the practical standpoint the fission process is primarily of interest as a mode of decay accessible to very heavy nuclei.

We shall now present the essence of the calculation of the activation energy made by Bohr and Wheeler.[13] This calculation is based upon the assumption that a heavy nucleus may be treated as a classical liquid droplet held together by a nuclear surface tension. According to this

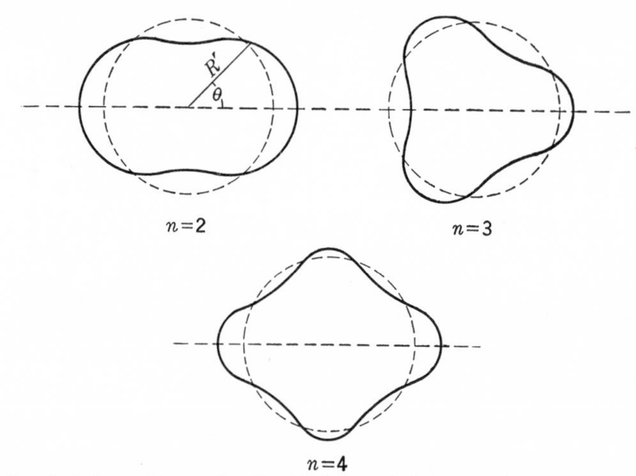

FIG. 9-7. Small deformations of a liquid drop of the type $R' = R + \alpha_n P_n \cos\theta$ for $n = 2$, 3, and 4. The figure corresponding to $n = 1$ is simply a circle displaced to the right a distance α_1. (*From Hill and Wheeler, Ref.* 14.)

model, if a nucleus acquires the excitation energy W^*, it will undergo vibratory distortions. When the excitation energy exceeds W^a, the critical activation energy, then the nucleus in its vibratory motion may reach a critical deformation for fission before it loses part or all of its excitation energy by some other process, such as radiation or neutron emission. In this event it will spontaneously subdivide, releasing the very large fission energy. To calculate W^a, we must solve the equilibrium problem of a liquidlike droplet in various conditions of distortion, a problem which is one of the very difficult problems arising in classical physics. Nevertheless, by making certain simplifying assumptions and approximations, Bohr and Wheeler obtained a solution which provides a reasonable interpretation of the results for distortions arising in the cases which are of interest.

The only terms in the semiempirical nuclear energy formula which are changed appreciably by nuclear deformations are E_s and E_c. To treat the energy changes connected with distortions, let us assume that, instead of a perfect sphere, the figure of the nucleus is described by a surface of revolution for which $R' = Rf(\theta)$. Since one may express an arbitrary continuous function of a periodic variable as an expansion in the Legendre polynomials, let us write

$$f(\theta) = 1 + \alpha_1 P_1(\cos\theta) + \alpha_2 P_2(\cos\theta) + \cdots + \alpha_n P_n(\cos\theta) + \cdots \tag{9-38}$$

where (see Fig. 9-7)

$$P_1 = \cos\theta \tag{9-39}$$
$$P_2 = \tfrac{1}{2}(3\cos^2\theta - 1) \tag{9-40}$$
$$P_3 = \tfrac{1}{2}(5\cos^3\theta - 3\cos\theta) \tag{9-41}$$
$$P_4 = \tfrac{1}{8}(35\cos^4\theta - 30\cos^2\theta + 3) \tag{9-42}$$
$$\cdots\cdots\cdots\cdots\cdots\cdots$$

and the α's are a set of constants which characterize the distortion. For any given $f(\theta)$ the deformation parameters (the α's) can be found by use of

$$\alpha_n = \frac{\int_0^\pi f(\theta) P_n(\cos\theta)\sin\theta\, d\theta}{\int_0^\pi P_n^2(\cos\theta)\sin\theta\, d\theta} \tag{9-43}$$

an equation which depends upon the well-known orthogonality properties of the Legendre functions. The surface area of any deformed droplet can then be calculated in terms of the deformation parameters by the formula

$$S = 2\pi R^2 \int_0^\pi f(\theta)\sin\theta \left[f^2 + \left(\frac{df}{d\theta}\right)^2\right]^{\frac{1}{2}} d\theta \tag{9-44}$$

The volume may be calculated using

$$V = \pi \int_{-1}^{1} y^2\, dx \tag{9-45}$$

where $y = R'\sin\theta$ and $x = R'\cos\theta$. Since the incompressibility condition requires that the volume of the nucleus be constant, it imposes a restriction upon the distortion parameters, a condition which becomes important when these parameters are large. Most studies of the fission problem have been confined to the symmetrical case, for which the odd distortion parameters, that is, $\alpha_1, \alpha_3, \ldots$, may be set to zero.

The total surface and coulomb energy can now in principle be calculated, the former rather simply since it is just the area multiplied by the surface tension. To obtain the coulomb energy, one must solve a rather complicated problem in electrostatics. Bohr and Wheeler in doing this carried their calculations to the fourth order in α_2 and the second order in α_4. They obtained for the potential energy of distortion

$$V = E_s' - E_s + E_c' - E_c$$
$$= E_s\left(\frac{2\alpha_2^2}{5} + \frac{116}{105}\alpha_2^3 + \frac{101}{35}\alpha_2^4 + \frac{2}{35}\alpha_2^2\alpha_4 + \alpha_4^2\right)$$
$$- E_c\left(\frac{\alpha_2^2}{5} + \frac{64}{105}\alpha_2^3 + \frac{58}{35}\alpha_2^4 + \frac{8}{35}\alpha_2^2\alpha_4 + \frac{5}{27}\alpha_4^2\right) \quad (9\text{-}46)$$

where

$$E_s = 4\pi R^2 \mathcal{O} = 4\pi b^2 A^{\frac{2}{3}} \mathcal{O} = a_2 A^{\frac{2}{3}} \quad (9\text{-}47)$$

and

$$E_c = \frac{3Z^2e^2}{5R} = \frac{3Z^2e^2}{5bA^{\frac{1}{3}}} = a_3 \frac{Z^2}{A^{\frac{1}{3}}} \quad (9\text{-}48)$$

are simply the undistorted surface and coulomb energies, respectively. The need for including the α_4 terms arises because of the strong coupling between α_2 and α_4; this coupling sets in when the distortion becomes appreciable because, if α_2 is large, the nucleus is elongated and must develop a concavity about its equatorial belt (α_4 negative) in order to preserve its volume.

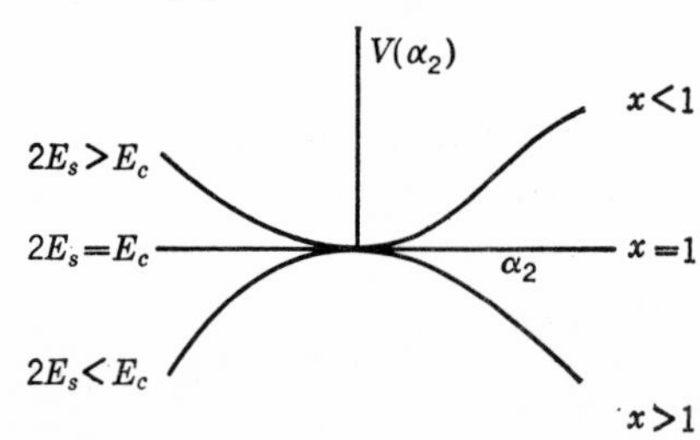

FIG. 9-8. Potential energy vs. small values of the distortion parameter α_2.

In the case of very small distortions the potential energy of distortion is approximately

$$V = (2E_s - E_c)\frac{\alpha_2^2}{5} \quad (9\text{-}49)$$

The sign of the variation of potential energy with α_2 obviously depends upon the relative magnitudes of $2E_s$ and E_c. If $2E_s > E_c$, the nucleus is metastable with respect to small distortions and will tend to restore itself. On the other hand if $2E_s < E_c$, the nucleus is completely unstable and will tend to keep going if the distortion is initiated. The borderline condition is (see Fig. 9-8)

$$2E_s = E_c \qquad \text{or} \qquad 8\pi b^2 A^{\frac{2}{3}} \mathcal{O} = \frac{3}{5}\frac{Z^2e^2}{bA^{\frac{1}{3}}}$$

or

$$2a_2 A^{\frac{2}{3}} = a_3 \frac{Z^2}{A^{\frac{1}{3}}} \quad (9\text{-}50)$$

Accordingly we may conclude that, for a nucleus to be metastable relative to decay by fission, it must have

$$\frac{Z^2}{A} \ll \left(\frac{Z^2}{A}\right)_l = \frac{40\pi b^3 \mathcal{O}}{3e^2} = \frac{2a_2}{a_3} \quad (9\text{-}51)$$

where subscript l denotes the borderline value. From the fission data Bohr and Wheeler inferred the value

$$\left(\frac{Z^2}{A}\right)_l = 47.8$$

The proximity of any nucleus to the borderline condition between metastability and instability may be conveniently characterized by a dimensionless parameter

$$x = \frac{Z^2/A}{(Z^2/A)_l} \tag{9-52}$$

If $x < 1$, the system is metastable, whereas if $x > 1$, the system is unstable. As is to be expected, the values of x for various naturally occurring heavy nuclei are always less than 1. For example, we note that for U^{236}

$$x = \frac{(92)^2/236}{47.8} = 0.75$$

We do not find substances in nature with x values much closer to the borderline value ($x = 1$), because such substances are unstable with respect to α-particle decay, with small half-lives.

Although nuclei with $x < 1$ are metastable with respect to small deformations, a large deformation may cause fission, since it will favor the repulsive long-range coulomb forces over the attractive short forces which give rise to the effect of surface tension. To obtain the critical activation energy, it is, therefore, necessary to calculate the critical deformation $(\alpha_2{}^c, \alpha_4{}^c)$ which will bring the nucleus to the critical equilibrium condition which corresponds to the verge of division. From dimensional considerations we may set

$$W^a = E_s\Phi(x) \tag{9-53}$$

where $\Phi(x)$ is an as yet unknown function of the fissionability parameter. If we could solve the problem of a surface in equilibrium under the action of surface-tension and coulomb forces for arbitrarily large distortion parameters, then we could determine $\Phi(x)$ for all values of x. However, as this is a very complicated problem, Bohr and Wheeler undertook only the task of finding $\Phi(x)$ for symmetrical fission and for certain restricted values of x.

Let us first find the value of W^a for a hypothetical nucleus of mass A for which $x = 0$ (that is, $Z = 0$). Since there is no repulsive force, W^a is now simply the work done against surface tension in separating the original sphere of volume V into two spheres, each having the volume $V_1 = V/2$ and the radius

$$R_1 = (\tfrac{1}{2})^{\frac{1}{3}}R \tag{9-54}$$

Consequently

$$W^a = 2(4\pi R_1^2\mathcal{O}) - 4\pi R^2\mathcal{O} = 4\pi R^2\mathcal{O}(2^{\frac{1}{3}} - 1) \tag{9-55}$$

and in view of Eq. (9-53)

$$\Phi(0) = 2^{\frac{1}{3}} - 1 = 0.260 \tag{9-56}$$

For a hypothetical system of mass number A for which x is small but not zero the critical shape is approximately that of two spheres held together by a narrow neck of radius r_n. Equilibrium now occurs when the repulsive coulomb forces between the two spheres with radii given by Eq. (9-54) are balanced by the surface tension. The equilibrium condition is thus approximately (see Fig. 9-9)

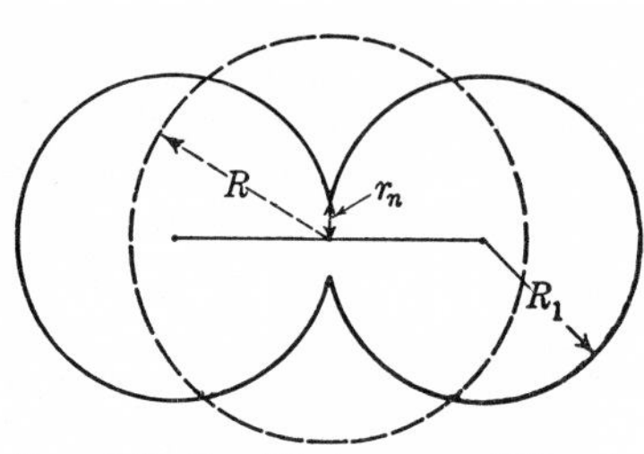

FIG. 9-9. Equilibrium condition for droplet held together by surface tension when a small charge is on droplet. The large sphere represents undistorted droplet.

$$\frac{(Ze/2)^2}{(2R_1)^2} = 2\pi r_n\mathcal{O} \tag{9-57}$$

To calculate Φ for this case, we again subtract the energy of the original system from the energy of the distorted equilibrium system. Ignoring the second order effects of the neck on the surface energy and the coulomb energy, the correction to the previous estimate of the potential energy is

$$\Delta V = 2\,\frac{3}{5}\,\frac{(Ze/2)^2}{R_1} + \frac{(Ze/2)^2}{2R_1} - \frac{3}{5}\,\frac{(Ze)^2}{R} \tag{9-58}$$

where the terms on the right are simply the self-energies of the two spheres plus their interaction energy, less the self-energy of the original sphere. Using

$$E_c = 2E_s x \tag{9-59}$$

[see Eqs. (9-50), (9-52), and (9-53)], we find

$$\Phi(x) = 0.260 - 0.215x \qquad \text{for } x \ll 1 \tag{9-60}$$

If desired, this expression could readily be corrected for the small energetic effects associated with the neck.

Let us next consider the more interesting case for which x is slightly less than 1. For this case it is necessary to find the deformation (α_2^c and α_4^c) for which the deformation energy reaches a maximum and is about to decrease. The dependence of the distortion energy upon α_2 and α_4 given by Eq. (9-46) can be represented as a surface on a diagram in which α_2 and α_4 are coordinates with equienergy lines as contours (see Fig. 9-10). The function is such that for a given α_2 there is a critical value of α_4 which will minimize V with respect to α_4. Bohr and Wheeler obtain for this critical value

$$\alpha_4{}^m = -\tfrac{243}{593}\alpha_2{}^2 \tag{9-61}$$

The function $V(\alpha_2, \alpha_4{}^m)$ obtained by using Eq. (9-61) in Eq. (9-46) gives the values of the distortion energy along a restricted path for which the energy is stationary to small variations in α_4. The maximum of this restricted function may now be obtained by equating to zero its derivative with respect to α_2. The critical parameters $\alpha_2{}^c$ and $\alpha_4{}^c$, when inserted into Eq. (9-61), then give the potential energy of the nucleus at the lowest unstable point of equilibrium. This is the activation energy W^a. These critical parameters also characterize the shape of the liquid

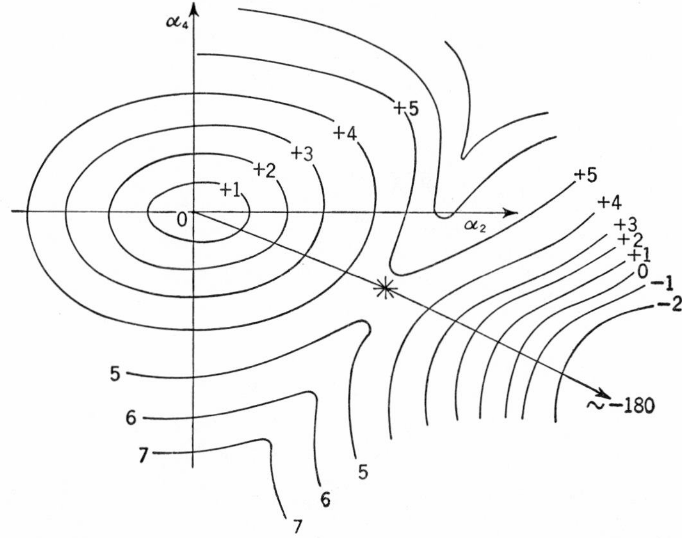

FIG. 9-10. Potential-energy surface vs. α_2 and α_4. The star denotes the saddle point. (*After Bohr and Wheeler, Ref.* 13.)

droplet at the equilibrium condition. In Fig. 9-11 we indicate the critical shapes of a liquid droplet for various values of the fissionability parameter x.

The appropriate name "saddle point" has been applied to this critical distortion. In relation to this deformation point, the energy goes down in one direction, but goes up in the perpendicular direction. Bohr and Wheeler suggest a classical analogue to the fission process consisting of a ball lying in a hollow. The height of the ball relative to the bottom of the hollow represents the deformation energy. "If the ball receives an impulse (neutron capture), it will execute complicated Lissajous figures of oscillation about its equilibrium. If its energy is sufficient, it will, in the course of time, happen to move in the proper direction to pass over the saddle point (after which fission will occur) unless it loses its energy (radiation or neutron re-emission)." In a similar way if the liquid droplet receives an impulse, it will execute complex vibratory motions. After many vibrations the total energy may happen to concentrate in a mode of distortion which corresponds to the critical shape, in which case the droplet will proceed to fission.

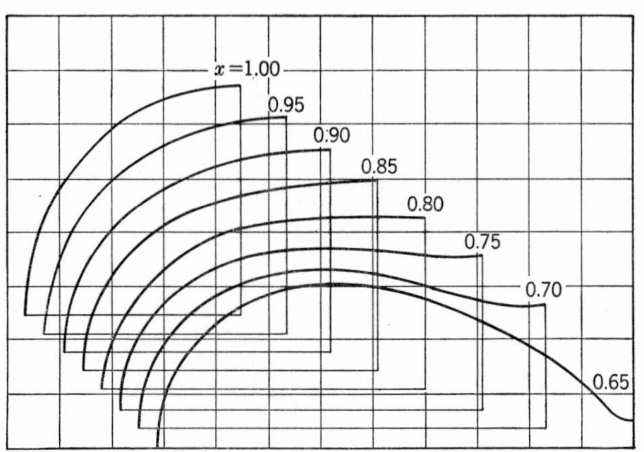

FIG. 9-11. Critical shapes at the saddle point for various values of x. *(From Hill and Wheeler, Ref. 14.)*

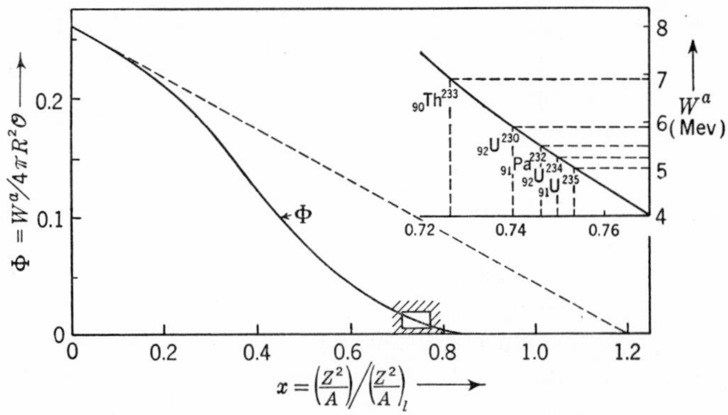

FIG. 9-12. $\Phi(x)$ vs. x, based upon calculations in the neighborhood of $x = 0$ and $x = 1$. The crosshatches show the region of interest. Since the surface energy changes only slightly in this region, the value $E_s = 530$ Mev, based upon $4\pi R^2\Theta = 14$ Mev, is used for the enlarged insert with $(Z^2/A)_l = 47.8$. *(From Bohr and Wheeler, Ref. 13.)*

The $\Phi(x)$ which was identified with the activation energy by Bohr and Wheeler as a result of their analysis is

$$\Phi(x) = 0.726(1 - x)^3 - 0.3292(1 - x)^4 \qquad x \lesssim 1 \qquad (9\text{-}62)$$

If this function is joined by a reasonable graphical interpolation to the $\Phi(x)$ function for $x \gtrsim 0$, we obtain a function for all x between 0 and 1 (see Fig. 9-12) which may be accepted with confidence.

Bohr and Wheeler chose the constant $a_2 = 14.0$ Mev from an early set of semiempirical constants and $(Z^2/A)_l = 47.8$, a value which led to the 1939 experimental activation energy for U^{239}. Since the range of x values for the very heavy nuclides is quite small, this adjustment procedure ensured that the computed values for W^a would be in approximate agreement with experimental values even if the theory had only an approximate validity. In column 1 of Table 9-2 we give the W^a values

TABLE 9-2. ACTIVATION ENERGIES (IN MEV) FOR SEVERAL HEAVY NUCLIDES

Nuclide	W^a (B and W) (1)	W^a (F and M) (2)	W^a (S) (3)	W^a (exptl.) (4)
Th^{232}	6.7	...	6.4	5.4
U^{233}	4.8	5.7	5.9	5.13
U^{235}	5.0	6.1	6.0	5.31
U^{238}	5.8	7.0	6.2	5.08
Pu^{239}	4.9	4.9	6.0	5.31

for several nuclides computed by Bohr and Wheeler. In column 2 we give the results of the more recent and more exact calculations made by Frankel and Metropolis[15] with the aid of the Eniac computer. In column 3 we list the results based upon

$$W^a = 19.0 - 0.36 \frac{Z^2}{A} \qquad \text{Mev} \tag{9-63}$$

a simple semiempirical equation proposed by Seaborg.[16] In the last column we list the experimental activation energies measured by Koch *et al.*[17] (see discussion below).

An examination of this table shows that the calculated activation energies agree with the experimental photofission thresholds in order of magnitude, but that there are significant discrepancies. In particular the fact that W^a for U^{238} is less than that for U^{235} appears to be in conflict with the theory, and the explanation of this discrepancy has not yet been given. It is probable that the classical liquid-drop model is useful only for obtaining the gross values of W^a, but that a more precise quantum model is needed for the fine energy structure.

Recently Hill and Wheeler[14] have explored a model which incorporates both the individual aspect of the independent-particle model and the collective aspects of the liquid-drop model. The anomalies discussed above have a natural explanation in their theory, although quantitative predictions have not yet been made with it.

9-11. Fissionability. The activation energy which we calculated in the previous section may be regarded as a barrier against fission somewhat as the coulomb potential is a barrier against alpha decay. Nevertheless a heavy nucleus may fission spontaneously by "tunneling" through the barrier against fission, although the probability for this process is quite small. Seaborg[16,18] has found on the basis of semi-empirical considerations that the half-lives for spontaneous fission are given approximately by

$$\tau_{\frac{1}{2}} = 10^{-21} \times 10^{178-3.75Z^2/A} \quad \text{sec} \tag{9-64}$$

In Fig. 9-13 we show the success of this relationship. If the fissioning nucleus is excited, the probability for fission increases rapidly with the

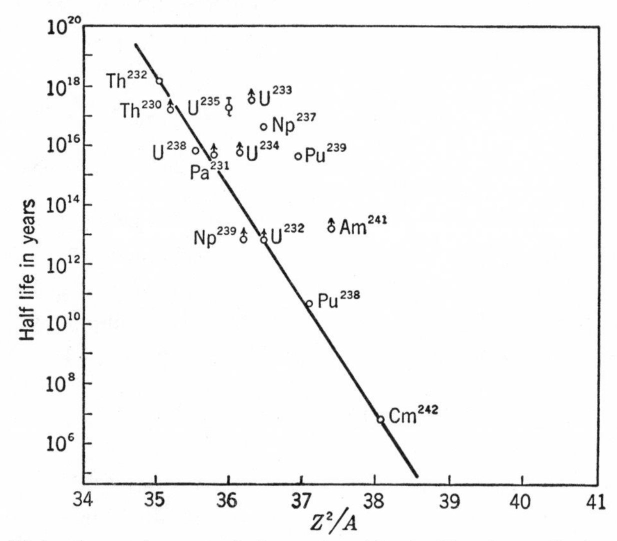

FIG. 9-13. Plot of spontaneous fission rates (ô signifies lower limit to half-life). (*From Seaborg, Ref.* 18.)

energy of excitation, especially when the excitation energy approaches W^a. Accordingly a rather straightforward method for measuring activation energies experimentally is to bombard heavy nuclides with gamma rays and to note the gamma-ray energy corresponding to the onset of appreciable fission yields. Such photofission experiments, using gamma rays obtained from a betatron, were the basis for the experimental W^a values quoted in Table 9-2.

The capture of neutrons also induces appreciable fission yields provided that the excitation energy of the compound nucleus exceeds the activation energy required for the fission of the compound nucleus. We recall [Eq. (7-18)] that the excitation energy of the compound nucleus after the capture of a slow neutron is given by

$$W^* = B_n^* + T \tag{9-65}$$

where B_n^* is the binding energy of the last neutron in the compound nucleus. Hence the threshold energy

$$T_{th} = W^a - B_n^* \tag{9-66}$$

determines whether a target nuclide is fissionable with respect to slow neutrons. If B_n^* exceeds W^a (that is, if $T_{th} < 0$), there is an appreciable cross section for fission for zero-energy neutrons. On the other hand, if W^a exceeds B_n^*, the cross sections for fission become appreciable only when the kinetic energy exceeds the threshold.

Recalling the composition of our empirical expression for B_n^* [see Eq. (9-36)], we may conclude that the slowly varying term $B_n(A)$ makes the major contribution ($\sim$6 Mev for $A = 235$) and that this term in itself almost cancels the slowly varying W^a ($\sim$6 Mev for U^{235}). Consequently the fission threshold energy is very sensitive to the small fluctuations in both W^a and B_n^*. Fluctuations in B_n^* may be identified with the parabolic correction, the pairing correction, and the shell correction. The parabolic correction is relatively small ($\sim$0.1 Mev) when the target nuclide is beta-stable, because the parabolic-width factor is small for heavy nuclides. The shell correction varies approximately linearly from about -1 Mev just beyond $N = 126$ to about $+1$ Mev at $N = 148$. The pairing term, on the other hand, is a fluctuating effect ($\sim$0.6 Mev for odd-neutron target nuclides and ~ -0.6 Mev for even-neutron target nuclides). This fluctuating term is probably the most important one in determining whether T_{th} is positive or negative. This fact is shown clearly in Table 9-3 in which we record the following information. In columns 1 and 2 we denote the symbol and proton number of the target and compound nucleus. In columns 3 and 4 we give the neutron and mass numbers of the target, whereas in columns 5 and 6 we indicate the corresponding numbers for the compound nucleus. In column 7 we indicate the pairing coefficient $\mathfrak{d} - \mathfrak{d}^*$. In column 8 we indicate by + and − whether the fission cross section for slow ($T \approx 0$) neutrons is greater than or less than 1 barn. In column 9 we give $-T_{th}$ calculated using Eq. (9-66), where B_n^* (column 11) has been computed from the experimental data and W^a (column 10) has been computed from Seaborg's formula [Eq. (9-63)]. An examination of this table reveals that with two exceptions (U^{232} and Pu^{238}) $\sigma_f(0)$, the slow-neutron fission cross section, is correlated with the oddness or evenness of the neutron number of the target and with the sign of $B_n^* - W^a$. Since these two substances lie far on the neutron-deficient side of the line of beta stability, the parabolic correction would readily account for the anomalies. The correlation between the signs of $\sigma_f(0)$ and $-T_{th}$ is almost perfect. This constitutes good evidence in support of Seaborg's formula.

9-12. Asymmetrical and Ternary Fission.[19] Experimental investigations have established the fact that the fragments resulting from slow-neutron fission of heavy nuclides are almost always unequal in mass, with the masses of the most frequent subdivisions having a ratio of about 2:3. In Fig. 9-14 we indicate the fragment-mass distributions from U^{235} bombarded by thermal neutrons. Mayer,[21] Wick,[22] and others have suggested that the anomalous stability in the neighborhood of $N = 50$ and $N = 82$ provides the explanation for the prevalence of asymmetric fission; indeed Fong[23] has arrived at a distribution formula based upon such considerations which is in quantitative agreement with the experimental distribution. On the other hand Hill and Wheeler[14] reject this explanation on the ground that the division takes place before the fissioning nucleus could "sense" the potential-energy structure of the unformed

TABLE 9-3. FISSION DATA FOR HEAVY NUCLIDES

Sym. (1)	Z (2)	N (3)	A (4)	N^* (5)	A^* (6)	$\mathfrak{d} - \mathfrak{d}^*$ (7)	$\sigma_f(0)$ (8)	$-T_{th}$ (9)	$W^a(X^*)$ (10)	B_n^* (11)
Ra	88	138	226	139	227	−	−	−1.8	6.7	4.9
	88	140	228	141	229	−	−	−2.2	6.8	4.6
Ac	89	138	227	139	228	−	−	−1.4	6.5	5.1
Th	90	137	227	138	228	+	+	0.8	6.2	7.0
	90	138	228	139	229	−	−	−0.9	6.3	5.4
	90	139	229	140	230	+	+	0.4	6.3	6.7
	90	140	230	141	231	−	−	−1.8	6.4	4.6
	90	142	232	143	233	−	−	−1.7	6.5	4.8
	90	144	234	145	235	−	−	−1.9	6.6	4.7
Pa	91	139	230	140	231	+	+	0.8	6.1	6.9
	91	140	231	141	232	−	−	−0.7	6.1	5.4
	91	141	232	142	233	+	+	0.5	6.2	6.7
	91	142	233	143	234	−	−	−1.2	6.3	5.1
U	92	140	232	141	233	−	+	0.0	5.9	5.9
	92	141	233	142	234	+	+	0.7	6.0	6.7
	92	142	234	143	235	−	−	−0.6	6.0	5.4
	92	143	235	144	236	+	+	0.4	6.1	6.5
	92	146	238	147	239	−	−	−1.4	6.2	4.8
Np	93	141	234	142	235	+	+	1.4	5.7	7.1
	93	144	237	145	238	−	−	−0.7	5.9	5.2
	93	145	238	146	239	+	+	0.4	6.0	6.4
	93	146	239	147	240	−	−	−1.0	6.0	5.0
Pu	94	144	238	145	239	−	+	0.0	5.7	5.7
	94	145	239	146	240	+	+	0.7	5.8	6.5
	94	147	241	148	242	+	+	0.3	5.9	6.2
Am	95	146	241	147	242	−	−	−0.2	5.5	5.3
	95	147	242	148	243	+	+	0.9	5.6	6.5
	95	148	243	149	244	−	?	−0.5	5.7	5.2
Cm	96	146	242	147	243	−	?	0.5	5.4	5.9

products. As an alternative explanation of the observed asymmetry they suggest a quantum-mechanical, shape-dependent viscosity effect or a hydrodynamical instability effect. Their preliminary calculations indicate that these explanations can account for the observations. At higher energies the products of fission tend to equal-mass values, a fact which conforms with expectations based upon all the explanations of asymmetric fission.

The possibility of fission into three parts was predicted on energetic grounds by Bohr and Wheeler.[13] Using the mass surface, it can be

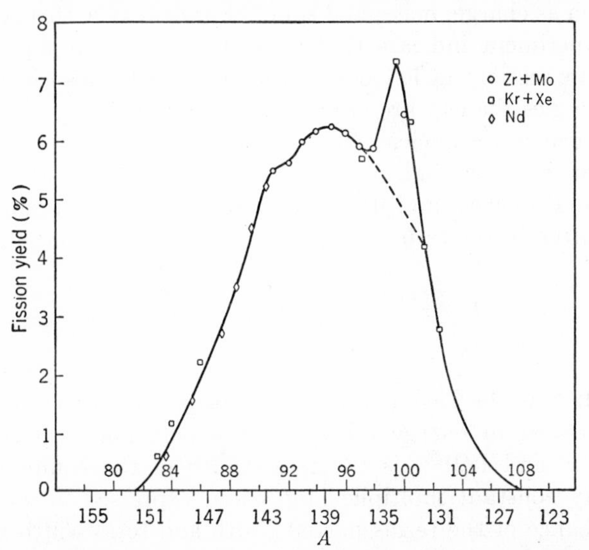

FIG. 9-14. Curve of mass spectrometer yield vs. mass in the U^{235} neutron reaction fission. The lower horizontal scale is the mass of the heavier fragment and the upper scale is the corresponding mass of the lighter fragment, under the assumption that, on the average, 2.5 neutrons "boil off" the fragments of the U^{236} nucleus. (*From Glendenin, Steinberg, Inghram, and Hess, Ref.* 20.)

shown that the energy available for such a process can be even greater than for binary fission. However, the probability is apparently small, experiments indicating that tripartition occurs about 7 times for 1 million binary fissions.[19]

9-13. Cross Sections in Neutron Fission Reactions. The general trends of the cross sections of the neutron fission process, as well as of competitive neutron-induced processes, can be interpreted in terms of a simplified theory which is based upon the Bohr picture of the compound nucleus. Treating the capture of the incident particle and the decay of the compound nucleus as completely independent, we write the cross section of a given reaction in the form

$$\sigma_{x,x'}(T) = \sigma_x(T)\eta_{x'}(W^*) \tag{9-67}$$

where $\sigma_x(T)$ is the cross section for the capture of the incident particle and $\eta_{x'}(W^*)$ is the probability for decay by the emission of x'. This factor is essentially the branching-ratio concept which we introduced in our discussion of radioactive decay. For most applications of Eq. (9-67) the symbols x and x' denote particles such as gamma rays, neutrons, protons, alpha particles, etc.; however, for application to fission we shall allow x' to represent also the fission process itself. The function $\sigma_x(T)$ depends upon the nature of the incident particle, the kinetic energy in the center-of-mass system, and also upon certain characteristics of the target nucleus such as charge, mass, and spin. For neutrons, theory (see Chap. 13) and experiment indicate that apart from irregular fluctuations the capture cross sections at low energies increase as $1/v$, as v becomes small. At high energies the capture cross section decreases as v increases, tending to the geometric nuclear cross section $\pi R^2(\sim 2 \text{ barns})$. The factor $\eta_{x'}(W^*)$, which, as we indicate, depends upon the excitation energy of the compound nucleus and upon the nature of the "outgoing particle," may be written in the form

$$\eta_{x'}(W^*) = \frac{\bar{\Gamma}_{x'}(W^*)}{\sum_{x''} \bar{\Gamma}_{x''}(W^*)} = \frac{\bar{\Gamma}_{x'}(W^*)}{\bar{\Gamma}(W^*)} \tag{9-68}$$

where $\bar{\Gamma}_{x'}(W^*)$ is the partial width (transition probability multiplied by $\hbar$ and expressed in energy units) for the emission by the compound nucleus of x' and $\bar{\Gamma}(W^*)$ is the total width of the compound nucleus (total decay constant multiplied by $\hbar$ and expressed in energy units). The significance of the terms partial width and total width and the bar over these symbols will be discussed in Chap. 13.

We shall not go into the details of the complicated and provisional statistical theories which lead to present estimates of these width functions. Nevertheless, it will be profitable to make certain observations concerning the general variations of partial widths for various processes with respect to the excitation energy W^*.

Whenever the excitation energy is below the binding energy of the x' particle in the compound nucleus, the corresponding partial width will be zero. The binding energy $B^*_{x'}$ thus may be regarded as the threshold energy for the x' mode of decay. Above the thresholds the partial width for neutron decay increases more rapidly and generally reaches larger values than the partial widths for the emission of charged particles. The coulomb barrier which exists for charged particles accounts for the reduced emission of charged particles and also makes the partial widths for p and α emission strongly energy-dependent and sensitive (inversely) to $Z'e$, the charge on the residual nucleus. We show in Fig. 9-15 the variations of several partial widths with the excitation energy of a typical heavy nucleus, as estimated by Bohr and Wheeler. $\bar{\Gamma}_\gamma$, $\bar{\Gamma}_f$, $\bar{\Gamma}_n$, and $\bar{\Gamma}_\alpha$ refer to radiation, fission, neutron, and alpha emission (proton emission is negligible until much higher energies). The curve for $\bar{\Gamma}_n$ indicates that decay by neutron emission is not permissible until the excitation energy is greater than the neutron binding energy (~6 Mev for heavy nuclei). Note, however, the sharp rise in this function after the threshold energy.

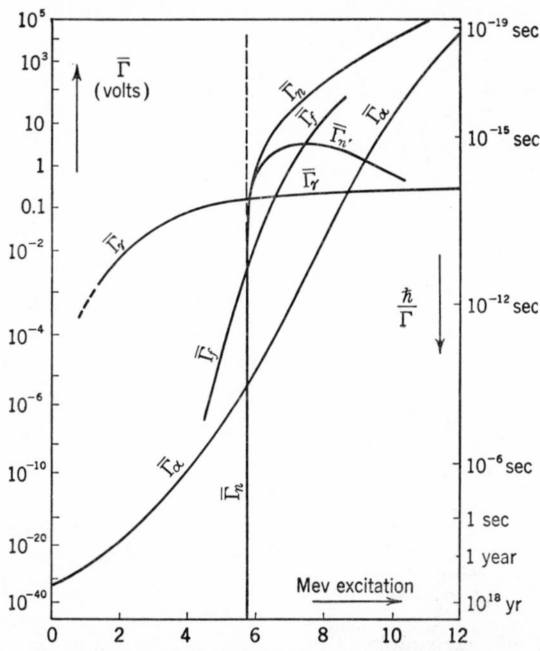

FIG. 9-15. Schematic diagram of the partial transition probabilities (multiplied by $\hbar$ and expressed in energy units) and their reciprocals (dimensions of a mean lifetime) for various excitation energies of a typical heavy nucleus. $\bar{\Gamma}_\gamma$, $\bar{\Gamma}_f$, and $\bar{\Gamma}_\alpha$ refer to radiation, fission, and alpha-particle emission, while $\bar{\Gamma}_n$ and $\bar{\Gamma}_{n'}$ determine, respectively, the probability of a neutron emission leaving the residual nucleus in its ground state or in any state. The latter quantities are, of course, zero if the excitation is less than the neutron binding energy, which is taken here to be about 6 Mev. (*From Bohr and Wheeler, Ref.* 13.)

Although fission is energetically possible for heavy nuclei even with zero excitation, the probability is small until the excitation energy becomes of the order of magnitude of or greater than W^a, the critical activation energy for fission (~6 Mev for heavy nuclei). This accounts for the sharp rise in $\bar{\Gamma}_f$ when $W^* > 6$ Mev. While all heavy nuclei are unstable relative to α decay, the partial width $\bar{\Gamma}_\alpha$ is small until excitation energy brings the energy close to the top of the coulomb barrier (~25 Mev). We note that, at low excitation energies, radiation is the predominant mode of decay, but for high excitations, $\bar{\Gamma}_\gamma$ approaches about 1 ev, which is usually small compared to the partial widths for other modes of decay.

To apply Fig. 9-15 to the interpretation of neutron-induced fission, we recall again the fact that the capture of slow neutrons brings the compound nucleus to the state of excitation $W^* = B_n^*$ (accordingly, the neutron-emission threshold is automatically reached). With the exception of those nuclides for which $B_n^* > W^a$, the gamma emission process is the most probable mode of decay of the compound nucleus formed by the capture of slow neutrons. Huizenger and Duffield[24] and Seaborg[16] recently have found an almost quantitative correlation between the ratio $\sigma_{nf}/\sigma_{n\gamma}$ [which according to Eqs. (9-67) and (9-68) should equal $\bar{\Gamma}_f/\bar{\Gamma}_\gamma$] and the energy $B_n^* - W^a$. In Fig. 9-16 we show this correlation.

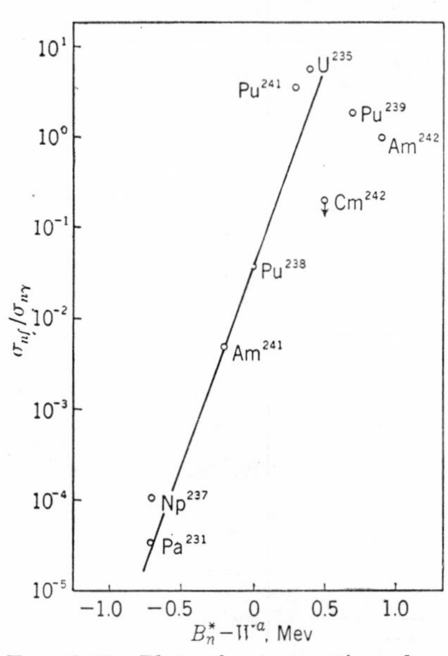

FIG. 9-16. Plot of comparative slow-neutron fissionability. $\sigma_{nf}/\sigma_{n\gamma}$ denotes ratio of slow-neutron fission to (n,γ) cross section (♀ signifies upper limit); $B_n^* - W^a$ denotes difference between neutron binding energy and activation energy. (*From Seaborg, Ref.* 16.)

The ratio $\sigma_{nf}/\sigma_{n\gamma}$ in conjunction with measured values for $\sigma_{n\gamma}$ might possibly be used to estimate cross sections for slow-neutron fission. At higher neutron energies the excitation energy of the compound nucleus becomes correspondingly large. According to Fig. 9-15 the neutron reemission process becomes dominant at high energies. Piecing together the parts of the discussion above, we may predict the general trends of the σ_{nf} cross section as a function of the neutron energy for heavy nuclides. The σ_{nf} cross sections for substances with positive thresholds (that is, $W^a > B_n^*$) are expected to be vanishingly small until the threshold energy is reached and then to approach a maximum rapidly. In Fig. 9-17 we show the neutron fission cross section for Np^{237}, which is typical of the substances with $W^a > B_n^*$.

On the other hand the curves of cross section vs. neutron energy for nuclides for which $B_n^* > W^a$ might be expected to start at a high value at $T = 0$ and descend gradually to about 1 barn as T becomes large. Information concerning these cross sections has appeared recently in the unclassified literature.[26–28] In Table 9-4 we list neutron fission cross sections and the neutron-gamma cross sections for thermal neutrons (neutrons having a Maxwellian distribution of velocities with a peak at 2.2×10^5 cm/sec) for several of the highly fissionable materials.

9-14. Sustained Fission Reactions.[29,30] Almost immediately after the correct interpretation of fission was given by Hahn and Strassman[12] in 1939, it was universally recognized by scientists that this reaction fulfilled the two requirements to serve as the basic process for a sustained nuclear-energy generator. Not only is the reaction markedly exoergic, but it also automatically reproduces the initiators (neutrons) of the reaction. Whether a sustained process could actually be attained under

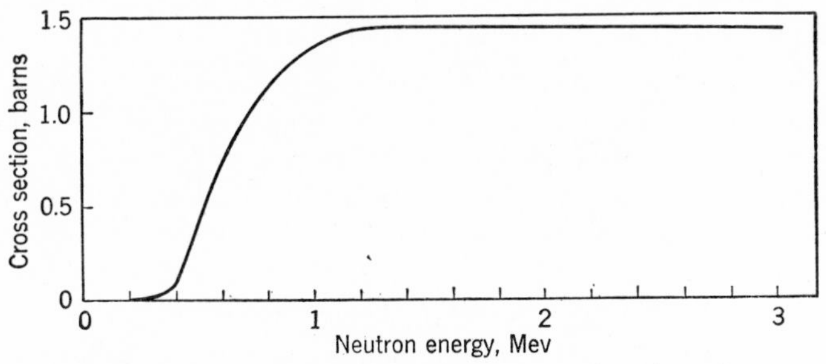

Fig. 9-17. Neutron fission cross section of Np^{237} as a function of neutron energy. (*From Ref.* 25.)

practical conditions was recognized to be dependent upon the values of certain nuclear parameters related to cross sections. The fact that these parameters were found suitable is recorded in history.

The basic nuclear reaction in a sustained fission process is the capture of a neutron by a very heavy nucleus, followed by a splitting of the composite nucleus into two approximately equal parts, with the ejection on the average of about $2\frac{1}{2}$ neutrons and the liberation of energy. A

Table 9-4. Thermal-neutron Cross Sections (in Barns)

Nucleus	σ_{nf}	$\sigma_{n\gamma}$
U^{233}	~500	
U^{235}	549	101
Pu^{239}	664	361
Pu^{241}	1000	400
Am^{242}	~6000	~2000

nuclear reactor or pile is a device for harnessing nuclear power by providing the conditions for reproduction or regeneration of the fission reaction. Thus in a reactor the fuel, or fissionable material, is arranged in a manner to promote the multiplication of neutrons which are the initiators and products of the reaction. Since some neutrons inevitably escape through the surface of the pile, it turns out that a sustained process will take place only when the pile is large enough. To secure a reactor of reasonable size, it is necessary that the fissionable fuel meet several stringent requirements. U^{235} is the only naturally occurring substance which meets these requirements. This isotope is present to the extent of 0.72 per cent in natural uranium, which is mostly (99.28 per cent) U^{238}. It has proved possible to operate a controlled reactor using natural uranium based upon the fission of U^{235}. For such a pile it is essential to use a moderator to slow down the fast neutrons ejected during fission and thereby improve their chances for fission capture with respect to radiative capture. At thermal energies the radiative-capture cross section of U^{238} is 2.8 barns, and, of course, the fission cross section is vanishingly small. Consequently at thermal-neutron energies the neutron fission cross section of natural uranium is $550 \times 0.72 = 3.9$ barns, whereas the (n,γ) cross section is $2.8 \times 99.28 + 101 \times 0.72 = 3.5$ barns. Accordingly at thermal energies somewhat more than half the neutrons moving through a mass of natural uranium will cause fission. It has recently been disclosed that on the average 2.5 neutrons are emitted per thermal fission. Thus we see that the accomplishment of a sustained fission process in natural uranium depends critically upon how well other losses of neutrons can be held to a minimum.

It is, perhaps, an amazing coincidence that a pile of natural uranium can be used to "breed" plutonium, another substance which meets the stringent requirements for a fissionable fuel. In the production of Pu^{239} some of the neutrons available from the U^{235} neutron fission reaction are captured by U^{238}. The compound nucleus decays instantly by gamma emission, leaving the neutron-rich odd-mass nuclide U^{239}. This decays to Pu^{239} through the following steps:

$$
\begin{aligned}
{}_{92}U^{239} &\rightarrow {}_{92}Np^{239} + \beta^- \qquad (23 \text{ min}) \\
{}_{93}Np^{239} &\rightarrow {}_{94}Pu^{239} + \beta^- \qquad (23 \text{ days})
\end{aligned}
$$

Th^{232} can also be converted into fissionable U^{233} in a similar way. The (n,γ) reaction here leads to the neutron-rich Th^{233}, which decays through the following steps:

$$
\begin{aligned}
{}_{90}Th^{233} &\rightarrow {}_{91}Pa^{233} + \beta^- \qquad (23.5 \text{ min}) \\
{}_{91}Pa^{233} &\rightarrow {}_{92}U^{233} + \beta^- \qquad (27.4 \text{ days})
\end{aligned}
$$

Thus the insertion of nonfissionable Th^{232} in a pile may yield fissionable U^{233}. The fact that significant quantities of U^{235} are available in nature is somewhat fortuitous, since it is now some 3 billion years (about four U^{235} half-lives) after the formation of the earth, so that only about one-sixteenth of what was originally present when the earth was created still exists. Other fissionable materials such as U^{233} and Pu^{239} were probably also present at the dawn of creation, but they have long since decayed away to insignificant quantities. Were the earth another 7 billion years (ten U^{235} half-lives) older, the amount of U^{235} present might have been too small to be utilizable and the harnessing of nuclear energy might have remained an academic question. As it is, however, by the Pu^{239} and the U^{233} production processes we have, in effect, turned back our geological clock.

Several methods have been devised for the separation of U^{235}, Pu^{239}, and U^{233}. By the use of such purified fissionable material in nuclear reactors it is possible to increase the rate of the fission process enormously. In an explosive reactor a fissionable mass of almost pure U^{235}, Pu^{239}, or U^{233} is assembled to critical size in a time which is so short that it must be measured in fractions of a microsecond. During the short period before the bomb bursts, an appreciable part of the material undergoes fission. It has been estimated that an energy equivalent to that of many thousands of tons of TNT is thereby released with the instantaneous creation of temperatures and pressures close to those at the interior of the sun. We shall not concern ourselves further with the design, operation, or construction of nuclear reactors, since these topics now belong to vast new technologies which must properly be regarded as special subdivisions of the munitions and power fields rather than of nuclear physics.

PROBLEMS

9-1. Compute E_v, E_s, E_c, E_{sym}, E^w, and Δ^w for the six nuclides of Prob. 8-3 using the constants of Fermi and the constants of Green and Engler. Compare these with the experimental values.

9-2. What values of b in $R = bA^{\frac{1}{3}}$ are implicit to each of the sets of constants in Table 9-1?

***9-3.** Derive the formulas for $\Delta_m{}^w(A)$, $D_m{}^w(A)$, and $J^w(A)$ when $Z(Z - 1)$ is used in the semiempirical equation in place of Z^2.

9-4. Derive a formula [which will compare with Eq. (8-20)] for the main contribution to nuclear Q values $Q_m{}^w(A)$ on the basis of the semiempirical equation.

9-5. Choose a heavy EE-type nuclide, and using only Δ_m and Δ_q, compute the approximate energy released in its symmetric fission.

9-6. What is the approximate energy released in the asymmetric fission of your heavy nuclide under the assumptions that the ratio of division is approximately 2:3 and that the two final D values lie approximately equal numbers of steps from the line of beta stability?

9-7. What is the approximate energy released in the symmetric tripartition of ${}_{93}Np^{240}$?

9-8. According to the Bohr-Wheeler theory, what is the critical activation energy of the compound nucleus formed by the capture of a slow neutron by your heavy nuclide? Let $a_2 = 14.0$ Mev, $(Z^2/A)_l = 47.8$, and $\Phi(x)$ be interpolated from:

x	$\Phi(x)$	x	$\Phi(x)$
0.700	0.0169	0.750	0.110
0.710	0.0154	0.760	0.0089
0.720	0.0140	0.770	0.0079
0.730	0.0126	0.780	0.0069
0.740	0.0112	0.790	0.0060

***9-9.** Using the liquid-drop-model equations with the Fermi constants, compute the limiting mass number for metastability with respect to spontaneous fission by beta-stable nuclides. Repeat this calculation, using Eq. (9-63) and the empirical line of beta stability.

9-10. What activation energies of U^{236} are implicit to each set of constants in Table 9-1?

REFERENCES

1. Weiszäcker, C. F. von: *Z. Physik,* **96,** 431 (1935).
2. Bethe, H. A., and R. F. Bacher: *Revs. Mod. Phys.,* **8,** 165 (1936).
3. Bohr, N., and J. A. Wheeler: *Phys. Rev.,* **56,** 426 (1939).
4. Feenberg, E.: *Revs. Mod. Phys.,* **19,** 239 (1947).
5. Green, A. E. S., and N. A. Engler: *Phys. Rev.,* **91,** 40 (1953).
6. Green, A. E. S., and D. F. Edwards: *Phys. Rev.,* **91,** 46 (1953).
7. Fermi, E.: unpublished. Quoted in C. Goodman (ed.), "The Science and Engineering of Nuclear Power," Vol. I, Addison-Wesley Publishing Company, Cambridge, Mass., 1947.
8. Mattauch, J., and S. Flugge: "Introduction to Nuclear Physics," Interscience Publishers, Inc., New York, 1946.
9. Pryce, M. H. L.: *Proc. Phys. Soc.* (*London*), **A63,** 692 (1950).
10. Metropolis, W., and G. Reitweiser: "Table of Atomic Masses," *U.S. Atomic Energy Comm. NP* 1980, March, 1950.
11. Fowler, W. A.: unpublished. Quoted in W. E. Siri, "Isotopic Tracers and Nuclear Radiations," p. 11, McGraw-Hill Book Company, Inc., New York, 1949.
12. Hahn, O., and F. Strassman: *Naturwiss.,* **27,** 11 (1939).
13. Bohr, N., and J. A. Wheeler: *Phys. Rev.,* **56,** 426 (1939).
14. Hill, D. L., and J. A. Wheeler: *Phys. Rev.,* **89,** 1102 (1953).
15. Frankel, S., and W. Metropolis: *Phys. Rev.,* **72,** 914 (1947).
16. Seaborg, G. T.: *Phys. Rev.,* **88,** 1429 (1952).
17. Koch, H. W., J. McElhinney, and E. L. Gasteiger: *Phys. Rev.,* **77,** 329 (1950).
18. Seaborg, G. T.: *Phys. Rev.,* **85,** 157 (1952).
19. Whitehouse, W. J.: *Progr. Nuclear Phys.,* **2,** 120 (1952).
20. Glendenin, L. E., E. P. Steinberg, N. G. Inghram, and D. C. Hess: *Phys. Rev.,* **84,** 860 (1951).
21. Mayer, M. G.: *Phys. Rev.,* **74,** 235 (1948).
22. Wick, G. C.: *Phys. Rev.,* **76,** 181 (1949).
23. Fong, P.: *Phys. Rev.,* **87,** 187 (1952).
24. Huizenger, J. R., and R. B. Duffield: *Phys. Rev.,* **88,** 959 (1953).
25. Atomic Energy Commission Neutron Cross Section Advisory Group: *U.S. Atomic Energy Comm.* Document AECU 2040, 1952.
26. Manning, W. M., A. Ghiorso, and G. T. Seaborg: Chap. 20 *in* G. T. Seaborg, J. J. Katz, and W. M. Manning, "The Transuranium Elements," *National Nuclear Energy Series,* Div. IV, Vol. 14B, McGraw-Hill Book Company, Inc., New York, 1950.
27. *Nature,* **169,** 871 (1952).
28. Street, K., Jr., A. Ghiorso, and S. G. Thompson: *Phys. Rev.,* **75,** 135 (1952).
29. Stephens, W. E. (ed.): "Nuclear Fission and Atomic Energy," The Science Press, Lancaster, Pa., 1948.
30. Goodman, C. (ed.): "The Science and Engineering of Nuclear Power," Vol. I (1947), Vol. II (1949), Addison-Wesley Publishing Company, Cambridge, Mass.
31. Green, A. E. S.: *Phys. Rev.,* **95,** 1006 (1954).

CHAPTER 10

QUANTUM MECHANICS AND THE NUCLEUS

We have attempted to organize and present some of the basic facts of nuclear physics as well as the simpler interpretations of the experimental observations. To go further into the interpretation of nuclear phenomena, we must come to closer grips with the methods of modern quantum mechanics. While it may eventually turn out that some other general theory will prove to be better for the description of nuclear phenomena, we are now faced with the fact that practically all current theoretical attempts to account for nuclear behavior are within the framework of modern quantum mechanics. Nor can we deny that several of these attempts have been successful in the explanation of certain substantial portions of nuclear physics, so much so that it seems probable that the future complete theory will share many features with the present theory.

The part of modern quantum mechanics we shall need most is the Schroedinger wave equation; in particular, the time-independent Schroedinger equation. However, before discussing this particular wave equation, let us consider some of the wave equations that arose earlier in other fields of physics, since many of the mathematical methods used in quantum mechanics have been borrowed bodily from the study of light, sound, and other types of wave motion.

10-1. Wave Equations. The mature particle dynamicist, when confronted with a system having a discrete number of degrees of freedom, first seeks the ordinary differential equations of motion of the system, since in effect these equations contain the totality of possible motions of the system. In a similar way the mature wave dynamicist, when confronted with a continuum (*i.e.*, a system having an infinite number of degrees of freedom), looks first for the partial differential equation of motion commonly called the wave equation. Just as in the case of particle dynamics, where there are many ways of arriving at the differential equations of motion, so also there are many ways of arriving at the wave equation by using various formulations of the basic laws. Indeed, in some treatments the wave equation itself is the basic statement of the law of motion. We list below several well-known wave equations which furnish accurate descriptions of various types of continuum phenomena in regions which do not contain sources.

1. The vibrations of a string

$$\frac{\partial^2 \mathbf{Y}}{\partial x^2} = \frac{1}{u^2}\frac{\partial^2 \mathbf{Y}}{\partial t^2} \tag{10-1}$$

where $u = (\tau/\rho)^{\frac{1}{2}}$ is the phase velocity, ρ is the density, τ the tension, and $\mathbf{Y}(x,t)$ is the instantaneous transverse displacement.

2. The vibrations of a surface or membrane

$$\frac{\partial^2 \mathbf{Z}}{\partial x^2} + \frac{\partial^2 \mathbf{Z}}{\partial y^2} = \frac{1}{u^2}\frac{\partial^2 \mathbf{Z}}{\partial t^2} \tag{10-2}$$

where u is the phase velocity and $\mathbf{Z}(x,y,t)$ is the transverse displacement.

3. The propagation of sound

$$\frac{\partial^2 \mathbf{\Phi}}{\partial x^2} + \frac{\partial^2 \mathbf{\Phi}}{\partial y^2} + \frac{\partial^2 \mathbf{\Phi}}{\partial z^2} = \frac{1}{u^2}\frac{\partial^2 \mathbf{\Phi}}{\partial t^2}$$

or

$$\Delta \mathbf{\Phi} = \frac{1}{u^2}\frac{\partial^2 \mathbf{\Phi}}{\partial t^2} \tag{10-3}$$

where u is the phase velocity and $\mathbf{\Phi}(x,y,z,t)$ is the velocity potential.

4. The propagation of heat in three dimensions

$$\Delta \mathbf{\Theta} = \frac{1}{\sigma}\frac{\partial \mathbf{\Theta}}{\partial t} \tag{10-4}$$

where σ is the thermal diffusivity and $\mathbf{\Theta}(x,y,z,t)$ is the temperature.

5. The propagation of electromagnetic fields in a vacuum

$$\Delta \mathbf{A}_\nu = \frac{1}{c^2}\frac{\partial^2 \mathbf{A}_\nu}{\partial t^2} \tag{10-5}$$

where c is the velocity of light, $\mathbf{A}_\nu(x,y,z,t)$ is the four-vector potential $\mathbf{A}_\nu = A_x,A_y,A_z,\phi$, and Δ is the Laplacian operator, *i.e.*,

$$\Delta = \frac{\partial^2}{\partial x^2} + \frac{\partial^2}{\partial y^2} + \frac{\partial^2}{\partial z^2} \tag{10-6}$$

A problem that arises often is the investigation of the motion in a continuum caused by an external source which is oscillating at a fixed frequency. In such cases it is possible to separate out the part of the wave function that depends upon time by assuming a solution of the form

$$\mathbf{Q}(x,y,z,t) = Q(x,y,z)T(t) \tag{10-7}$$

where

$$T = \exp(-i\omega t) \tag{10-8}$$

The use of exponentials instead of sine or cosine functions generally simplifies the algebraic steps. In many cases it is agreed that only the real part of the result is to be used. If now we substitute Eqs. (10-7) and (10-8) into the wave equation, we obtain the differential equation for Q which is independent of time. The time-independent or amplitude equations corresponding to Eqs. (10-1) to (10-5) are

$$\frac{d^2Y}{dx^2} + \frac{\omega^2}{u^2} Y = 0 \tag{10-9}$$

$$\frac{\partial^2 Z}{\partial x^2} + \frac{\partial^2 Z}{\partial y^2} + \frac{\omega^2}{u^2} Z = 0 \tag{10-10}$$

$$\Delta\Phi + \frac{\omega^2}{u^2} \Phi = 0 \tag{10-11}$$

$$\Delta\Theta + i\frac{\omega}{\sigma} \Theta = 0 \tag{10-12}$$

$$\Delta A_\nu + \frac{\omega^2}{c^2} A_\nu = 0 \tag{10-13}$$

When confronted with de Broglie's(1) suggestion that $E = \hbar\omega$ and $p = \hbar k$ apply to matter waves, Schroedinger(2) concluded that there ought to be a wave equation. Assuming that the energy-frequency relation implies that the matter waves associated with an energy state have fixed frequency, Schroedinger was led to investigate possible forms of time-independent wave equations. It turned out that he met with success without looking very far. The time-independent Schroedinger equation is just the corresponding equation for electromagnetic wave functions when certain replacements are made which, when viewed with hindsight, seem quite plausible. In essence, Schroedinger by his generalization made the following replacements:

$$\left(\frac{\omega}{u}\right)^2 = k^2 = \left(\frac{p}{\hbar}\right)^2 = \frac{2m}{\hbar^2}\frac{p^2}{2m} = \frac{2mT}{\hbar^2} \tag{10-14}$$

If a particle has the total energy W and is in a field of force characterized by the potential energy

$$V = V(x,y,z) \tag{10-15}$$

it has the kinetic energy

$$T = W - V(x,y,z) \tag{10-16}$$

hence we find, upon using Eqs. (10-14) and (10-16) in Eq. (10-11) or Eq. (10-13) and denoting the matter-wave wave function by the usual symbol Ψ, the amplitude equation

$$\Delta\Psi + \frac{2m}{\hbar^2}[W - V(x,y,z)]\Psi = 0 \tag{10-17}$$

We may note that the third equality in Eq. (10-14) is the main generalization, since here an expression valid for massless particles (photons) is adapted to particles with mass. In addition, for matter waves we permit the wave functions to be complex functions, *i.e.*, expressible in the form

$$\Psi(x,y,z) = \Upsilon(x,y,z) + i\Phi(x,y,z) \tag{10-18}$$

where Υ and Φ are real functions of the space variables.

In the next few sections we shall consider the interpretation and applications of this Schroedinger amplitude equation to a system consisting of a single particle in a field of force.

10-2. Wave Mechanics for Energy States. In Schroedinger's theory the wave function $\Psi(x,y,z)$ is assumed to be the spatial part of a complex, time-dependent wave function which has the form

$$\boldsymbol{\Psi}(x,y,z,t) = \Psi(x,y,z) \exp\left(-\frac{iWt}{\hbar}\right) \tag{10-19}$$

Physical substance is given to these wave functions by assuming that

$$P(x,y,z,t) = \boldsymbol{\Psi}^*(x,y,z,t)\,\boldsymbol{\Psi}(x,y,z,t) \tag{10-20}$$

is the probability per unit volume for finding a particle in a small volume element in the neighborhood of the point x, y, z at the time t. We note that, for wave functions of the type given by Eq. (10-19), this probability is independent of time, since the factor $\exp(iWt/\hbar)$ in $\boldsymbol{\Psi}^*$ cancels the factor $\exp(-iWt/\hbar)$ in $\boldsymbol{\Psi}$. In view of the probability interpretation we may compute the average value or expectation $\langle f\rangle$ of any function f of the coordinates of a particle state by

$$\langle f\rangle = \iiint_{-\infty}^{\infty} P(x,y,z,t)f(x,y,z)\,dx\,dy\,dz \tag{10-21}$$

The average value or expectation of a classical dynamical variable Ω which depends upon the components of momentum, however, must be computed, according to a basic postulate of the Schroedinger theory, by use of the expectation formula

$$\langle\Omega\rangle = \iiint_{-\infty}^{\infty} \boldsymbol{\Psi}^*(x,y,z,t)[\Omega_{op}\boldsymbol{\Psi}(x,y,z,t)]\,dx\,dy\,dz \tag{10-22}$$

where Ω_{op} is the Schroedinger operator identified with the classical dynamical variable. The rules for associating a Schroedinger operator with a classical dynamical variable are:

1. Express the dynamical variables as functions of x, y, z, p_x, p_y, and p_z.
2. Replace p_x, p_y, and p_z by $-i\hbar\,\partial/\partial x$, $-i\hbar\,\partial/\partial y$, and $-i\hbar\,\partial/\partial z$.

As an example we shall find the operator associated with the classical

Hamiltonian (*i.e.*, the total energy) of a one-dimensional harmonic oscillator. In terms of momentum and position variables the total energy is

$$H(x,p_x) = \frac{p_x^2}{2m} + \frac{kx^2}{2}$$

Replacing p_x by $-i\hbar\, \partial/\partial x$, we obtain the Hamiltonian operator

$$\begin{aligned} H_{op} &= \frac{1}{2m}\left(-i\hbar \frac{\partial}{\partial x}\right)\left(-i\hbar \frac{\partial}{\partial x}\right) + \frac{kx^2}{2} \\ &= -\frac{\hbar^2}{2m}\frac{\partial^2}{\partial x^2} + \frac{kx^2}{2} \end{aligned}$$

As a second example let us find the operator associated with the x component of the angular momentum of an electron located at the position $\mathbf{r}$ relative to a stationary nucleus and having the momentum $\mathbf{p}$. The classical expression for the x component cf angular momentum is

$$l_x = (\mathbf{r} \times \mathbf{p})_x = yp_z - zp_y$$

Replacing the momentum components by the corresponding operators, we obtain

$$l_{x,op} = y\left(-i\hbar \frac{\partial}{\partial z}\right) - z\left(-i\hbar \frac{\partial}{\partial y}\right) = -i\hbar\left(y \frac{\partial}{\partial z} - z \frac{\partial}{\partial y}\right)$$

In this manner a Schroedinger operator may be found for dynamical variables which are expressible in terms of the components of position and momentum.

In the expectation formula and elsewhere we assume that an operator acts upon the wave function to the right of it in conformity with the usual rules for multiplication and differentiation. For example

$$p_{x,op}\Psi(x,y,z,t) = -i\hbar \frac{\partial}{\partial x}\Psi(x,y,z,t) = -i\hbar \frac{\partial \Psi}{\partial x}$$

and

$$x_{op}\Psi(x,y,z,t) = x\Psi$$

Because of the physical interpretation implied in the probability and expectation formulas, the wave function $\Psi(x,y,z,t)$ and its first spatial derivatives must be continuous, finite, and single-valued functions of position. We shall refer to functions which possess these properties as "well-behaved." Since the particle exists, the wave functions must satisfy the normalization condition

$$\iiint_{-\infty}^{\infty} \Psi^*(x,y,z,t)\Psi(x,y,z,t)\, dx\, dy\, dz = 1 \qquad (10\text{-}23)$$

To find the Schroedinger wave equation associated with a system consisting of a single particle held in a known field of force, we simply insert for the V in Schroedinger's equation the potential-energy expression which is appropriate for the problem under consideration. For example, to investigate the linear-harmonic-oscillator problem, we use $V = \frac{1}{2}kx^2$. To investigate the problem of a one-dimensional particle in a box, we use $V = 0$, when $0 < x < a$, $V = \infty$ elsewhere. Important potential functions which are often assumed in atomic, molecular, and nuclear physics are the following:

The coulomb potential:

$$V = -\frac{Ze^2}{r} \tag{10-24}$$

The Hooke's law potential function:

$$V = \tfrac{1}{2}k(r - r_0)^2 \tag{10-25}$$

The Morse function:

$$V = V_0\{1 - \exp[-\kappa(r - r_0)]\}^2 \tag{10-26}$$

The three-dimensional harmonic oscillator:

$$V = \tfrac{1}{2}kr^2 \tag{10-27}$$

The spherical box:

$$\begin{aligned} V &= 0 \qquad 0 < r < a \\ &= \infty \qquad \text{elsewhere} \end{aligned} \tag{10-28}$$

The spherical well (also called the square well):

$$\begin{aligned} V &= -V_0 \qquad 0 < r < a \\ &= 0 \qquad \text{elsewhere} \end{aligned} \tag{10-29}$$

The exponential function:

$$V = -V_0 \exp\left(-\frac{r}{a}\right) \tag{10-30}$$

The Gaussian function:

$$V = -V_0 \exp\left(-\frac{r^2}{a^2}\right) \tag{10-31}$$

The Yukawa function:

$$V = -V_0 \frac{a}{r} \exp\left(-\frac{r}{a}\right) \tag{10-32}$$

Each of these is of the central-field type in that the potential function depends only upon the distance from the origin of the field of force. More complicated potentials have also been explored in the study of complex molecules, atoms, and nuclei.

10-3. The Particle in a Box. To illustrate the manner in which the Schroedinger theory may be applied to obtain the allowed energy, let us consider a hypothetical system consisting of a particle of mass m bound by a potential of the form

$$\begin{aligned} V &= 0 \qquad 0 < x < a \\ &= \infty \qquad \text{elsewhere} \end{aligned} \tag{10-33}$$

This is the problem of a particle in a one-dimensional box. The amplitude equation for the region inside the box is

$$\frac{d^2\Psi}{dx^2} + \frac{2mW}{\hbar^2}\Psi = 0 \tag{10-34}$$

We must find the well-behaved solutions of this simple differential equation.

Usually, in physical problems in which a second-order differential equation such as this arises, we know the value of the constant parameters in the equation. To obtain a solution, we first seek the general solution, which contains two arbitrary constants, and then adjust these constants to satisfy given initial or boundary conditions. The problem of obtaining the well-behaved solutions of an ordinary differential equation which contains an unknown parameter (such as W above) and at the same time finding the corresponding allowed values of this parameter, is quite different, although, of course, it has several features in common with the usual problem.

The general solution of Eq. (10-34) is

$$\Psi(x) = A \sin\left[\left(\frac{2mW}{\hbar^2}\right)^{\frac{1}{2}} x\right] + B \cos\left[\left(\frac{2mW}{\hbar^2}\right)^{\frac{1}{2}} x\right] \tag{10-35}$$

The fact that an infinite potential confines the particle suggests that the wave function associated with the particle vanishes identically outside the box. Using now the requirement of Schroedinger's theory that the wave functions are continuous, we conclude in the present case that the interior wave function must vanish at $x = 0$ and $x = a$. The former requirement may be satisfied simply by letting $B = 0$. However, we cannot satisfy the latter requirement (at $x = a$) by any adjustment of the constant A except the trivial one $A = 0$ (no wave function at all). Because of the properties of the sine function, however, the boundary condition may be satisfied if

$$\left(\frac{2mW}{\hbar^2}\right)^{\frac{1}{2}} a = n\pi \tag{10-36}$$

where $n \doteq 1, 2, 3, \ldots$. Solving for W, we find

$$W = n^2\pi^2 \frac{\hbar^2}{2ma^2} \tag{10-37}$$

which is exactly Eq. (1-65).

We have given here the very simplest illustration of the manner in which the allowed energies of a system may be determined on the basis of the Schroedinger equation and the requirement of good behavior. Of course all real problems are concerned with particles in three-dimensional space; hence the amplitude equation is a partial differential equation, and in consequence the mathematical problem of finding the well-behaved solutions is more complicated. Since the problem of a particle in a three-dimensional box is a particularly simple example of a three-dimensional problem which not only has some practical interest but also serves to illustrate the important mathematical step known as separation of variables, we shall now give consideration to it.

For the case of a cubic box with sides a, the Schroedinger amplitude equation for the internal region ($0 < x < a$, $0 < y < a$, and $0 < z < a$) is

$$\frac{\partial^2\Psi}{\partial x^2} + \frac{\partial^2\Psi}{\partial y^2} + \frac{\partial^2\Psi}{\partial z^2} + \frac{2m}{\hbar^2} W\Psi = 0 \tag{10-38}$$

Let us assume that the wave function $\Psi(x,y,z)$ may be separated into the form

$$\Psi(x,y,z) = X(x) \cdot Y(y) \cdot Z(z) \tag{10-39}$$

where X, Y, and Z are functions of the arguments x, y, and z, respectively. Carrying through the differentiations, we find

$$X''YZ + XY''Z + XYZ'' + \frac{2m}{\hbar^2} WXYZ = 0 \tag{10-40}$$

where we use primes to denote differentiation relative to the argument of the dependent variable. If we divide through by XYZ, we obtain

$$\frac{X''}{X} + \frac{Y''}{Y} + \frac{Z''}{Z} + \frac{2m}{\hbar^2} W = 0 \tag{10-41}$$

Taking X''/X over to the right, we have

$$\frac{Y''}{Y} + \frac{Z''}{Z} + \frac{2m}{\hbar^2} W = -\frac{X''}{X} \tag{10-42}$$

Since the right side of this equation is a function of x alone, it is independent of y and z. On the other hand this equation states that $-X''/X$ is equal to the function of y and z given by the left side. To satisfy both of these conditions, *i.e.*, to be a function of y and z which is not a function of y and z, $-X''/X$ must be a constant. Using the symbol α to denote this unknown constant, we have

$$\frac{Y''}{Y} + \frac{Z''}{Z} + \frac{2m}{\hbar^2} W = \alpha = -\frac{X''}{X} \tag{10-43}$$

The equation on the left may now be arranged in the form

$$\frac{Z''}{Z} + \frac{2m}{\hbar^2} W - \alpha = -\frac{Y''}{Y} \tag{10-44}$$

Reasoning again as before and introducing a second unknown constant β, we find

$$\frac{Z''}{Z} + \frac{2m}{\hbar^2} W - \alpha = -\frac{Y''}{Y} = \beta \tag{10-45}$$

We may finally collect our results in the form

$$X'' + \alpha X = 0 \qquad Y'' + \beta Y = 0 \qquad Z'' + \gamma Z = 0 \tag{10-46}$$

where

$$\alpha + \beta + \gamma = \frac{2m}{\hbar^2} W \tag{10-47}$$

We have succeeded in separating the variables of this problem and have obtained three ordinary differential equations in place of a single partial differential equation with three independent variables. Since each of these three differential equations has exactly the form of the differential equation which arises in the one-dimensional problem of the particle in a box, we may conclude by the identical reasoning used in that problem that

$$\alpha^{\frac{1}{2}}a = n_x\pi \qquad \beta^{\frac{1}{2}}a = n_y\pi \qquad \gamma^{\frac{1}{2}}a = n_z\pi \tag{10-48}$$

and consequently that

$$W = \pi^2 \frac{\hbar^2}{2ma^2} (n_x^2 + n_y^2 + n_z^2) \tag{10-49}$$

where n_x, n_y, and n_z are positive integers. The normalized solution corresponding to a particular set of quantum numbers is

$$\Psi_{n_xn_yn_z}(x,y,z) = \left(\frac{8}{a^3}\right)^{\frac{1}{2}} \sin\left(\frac{n_x\pi x}{a}\right) \sin\left(\frac{n_y\pi y}{a}\right) \sin\left(\frac{n_z\pi z}{a}\right) \tag{10-50}$$

Before leaving the problem of the particle in the box, we might point out that the assumption that the potential becomes infinite at the walls leads to considerable analytical simplification which is not usually realized in real problems. This assumption also leads to a discontinuity of the first derivative of the wave function at the boundary, which, according to the definition of good behavior, is inadmissible for the wave functions associated with real physical systems. The particle in a box must therefore be regarded as a hypothetical limiting case of problems with finite potentials.

10-4. The Central-field Problem. The success of an attempt to separate a partial differential equation into ordinary differential equations usually depends upon the coordinate system chosen for the investigation of the problem. In electrostatics and other field theories the symmetry of the boundaries or source conditions suggests the coordinate system which is suitable for the study of the problem; so also the best coordinate system for the solution of Schroedinger's equation is usually suggested by the symmetry of the potential function. For the central-field type

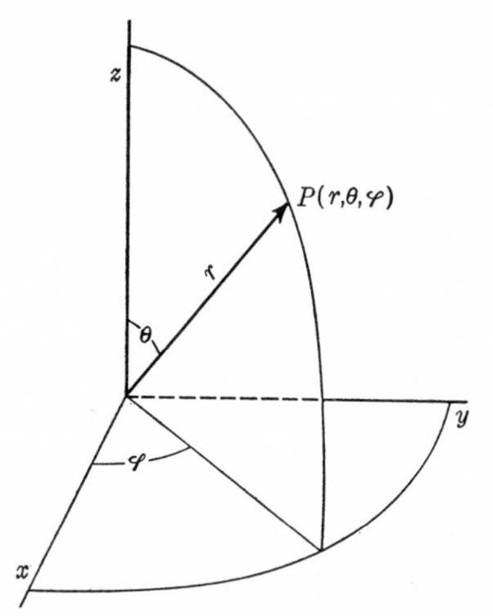

FIG. 10-1. Diagram showing the spherical polar coordinates of a point.

of potential, separation of variables may be accomplished by using spherical polar coordinates to characterize the position of the particle (see Fig. 10-1). Using Laplace's operator in spherical coordinates (see any book on vector analysis), Schroedinger's equation becomes

$$\left\{\frac{1}{r^2}\frac{\partial}{\partial r}\left(r^2\frac{\partial}{\partial r}\right) + \frac{1}{r^2\sin^2\theta}\frac{\partial^2}{\partial\varphi^2} + \frac{1}{r^2\sin\theta}\frac{\partial}{\partial\theta}\left(\sin\theta\frac{\partial}{\partial\theta}\right) + \frac{2m}{\hbar^2}[W - V(r)]\right\}\Psi(r,\theta,\varphi) = 0 \quad (10\text{-}51)$$

Let us now attempt to separate variables by writing

$$\Psi(r,\theta,\varphi) = R(r)\Theta(\theta)\Phi(\varphi) \quad (10\text{-}52)$$

Substituting this into Eq. (10-51), carrying out the differentiations, and then dividing by $R\Theta\Phi$, we obtain

$$\frac{1}{Rr^2}\frac{d}{dr}\left(r^2\frac{dR}{dr}\right) + \frac{1}{\Phi r^2\sin^2\theta}\frac{d^2\Phi}{d\varphi^2} + \frac{1}{\Theta r^2\sin\theta}\frac{d}{d\theta}\left(\sin\theta\frac{d\Theta}{d\theta}\right) + \frac{2m}{\hbar^2}[W - V(r)] = 0 \quad (10\text{-}53)$$

We may now multiply through by $r^2 \sin^2 \theta$ and transpose the second term to the right. The right side of the equation, $-\Phi''/\Phi$, is then a function of φ alone, whereas the left side is a function of r and θ. Such a relation can for arbitrary values of the independent variables r, θ, and φ be true only when both sides are equal to a constant (α). We have thus obtained one ordinary differential equation, the Φ equation, and a second partial differential equation in two variables. Both differential equations involve a presently unknown constant. The ordinary differential equation may be written in the form

$$\frac{d^2\Phi}{d\varphi^2} + \alpha\Phi = 0 \tag{10-54}$$

If the second partial differential equation, mentioned above, is divided through by $\sin^2 \theta$, it is possible to arrange it in the form $F(r) = G(\theta)$, which again can be true only if both sides are equal to another constant (β). We thus obtain two additional ordinary differential equations: the Θ equation,

$$\frac{1}{\sin \theta}\frac{d}{d\theta}\left(\sin \theta \frac{d\Theta}{d\theta}\right) - \frac{\alpha\Theta}{\sin^2 \theta} + \beta\Theta = 0 \tag{10-55}$$

and the R equation,

$$\frac{1}{r^2}\frac{d}{dr}\left(r^2 \frac{dR}{dr}\right) + \frac{2m}{\hbar^2}[W - V(r)]\,R - \frac{\beta}{r^2}R = 0 \tag{10-56}$$

In spherical coordinates the normalization condition becomes

$$\int_0^\infty \int_0^\pi \int_0^{2\pi} R^*(r)\Theta^*(\theta)\Phi^*(\varphi)R(r)\Theta(\theta)\Phi(\varphi)r^2 \sin \theta \, dr\, d\theta\, d\varphi = 1 \tag{10-57}$$

Since it is a matter of considerable convenience if the three integrals involved in Eq. (10-57) are normalized separately, we shall assume that

$$\int_0^{2\pi} \Phi^*(\varphi)\Phi(\varphi)\, d\varphi = 1 \tag{10-58}$$

$$\int_0^\pi \Theta^*(\theta)\Theta(\theta) \sin \theta \, d\theta = 1 \tag{10-59}$$

$$\int_0^\infty R^*(r)R(r)r^2\, dr = 1 \tag{10-60}$$

10-5. Solution of the Φ Equation. The general solution of Eq. (10-54) may be written as

$$\Phi = A \exp (i\alpha^{\frac{1}{2}}\varphi) + B \exp (-i\alpha^{\frac{1}{2}}\varphi) \tag{10-61}$$

where A and B are arbitrary constants. Since φ is a periodic variable, the angles φ, $\varphi + 2\pi$, $\varphi + 4\pi$, . . . are the same physical angle. If Φ is to be single-valued, then it must satisfy

$$\Phi(\varphi) = \Phi(\varphi + 2\pi) = \Phi(\varphi + 4\pi) = \cdots$$

The two particular solutions in Eq. (10-61) will satisfy these requirements only if

$$\alpha^{\frac{1}{2}} = m_l \qquad \text{or} \qquad \alpha = m_l^2 \tag{10-62}$$

where m_l can take on only the positive or negative integral values or zero. One may readily verify by expanding both particular solutions in terms of cosine and sine functions that the composite solution has the required periodicity in φ. For a given $\alpha^{\frac{1}{2}}$ the two particular solutions in Eq. (10-61) correspond to the positive and negative integers $\pm m_l$. We may thus conclude that all well-behaved functions are given by

$$\Phi = Ce^{im_l\varphi} \tag{10-63}$$

or linear combinations of these functions, where

$$m_l \doteq 0, \pm 1, \pm 2, \ldots \tag{10-64}$$

The normalization condition [Eq. (10-58)] then requires that

$$\int_0^{2\pi} C^* e^{-im_l\varphi} C e^{im_l\varphi} \, d\varphi = 1$$

which is satisfied if $C = 1/(2\pi)^{\frac{1}{2}}$. Thus the normalized Φ functions are

$$\Phi = \frac{1}{(2\pi)^{\frac{1}{2}}} e^{im_l\varphi} \tag{10-65}$$

10-6. Solution of the Θ Equation. Using Eq. (10-62) for α, the Θ equation becomes

$$\frac{1}{\sin\theta}\frac{d}{d\theta}\left(\sin\theta\frac{d\Theta}{d\theta}\right) + \left(\beta - \frac{m_l^2}{\sin^2\theta}\right)\Theta = 0 \tag{10-66}$$

This may be simplified by letting

$$z = \cos\theta \tag{10-67}$$

where z is here simply a new variable which ranges between ± 1 and is not to be confused with the rectangular coordinate. With this substitution we have

$$\frac{d\Theta}{d\theta} = \frac{dz}{d\theta}\frac{d\Theta}{dz} = -\sin\theta\frac{d\Theta}{dz} \tag{10-68}$$

Thus Eq. (10-66) becomes

$$\frac{d}{dz}\left[(1 - z^2)\frac{d\Theta}{dz}\right] + \left(\beta - \frac{m_l^2}{1 - z^2}\right)\Theta = 0 \tag{10-69}$$

For simplicity let us consider the case $m_l = 0$ and rewrite this equation as

$$\Theta'' - z^2\Theta'' - 2z\Theta' + \beta\Theta = 0 \tag{10-70}$$

This can be solved by the well-known power-series method. We assume the solution

$$\Theta = a_0 + a_1 z + \cdots + a_j z^j + \cdots \tag{10-71}$$

Upon differentiating once and twice, we obtain

$$\Theta' = a_1 + 2a_2 z + \cdots + j a_j z^{j-1} + \cdots \tag{10-72}$$
$$\Theta'' = 2a_2 + 3 \cdot 2a_3 z + \cdots + j(j-1)a_j z^{j-2} + \cdots \tag{10-73}$$

Substituting these in Eq. (10-70), we get

$$\begin{aligned} 2 \cdot 1a_2 + 3 \cdot 2a_3 z + \cdots + j(j-1)a_j z^{j-2} + \cdots - 2 \cdot 1a_2 z^2 - 3 \cdot 2a_3 z^3 \\ - \cdots - j(j-1)a_j z^j - \cdots \quad - 2a_1 z - 2 \cdot 2a_2 z^2 - \cdots - 2ja_j z^j \\ - \cdots + \beta a_0 + \beta a_1 z + \cdots + \beta a_j z^j = 0 \end{aligned} \tag{10-74}$$

Since this must be identically zero for all z, the coefficient of each power of z must vanish. Equating to zero the coefficients of $z^0, z^1, \ldots, z^j$, we find

$$\begin{aligned} 2 \cdot 1a_2 + \beta a_0 &= 0 \\ 3 \cdot 2a_3 - 2a_1 + \beta a_1 &= 0 \\ \cdots\cdots\cdots\cdots\cdots \\ (j+2)(j+1)a_{j+2} + [\beta - 2j - j(j-1)]a_j &= 0 \end{aligned} \tag{10-75}$$

Accordingly, for any j, a_{j+2} may be obtained in terms of a_j by the recursion formula

$$a_{j+2} = \frac{j(j+1) - \beta}{(j+1)(j+2)} a_j \tag{10-76}$$

If we fix a_0, the recursion formula may be used to find $a_2, a_4, a_6, \ldots,$ and if we fix a_1, the recursion formula may be used to find $a_3, a_5, a_7, \ldots.$ In this way we obtain $\Theta(z)$ as a sum of two independent series, one comprising all the even powers of z, which starts with a_0, and the second comprising all the odd powers of z, which starts with $a_1 z$.

Since β is a constant, if we let j become large enough, we may ignore β and the small integers in Eq. (10-76). Consequently for very large j, we find

$$a_{j+2} \approx a_j$$

Now an infinite power series in z^2 will diverge at $z = \pm 1$ if successive coefficients of the higher-order terms are equal. In consequence our solutions violate the good-behavior requirement of finiteness. However, we can generate well-behaved solutions of the Θ equation by two rather simple expedients. We let

$$\beta = j'(j'+1) \tag{10-77}$$

where j' is a fixed even (odd) integer. Since all coefficients in the even (odd) series past j' vanish [see Eq. (10-76)], the even (odd) series is a well-behaved polynomial whose highest power is $z^{j'}$. Second we set

a_1 (a_0) equal to zero so that the odd (even) power series, which is not terminated by Eq. (10-77), vanishes altogether. In this manner we may secure a well-behaved solution for every integral value of j', or every value of β which has the form given in Eq. (10-77). Using the recursion formula, we can readily generate these polynomials. Apart from the normalization constants they turn out to be the well-known Legendre polynomials. The first few of these are

$$P_0 = 1 \qquad P_1 = z \qquad P_2 = \tfrac{1}{2}(3z^2 - 1)$$
$$P_3 = \tfrac{1}{2}(5z^3 - 3z) \qquad P_4 = \tfrac{1}{8}(35z^4 - 30z^2 + 3) \tag{10-78}$$

We have shown again how the good-behavior requirement restricts the values of an unknown constant parameter (β) which appears in a differential equation. The problem of finding the solution of the equation when m_l is an integral value other than zero is quite similar to the above case. For this general case it is convenient to define the azimuthal quantum number

$$l = j' + |m_l| \tag{10-79}$$

where j' is integral. In terms of l, the separation constant β which leads to well-behaved solutions is given by

$$\beta = l(l + 1) \tag{10-80}$$

It can be shown that the azimuthal quantum number l and the magnetic quantum number m_l have important physical significance in that they characterize the orbital angular momentum by Eqs. (1-75) and (1-77). The restriction of m_l values [Eq. (1-78)] follows immediately from Eq. (10-79). Further it can be shown[3] that the normalized well-behaved solutions associated with each allowed l and m_l are the well-known associated Legendre functions

$$\Theta_l^{m_l}(z) = \left[\frac{(l - |m_l|)!}{(l + |m_l|)!}\,\frac{2l + 1}{2}\right]^{\frac{1}{2}} (1 - z^2)^{|m_l|/2} \frac{d^{|m_l|}}{dz^{|m_l|}} P_l(z) \tag{10-81}$$

Figure 1-4 is a graphical representation of the probability functions $(\Theta_l^{|m_l|})^2$ for several small values of l and m_l.

10-7. Radial Wave Equation. Inserting $l(l + 1)$ for β in Eq. (10-56), the radial wave equation becomes

$$\frac{1}{r^2}\frac{d}{dr}\left(r^2 \frac{dR}{dr}\right) + \frac{2m}{\hbar^2}\left[W - V(r) - \frac{\hbar^2 l(l + 1)}{2mr^2}\right] R = 0 \tag{10-82}$$

The substitution

$$R(r) = \frac{G(r)}{r} \tag{10-83}$$

then changes the radial wave equation to

$$\frac{d^2G}{dr^2} + \frac{2m}{\hbar^2}\left[W - V(r) - \frac{\hbar^2 l(l+1)}{2mr^2}\right]G = 0 \tag{10-84}$$

If we define the effective potential

$$V_e = V(r) + \frac{\hbar^2 l(l+1)}{2mr^2} \tag{10-84a}$$

the radial wave equation with G as the wave function becomes identical in form with the one-dimensional wave equation. Since the quantity $\hbar^2 l(l+1)$ is the square of the magnitude of the orbital angular momentum of the particle about the origin, we may take the term $\hbar^2 l(l+1)/2mr^2$ as the quantum counterpart of the classical "centrifugal energy"

$$T_{cent} = \frac{|l|^2}{2\mathcal{I}}$$

where $\mathcal{I} = mr^2$. Accordingly we may say that the effective potential energy is the true potential energy plus the centrifugal energy. $V(r)$ can be intrinsically negative or positive, depending upon whether the associated force is attractive or repulsive. However, since the centrifugal energy is always positive, it corresponds to a repulsive force, the centrifugal force.

The radial wave equation differs in the following important respects from the one-dimensional wave equation: (1) The variable r by its very nature is restricted to positive values from 0 to ∞, whereas x ranges from $-\infty$ to ∞. Using Eq. (10-60), we see that the normalization condition for the radial wave function G is

$$\int_0^\infty G^*G\,dr = 1 \tag{10-85}$$

(2) Since the complete radial wave function is given by Eq. (10-83), $R(r)$ can be finite at the origin only if $G(r)$ always satisfies the boundary condition

$$G(0) = 0 \tag{10-86}$$

In fact, $G(r)$ must go to zero at least as fast as a constant times r if $R(r)$ is to be finite at the origin.

The well-behaved solutions of the Schroedinger wave equation may be divided into the two general classes corresponding to negative W values and positive W values. The former class pertains to the states of binding analogous to the closed orbits of a planetary system. The latter class pertains to the unbound states analogous to the hyperbolic orbits of a planetary system. We can have states of binding only if the potential function corresponds to a strong enough attractive force (negative V). For the types of attractive potentials which arise in physical problems, well-behaved radial wave functions usually exist only when W is one of a discrete set of negative values. The particular set of allowed negative energy values depends upon the detailed characteristics of the potential function and the mass of the particle. Although no general proof has been given for this assertion, its plausibility is perhaps indicated by the following discussion.

At long ranges the effective-potential-energy function in Eq. (10-84) may be ignored so that, as may readily be verified by differentiation,

$$\overrightarrow{G} = C \exp\left[-\left(\frac{2m|W|}{\hbar^2}\right)^{\frac{1}{2}} r\right] \tag{10-87}$$

is a well-behaved solution of Eq. (10-87) for any negative value of W and for any constant C. We use the symbol $\rightarrow$ to signify "in the asymptotic limit at infinity." The corresponding radial wave function $R = G/r$ is also well-behaved. Now if we know a well-behaved solution at long ranges, it is always possible in principle to integrate Eq. (10-84) inward by a stepwise procedure. Thus we express G and its first derivative in the form of a Taylor's expansion about an arbitrary point, *i.e.*,

$$G(r_0 + h) = G(r_0) + hG'(r_0) + \frac{h^2}{2!}G''(r_0) + \cdots \tag{10-88}$$

and

$$G'(r_0 + h) = G'(r_0) + hG''(r_0) + \frac{h^2}{2!}G'''(r_0) + \cdots \tag{10-89}$$

But Eq. (10-84) itself may be used to relate the values of all higher derivatives at the point r_0 to $G(r_0)$ and to $G'(r_0)$. If this is done, Eqs. (10-88) and (10-89) become

$$G(r_0 + h) = P(r_0,h)G(r_0) + Q(r_0,h)G'(r_0) \tag{10-90}$$

and

$$G'(r_0 + h) = P'(r_0,h)G(r_0) + Q'(r_0,h)G'(r_0) \tag{10-91}$$

where P and Q are power-series representations of functions which may be evaluated to any desired degree of accuracy. Thus the values of G and G' at any point may be used to determine the values of these functions at a neighboring interior point (h negative). If we start at a point at very long range, where Eq. (10-87) is valid, Eqs. (10-90) and (10-91) can be used to determine $G(r_0 + h)$ and $G'(r_0 + h)$. Proceeding inward step by step from this point, we may generate the function $G(r)$. In the region in which the potential function V_e becomes important, the curve will deviate quite appreciably from Eq. (10-87). In fact, at the point

r_1 (see Fig. 10-2), the curvature reverses, and G becomes concave toward the r axis. Proceeding farther inward, the value of G at the origin can finally be determined. But since we have chosen a particular value for W and have integrated inward from the corresponding long-range function [Eq. (10-87)], the value of $G(0)$ is predestined to be a particular value, which depends largely on the detailed characteristics of the effective-potential function. In view of the infinity of possible values for $G(0)$, it

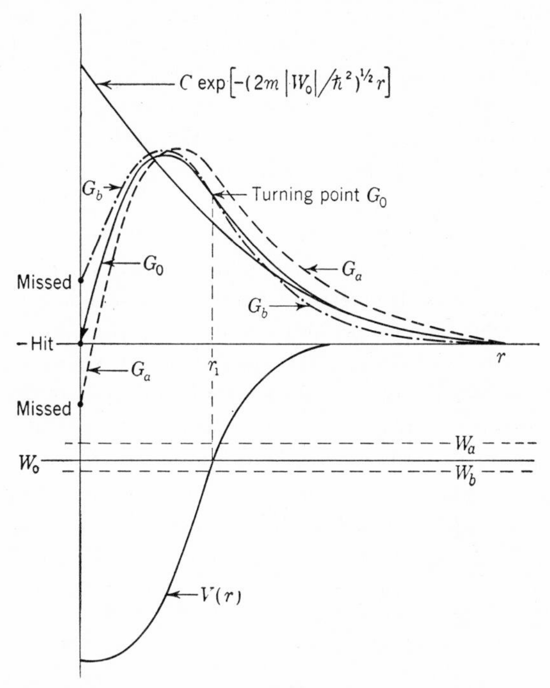

FIG. 10-2. Diagram illustrating the inward integration of the radial wave equation from its long-range solution for an arbitrary energy. W_a and W_b lead to solutions which miss the origin and hence are unacceptable. W_0 leads to a well-behaved solution.

will be a rare instance that the initial choice of W will lead to a $G(0)$ which just happens to "hit" the origin, *i.e.*, satisfies Eq. (10-86). Any attempt to "aim" at the origin by altering the constant C in Eq. (10-87) will be to no avail, since the radial wave equation is homogeneous and therefore the alteration of C will simply multiply all values of G including $G(0)$ by the same factor.

From the above discussion it is apparent that, to determine the allowed values of the total energy of a particle in a central field, we must in some way find the rare values of W, if any, which go with the correspondingly rare well-behaved radial wave functions. If this investigation is carried out by analytical methods, the result usually appears in the form of a relationship between W and the parameters which characterize the potential function and the value of l. This relationship, called the energy eigenvalue equation, is such that it can be satisfied only by certain discrete values of W. The detailed analytical steps used to find the radial wave functions and the eigenvalue equation change very markedly if one changes the analytical form of the potential function. For a few potentials, one can readily find closed expressions for the radial wave functions and a simple eigenvalue equation. However, in most cases it is impossible to obtain the results in analytical form, and one must resort to numerical or approximation methods. This seems to be an intrinsic limitation of the mathematical analysis. When strictly numerical methods are used, no sharp differences arise in the task of finding the radial wave functions and eigenvalues for potentials which are similar in width, depth, and shape.

We shall consider now the detailed solution of the radial wave equation for the coulomb potential and for the spherical well. These two potentials in many respects are the extreme types of potentials arising in atomic and nuclear physics, one representing a long-range potential and the other a short-range potential. By confining our main attention to s waves ($l = 0$), we shall avoid the most difficult mathematics without sacrificing the essential ideas of the quantum-mechanical method.

It is convenient to work with dimensionless quantities when solving the radial wave equation. To this end we refer lengths to some convenient base length a, such as the Bohr radius in the atomic case or the range of forces in the nuclear case. If we define the dimensionless distance parameter

$$\rho = \frac{r}{a} \tag{10-92}$$

we find it also convenient to refer energies to the natural energy unit

$$E_0 = \frac{\hbar^2}{2ma^2} \tag{10-93}$$

Accordingly we define the dimensionless total-energy parameter ϵ_W by

$$\epsilon_W{}^2 = \mp \frac{W}{(\hbar^2/2ma^2)} = \mp \frac{W}{E_0} \tag{10-94}$$

where the upper sign is used for the study of negative energy states and the lower sign for the study of positive energy states. For *attractive* potentials we define the dimensionless potential-energy parameter $\epsilon(\rho)$ by

$$\epsilon^2(\rho) = -\frac{V(r)}{(\hbar^2/2ma^2)} = -\frac{V(r)}{E_0} \tag{10-95}$$

The radial wave equation for negative energy states and negative potential energies becomes

$$G'' + \left[\epsilon^2(\rho) - \frac{l(l+1)}{\rho^2} - \epsilon_W{}^2\right] G = 0 \tag{10-96}$$

where a prime here denotes differentiation with respect to ρ.

10-8. The Hydrogenic-system Problem. If we assume the nucleus to be infinitely massive, a convenient unit of length is the hydrogenic Bohr radius

$$a = \frac{a_B}{Z} = \frac{\hbar^2}{m_e e^2 Z} \tag{10-97}$$

The corresponding natural unit of energy is

$$E_0 = \frac{\hbar^2}{2m_e a^2} = \frac{Z^2 e^4 m_e}{2\hbar^2} \tag{10-98}$$

which is precisely the magnitude of the ground-state energy of a hydrogenic system according to Bohr's theory. For the case $l = 0$ we find, upon using $V = -Ze^2/r$ in conjunction with Eqs. (10-95) and (10-96), that the wave equation becomes

$$G'' + \left(\frac{2}{\rho} - \epsilon_W{}^2\right) G = 0 \tag{10-99}$$

If we attempt to use the power series method to solve Eq. (10-99), we obtain a three-term recursion formula. However, the long-range solution and the boundary condition at the origin suggest that we try the substitution

$$G = \rho\,[\exp\,(-\epsilon_W \rho)] L(\rho) \tag{10-100}$$

The differential equation for L is

$$\rho L'' + 2(1 - \epsilon_W \rho) L' + 2(1 - \epsilon_W) L = 0 \tag{10-101}$$

Assuming the power series

$$L = a_0 + a_1 \rho + \cdots + a_j \rho^j + \cdots \tag{10-102}$$

differentiating, substituting into Eq. (10-101), and equating the coefficient of the jth power of ρ to zero, we find the two-term recursion formula

$$[(j+1)j + 2(j+1)]a_{j+1} + 2[1 - \epsilon_W(j+1)]a_j = 0 \tag{10-103}$$

In the limit of large j the ratio of successive terms in this representation of L is $2\epsilon_W \rho / j$; this fact leads us to the conclusion that the higher terms in $L(\rho)$ approach the higher terms in the expansion of $\exp 2\epsilon_W \rho$. Consequently G is divergent at infinity and unsatisfactory as a wave function unless the power series terminates. Examining Eq. (10-103), we see that termination occurs if

$$\epsilon_W = \frac{1}{n} \tag{10-104}$$

where

$$n \doteq 1, 2, 3, \ldots \tag{10-105}$$

This restriction upon ϵ_W leads immediately to

$$W = -\epsilon_W{}^2 \frac{\hbar^2}{2m_e a^2} = -\frac{Z^2 e^4 m_e}{2\hbar^2 n^2} \tag{10-106}$$

Accordingly the energy levels for s states are exactly those given by the Bohr formula.

Let us now consider briefly the wave function for the ground and first excited s states (*i.e.*, for $n = 1$ and 2). Inserting $\epsilon_W = 1$ into Eq. (10-103), we find, if $a_0 \neq 0$, that $a_1, a_2, a_3, \ldots$ all vanish. The radial wave function for the ground state hence has the form

$$G_1 = a_0\rho \exp(-\epsilon_W \rho) \tag{10-107}$$

This wave function has no intermediate zeros between the zero at the origin and the zero at infinity. Setting $\epsilon_W = \frac{1}{2}$ in Eq. (10-103), we find that $a_1 = -a_0/2$ and that $a_2, a_3, \ldots$ all vanish. Hence the radial wave function for the first excited s state is

$$G_2 = a_0\rho\left(1 - \frac{\rho}{2}\right)\exp(-\epsilon_W \rho) \tag{10-108}$$

a function which has one intermediate node (at $\rho = 2$). The wave functions for $n = 3, 4, 5, \ldots$ can be generated by the use of Eqs. (10-103) and (10-104). One finds in a similar manner that these wave functions have two, three, four, etc., intermediate nodes.

Thus we see that for s waves the number of intermediate nodes of the radial wave function correlates directly with the order number for the energy level; *i.e.*, the ground state has zero nodes, the first excited s state has one intermediate node, the second excited state has two nodes, etc. This correlation between number of intermediate nodes and the order of the energy level holds true for $p, d, f, \ldots$ waves as well and for any type of potential function. For this reason it is convenient to introduce a nodal quantum number v, which designates directly the number of intermediate nodes in the radial wave function.

If we investigate the hydrogenic-system problem for $l \neq 0$, we find that an unusual degeneracy occurs in which the energy depends upon the integral combination

$$n = v + 1 + l \tag{10-109}$$

It is customary in atomic physics to use the n defined by Eq. (10-109) in conjunction with l for designating energy states. This convention is adhered to, even for the noncoulombic fields which arise in the explanation of the atomic periodic table, because when the n values of several states as defined by Eq. (10-109) are equal, those states usually lie fairly close together. However, in nuclear and molecular physics this grouping rarely takes place, so that there is no advantage to the use of a principal quantum number defined by Eq. (10-109). Instead, the notation which is gaining acceptance and which we shall follow in the remainder of this book defines

$$n = v + 1 \tag{10-110}$$

an integer which is simply one unit greater than the number of nodes in the radial wave function. In view of this ambiguity in the meaning of n for other than s waves, the reader must exercise some caution in reading the nuclear literature.

10-9. Particle in a Spherical Box. Before taking up the problem of a particle in a spherical well, let us consider the somewhat artificial problem of a particle held by a field of force which is defined by

$$\begin{aligned} V(r) &= -V_0 \qquad 0 < r < a \\ &= \infty \qquad r > a \end{aligned} \tag{10-111}$$

(the spherical box). On physical grounds the wave function must vanish identically for $r \geq a$ or $\rho \geq 1$. This attribute of the problem greatly simplifies the mathematics and provides us with a simple point of departure from which to examine more realistic problems. The potential-energy parameter here is given by

$$\begin{aligned} \epsilon^2(\rho) &= \epsilon_0^2 = \frac{V_0}{E_0} \qquad \rho < 1 \\ &= -\infty \qquad \rho > 1 \end{aligned} \tag{10-112}$$

The wave equation for the interior region when $l = 0$ is

$$G_i'' + (\epsilon_0^2 - \epsilon_W^2)G_i = 0 \tag{10-113}$$

where the subscript i denotes the word interior. The solution of Eq. (10-113) which vanishes at the origin [see Eq. (10-86)] is

$$G_i = C_i \sin\,(\epsilon_0^2 - \epsilon_W^2)^{\frac{1}{2}}\rho \tag{10-114}$$

where C_i is a constant which must be fixed by the normalization requirement.

In view of the properties of the sine function we see that G_i will vanish at $\rho = 1$ if

$$(\epsilon_0^2 - \epsilon_W^2)^{\frac{1}{2}} = (v + 1)\pi \tag{10-115}$$

where

$$v \doteq 0, 1, 2, 3 \tag{10-116}$$

We conclude that the allowed total-energy parameters in this case are given by

$$\epsilon_W^2 = \epsilon_0^2 - (v + 1)^2\pi^2 \tag{10-117}$$

or using Eqs. (10-94) and (10-95), we find

$$W = -V_0 + (v + 1)^2 \frac{\pi^2\hbar^2}{2ma^2} \tag{10-118}$$

This is precisely the form of the energy eigenvalue equation for a particle in a one-dimensional box. When consideration is given to the normalization condition

$$\int_0^a |G_i|^2 \, dr = 1 \tag{10-119}$$

we find that the well-behaved radial wave functions for s waves are

$$G = \left(\frac{2}{a}\right)^{\frac{1}{2}} \sin\left[(v + 1)\frac{\pi r}{a}\right] \tag{10-120}$$

The total wave functions for s waves are therefore given by [see Eqs. (10-65) and (10-81)]

$$\Psi(r,\theta,\varphi) = \frac{1}{(2\pi a)^{\frac{1}{2}}} \frac{1}{r} \sin\left[(v + 1)\frac{\pi r}{a}\right] \tag{10-121}$$

Here again we observe that v determines the number of nodes in the radial wave function.

While the s-wave energy values for the particle in a spherical box correspond identically to the energy eigenvalues for the particle in a one-dimensional box, the energy eigenvalues for the p, d, f, . . . waves are quite different. The radial wave equation for $\rho < 1$ in the case of p waves is

$$G_i'' + \left(\epsilon_0^2 - \frac{2}{\rho^2} - \epsilon_W^2\right) G_i = 0 \tag{10-122}$$

We may verify by differentiation that a solution of this equation which vanishes at the origin is

$$G_{ip} = C_{ip}\left[\frac{\sin\,(\epsilon_0^2 - \epsilon_W^2)^{\frac{1}{2}}\rho}{(\epsilon_0^2 - \epsilon_W^2)^{\frac{1}{2}}\rho} - \cos\,(\epsilon_0^2 - \epsilon_W^2)^{\frac{1}{2}}\rho\right] \tag{10-123}$$

Assuming that this wave function must vanish at $\rho = 1$, we find the eigenvalue condition

$$\tan\,(\epsilon_0^2 - \epsilon_W^2)^{\frac{1}{2}} = (\epsilon_0^2 - \epsilon_W^2)^{\frac{1}{2}} \tag{10-124}$$

The equation $\tan\theta = \theta$ is satisfied by values of θ which are a trifle smaller than $3\pi/2$, $5\pi/2$, $7\pi/2$, etc. Accordingly, using Eq. (10-94), we find that the energy eigenvalues for p states are approximately given by

$$W \approx -V_0 + \left(v + \frac{3}{2}\right)^2 \frac{\pi^2\hbar^2}{2ma^2} \tag{10-125}$$

The complete normalized wave functions may be constructed by straightforward methods from the associated Legendre functions for p waves and the radial wave functions given by Eq. (10-123).

The solutions for $d, f, \ldots$ states may each be investigated in turn and the corresponding eigenvalues determined by the analysis of the radial wave equation belonging to each case. However, a more systematic method is to find the well-behaved solutions of the general radial wave equation

$$G_i'' + \left[\epsilon_0^2 - \frac{l(l+1)}{\rho^2} - \epsilon_W^2\right] G_i = 0 \qquad (10\text{-}126)$$

It can be shown[4] that the solutions of Eq. (10-126) which vanish at $\rho = 0$ are

$$G_i = \left[\frac{(\epsilon_0^2 - \epsilon_W^2)^{\frac{1}{2}}\rho\pi}{2}\right]^{\frac{1}{2}} J_{l+\frac{1}{2}}[(\epsilon_0^2 - \epsilon_W^2)^{\frac{1}{2}}\rho] \qquad (10\text{-}127)$$

where $J_{l+\frac{1}{2}}$ are Bessel functions of half-integral order. To satisfy the condition that the wave functions vanish at $\rho = 1$, the values of ϵ_W must be such that

$$J_{l+\frac{1}{2}}[(\epsilon_0^2 - \epsilon_W^2)^{\frac{1}{2}}] = 0 \qquad (10\text{-}128)$$

The roots of the equation $J_{l+\frac{1}{2}}(\theta) = 0$ may be found in tables of Bessel functions. For a fixed value of l the first and successively larger roots correspond to the lowest and successively higher energy states, and the corresponding wave functions have zero, one, two, etc., intermediate nodes.

10-10. Particle in a Spherical Well. The potential function in this case is

$$\begin{aligned} V &= -V_0 \qquad 0 < r < a \\ &= 0 \qquad\quad\; r > a \end{aligned} \qquad (10\text{-}129)$$

The fact that V vanishes as r goes to infinity is, of course, a basic physical requirement for any real potential. Because of this feature of the spherical-well potential the wave function no longer need vanish identically outside the well. Instead the exterior wave function for s waves must be a well-behaved function which satisfies

$$G_e'' - \epsilon_W^2 G_e = 0 \qquad (10\text{-}130)$$

where the subscript e denotes the word exterior. The solution of this equation which is well-behaved at infinity is

$$G_e = C_e \exp(-\epsilon_W \rho) \qquad (10\text{-}131)$$

where C_e is a normalization constant. The interior wave equation and interior wave function are given by Eqs. (10-113) and (10-114) just as in the spherical box. To satisfy the good-behavior requirement, the interior and exterior wave functions must now join smoothly at $\rho = 1$. We may therefore impose the conditions that

$$G_i(1) = G_e(1) \tag{10-132}$$

and

$$G_i'(1) = G_e'(1) \tag{10-133}$$

These two equations furnish two algebraic relations between C_i and C_e in terms of ϵ_0 and ϵ_W. A third relation follows from the normalization condition

$$\int_0^a |G_i|^2 dr + \int_a^\infty |G_e|^2 \, dr = 1 \tag{10-134}$$

In general the three equations for C_i and C_e can be satisfied only for special values of ϵ_W in relation to ϵ_0. The simplest and most direct method for finding the condition which must be fulfilled by the energy parameter ϵ_W and the well parameter ϵ_0 is to set

$$\left.\frac{G_i'}{G_i}\right|_{\rho=1} = \left.\frac{G_e'}{G_e}\right|_{\rho=1} \tag{10-135}$$

The C_i's and C_e's automatically cancel in this equation, and we obtain immediately the eigenvalue equation

$$(\epsilon_0^2 - \epsilon_W^2)^{\frac{1}{2}} \cot (\epsilon_0^2 - \epsilon_W^2)^{\frac{1}{2}} = -\epsilon_W \tag{10-136}$$

or

$$\tan (\epsilon_0^2 - \epsilon_W^2)^{\frac{1}{2}} = -\frac{(\epsilon_0^2 - \epsilon_W^2)^{\frac{1}{2}}}{\epsilon_W} \tag{10-137}$$

For a well which has a large ϵ_0, ϵ_W will be close to ϵ_0 for low-lying states, and hence the right side of Eq. (10-137) will be small. Hence for this case Eq. (10-115) will furnish a good approximation for the energy values of the low-lying states. When the well is shallow, it is impossible to express the energy levels in terms of an explicit formula. Instead for a given ϵ_0 we must find the roots of Eq. (10-137) by approximate numerical or graphical methods. The number of ϵ_W roots which exist depends, of course, upon the value of the well parameter ϵ_0. In Table 10-1 we show

TABLE 10-1. ROOTS OF EIGENVALUE EQUATION

ϵ_0	No.	ϵ_W Value			
		1s	2s	3s	4s
0	None				
$1.5708 = \pi/2$	One	0			
$4.7124 = 3\pi/2$	Two	3.950	0		
$7.8540 = 5\pi/2$	Three	7.345	5.600	0	
$10.9956 = 7\pi/2$	Four	10.612	9.382	6.931	0

the number of ϵ_W roots and their values for small critical values of ϵ_0. In the range of ϵ_0 between critical values the number of roots is the same as for the lower ϵ_0 value. By inserting $\epsilon_W = 0$ into Eq. (10-137) we obtain

$$\tan \epsilon_0 = -\infty \tag{10-138}$$

The roots of this equation are the critical values which give rise to an s state of zero energy. These are $\epsilon_0 = \pi/2, 3\pi/2, 5\pi/2, \ldots$. The ϵ_W values corresponding to the more stable s states at the critical ϵ_0 values are listed in the four right-hand columns.

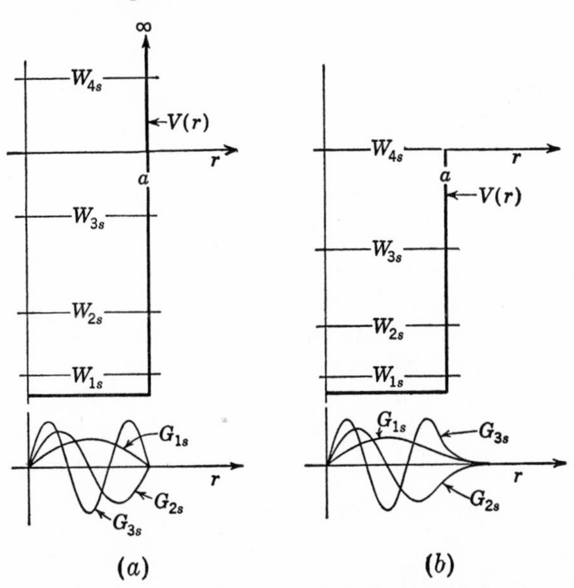

FIG. 10-3. Schematic diagram showing low-lying s states and the corresponding wave functions when $\epsilon_0 = 7\pi/2$ in (a) a spherical box and (b) a spherical well.

Once the roots of the eigenvalue equation for any given well parameter are found, we can readily construct the wave functions corresponding to each root by use of Eqs. (10-114) and (10-131). If this is done, it is again found that the ground s state has no intermediate nodes, etc. In Fig. 10-3 we indicate schematically the energy values and the radial wave functions for the several low-lying s states in the case of a particle in a box and for the case of a particle in a deep well. We note that in each of the latter cases the wave function extends into the external region. This region would be inaccessible to the particle if classical laws were obeyed, since here the classical kinetic energy ($T = W - V$) would be negative. The eigenfunctions and $\epsilon_0^2 - \epsilon_w^2$ eigenvalues of the spherical well go over to those of the spherical box as $V_0 \rightarrow \infty$ (the infinite spherical well).

Let us now consider briefly the p states of binding ($l = 1$) for the spherical well. We may verify by differentiation that the interior solution and exterior solution which satisfy the desired boundary conditions at the origin and at infinity are

$$G_{ip} = C_{ip}\left[\frac{\sin(\epsilon_0{}^2 - \epsilon_W{}^2)^{\frac{1}{2}}\rho}{(\epsilon_0{}^2 - \epsilon_W{}^2)^{\frac{1}{2}}\rho} - \cos(\epsilon_0{}^2 - \epsilon_W{}^2)^{\frac{1}{2}}\rho\right] \tag{10-139}$$

and

$$G_{ep} = C_{ep}\left(1 + \frac{1}{\epsilon_W\rho}\right)\exp(-\epsilon_W\rho) \tag{10-140}$$

The energy eigenvalue equation obtained by matching G'/G at $\rho = 1$ is

$$\frac{\cot(\epsilon_0{}^2 - \epsilon_W{}^2)^{\frac{1}{2}}}{(\epsilon_0{}^2 - \epsilon_W{}^2)^{\frac{1}{2}}} - \frac{1}{\epsilon_0{}^2 - \epsilon_W{}^2} = \frac{1}{\epsilon_W} + \frac{1}{\epsilon_W{}^2} \tag{10-141}$$

For a very deep well we may show that the energy values are given approximately by Eq. (10-125). Investigating the case of a shallow well, we find that the critical ϵ_0 values, each of which gives rise to a p state of zero energy ($\epsilon_W = 0$), are π, 2π, 3π, . . . , corresponding to the relation

$$\tan\epsilon_0 = 0 \tag{10-142}$$

The solutions for $d, f, g,$ . . . states and other states of higher orbital angular momentum may each be investigated in turn, and the corresponding eigenvalues determined by the analysis of the radial wave equation belonging to each case. However, again a more systematic method which makes it unnecessary to investigate each value of l separately is to find the general solutions of the radial equations inside and outside the well for an arbitrary value of l. It can be shown[(4)] that these solutions are

$$G_{il} = \left[\frac{(\epsilon_0{}^2 - \epsilon_W{}^2)^{\frac{1}{2}}\rho\pi}{2}\right]^{\frac{1}{2}} J_{l+\frac{1}{2}}[(\epsilon_0{}^2 - \epsilon_W{}^2)^{\frac{1}{2}}\rho] \tag{10-143a}$$

$$G_{el} = \left(\frac{\rho\pi}{2}\right)^{\frac{1}{2}} H_{l+\frac{1}{2}}(i\epsilon_W\rho) \tag{10-143b}$$

where $J_{l+\frac{1}{2}}$ and $H_{l+\frac{1}{2}}$ are Bessel and Hankel functions of half-integral order. On the basis of the properties of these functions the eigenvalues and the eigenfunctions can be determined for any value of ϵ_0. Using a comprehensive table[(10)] of $J_{l+\frac{1}{2}}$, Lee and Green[(11)] have calculated the eigenvalues of $\epsilon_0{}^2 - \epsilon_W{}^2$ for the complete range of $\epsilon_0{}^2$ of interest in nuclear physics. These eigenvalues are presented in Fig. 10-4.

10-11. Other Short-range Potentials. Most of the general features of the eigenvalues and eigenfunctions of the square well also appear in problems concerned with other short-range potentials such as the exponential, Gaussian, and Yukawa potentials. In each of these cases we may define a parameter ϵ_0 which depends upon the well depth, the well width, and the mass of the particle. For a large value of ϵ_0 there exist many states of binding. On the other hand for ϵ_0 of the order of unity, only a few states of binding exist, and again there are critical values which give rise to a state of zero binding. For each value of ϵ_0 we may number the states by the quantum number v, which determines the number of intermediate nodes in the wave function and at the same time specifies the order of the state on an energy scale. The order of states characterized

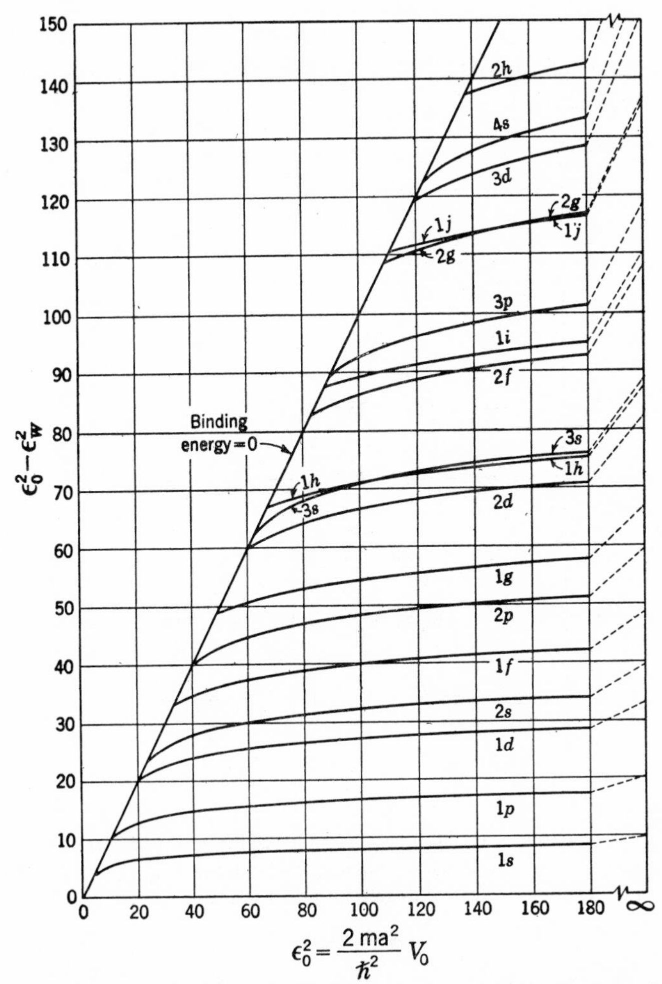

FIG. 10-4. The energy levels of a spherical well. The abscissas correspond to values of $\epsilon_0{}^2$; that is, V_0 in the natural unit $\hbar^2/2ma^2$ and the ordinate give $\epsilon_0{}^2 - \epsilon_W{}^2$ or $V_0 - |W|$ in the natural unit $\hbar^2/2ma^2$. The vertical scale on the right gives the levels for a spherical box. (*From Lee and Green, Ref. 11, after Moszkowski, Ref. 5.*)

by both quantum numbers v and l depends upon the potential function. However, the ordering varies only slightly for potentials which have the same general shape, width, and depth.

The three-dimensional harmonic oscillator [Eq. (10-27)] has been used in many discussions in nuclear physics to furnish a simple reference set of levels. The energy levels for this potential are given by

$$W = (2v + l + \tfrac{3}{2})\hbar\omega_c \tag{10-144}$$

where

$$\omega_c = \left(\frac{k}{m}\right)^{\frac{1}{2}} \tag{10-145}$$

We note here that there is a degeneracy in the energy for states with the same value of $2v + l$. In some treatments the oscillator number

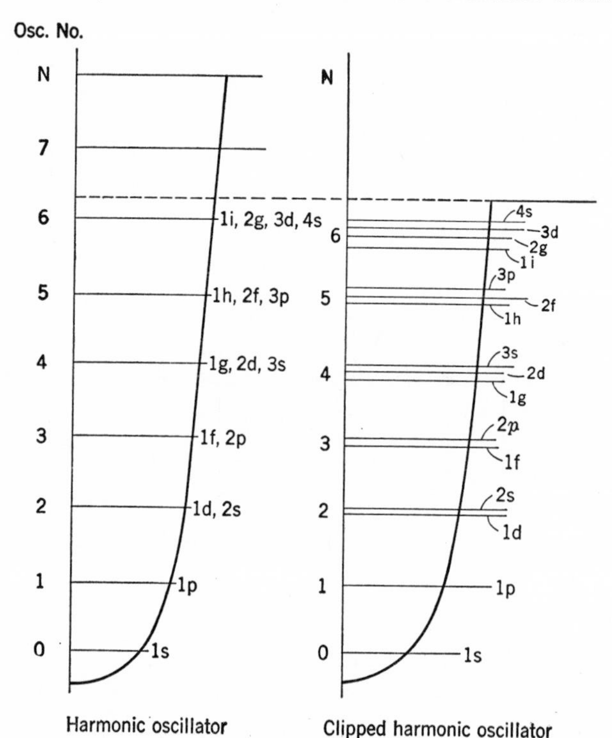

FIG. 10-5. The energy levels of the harmonic oscillator and the clipped harmonic oscillator, showing the removal of degeneracy in the latter case.

$$N = 2v + l \tag{10-146}$$

is introduced. In terms of N the energy of a three-dimensional oscillator is just

$$W = (N + \tfrac{3}{2})\hbar\omega_c \tag{10-147}$$

If a constant $-V_0$ is added to this potential, the allowed energies are simply changed by this constant. The low-lying states of this hypothetical field may be expected to correspond closely to the low-lying states of a similar potential which satisfies the physical requirement that V approaches zero as r goes to infinity. In Fig. 10-5 we show a hypothetical well shape alongside a similar well shape which meets the physical requirement stated above. If the oscillator potential function [Eq. (10-27)] is "clipped" in the manner shown in Fig. 10-5, the "accidental" degeneracy of the harmonic-oscillator potential is eliminated. The split-

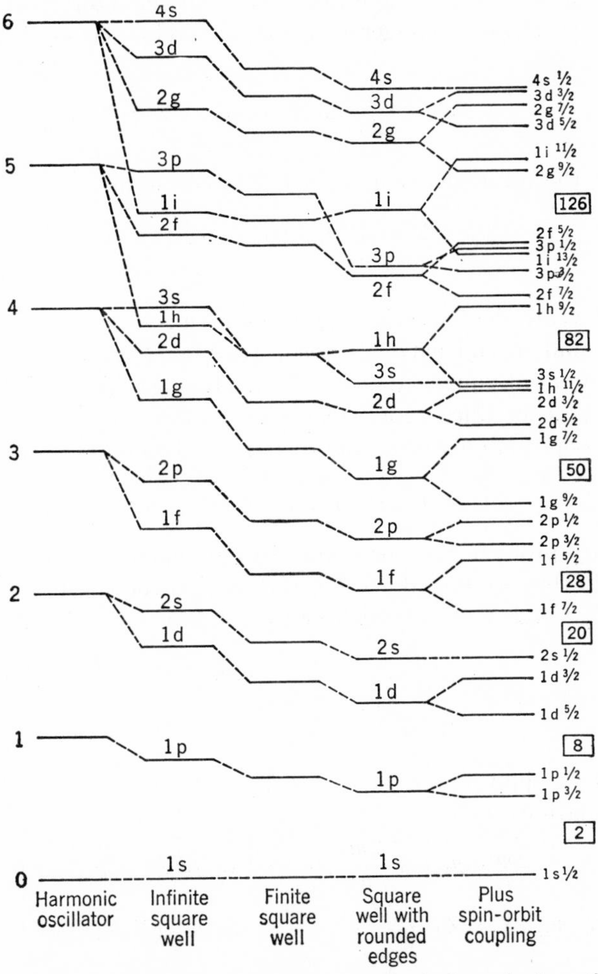

FIG. 10-6. Order of energy levels according to the independent-particle model of nuclei under various assumptions concerning the shape of the nuclear potential and including the effects of spin-orbit coupling. The energy is not to scale, nor should the exact order of the levels within a given shell be taken too seriously. (*From Feld, Ref.* 6.)

ting of the degenerate levels occurs in such a way that the states with higher l value belonging to a given oscillator number are more stable. A similar ordering of levels may be expected from a square well with rounded corners. In Fig. 10-6 we show the level sequences corresponding to several central fields. The significance of the last set of levels will be discussed in Chap. 11.

10-12. Two-body and Many-body Problems. The quantum mechanics which we have presented applies to hypothetical problems in which a single particle is bound to an infinitely heavy center of force. For the two-body problem the Schroedinger equation, an obvious generalization of Eq. (10-17), is

$$\frac{\hbar^2}{2m_1}\Delta_1\Psi + \frac{\hbar^2}{2m_2}\Delta_2\Psi + (W - V)\Psi = 0 \qquad (10\text{-}148)$$

where W is the total energy of the two-body system,

$$V = V(x_1,y_1,z_1,x_2,y_2,z_2) \qquad (10\text{-}149)$$

$$\Psi = \Psi(x_1,y_1,z_1,x_2,y_2,z_2) \qquad (10\text{-}150)$$

and Δ_1 and Δ_2 are the Laplacian operators with respect to the coordinates of the first and second particles, respectively. The direct solution of a partial differential equation such as Eq. (10-148) for a general type of potential is an exceedingly complex task. However, whenever the potential energy depends only upon the relative coordinates, *i.e.*, when

$$V = V(x_1 - x_2,\ y_1 - y_2,\ z_1 - z_2) \qquad (10\text{-}151)$$

the two-body problem may be reduced to an equivalent one-body problem. To do this, we introduce the relative and the center-of-mass coordinates x, y, z and X, Y, Z which are defined by

$$x = x_1 - x_2 \qquad \text{etc.} \qquad (10\text{-}152)$$

$$X = \frac{m_1x_1 + m_2x_2}{m_1 + m_2} \qquad \text{etc.} \qquad (10\text{-}153)$$

Schroedinger's equation for the two-body problem can then be separated into two equations

$$\Delta\Psi(x,y,z) + \frac{2m_r}{\hbar^2}[W - V(x,y,z)]\Psi(x,y,z) = 0 \qquad (10\text{-}154)$$

$$\Delta_{cm}\Psi_{cm}(X,Y,Z) + \frac{2(m_1 + m_2)}{\hbar^2}W_{cm}\Psi_{cm}(X,Y,Z) = 0 \qquad (10\text{-}155)$$

where

$$m_r = \frac{m_1m_2}{m_1 + m_2} \qquad (10\text{-}156)$$

Equation (10-155) has little interest, as it simply accounts for the constant translational motion of the center of mass of the entire system and has no effect upon the internal motion. The interesting aspects of the two-body problem are inherent in Eq. (10-154), which relates to the internal motion of the system. We observe that this equation is in all respects identical with the one-body Schroedinger equation except that the reduced mass m_r replaces the mass m.

The principles of the Schroedinger theory also extend readily to the multibody problem. The wave equation for the case of n particles may be written in the form

$$\sum_{i=1}^{n} \frac{\hbar^2}{2m_i} \Delta_i \Psi + (W - V)\Psi = 0 \tag{10-157}$$

where again W is the total energy of the system and V and Ψ depend upon the coordinates of all the particles. In multibody problems the potential function usually contains terms which depend upon the coordinates of pairs of particles. Whereas in the two-body problem such terms can readily be handled by the use of the transformations Eqs. (10-152) and (10-153), these same types of terms render almost hopeless the direct solution of a many-body problem. In some cases, however, we may replace the exact potential energy by an approximate potential of the form

$$V_0(\mathbf{r}_1, \mathbf{r}_2, \ldots, \mathbf{r}_n) = \sum_{i=1}^{n} V_0(r_i) \tag{10-158}$$

With this approximation we may effect an immediate separation of variables by assuming a solution of the product form

$$\Psi(\mathbf{r}_1, \mathbf{r}_2, \ldots, \mathbf{r}_n) = \Psi_1(\mathbf{r}_1)\Psi_2(\mathbf{r}_2) \cdots \Psi_n(\mathbf{r}_n) \tag{10-159}$$

and a total energy of the form

$$W = W_1 + W_2 + \cdots + W_n \tag{10-160}$$

It follows by the usual arguments that Eq. (10-157) is equivalent to a set of independent wave equations each of the form

$$\frac{\hbar^2}{2m_i} \Delta_i \Psi_i + [W_i - V_0(r_i)]\Psi_i = 0 \tag{10-161}$$

According to this method each particle has associated with it a set of Ψ functions and energy eigenvalues appropriate for a single particle in the field $V_0(r)$. If the particles are all identical, we need find the set of solutions and energy eigenvalues of only a single wave equation. The total energy and wave function then depend simply upon the set of single-particle states occupied by the n-particle system. For the ground state of the multibody problem consisting of identical spin $\frac{1}{2}$ particles which obey an exclusion principle, this set of solutions and energy eigenvalues, of course, would consist of the n lowest energy states of the single-particle system.

This entire method of approximation has been applied quite successfully in atomic physics, in which case it is known as the Hartree method,[7] or the method of self-consistent fields. The latter designation has been given because, in the atomic case, it is possible to use the wave functions obtained in the zero approximation to infer a more accurate effective central field for each particle. On the basis of this improved potential one can find still better wave functions. The process is repeated until finally the wave functions are self-consistent with the potential function. Still further refinements of energy values are possible by the use of the various perturbation methods, in which the effects of remaining noncentral components are calculated. Because we do not know the basic law of force between nucleons, the Hartree method cannot be carried as far in the nuclear case. However, as we shall see in the next few chapters, the limited application of this method has already led to several outstanding successes.

10-13. Time-dependent Wave Equation. We began this chapter with a discussion of Schroedinger's time-independent wave equation in relation to classical time-independent wave equations. This equation is applicable to stationary states whose energies are precisely fixed and whose probability distributions are independent of time. Schroedinger has also postulated a more general time-*dependent* wave equation

$$\left[\frac{\hbar^2}{2m}\Delta - V(x,y,z) + i\hbar\frac{\partial}{\partial t}\right]\Psi(x,y,z,t) = 0 \qquad (10\text{-}162)$$

which is the basic quantum-mechanical law of motion.

If we substitute into this general wave equation the special type of wave function for the ith stationary state

$$\Psi_i(x,y,z,t) = \Psi_i(x,y,z)\exp\left(-\frac{iW_it}{\hbar}\right) \qquad (10\text{-}163)$$

we obtain upon differentiation with respect to the time precisely the Schroedinger time-*independent* wave equation [Eq. (10-17)]. The most important problems which require the use of the general Schroedinger wave equation deal with the phenomena of transitions between energy states and the decay of excited states. It is a well-known experimental fact that a system in an excited state may jump to a lower energy state by emitting a photon or (in nuclear physics) by emitting a nuclear or beta particle. The fact that excited states decay implies that they are not exactly representable by functions which vary harmonically with time. As a better approximation we might represent a decaying state by a damped harmonic wave function of the form

$$\Psi_i(x,y,z,t) = \Psi_i(x,y,z)\exp\left(-\frac{iW_it}{\hbar}\right)\exp\left(-\frac{\lambda_it}{2}\right) \qquad (10\text{-}164)$$

We note that such a wave function yields the probability density

$$\boldsymbol{\Psi}_i^* \boldsymbol{\Psi}_i = \Psi_i^* \Psi_i \exp(-\lambda_i t) \tag{10-165}$$

According to this expression the probability distribution function of a decaying state decreases exponentially with time, with a decay constant λ_i. We may define a corresponding lifetime for the state by

$$\tau_i = \lambda_i^{-1} \tag{10-166}$$

We may modify our earlier treatment of excited states to allow for the phenomenon of decay simply by replacing W in Eq. (10-19) by $W_i - (i\hbar\lambda_i/2)$. From the formal standpoint, energy values become complex whenever we deal with decaying states. An analogous formalism appears in electric-circuit transient theory, in which case the presence of dissipative forces may be accommodated by introducing complex characteristic frequencies.

Formulas in which the energy is allowed to have a small imaginary component take on a somewhat neater form if we define

$$\Gamma_i = \hbar\lambda_i = \hbar\tau_i^{-1} \tag{10-167}$$

where Γ_i is known as the total energy width for the ith state and is measured in energy units. The time-dependent wave function and probability function for a decaying state are therefore

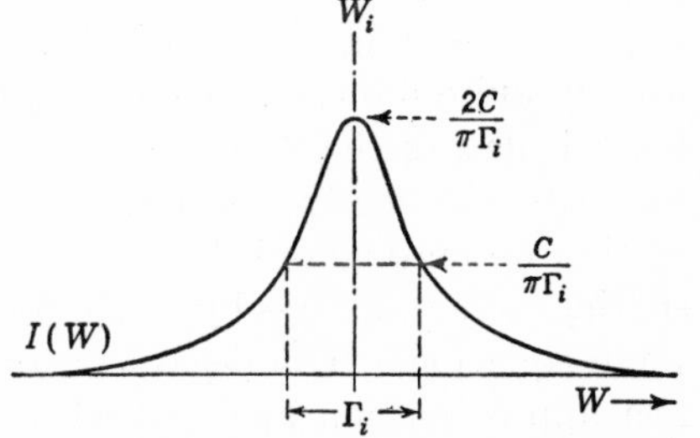

FIG. 10-7. Diagram showing schematically the distribution in energies of an excited state.

$$\boldsymbol{\Psi}_i(x,y,z,t) = \Psi_i(x,y,z) \exp\left[-i\left(W_i - i\frac{\Gamma_i}{2}\right)\frac{t}{\hbar}\right] \tag{10-168}$$

and

$$\boldsymbol{\Psi}_i^* \boldsymbol{\Psi}_i = \Psi_i^*(x,y,z)\Psi_i(x,y,z) \exp\left(-\frac{\Gamma_i t}{\hbar}\right) \tag{10-169}$$

A wave function of the form given by Eq. (10-168) may be viewed as a continuous superposition of perfectly harmonic functions. The method of Fourier analysis may be applied to the time-dependent part of Eq. (10-168) to obtain the corresponding frequency (or energy) distribution function. The distribution function for energies which follows directly from such an analysis is (see Fig. 10-7)

$$I(W) = C\frac{\Gamma_i/2\pi}{(W - W_i)^2 + (\Gamma_i/2)^2} \tag{10-170}$$

where C is a constant. This distribution function is centered about the "resonance" energy W_i and has Γ_i as the half width (*i.e.*, the distance on the energy scale between the two points at which the distribution function has one-half its peak value). We have thus justified our use of the word "width" for Γ_i. The equation

$$\Gamma_i \tau_i = \hbar \tag{10-171}$$

implies that a state with a short lifetime has a wide distribution of energy values, and a state with a long lifetime has a narrow distribution of energy values. This equation is the time-energy counterpart of the position-momentum uncertainty principle [Eq. (2-56)].

To find the allowed complex energy eigenvalues for the excited states of a system, we might in principle substitute Eq. (10-168) into Eq. (10-162). The spatial wave function then has the complex energy value in it. Presumably, by considering the wave equation for the total system, we might attempt a direct evaluation of the allowed energies and the corresponding energy widths. In practice such a direct approach is usually quite difficult. Consequently various indirect methods are used for calculating the values of energy widths or decay constants. Such methods are usually based upon the assumption that in the 0th approximation we may ignore the energy width of a decaying state and find the spatial wave functions by using the usual time-independent Schroedinger wave equation. The decay constant is then evaluated by various indirect approximation methods when consideration is given to the mechanism by which the decay takes place.

When the situations arise in nuclear physics whose treatment must be based upon the general Schroedinger equation, we usually use the formula for w, the transition probability per unit time, which is a consequence of the general Schroedinger equation. This formula, first derived by Dirac[8] using the so-called time-dependent perturbation theory, is

$$w = \frac{2\pi}{\hbar} \left| \int \Psi_i^* H_{op} \Psi_f \, d\tau \right|^2 \frac{d\mathfrak{N}}{dW} \tag{10-172}$$

where Ψ_i and Ψ_f are the time-independent functions for the initial and final states of the system, $d\mathfrak{N}/dW$ is the energy density of final states per unit volume of real space (see Sec. 11-4), and H_{op} is the operator associated with the interaction energy which causes the transition. The wave functions Ψ_i and Ψ_f must be normalized so that the corresponding probabilities per unit volume are unity.

Conservation of energy, a basic principle of macroscopic physics, is one of the important consequences of the time-dependent perturbation theory when it is applied to real processes. Thus although the initial and final states of the system may be different in many respects, they nevertheless must have the same total energy. For example, a transition from an excited state of a system to the ground state by the emission of a quantum with energy $h\nu$ may be viewed as a transition between two energy states which satisfy

$$W_i = W_f + h\nu \tag{10-173}$$

Here the final state is regarded as the state in which the original system is in the ground state and a quantum exists. A transition from an excited state by the emission of a heavy particle must satisfy

$$M_i + W_i = T + M_f + m + W_f \tag{10-174}$$

where the masses are now included because they do not cancel in this case. Several applications of Eq. (10-172) will be discussed as they arise in the remainder of this book.

10-14. Perturbation Methods. It happens almost always in nature that the total physical situation is far too complicated for a complete direct analysis. Fortunately, however, physical situations arise or can be arranged in which various effects have different orders of magnitude so that the problem may be treated by a method of successive approximations. Atomic and nuclear physics provide an abundance of problems which can be approached in this way. In these problems we proceed theoretically by investigating first the effect of the largest energy term, ignoring completely the smaller interactions. After this first approximation has been resolved, we proceed to the study of the next largest interaction (*i.e.*, the second approximation). Continuing in this way, we frequently find the most difficult problems to be tractable.

A result of both classical and quantum-mechanical perturbation theory which is practically indispensable for the resolution of problems arising in atomic and nuclear physics may be stated in the form of the following basic theorem:

The change in the total energy of a state which is caused by a small perturbation is the average of the perturbation energy calculated on the basis of the unperturbed state. Symbolically we may write

$$\Delta W = \langle W \rangle \tag{10-175}$$

If the perturbation energy may be expressed as a Schroedinger operator, the average is simply obtained from the expectation formula

$$\langle W \rangle = \int \Psi_i^* W_{op} \Psi_i \, d\tau \tag{10-176}$$

where Ψ_i is the atomic wave function which characterizes the unperturbed energy state. However, if, as is often the case when spin angular momentum is involved, it is impossible to identify a Schroedinger operator with the perturbation energy, then the computation of the average energy or energy shift can be carried out quantitatively only by using the most advanced quantum-mechanical methods. The mathematics required for such work is beyond the scope of this book. To proceed further, it will be necessary to adopt some sort of compromise between an advanced quantum-mechanical approach and an elementary approach. In the treatment which we shall follow the quantization rules given in Chap. 1, which were extracted from advanced quantum theory, will be accepted as postulates. Having accepted these basic postulates, we shall use for final calculations the semiclassical methods which were developed and successfully applied to a great number of situations before the discovery of quantum theory. By way of apology for this departure from the rigorous route we might state that most of the quantitative results which we will obtain here agree with those obtained by strict quantum-mechanical methods.

10-15. Quasi-quantum-mechanical Methods for Angular Momenta.[9] Angular momenta usually enter into simple nuclear problems in the form of an energy term which depends upon the scalar product of an angular-momentum vector and the magnetic-field vector or a scalar product of two angular momenta. If the circumstances are such that the angle between the two vectors is constant, the allowed values of the scalar product can be computed quite simply. For example, to obtain the value of $\mathbf{K} \cdot \mathbf{H}$ when $\mathbf{K}$ makes a fixed angle relative to $\mathbf{H}$, we accept the z direction as the direction of $\mathbf{H}$. Then using Eq. (1-73), we get immediately

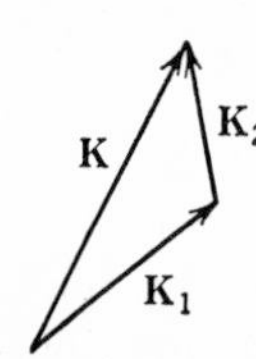

FIG. 10-8. Diagram illustrating the coupling of angular-momentum vectors.

$$\mathbf{K} \cdot \mathbf{H} = K_z H = M_K \hbar H \tag{10-177}$$

where M_K conforms to Eq. (1-74). When the scalar product involves two angular-momentum vectors which are rigidly coupled to form a third vector

$$\mathbf{K} = \mathbf{K}_1 + \mathbf{K}_2 \tag{10-178}$$

we find according to the law of cosines or vector algebra (see Fig. 10-8)

$$\mathbf{K}_1{}^2 + \mathbf{K}_2{}^2 + 2\mathbf{K}_1 \cdot \mathbf{K}_2 = \mathbf{K}^2$$

or

$$\mathbf{K}_1 \cdot \mathbf{K}_2 = \tfrac{1}{2}(\mathbf{K}^2 - \mathbf{K}_1{}^2 - \mathbf{K}_2{}^2)$$

Using for each vector the quantization rule

$$\mathbf{K}^2 = \mathbf{K} \cdot \mathbf{K} = K(K+1)\hbar^2 \tag{10-179}$$

we obtain

$$\mathbf{K}_1 \cdot \mathbf{K}_2 = \frac{\hbar^2}{2}[K(K+1) - K_1(K_1+1) - K_2(K_2+1)] \tag{10-180}$$

By a similar calculation we find

$$\mathbf{K} \cdot \mathbf{K}_1 = \frac{\hbar^2}{2}[K(K+1) + K_1(K_1+1) - K_2(K_2+1)] \tag{10-181}$$

and

$$\mathbf{K} \cdot \mathbf{K}_2 = \frac{\hbar^2}{2} [K(K + 1) - K_1(K_1 + 1) + K_2(K_2 + 1)] \quad (10\text{-}182)$$

We shall refer to Eqs. (10-177) and (10-180) to (10-182) simply as the Landé formulas. Some values of $\mathbf{K}_1 \cdot \mathbf{K}_2$, $\mathbf{K}_1 \cdot \mathbf{K}$, $\mathbf{K}_2 \cdot \mathbf{K}$, and $\mathbf{K} \cdot \mathbf{K}$ are given in Table 10-2.

TABLE 10-2. VALUES OF SCALAR PRODUCTS IN UNITS OF $\hbar^2$

(The first column in each block denotes the values of K; the second, third, fourth, and fifth figures in each block give the corresponding values of $\mathbf{K}_1 \cdot \mathbf{K}_2$, $\mathbf{K}_1 \cdot \mathbf{K}$, $\mathbf{K}_2 \cdot \mathbf{K}$, and $\mathbf{K} \cdot \mathbf{K}$, respectively.)

K	K_2 \ K_1	0					$\frac{1}{2}$				
$K = K_1$	0	0	0	0	0	0	$\frac{1}{2}$	0	$\frac{3}{4}$	0	$\frac{3}{4}$
$K = K_1 + \frac{1}{2}$	$\frac{1}{2}$	$\frac{1}{2}$	0	0	$\frac{3}{4}$	$\frac{3}{4}$	1	$\frac{1}{4}$	1	1	2
$K = K_1 - \frac{1}{2}$	$\frac{1}{2}$	...	...	...	...	...	0	$-\frac{3}{4}$	0	0	0
$K = K_1 + 1$	1	1	0	0	2	2	$\frac{3}{2}$	$\frac{1}{2}$	$\frac{5}{4}$	$\frac{5}{2}$	$\frac{15}{4}$
$K = K_1$	1	...	...	...	...	...	$\frac{1}{2}$	-1	$-\frac{1}{4}$	1	$\frac{3}{4}$
$K = K_1 - 1$	1	...	...	...	...	...	...	...	...	...	...
$K = K_1 + \frac{3}{2}$	$\frac{3}{2}$	$\frac{3}{2}$	0	0	$\frac{15}{4}$	$\frac{15}{4}$	2	$\frac{3}{4}$	$\frac{3}{2}$	$\frac{9}{2}$	6
$K = K_1 + \frac{1}{2}$	$\frac{3}{2}$	...	...	...	...	...	1	$-\frac{5}{4}$	$-\frac{1}{2}$	$\frac{5}{2}$	2
$K = K_1 - \frac{1}{2}$	$\frac{3}{2}$	...	...	...	...	...	...	...	...	...	...
$K = K_1 - \frac{3}{2}$	$\frac{3}{2}$	...	...	...	...	...	...	...	...	...	...
$K = K_1 + 2$	2	2	0	0	6	6	$\frac{5}{2}$	1	$\frac{7}{4}$	7	$\frac{35}{4}$
$K = K_1 + 1$	2	...	...	...	...	...	$\frac{3}{2}$	$-\frac{3}{2}$	$-\frac{3}{4}$	$\frac{9}{2}$	$\frac{15}{4}$
$K = K_1$	2	...	...	...	...	...	...	...	...	...	...
$K = K_1 - 1$	2	...	...	...	...	...	...	...	...	...	...
$K = K_1 - 2$	2	...	...	...	...	...	...	...	...	...	...

K	K_2 \ K_1	1					$\frac{3}{2}$				
$K = K_1$	0	1	0	2	0	2	$\frac{3}{2}$	0	$\frac{15}{4}$	0	$\frac{15}{4}$
$K = K_1 + \frac{1}{2}$	$\frac{1}{2}$	$\frac{3}{2}$	$\frac{1}{2}$	$\frac{5}{2}$	$\frac{5}{4}$	$\frac{15}{4}$	2	$\frac{3}{4}$	$\frac{9}{2}$	$\frac{3}{2}$	6
$K = K_1 - \frac{1}{2}$	$\frac{1}{2}$	$\frac{1}{2}$	1	1	$-\frac{1}{4}$	$\frac{3}{4}$	1	$-\frac{5}{4}$	$\frac{5}{2}$	$-\frac{1}{2}$	2
$K = K_1 + 1$	1	2	1	3	3	6	$\frac{5}{2}$	$\frac{3}{2}$	$\frac{21}{4}$	$\frac{7}{2}$	$\frac{35}{4}$
$K = K_1$	1	1	-1	1	1	2	$\frac{3}{2}$	-1	$\frac{11}{4}$	1	$\frac{15}{4}$
$K = K_1 - 1$	1	0	-2	0	0	0	$\frac{1}{2}$	$-\frac{5}{2}$	$\frac{5}{4}$	$-\frac{1}{2}$	$\frac{3}{4}$
$K = K_1 + \frac{3}{2}$	$\frac{3}{2}$	$\frac{5}{2}$	$\frac{3}{2}$	$\frac{7}{2}$	$\frac{21}{4}$	$\frac{35}{4}$	3	$\frac{9}{4}$	6	6	12
$K = K_1 + \frac{1}{2}$	$\frac{3}{2}$	$\frac{3}{2}$	-1	1	$\frac{11}{4}$	$\frac{15}{4}$	2	$-\frac{3}{4}$	3	3	6
$K = K_1 - \frac{1}{2}$	$\frac{3}{2}$	$\frac{1}{2}$	$-\frac{5}{2}$	$-\frac{1}{2}$	$\frac{5}{4}$	$\frac{3}{4}$	1	$-\frac{11}{4}$	1	1	2
$K = K_1 - \frac{3}{2}$	$\frac{3}{2}$	...	...	...	...	...	0	$-\frac{15}{4}$	0	0	0
$K = K_1 + 2$	2	3	2	4	8	12	$\frac{7}{2}$	3	$\frac{27}{4}$	9	$\frac{63}{4}$
$K = K_1 + 1$	2	2	-1	1	5	6	$\frac{5}{2}$	$-\frac{1}{2}$	$\frac{13}{4}$	$\frac{11}{2}$	$\frac{35}{4}$
$K = K_1$	2	1	-3	-1	3	2	$\frac{3}{2}$	-3	$\frac{3}{4}$	4	$\frac{15}{4}$
$K = K_1 - 1$	2	...	...	...	...	...	$\frac{1}{2}$	$-\frac{9}{2}$	$-\frac{3}{4}$	$\frac{3}{2}$	$\frac{3}{4}$
$K = K_1 - 2$	2	...	...	...	...	...	...	...	...	...	...

K	K_2 \ K_1	2				
$K = K_1$	0	2	0	6	0	6
$K = K_1 + \frac{1}{2}$	$\frac{1}{2}$	$\frac{5}{2}$	1	7	$\frac{7}{4}$	$\frac{35}{4}$
$K = K_1 - \frac{1}{2}$	$\frac{1}{2}$	$\frac{3}{2}$	$-\frac{3}{2}$	$\frac{9}{2}$	$-\frac{3}{4}$	$\frac{15}{4}$
$K = K_1 + 1$	1	3	2	8	4	12
$K = K_1$	1	2	-1	5	1	6
$K = K_1 - 1$	1	1	-3	3	-1	2
$K = K_1 + \frac{3}{2}$	$\frac{3}{2}$	$\frac{7}{2}$	3	9	$\frac{27}{4}$	$\frac{63}{4}$
$K = K_1 + \frac{1}{2}$	$\frac{3}{2}$	$\frac{5}{2}$	$-\frac{1}{2}$	$\frac{11}{2}$	$\frac{13}{4}$	$\frac{35}{4}$
$K = K_1 - \frac{1}{2}$	$\frac{3}{2}$	$\frac{3}{2}$	-3	3	$\frac{3}{4}$	$\frac{15}{4}$
$K = K_1 - \frac{3}{2}$	$\frac{3}{2}$	$\frac{1}{2}$	$-\frac{9}{2}$	$\frac{3}{2}$	$-\frac{3}{4}$	$\frac{3}{4}$
$K = K_1 + 2$	2	4	4	10	10	20
$K = K_1 + 1$	2	3	0	6	6	12
$K = K_1$	2	2	-3	3	3	6
$K = K_1 - 1$	2	1	-5	1	1	2
$K = K_1 - 2$	2	0	-6	0	0	0

Frequently we must evaluate the average scalar product of two vectors whose relative angles change periodically. The classical model attributes such changes to the complex precessional motions which take place because of the torques associated with various interaction energies. Thus a strong energy term of the type

$$W = a\, \mathbf{K}_1 \cdot \mathbf{K}_2 \quad (10\text{-}183)$$

is assumed to produce a rigid coupling of the two vectors $\mathbf{K}_1$ and $\mathbf{K}_2$ and a rapid precession of $\mathbf{K}_1$ and $\mathbf{K}_2$ about the resultant $\mathbf{K}$. Since this motion does not affect the angle between $\mathbf{K}_1$ and $\mathbf{K}_2$, the energy in Eq. (10-183) follows simply from the Landé formula.

Let us now suppose that, in addition to a strong interaction of the type described by Eq. (10-183), there is a small magnetic energy of the type

$$W = g_I \frac{\mu_0\, \mathbf{K}_1 \cdot \mathbf{H}}{\hbar} \quad (10\text{-}184)$$

If $\mathbf{K}_1$ were free, the magnetic field would cause $\mathbf{K}_1$ to precess independently and slowly about $\mathbf{H}$ (see discussion of the Larmor precession in Chap. 2). However, since $\mathbf{K}_1$ is strongly coupled to $\mathbf{K}$, the net effect of the large interaction energy and the magnetic energy, according to the classical model, is a complex precessional motion in which $\mathbf{K}_1$ and $\mathbf{K}_2$ precess rapidly about $\mathbf{K}$, and $\mathbf{K}$ precesses slowly about $\mathbf{H}$ (see Fig. 10-9). In such a motion the angle between $\mathbf{K}_1$ and $\mathbf{H}$ varies, and hence $\mathbf{K}_1 \cdot \mathbf{H}$ varies. To evaluate the effect of the small-energy term, we make use of the postulate of perturbation theory quoted in the preceding section. We must therefore find the average of $\mathbf{K}_1 \cdot \mathbf{H}$ for the complex precessional motion indicated in Fig. 10-9.

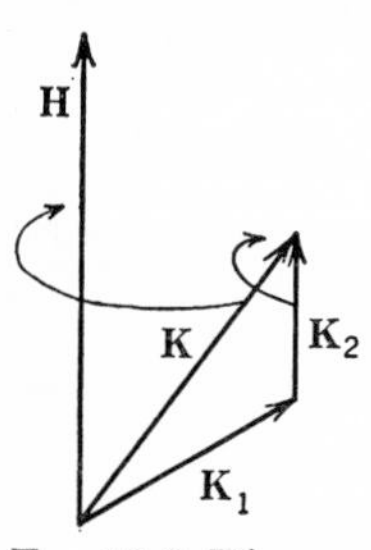

FIG. 10-9. Diagram illustrating the coupling and precession of angular-momentum vectors in a magnetic field.

Now it can be shown from simple trigonometric and statistical considerations that, for the assumed type of motion,

$$\langle \cos \widehat{K_1 H} \rangle = \cos \widehat{K_1 K} \cos \widehat{KH} \qquad (10\text{-}185)$$

where we use the symbol $\widehat{K_1 H}$ to mean the angle between K_1 and H, etc. This theorem may be written in the convenient and mnemonic form

$$\langle \mathbf{K}_1 \cdot \mathbf{H} \rangle = \frac{(\mathbf{K}_1 \cdot \mathbf{K})(\mathbf{K} \cdot \mathbf{H})}{(\mathbf{K} \cdot \mathbf{K})} = \frac{\mathbf{K}_1 \cdot \mathbf{K}\, \mathbf{K} \cdot \mathbf{H}}{\mathbf{K} \cdot \mathbf{K}} \qquad (10\text{-}186)$$

where all the scalar products on the right can be evaluated using quantization rules and the Landé formulas. We may visualize the $\mathbf{K}$ in Eq. (10-186) as the intermediate link in a chain connecting $\mathbf{K}_1$ to $\mathbf{H}$, in analogy with the fact that $\mathbf{K}_1$ precesses about $\mathbf{K}$, which precesses about $\mathbf{H}$. With this interpretation we may readily infer more elaborate "chain" formulas which are appropriate for more complex precessional motions. For example, in the precessional motion indicated in Fig. 10-10, in which the rigidly coupled $\mathbf{s}_1$ and $\mathbf{s}_2$ precess very rapidly about the resultant $\mathbf{S}$ and the rigidly coupled $\mathbf{S}$ and $\mathbf{L}$ precess less rapidly about $\mathbf{I}$, which precesses slowly about $\mathbf{H}$, we have

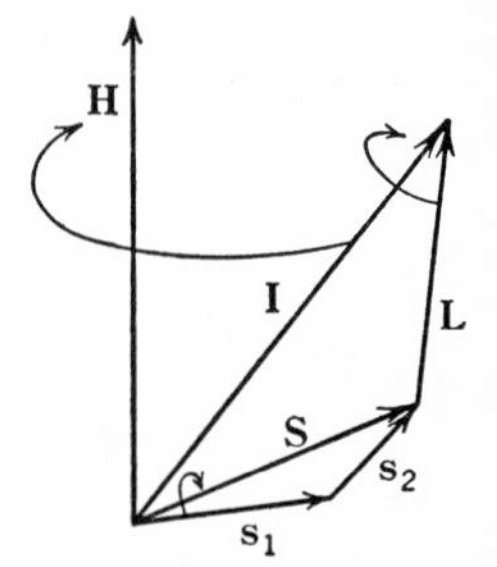

FIG. 10-10. Diagram illustrating the couplings and precessions of several angular-momentum vectors in a magnetic field.

$$\langle \mathbf{s}_1 \cdot \mathbf{H} \rangle = \frac{\mathbf{s}_1 \cdot \mathbf{S}\, \mathbf{S} \cdot \mathbf{I}\, \mathbf{I} \cdot \mathbf{H}}{\mathbf{S} \cdot \mathbf{S}\, \mathbf{I} \cdot \mathbf{I}} \qquad (10\text{-}187)$$

where again all the quantities on the right can be evaluated using the quantization rules and Landé formulas. Equation (10-187) may be verified directly by the use of simple statistical and trigonometric theorems. These perturbation methods will find many applications in Chap. 11 and the remainder of this book.

PROBLEMS

10-1. By normalizing, show that A in Eq. (10-35) is equal to $(2/a)^{\frac{1}{2}}$, apart from an arbitrary complex constant of unit magnitude.

10-2. Carry through the detailed steps leading to Eqs. (10-54) to (10-56).

10-3. Evaluate $\langle x \rangle$, $\langle x^2 \rangle$, $\langle p_x \rangle$, $\langle p_x{}^2 \rangle$, Δx, and Δp, where $\Delta x = (\langle x^2 \rangle - \langle x \rangle^2)^{\frac{1}{2}}$ and $\Delta p = (\langle p^2 \rangle - \langle p \rangle^2)^{\frac{1}{2}}$, for a particle in a one-dimensional box in the nth state. What is the value of $\Delta x \, \Delta p$? What are the implications of this result?

10-4. Generate the 3s wave function for the coulomb well.

10-5. What are the ϵ_w values of all bound s states (to four significant figures) for the square-well potential (*a*) when $\epsilon_0 = 8$? (*b*) when $\epsilon_0 = 9\pi/2$?

10-6. At what value of the well-strength parameter ϵ_0 is the binding-energy parameter ϵ_w for the lowest s state for the square well precisely one-half the magnitude of the potential-energy parameter?

***10-7.** What are the ϵ_w values of all bound p states (*a*) when $\epsilon_w = 3\pi/2$? (*b*) When $\epsilon_w = 2\pi$? (*c*) When $\epsilon_w = 8$?

***10-8.** Verify Eq. (10-127).

***10-9.** Find the three lowest eigenvalues and eigenfunctions for the one-dimensional motion of a particle bound by the potential $V = \frac{1}{2}kx^2$. What is the value of $\langle V \rangle + \langle T \rangle$ in these states? What are the implications of these results? What is the value of $\Delta x \, \Delta p$ for these states?

***10-10.** Find the three lowest s-wave eigenvalues and eigenfunctions for the three-dimensional harmonic-oscillator potential [Eq. (10-27)].

10-11. Verify Eqs. (10-154) and (10-155).

10-12. Show that the chain rule is applicable to the computation of $\langle \mathbf{K}_1 \cdot \mathbf{K}_2 \rangle$ when $\mathbf{K}_1$ and $\mathbf{K}_2$ precess independently about a third vector $\mathbf{A}$. (*Hint:* Use $\cos \widehat{K_1 K_2} = \alpha_1\alpha_2 + \beta_1\beta_2 + \gamma_1\gamma_2$, where α, β, and γ denote the direction cosines relative to the x, y, and z axes. Also use the statistical theorems that the average of a sum is the sum of the averages, and for the independent distributions the average of a product is the product of the averages.)

10-13. Verify Eqs. (10-186) and (10-187) by extending the arguments in Prob. 10-12.

REFERENCES

1. De Broglie, L.: *Ann. phys.*, **3,** 22 (1925).
2. Schroedinger, E.: *Ann. Physik*, **79,** 361, 489; **80,** 437; **81,** 109 (1926).
3. Pauling, L., and E. B. Wilson: "Introduction to Quantum Mechanics," p. 124, McGraw-Hill Book Company, Inc., New York, 1935.
4. Schiff, L. I.: "Quantum Mechanics," McGraw-Hill Book Company, Inc., New York, 1949.
5. Moszkowski, S. A.: *Phys. Rev.*, **89,** 482 (1953).
6. Feld, B. T.: *Ann. Rev. Nuclear Sci.*, **2,** 249 (1953).
7. Hartree, D. R.: *Proc. Cambridge Phil. Soc.*, **24,** 111 (1928).
8. Dirac, P. A. M.: *Proc. Roy. Soc. (London)*, **A112,** 661 (1925); **A114,** 243 (1927).
9. Back, E., and A. Landé: "Zeeman effect und Multiplett Structur," Springer-Verlag, Berlin, 1927.
10. Mathematical Tables Project, National Bureau of Standards: "Tables of Spherical Bessel Functions," Vols. 1 and 2, Columbia University Press, New York, 1947.
11. Lee, K., and A.E.S. Green: unpublished.

CHAPTER 11

NUCLEAR PERIODIC TABLE

Despite the fact that we still do not understand the basic nature of the neutron and proton and the neutron-proton, neutron-neutron, and proton-proton interactions, there have been many attempts to devise a theory to explain some of the properties of complex nuclei. Such theories usually take as basic assumptions a specific nuclear model, the laws of quantum mechanics, a set of nucleon-nucleon interactions, and the experimentally known properties of the neutron and the proton. In most theories which have been investigated thus far, the detailed nature of the nucleon-nucleon force does not affect some of the general properties of complex nuclei. Thus, as far as these general properties are concerned, the model chosen essentially characterizes the theory. The properties of complex nuclei which theoreticians are seeking to explain are (1) the systematics and tendencies of complex nuclei, (2) the energy values of the ground state and the low-lying excited states of complex nuclear systems, (3) nuclear, mechanical, magnetic, and electric moments, and (4) the measurable parameters connected with various nuclear transitions and processes. We shall devote this chapter to a description of several nuclear theories and a comparison of some of the experimental and theoretical properties listed under items (1) to (3).

11-1. Liquid-drop Model. We have already discussed the liquid-drop model, which is based upon the assumption that the nuclear constituents are so numerous that their individuality may be disregarded in the explanation of most nuclear properties. This continuum model is an extremely simple and appealing one, which has served well for a description of certain types of nuclear phenomena. However, it cannot be applied to light nuclei or to the explanation of the irregularities in the mass surface which are attributed to nuclear shell structure.

On the basis of the liquid-drop model some of the excited states of nuclei correspond to the rotational levels of the system which is behaving approximately as a rigid body. These energies are expected to conform to the formula for the rigid rotator ($\mathcal{I}$ is the moment of inertia and L is the rotational quantum number)

$$W_L = \frac{\hbar^2}{2\mathcal{I}} L(L + 1) \qquad (11\text{-}1)$$

If one uses for the moment of inertia of a rotating sphere

$$\mathcal{I} = \tfrac{2}{5}MR^2 \approx \tfrac{2}{5}M_n b^2 A^{\frac{5}{3}} \tag{11-2}$$

the theoretical rotational levels become (see Fig. 11-1)

$$W_L = \frac{5}{4}\frac{\hbar^2}{M_n b^2}\frac{L(L+1)}{A^{\frac{5}{3}}} \approx \frac{25L(L+1)}{A^{\frac{5}{3}}} \quad \text{Mev} \tag{11-3}$$

If the intrinsic spin quantum number associated with the ground state of a nucleus is zero, the total angular-momentum quantum number of a

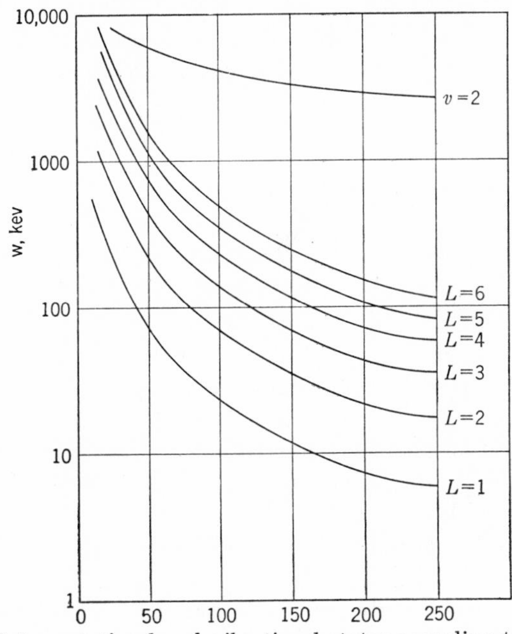

FIG. 11-1. Low-lying rotational and vibrational states according to the elementary liquid-drop model.

given excited rotational state will be simply the value of L. The observations of low-lying excited states of nuclei whose ground-state angular momenta vanish fail to exhibit levels which are spaced as close and as regularly as these formulas indicate. Experimental evidence further tends to rule out the efforts to account for the observed states simply by assuming that some L values are forbidden because of symmetry requirements. It thus does not appear that the excited levels of nuclei can be accounted for simply as the rotational levels of a liquid droplet as a whole.

The low-lying excited levels of a complex nucleus, according to the liquid-drop model, also might be identified with surface vibrations which preserve the volume of the droplets. Bohr and Kalckar,[1] on the basis of such an interpretation, have shown that the characteristic angular frequency of the fundamental mode of a droplet having a radius R, a density ρ, and a surface tension $\mathcal{O}$ is given by

$$\omega = \left(\frac{4}{3}\frac{\pi\mathcal{O}}{AM_n}\right)^{\frac{1}{2}} [v(v-1)(v+2)]^{\frac{1}{2}} \tag{11-4}$$

where v denotes the order of the Legendre function which characterizes the mode of distortion (see Chap. 9). We note that $\omega = 0$ for $v = 1$, a circumstance which is related to the fact that such vibration would violate conservation of momentum. Recalling that $4\pi R^2\mathcal{O} = a_2A^{\frac{2}{3}}$, we see that the energy of the first excited vibrational state ($v = 2$) for a nuclear droplet is (see Fig. 11-1)

$$W_v = \hbar\omega = \left(\frac{\hbar^2}{M_nb^2}\frac{a_2}{3}\right)^{\frac{1}{2}} \frac{2\sqrt{2}}{A^{\frac{1}{2}}}$$

$$\approx \frac{41.5}{A^{\frac{1}{2}}} \text{ Mev} \tag{11-5}$$

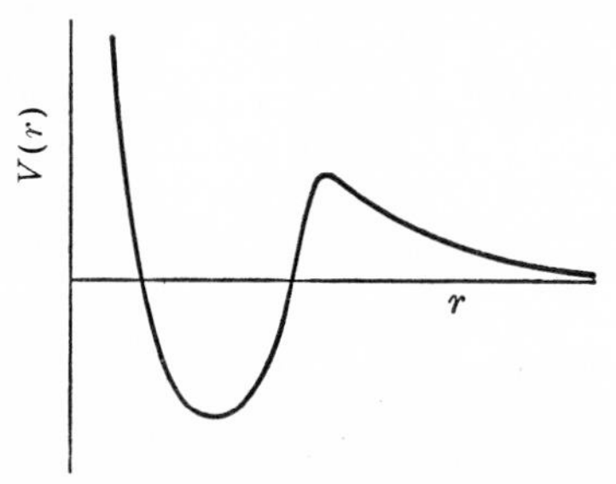

FIG. 11-2. Schematic diagram of a possible potential function for alpha particles.

The variation of $A^{\frac{1}{2}}$ does roughly characterize the general trend of the energy of the first excited states of nuclei, but the theoretical magnitude is much greater than experimental observations indicate. The coulomb repulsion, which we have thus far neglected, tends to lower the energy of these surface vibrations; however, the effect is not large enough to bring the theoretical results into line with experiment.

The fact that the liquid-drop model in its elementary form does not provide a basis for a good estimate for low-lying levels is not entirely unexpected. For low states of excitation the nuclear fluid should not actually behave like a classical fluid, but should instead show the anomalous quantum effects, when it is near absolute zero, of a fluid of Fermi-Dirac particles. The classical liquid-drop model might, however, be expected to be useful for studies of highly excited states. Recently a modified form of the liquid-drop model, known as the collective model, has been proposed which shows promise of accounting for some of the experimental evidence on excited states. We shall discuss this model and this evidence in Sec. 11-8.

11-2. Alpha-particle Model. One effort to account for the properties of light nuclei is based upon the assumption that alpha particles are important subgroups within nuclei. The so-called alpha nuclei (light nuclei with $A = 4n$, $Z = N = 2n$, with n integral) are assumed to consist solely of alpha particles bound into simple geometrical configurations by weak forces of the van der Waals type. In Fig. 11-2 we indicate a type of potential function which may be appropriate for a pair of alpha particles. Such a potential corresponds to a strong, short-range repulsive force, an attractive force of the van der Waals type at intermediate ranges, and a long-range repulsive coulomb force. The geometric configurations assumed for alpha nuclei correspond to the simplest types of closest-packing arrangements of rigid spheres which are familiar in the study of molecular structure. The total alpha binding energy of alpha nuclei is

$$B = nM_\alpha - M \tag{11-6}$$

A striking aspect of the experimental data which appears at first to support the alpha model is the almost constant value 2.4 mMU for the alpha binding energy per bond. This is indicated in Table 11-1. While the

TABLE 11-1. BINDING ENERGIES OF ALPHA NUCLEI

n	Symbol	Configuration	Δ	B_α, mMU	No. bonds	Energy per bond
1	He^4	....	3.873	....	0	
2	Be^8	Dumbbell	7.850	0.104	1	−0.104
3	C^{12}	Triangle	3.804	7.815	3	2.60
4	O^{16}	Tetrahedron	0	15.492	6	2.58
5	Ne^{20}	Trigonal bipyramid	−1.223	20.588	9	2.29
6	Mg^{24}	Tetragonal bipyramid	−7.372	30.610	12	2.55
7	Si^{28}	Pentagonal bipyramid	−14.175	41.286	15	2.58
8	S^{32}	Hexagonal bipyramid	−17.817	48.801	~19	2.57
9	A^{36}	....	~−21.93	~56.78	~21	2.66
10	Ca^{40}	....	~−24.55	~63.28	~25	2.53
11	Ti^{44}	....	~−27.00	~69.60	~28	2.44
12	Cr^{48}	....	~−31.53	~77.91	~32	2.43
13	Fe^{52}	Centered icosahedron	~−35.30	~85.65	~36	2.38
14	Ni^{56}	....	~−41.33	~95.55	~40	2.38
15	Zn^{60}	....	~−47.00	~105.09	~44	2.39
16	Ge^{64}	....	~−48.00	~109.5	~48	2.28
17	Se^{68}	....	~−49.00	~113.84	~52	2.18

simplest alpha nucleus Be^8, which is assumed to have a dumbbell-type structure, is exceptional in this regard, since the ground state of this nucleus is unstable relative to alpha decay, the agreement among the other alpha nuclei is very good.

A closely related observation in favor of the alpha model is the "four-structure" type of irregularity in the trend of light nuclear masses. On the other hand, a four-structure type of irregularity might also be explained on the basis of the independent-particle model. Further, detailed studies of alpha nuclei[(2)] suggest that the apparent additivity of the energies of alpha-particle bonds is a fortuitous result of complicated, essentially nonadditive interaction effects.

Because of the spin saturation of the alpha-particle subgroups, alpha nuclei are expected, in conformity with experiment, to have zero mechanical and magnetic moments. Again, however, this expectation follows from the independent-particle model, so that it cannot be regarded as evidence in favor of the alpha-particle model.

The low-lying excited states of the simplest alpha nuclei have been studied by methods similar to those used in the study of molecular energy levels. The analysis indicates that the levels of these alpha nuclei may be expressed in terms of a rotational quantum number and a characteristic moment of inertia by the formula

$$W_L = \frac{\hbar^2}{2\mathcal{J}} L(L + 1) \tag{11-7}$$

and in terms of various vibrational quantum numbers and the associated vibrational frequencies ν_i according to

$$W_{vib} = \sum_i n_i h\nu_i + W_0 \tag{11-8}$$

Be^8, the simplest alpha nucleus, is completely analogous to a diatomic molecule consisting of two nuclei with zero spin. The rotational quantum numbers in this case are restricted by symmetry requirements to the values $L = 0, 2, 4, \ldots$. This nucleus has been investigated by Dee and Gilbert[3] in experiments on scattering of alpha particles by helium. These experiments have revealed the existence of a virtual ground state having an energy of about 0.125 Mev and a virtual first excited state with $W = 2.8$ Mev. If this excited state is identified with $L = 2$, we obtain $\hbar^2/2\mathcal{J} \approx 0.5$ Mev from Eq. (11-7). This value gives a moment of inertia which is much larger than one would expect from the alpha-particle model. Dennison[4] in 1940 attempted to correlate the low-lying excited states of the four simplest alpha nuclei in terms of only two adjusted experimental parameters associated with vibrational and rotational motion, respectively. This work has been reexamined in the light of recent data by Inglis,[5] who finds considerable success in accounting for the first few excited states of O^{16} but finds difficulties with C^{12}. On the other hand Haefner[6] meets with limited successes in ascribing some of the observed excited states of alpha nuclei to rotational states.

The alpha-particle model has been extended by Hafstad and Teller[7] to nuclei of mass number $4n \pm 1$. These nuclei are viewed as clusters of alpha particles with an extra or missing nucleon. The geometrical symmetries of the alpha-particle structure serve as a guide in the choice of the wave functions which characterize the extra or missing nucleon. Besides rotational and vibration levels one here encounters nucleonic levels which are the analogues of the electronic levels of molecular spectroscopy. Unfortunately the perturbation methods used successfully in molecular physics are not well justified in nuclear physics, so that the significance of the results based upon such methods is still obscure.

11-3. Wigner's Uniform Model. As an important preliminary to the discussion of Wigner's uniform model let us first calculate the number of standing waves per unit volume in an enclosure which is assumed to be large compared to the majority of wavelengths present. This result will have several other applications in the remainder of this book.

The conditions for standing waves in a cubic box with sides of length a are

$$k_x a = n_x \pi \qquad k_y a = n_y \pi \qquad k_z a = n_z \pi \tag{11-9}$$

where n_x, n_y, and n_z are positive integers. These equations, which must be fulfilled for each mode, restrict the propagation constants to discrete quantities. However, when the integers which characterize a state are very large, we may view unit changes as differentials and accept these equations as relations between the continuous variables k_x and n_x, k_y and n_y, and k_z and n_z. With this convention the number of states per unit volume of real space in the propagation-constant intervals $k_x \rightarrow k_x + dk_x$, $k_y \rightarrow k_y + dk_y$, $k_z \rightarrow k_z + dk_z$ is found to be

$$d\mathfrak{N} = \frac{dn_x\,dn_y\,dn_z}{a^3} = \frac{dk_x\,dk_y\,dk_z}{\pi^3} \tag{11-10}$$

The factor $dk_x\,dk_y\,dk_z$ is just a volume element in a space in which the propagation constants are the coordinates. Since the components of the propagation constant are always positive quantities, our propagation-constant space extends only over a positive octant. We may compute the number of states per unit volume of real space having propagation constants less than or equal to k_m, a specific large propagation constant, by integrating Eq. (11-10), placing limits upon k_x, k_y, and k_z such that

$$k_m = (k_x^2 + k_y^2 + k_z^2)^{\frac{1}{2}} \tag{11-11}$$

The results of such an integration follow simply from the formula for the volume of an octant of a sphere of radius k_m. Thus we have

$$\mathfrak{N} = \frac{1}{8\pi^3}\frac{4\pi k_m{}^3}{3} = \frac{k_m{}^3}{6\pi^2} \tag{11-12}$$

It follows immediately that the number of states per unit volume of real space in the propagation-constant range from k to $k + dk$ is

$$d\mathfrak{N}(k) = \frac{k^2}{2\pi^2}\,dk \tag{11-13}$$

In the uniform model the neutrons and protons in the ground state of a nucleus are assumed to behave like a Fermi gas, in that they occupy the lowest available momentum states of a standing-wave field in the spherical enclosure having the volume of the nucleus ($V = \frac{4}{3}\pi b^3 A$). As a 0th approximation the enclosure is considered to be large compared to the wavelengths, and consequently the volume density of states is accepted as uniform. In a nucleus with an even number of neutrons the total number of neutron states or neutrons with propagation constants less than k_m is

$$N = 2\frac{4\pi b^3 A}{3}\frac{k_m{}^3}{6\pi^2} \tag{11-14}$$

where the factor 2 allows for both possible spin orientations. The maximum neutron propagation constant is thus

$$k_m = \frac{1}{b}\left(\frac{9\pi}{4}\right)^{\frac{1}{3}}\left(\frac{N}{A}\right)^{\frac{1}{3}} \tag{11-15}$$

The total neutron kinetic energy is

$$\begin{aligned} T_n &= 2\frac{4\pi b^3 A}{3}\int_0^{k_m}\frac{\hbar^2 k^2}{2M_n}\frac{k^2}{2\pi^2}\,dk = \frac{\hbar^2}{2M_n}\frac{4\pi b^3 A}{3\pi^2}\frac{k_m{}^5}{5} \\ &= \frac{3}{10}\frac{\hbar^2}{M_n b^2}\left(\frac{9\pi}{4}\right)^{\frac{2}{3}}\frac{N^{\frac{5}{3}}}{A^{\frac{2}{3}}} \end{aligned} \tag{11-16}$$

Similar expressions follow for the maximum proton propagation constant and the total proton kinetic energy in an even-Z nucleus. The total kinetic energy of a complex even-even nucleus therefore is (letting $M_n = M_p = M$)

$$T = \frac{3}{10}\frac{\hbar^2}{Mb^2}\left(\frac{9\pi}{4}\right)^{\frac{2}{3}}\frac{N^{\frac{5}{3}} + Z^{\frac{5}{3}}}{A^{\frac{2}{3}}} \tag{11-17}$$

Substituting $(A/2)(1 + D/A)$ for N, $(A/2)(1 - D/A)$ for Z, and assuming D/A is small compared to 1, it follows that

$$T = T_0 A\left(1 + \frac{5}{9}\frac{D^2}{A^2}\right) \tag{11-18}$$

where

$$T_0 = \frac{3}{10}\frac{\hbar^2}{Mb^2}\left(\frac{9\pi}{8}\right)^{\frac{2}{3}} \tag{11-19}$$

From the standpoint of statistical mechanics this energy is the zero-point energy (kinetic energy at absolute zero) of the assembly of neutrons and protons.

In order to determine the total potential energy of a nucleus, we must now make some assumptions as to the nature of the interaction between nucleons. As a starting point Wigner[8] has suggested the use of simple short-range ordinary and exchange forces which are independent of charge and spin. The coulomb force is ignored in the 0th approximation. The ordinary and exchange forces assumed by Wigner may be divided into two sets. For one set the interaction between two particles is completely indifferent to the states occupied by the two particles or to their spin or isobaric spin. For the second set the interaction between two particles depends upon the states occupied by these particles as well as the spin and isobaric spin of these particles.

To develop an expression for the total potential energy associated with the first-mentioned type of force, we note that in a complex nucleus the total number of pairs of nucleons or the total number of couplings is $\frac{1}{2}A(A-1)$. In the so-called Wigner approximation it is assumed (1) that the motion of particles in a complex nucleus is so complicated that each coupling has equal a priori probability, (2) that a pair of particles interact only when the two particles come within a range r'_0 which is small compared to R, and (3) that within this range the potential energy is $-V'_0$. In view of these assumptions it follows that the total potential energy associated with the forces which are indifferent to the state, spin, or isobaric spin of the two nucleons is approximately

$$V' = -\frac{1}{2}A(A-1)\frac{\frac{4}{3}\pi r_0'^3}{\frac{4}{3}\pi R^3}V'_0 \tag{11-20}$$

Using $R = bA^{\frac{1}{3}}$ and letting c' be an energy constant given by

$$c' = \frac{r_0'^3 V'_0}{b^3} \tag{11-21}$$

Eq. (11-20) becomes

$$V' = -\tfrac{1}{2}c'(A-1) \tag{11-22}$$

Because of the uncertainties in all the quantities which make up c', this constant is usually allowed to be an adjustable one.

Using group-theoretic methods, Wigner has shown that the exchange force which he assumed gives rise to the contribution

$$V'' = -\Xi\frac{r_0''^3}{R^3}V''_0 = -\Xi\frac{c''}{A} \tag{11-23}$$

where r''_0, V''_0, and c'' are the corresponding range, depth, and adjustable constants associated with the exchange force and Ξ is a quantity which depends only upon the symmetry properties of the distribution of nucleons. The nature of the exchange force assumed by Wigner is effectively such that the $\frac{1}{2}A(A-1)$ couplings may be divided into three groups: (1) couplings between particles in the same state each of which contributes $+1$ to Ξ, (2) couplings between identical particles (same spin and isobaric spin) in different states each of which contributes -1 to Ξ, (3) couplings between unlike particles in different states each of which contributes zero to Ξ. As a justification for this last rule we might note that, when at least one of the two particles lies in a fully occupied state, an exchange of two nonidentical particles would produce a state which violates the exclusion principle.

Using the rules above, we can readily evaluate Ξ for the important cases of interest. Let us first consider an even-even type of nuclide with

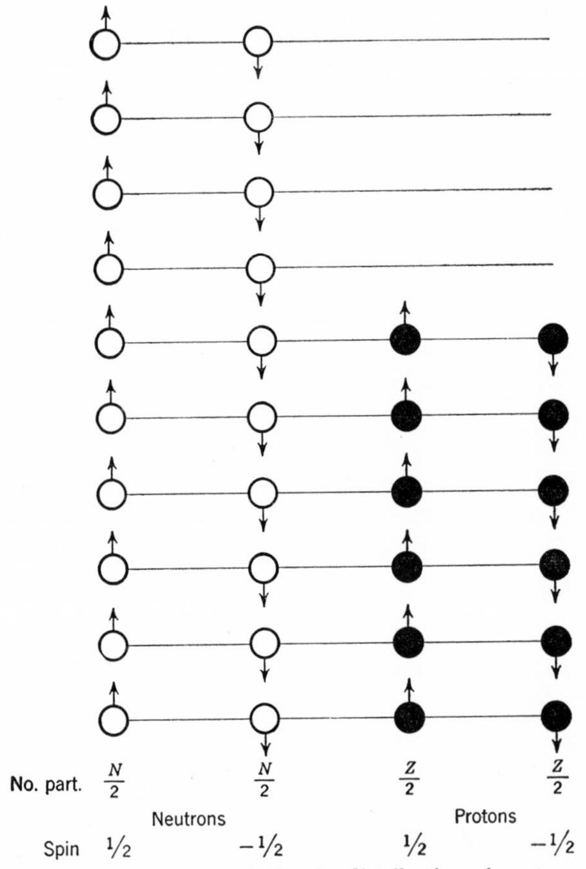

Fig. 11-3. Diagram showing schematically the distribution of neutrons and protons among hypothetical nuclear energy states in an EE nucleus. It is assumed that the coulomb force between protons is absent and that neutrons and protons have the same mass.

a positive neutron excess. Such a nuclide is represented diagrammatically by Fig. 11-3. We see that there are $Z/2$ states with four particles. Each of these contributes six positive couplings. In addition there are $(N - Z)/2$ states with two particles, each of which contributes one positive coupling. The up-spin neutrons and down-spin neutrons each contribute $\frac{1}{2}(N/2)[(N/2) - 1]$ negative couplings, and the up-spin protons and down-spin protons each contribute $\frac{1}{2}(Z/2)[(Z/2) - 1]$. Gathering together these contributions, we have

$$\Xi = 6\frac{Z}{2} + \frac{N - Z}{2} - \frac{N}{2}\left(\frac{N}{2} - 1\right) - \frac{Z}{2}\left(\frac{Z}{2} - 1\right)$$
$$= -\frac{N^2}{4} - \frac{Z^2}{4} + N + 3Z \tag{11-24}$$

Letting $N = (A + D)/2$ and $Z = (A - D)/2$, we find

$$\Xi = -\frac{A^2}{8} - \frac{D^2}{8} + 2A - D \tag{11-25}$$

This value of Ξ was derived with the assumption that the neutron excess is positive. Since the exchange force is symmetrical with respect to the isobaric spin, we would have the same number for Ξ if the number of protons were interchanged with the number of neutrons (*i.e.*, if D were negative). Hence for the general case we should replace the D in Eq. (11-25) by $|D|$. Inserting the resulting expression into Eq. (11-23), we find for the potential energy connected with the exchange force

$$V'' = c''\left(\frac{A}{8} - 2\right) + c''\left(\frac{D^2}{8A} + \frac{|D|}{A}\right) \tag{11-26}$$

In addition to the potential energy associated with strictly nuclear forces, we must add a correction for the small coulomb interaction energy. Since the proton density is assumed to be uniform, we may take as a reasonable approximation the classical coulomb expression

$$E_c = \frac{3}{5}\frac{Z(Z - 1)e^2}{R} = \frac{a_3 Z(Z - 1)}{A^{\frac{1}{3}}} \tag{11-27}$$

where

$$a_3 = \frac{3}{5}\frac{e^2}{b} \tag{11-27a}$$

The quantum-mechanical calculation also predicts a term which may be interpreted as a surface energy. Part of this energy arises as a result of a slight overestimate of the number of states [Eq. (11-12)] in an octant of k space bounded by k_m, and part of this energy term arises as a result of the assumption of the standing-wave conditions [Eq. (11-9)] appropriate for a potential which rises to infinity at the walls instead of for a finite potential. When consideration is given to these two effects, a surface term is found[9,10] approximately of the form which we discussed in Chap. 9, namely,

$$E_s = 4\pi b^2 \mathcal{O} A^{\frac{2}{3}} = a_2 A^{\frac{2}{3}} \tag{11-28}$$

Collecting all the energy terms, we obtain for the total energy

$$
\begin{aligned}
E &= T + V + E_s + E_c \\
&= -A\left(\frac{c'}{2} - \frac{c''}{8} - T_0\right) + \frac{c'}{2} - 2c'' + \left(\frac{c''}{8} + 5\, T_0\right)\frac{D^2}{A} + c''\frac{|D|}{A} \\
&\qquad + a_2 A^{\frac{2}{3}} + a_3 \frac{Z(Z-1)}{A^{\frac{1}{3}}} \qquad (11\text{-}29)
\end{aligned}
$$

One of the principal successes of this theory is the automatic appearance of a symmetry energy which accounts for the tendency of the strictly nuclear force to states with $D = 0$.

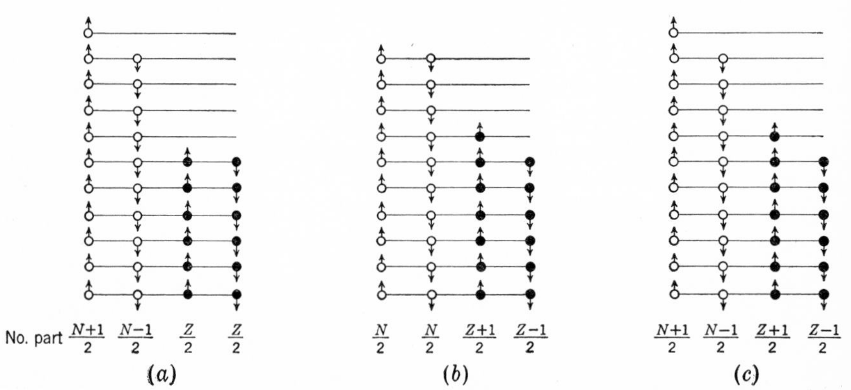

FIG. 11-4. Diagrams showing schematically the distribution of neutrons and protons among hypothetical nuclear energy states in (a) an OE nucleus, (b) an EO nucleus, and (c) an OO nucleus.

The energy given by Eq. (11-29) may be converted into a mass decrement in a manner similar to that which we used for the Weiszäcker mass surface. The functional form of the result is quite promising and suggests that a comparison with experiment would lead to agreement as favorable as in the case of the Weiszäcker formula.

An additional success of the Wigner model (sometimes referred to as the uniform model) is the fact that it automatically predicts the pairing tendency of nuclei. To show this, let us consider an OE-type nuclide (see Fig. 11-4a). In this case we have

$$
\begin{aligned}
\Xi &= 6\frac{Z}{2} + \left(\frac{N-1}{2} - \frac{Z}{2}\right) - \frac{1}{2}\frac{N-1}{2}\left(\frac{N-1}{2} - 1\right) \\
&\qquad - \frac{1}{2}\frac{N+1}{2}\left(\frac{N+1}{2} - 1\right) - \frac{Z}{2}\left(\frac{Z}{2} - 1\right) \\
&= 2A - \frac{A^2}{8} - \frac{D^2}{8} - D - \frac{3}{4} \qquad (11\text{-}30)
\end{aligned}
$$

For EO-type nuclides (see Fig. 11-4b) we have

$$\Xi = 6\,\frac{Z-1}{2} + 3 + \left(\frac{N}{2} - \frac{Z+1}{2}\right) - \frac{N}{2}\left(\frac{N}{2} - 1\right) - \frac{1}{2}\,\frac{Z+1}{2}\left(\frac{Z+1}{2} - 1\right) - \frac{1}{2}\,\frac{Z-1}{2}\left(\frac{Z-1}{2} - 1\right)$$
$$= 2A - \frac{A^2}{8} - \frac{D^2}{8} - D - \frac{3}{4} \tag{11-31}$$

In an OO-type nuclide (see Fig. 11-4c) we have

$$\Xi = 6\,\frac{Z-1}{2} + 3 + \left(\frac{N-1}{2} - \frac{Z+1}{2}\right) - \frac{1}{2}\,\frac{N+1}{2}\left(\frac{N+1}{2} - 1\right) - \frac{1}{2}\,\frac{N-1}{2}\left(\frac{N-1}{2} - 1\right) - \frac{1}{2}\,\frac{Z+1}{2}\left(\frac{Z+1}{2} - 1\right) - \frac{1}{2}\,\frac{Z-1}{2}\left(\frac{Z-1}{2} - 1\right)$$
$$= 2A - \frac{A^2}{8} - \frac{D^2}{8} - D - \frac{3}{2} \tag{11-32}$$

Accordingly in relation to the potential energy of EE nuclides given by Eq. (11-26) we find

$$V_{\text{OE}} = V_{\text{EO}} = V_{\text{EE}} + \frac{3}{4}\,\frac{c''}{A} \tag{11-33}$$

and

$$V_{\text{OO}} = V_{\text{EE}} + \frac{3}{2}\,\frac{c''}{A} \tag{11-34}$$

An odd-even effect also appears in connection with the kinetic-energy term. By modifying Eq. (11-14) to Eq. (11-16) appropriately one finds that for an OE-type nuclide (see Fig. 11-4a) the kinetic energy is

$$T_{\text{OE}} = (2)^{\frac{4}{3}}\,\frac{T_0}{A^{\frac{2}{3}}}\left[\left(\frac{N+1}{2}\right)^{\frac{5}{3}} + \left(\frac{N-1}{2}\right)^{\frac{5}{3}} + \left(\frac{Z}{2}\right)^{\frac{5}{3}} + \left(\frac{Z}{2}\right)^{\frac{5}{3}}\right]$$
$$\approx T_{\text{EE}} + \frac{10T_0}{9A} \tag{11-35}$$

where we first assumed that $N \gg 1$ and finally that $N \approx A/2$. By an identical procedure we find

$$T_{\text{EO}} \approx T_{\text{EE}} + \frac{10T_0}{9A} \tag{11-36}$$

and

$$T_{\text{OO}} \approx T_{\text{EE}} + \frac{20}{9}\,\frac{T_0}{A} \tag{11-37}$$

Hence in relation to the total energy for EE nuclides, odd-mass nuclides have the additional pairing energy

$$\Delta E = \frac{1}{A}\left(\frac{3}{4}c'' + \frac{10T_0}{9}\right) \tag{11-38}$$

and OO-type nuclides have a pairing energy twice as great. In relation to the odd mass surface we may place the Wigner pairing correction in the form of Eq. (8-3) with

$$H(A) = \frac{1}{A}\left(\frac{3}{4}c'' + \frac{10T_0}{9}\right) \tag{11-39}$$

We recall from our discussion of Sec. 8-2 that such a pairing correction is in rough conformity with experiment.

Another successful qualitative feature of the theory is the fact that the type of exchange force used in this theory, the so-called Majorana force, can automatically lead to the saturation of nucleon densities. To exhibit this feature of the theory, we would have to use more accurate expressions for the radial dependence of the potential energy than Eqs. (11-20) and (11-23). A study with these more accurate potentials shows that changes in the relative contributions of the repulsive forces and the attractive forces to the total potential energy would occur if the radius of an assembly of nucleons were varied. The net effect is such that the total potential energy has a minimum at some value between $r = 0$ and $r = \infty$. In the absence of an exchange force the minimum would occur at $r = 0$. However, if the exchange force is sufficiently large so that $c'' \gtrsim c'$, this minimum occurs in the neighborhood of actual nuclear radii.

A number of attempts[11,34,35] have been made to adjust the constants of the Wigner mass surface to secure quantitative agreement with the experimental data and to account for the saturation of nuclear densities. In these attempts it has been traditional to ignore the surface energy and to proceed essentially in the following fashion. First, one inserts into Eqs. (11-19) and (11-27*a*) the radius constant obtained from studies of the mass differences of mirror nuclides. The mass differences between isobars are then used to evaluate c''. Finally absolute masses are used to obtain c'.

Unfortunately the results of such attempts have been disappointing. It has not been possible to give a quantitative account of all the mass differences between isobars with only a single adjustable parameter c''. Better results for isobaric mass differences are obtained if T_0 is also taken as an adjustable parameter. However, the fit of the absolute masses is still poor no matter what one uses for c'. One can do much better in the fitting of the absolute masses by using a finite surface-energy constant a_2 whose magnitude is of the same order as that used in the Weiszäcker equation.[36] Indeed if T_0, c', c'', and a_2 are taken as adjustable parameters, one can do quite well with the Wigner equation in fitting both the general trends of isobaric differences and absolute nuclear masses. However, to achieve a reasonable fit to the experimental mass surface, the constant c' must be taken to be considerably greater than c''. This is contrary to the condition needed to prevent the collapse of the nucleus. This serious difficulty has yet to be overcome.

A second objection which has been raised to the Wigner model is that it fails to reproduce the fine details of the mass surface which are related to shell effects and the pairing tendency. However, such refinements should hardly be expected of a statistical model. Instead, to account for the details of the mass surface as well as the energies of low-lying excited states requires a model with features diametrically opposed to the uniform model.

11-4. Independent-particle Model. The nuclear model which has been investigated most extensively is one in which it is assumed that in the ground state of a complex nucleus each nucleon occupies the lowest available orbital of a single nucleon in an average central field due to all the other nucleons. Apart from its simplicity this model has the great appeal that it leads naturally to the conclusion that the nuclei which have completely filled outer shells will be exceptionally stable structures. Although there remain experimental data which have still not been explained on the basis of the independent-particle model, nevertheless the accumulation of successes of this simple model during the past few years is highly impressive. For this reason we shall devote considerable attention to this particular theory of nuclear structure.

As early as 1933 Elsasser,(12) using mass data and abundance data, pointed out that certain nuclei possess greater stability than that to be expected from a smooth nuclear energy surface. It now appears(15) that the exceptional nuclei are those which have the neutron number or proton number 2, 8, 20, 28, 50, 82, and 126. These "magic numbers" apparently play a role analogous to that played by the numbers 2, 10, 18, 36, 54, and 86 in the atomic periodic table. Recall that in the atomic case the magic numbers follow simply from the degeneracy of various hydrogen orbitals if we allow for certain departures from the normal order of the hydrogen orbitals. The departures are readily explained as the effect of the coulomb repulsion between electrons. The basic assumption is then made that in a multielectron system the electrons occupy the lowest available orbitals of a single electron in the modified central field. The Pauli exclusion principle is used to account for the fact that all the electrons do not go into the lowest orbital.

There is very little theoretical ground for supposing that such an extreme single-particle model will also be successful when applied to the nucleus. In the nucleus there is no dominant long-range nuclear potential which may have the counterpart of the atomic role of the coulomb potential set up by the nucleus. Nevertheless, investigations were carried out based upon the assumption that each nucleon is effectively bound by an average central field created by the remaining nucleus. The shape of this central field determines the order of the quantum states and the corresponding degeneracy numbers. The earliest efforts based upon the one-particle model sought to find a well shape, which had a reasonable theoretical basis, which would give rise to the observed magic numbers. An excellent review of this early work is contained in a paper by Feenberg.[13]

In light nuclei a bell-shaped central field (see Fig. 11-5) serves nicely to produce the magic numbers 2, 8, and 20. However, in heavy nuclei the observed closed shells at 50 and 82 seem to require a "wine-bottle

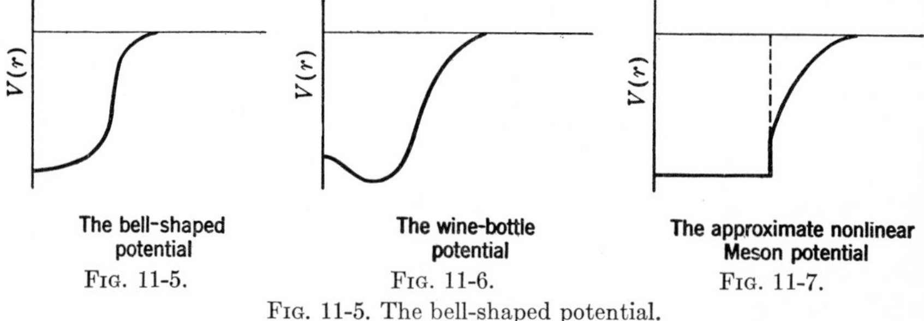

FIG. 11-5. FIG. 11-6. FIG. 11-7.

FIG. 11-5. The bell-shaped potential.
FIG. 11-6. The wine-bottle potential.
FIG. 11-7. The approximate nonlinear meson potential. (*From Malenka, Ref.* 17.)

potential" (see Fig. 11-6). Some justification for an effective potential with this shape has been given on the basis of the decreased central density of nucleons caused by the repulsion between protons. However, Swiatecki[14] has shown that this explanation is not adequate to produce a nucleus with a sufficiently hollow core to give rise to the magic numbers 50 and 82.

11-5. Spin-orbit Coupling Model. A promising proposal for generating the observed magic numbers has been made by Maria Mayer[15] and by Haxel, Jensen, and Suess,[16] who suggest that each nucleon possesses a strong spin-orbit energy of the type

$$W_{so} = -\beta \frac{\mathbf{l} \cdot \mathbf{s}}{\hbar^2} \qquad (11\text{-}40)$$

where β is a positive constant. Letting $\mathbf{i} = \mathbf{l} + \mathbf{s}$ denote the total angular momentum of an individual nucleon, it follows that $i \doteq l \pm \frac{1}{2}$. Inserting these into the Landé formula, we find

$$\begin{aligned} \Delta W_{so}(i = l - \tfrac{1}{2}) &= \tfrac{1}{2}\beta(l + 1) \\ \Delta W_{so}(i = l + \tfrac{1}{2}) &= -\tfrac{1}{2}\beta l \end{aligned} \qquad (11\text{-}41)$$

These doublets are called inverted doublets, since the state of highest total angular momentum is the most stable, whereas in the well-known alkali-metal doublets the state of lowest total angular momentum is the most stable. By applying this spin-orbit splitting to the energy levels which go with the square well with rounded corners or the clipped oscillator potential and by using a reasonable value for β, it is possible to generate a level sequence which gives the magic numbers 2, 8, 20, 28, 50, 82, and 126 immediately.

Malenka[17] has carried out a quantitative calculation based upon the well (see Fig. 11-7)

$$\begin{aligned} V &= -V_0 & r &< R \\ &= -\tfrac{3}{4}V_0 \exp\left[-\kappa(r - R)\right] & r &> R \end{aligned} \tag{11-42}$$

with the well constants $V_0 = 34.1$ Mev, $R = 8.77 \times 10^{-13}$ cm, and $\kappa = 1.31 \times 10^{13}$ cm^{-1} and with the spin-orbit energy constant $\beta = 0.54$ Mev. This well, which has a possible theoretical basis in nonlinear meson theory, is quite similar to the square well with rounded corners so that the results obtained with it are consistent with those obtained from the scheme of Mayer and Haxel, Jensen, and Suess. In Fig. 11-8 we give the level sequence, degeneracy numbers, and magic numbers for Malenka's well without and with spin-orbit splitting. The success and reasonableness of this scheme for generating magic numbers should be immediately apparent.

We must call attention to the fact that we cannot draw a single set of energy levels appropriate to all nuclei and to both neutron states and proton states. Even assuming a universal nuclear well-depth constant V_0, the number and spacing of the energy levels vary with the radius, which, of course, depends upon A. Furthermore, the coulomb interaction between protons shifts the proton levels upward relative to the neutron levels to an extent which depends upon Z. In addition, interactions between individual particles, whose effects we shall discuss in the next section, raise or depress the individual-particle levels to an extent which depends upon the numbers of occupants of the levels. Nevertheless, it is possible to represent schematically the approximate energy levels of nuclei by a filling-order diagram which indicates the information which is most useful to the physicist. Figure 11-9 is such a diagram. The neutron orbitals shown are based upon the assignments of Klinkenberg,[20] which have been arrived at on the basis of the shell model with the aid of spin and magnetic-moment data. The proton orbitals have been positioned in relation to the neutron orbitals with consideration given to the effects of the coulomb interactions as well as the experimental spin and magnetic-moment data. Competing orbitals are grouped together. In nuclear physics this diagram may be used for all nuclei as a guide in assigning the ground-state configuration and possible low-lying excited-state configurations just as Fig. 1-6 may be used in atomic physics. The spacings of the levels on this diagram should not be regarded

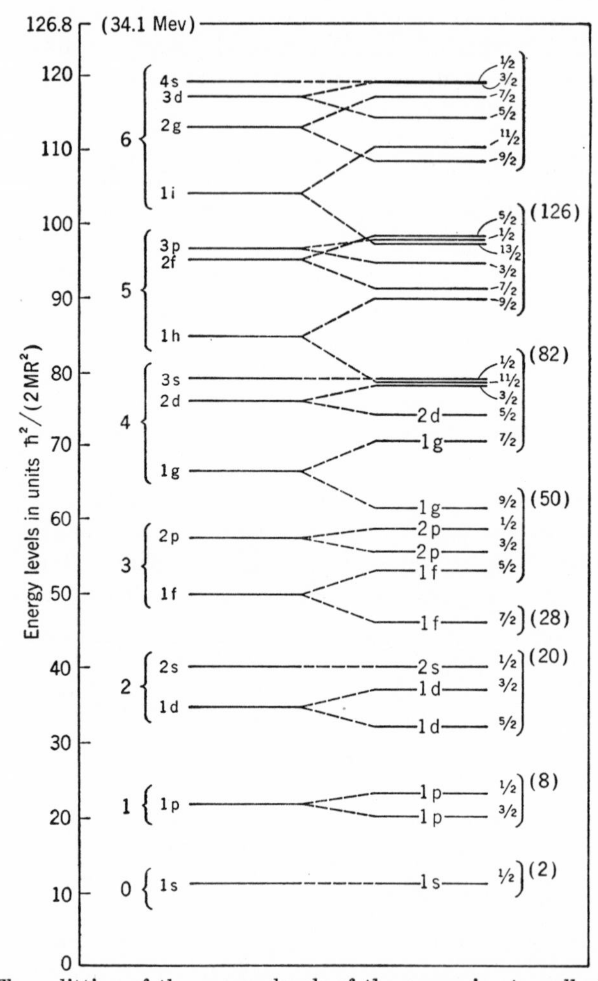

Fig. 11-8. The splitting of the energy levels of the approximate well of Eq. (11-42) because of the phenomenological spin-orbit coupling [Eq. (11-41)]. The brackets at the left indicate the levels that are degenerate in the oscillator potential. The numbers at the right are the magic numbers which correspond to the number of neutrons and protons that completely fill all the preceding levels. (*From Malenka, Ref.* 17.)

very literally, nor, in view of the effects discussed in the next section, should the specific order of competing orbitals be regarded as significant.

11-6. Nuclear Angular Momenta. If an extreme one-particle model is successful, we may expect that only the nucleons in a given nucleus which are outside closed shells will contribute to the total nuclear angular

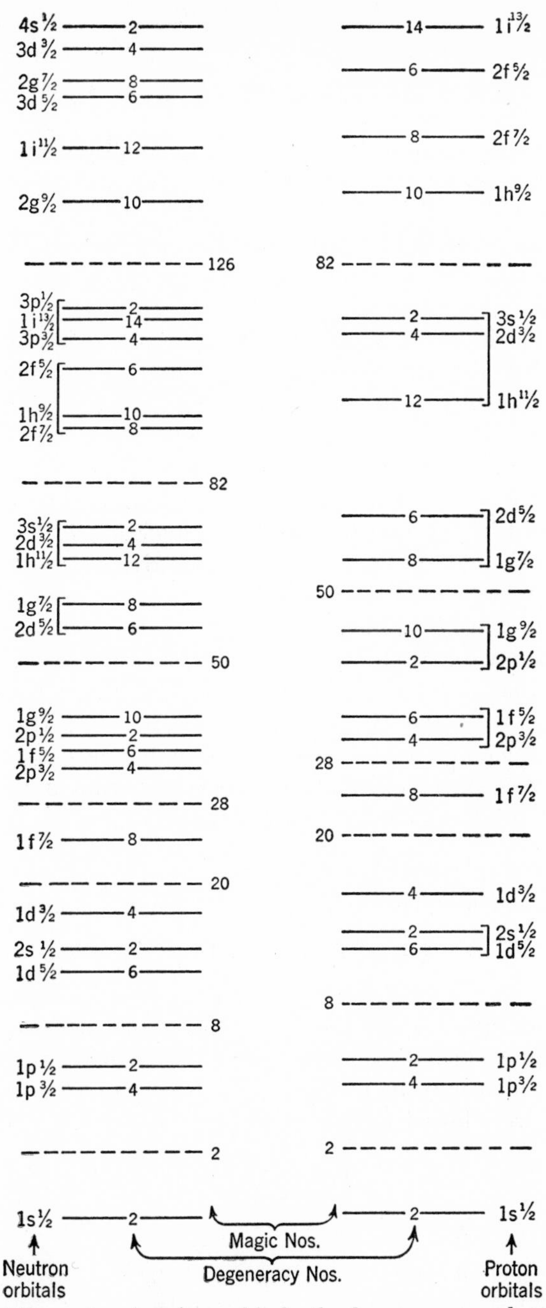

FIG. 11-9. The filling order of nuclear orbitals, the degeneracy numbers, and the magic numbers of the nuclear periodic table. The neutron orbitals follow approximately the level assignments of Klinkenberg (see Ref. 20). The proton orbitals are positioned in relation to the neutron orbitals so as to include schematically the effects of the coulomb interactions.

momentum. The nucleons inside the closed shell, because of the exclusion principle, will couple in such a way that their net contribution to the total angular momentum will vanish.

The bold assumption of Mayer, which we shall tentatively accept, is that a strong coupling exists between the spin and orbital motions of each nucleon. Thus the $(n, l, i = l + \frac{1}{2})$ and the $(n, l, i = l - \frac{1}{2})$ substates of an (n,l) state of a single nucleon are relatively far apart. For large l the spin-orbit splitting is sometimes sufficient to depress the $(n, l, i = l + \frac{1}{2})$ state below an $(n', l', i' = l' - \frac{1}{2})$ state, which would be more stable if spin-orbital coupling did not exist, *e.g.*, the $1h_{\frac{11}{2}}$ is depressed below the $3s_{\frac{1}{2}}$. We shall therefore, for convenience, use the term "nuclear orbital" to refer to an (n,l,i) state in contrast to the atomic orbital which refers to an (n,l) state (n here denotes $v + 1$). We shall call identical nucleons (such as two neutrons) which are in the same orbital "equivalent nucleons." The nuclear configuration will be designated by indicating the number of occupied nuclear orbitals by exponents. As in the atomic case we shall in most cases give only the configuration of the nucleons outside of closed shells.

The known pairing tendencies of equivalent nucleons suggest that there exists a moderately strong spin-spin force in addition to the spin-orbit force. Such a force will give rise to $(\mathbf{i}, \mathbf{i}, \ldots, \mathbf{i})$ coupling in an exact analogy with the $(\mathbf{j}, \mathbf{j}, \ldots, \mathbf{j})$ coupling of the atomic case. Accordingly, the equivalent nucleons outside of a closed shell will couple into the various states of total angular momentum $\mathcal{I}$ for the nuclear orbital. The total angular momentum for an orbital is given by

$$\mathcal{I} = \Sigma \mathbf{i} \tag{11-43}$$

The total angular momentum of the entire nucleus is given by

$$\mathbf{I} = \mathcal{I}_\nu + \mathcal{I}_\pi = \sum_\nu \mathbf{i}_\nu + \sum_\pi \mathbf{i}_\pi \tag{11-44}$$

where the subscripts ν and π denote neutrons and protons, respectively. Because of the exclusion principle for spin $\frac{1}{2}$ particles, the number of $\mathcal{I}_\nu$ or $\mathcal{I}_\pi$ states which may be formed is much smaller than the number of states which are allowed for nonequivalent nucleons. Table 11-2 gives

TABLE 11-2. $\mathcal{I}$ VALUES FOR EQUIVALENT NUCLEONS†

r	$l_{\frac{1}{2}}{}^r$	$l_{\frac{3}{2}}{}^r$	$l_{\frac{5}{2}}{}^r$	$l_{\frac{7}{2}}{}^r$
±0	0	0	0	0
±1	$\frac{1}{2}$	$\frac{3}{2}$	$\frac{5}{2}$	$\frac{7}{2}$
±2	. .	0, 2	0, 2, 4	0, 2, 4, 6
±3	. .	. . .	$\frac{3}{2}, \frac{5}{2}, \frac{9}{2}$	$\frac{3}{2}, \frac{5}{2}, \frac{7}{2}, \frac{9}{2}, \frac{11}{2}, \frac{15}{2}$
±4	. .	. . .	. . . . .	0, 2, 2, 4, 4, 5, 6, 8

† From Condon and Shortley, Ref. 18.

the allowed $\mathcal{J}$ values for various $(n,l,i)^r$ states for equivalent nucleons. Positive values of the symbol r denote the number of nucleons in the orbital, whereas negative values denote the number of missing nucleons, *i.e.*, the number of nucleons needed to fill the orbital completely.

Besides the assumption of strong spin-orbit coupling (assumption 1) Mayer[15] and Nordheim[19] use four additional assumptions to predict the I values for the ground states of nuclei. These assumptions are as follows: (2) An even number of equivalent nucleons will always couple in the ground state such that

$$\mathcal{J} = \Sigma \mathbf{i} = 0 \tag{11-45}$$

(3) An odd number of equivalent nucleons in the ground state will always couple such that

$$\mathcal{J} = \Sigma \mathbf{i} = \mathbf{i} \tag{11-46}$$

(4) For a given nucleus the pairing energy of the nucleon in the same (n,l) state is greater for the orbital with larger i. (5) For odd-odd nuclei

$$I = |i_\nu - i_\pi| \tag{11-47}$$

when the correspondence is such that

$$i_\nu = l_\nu \pm \tfrac{1}{2} \qquad \text{and} \qquad i_\pi = l_\pi \mp \tfrac{1}{2} \tag{11-48}$$

However

$$i_\nu + i_\pi \geq I > |i_\nu - i_\pi| \tag{11-49}$$

when

$$i_\nu = l_\nu \pm \tfrac{1}{2} \qquad \text{and} \qquad i_\pi = l_\pi \pm \tfrac{1}{2} \tag{11-50}$$

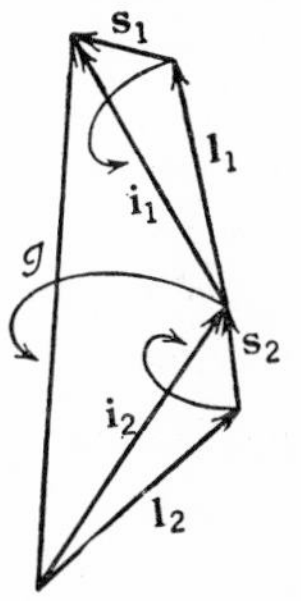

FIG. 11-10. Diagram illustrating the angular-momentum couplings of equivalent nucleons.

When we have just a single nucleon in an outer orbital, Eq. (11-46) is, of course, merely an identity. The assumption contained in Eq. (11-45) for two nucleons implies that the $\mathcal{J} = 0$ substate is always the most stable substate of a system containing an outermost pair of nucleons. Of course for the $l_{\frac{1}{2}}{}^2$ configurations the $\mathcal{J} = 0$ substate is the only allowed substate. The fact that there should be an energy difference between states for which more than one value of $\mathcal{J}$ is allowed may be attributed to the pairing tendency. To illustrate this point, let us assume that the observed pairing tendency is a manifestation of an effective spin-spin force and compute the separation of the various $l_i{}^2$ substates by semi-classical methods (see Fig. 11-10). We can evaluate the energy shift by calculating the expectation of the perturbation term

$$W_{ss} = a_{ss}\, \mathbf{s}_1 \cdot \mathbf{s}_2 \tag{11-51}$$

where a_{ss} is here taken as a constant. Using the chain rule, we obtain

$$\begin{aligned} W_{ss} &= a_{ss}\langle \mathbf{s}_1 \cdot \mathbf{s}_2 \rangle = a_{ss} \frac{\mathbf{s}_1 \cdot \mathbf{i}_1\, \mathbf{i}_1 \cdot \mathbf{i}_2\, \mathbf{i}_2 \cdot \mathbf{s}_2}{\mathbf{i}_1 \cdot \mathbf{i}_1\, \mathbf{i}_2 \cdot \mathbf{i}_2} \\ &= a_{ss} \left(\frac{\mathbf{s} \cdot \mathbf{i}}{\mathbf{i} \cdot \mathbf{i}} \right)^2 \mathbf{i}_1 \cdot \mathbf{i}_2 \end{aligned} \tag{11-51a}$$

where in the last step we have made use of the identity of the two sets of quantum numbers. These scalar products may be evaluated for any l, i, and $\mathcal{I}$ by using the Landé formulas; Mayer's assumption that the ground state is the state in which $\mathcal{I} = 0$ here simply implies that a_{ss} is a *positive* number.

In the case of three equivalent nucleons, whenever the exclusion principle permits more than one value for $\mathcal{I}$, the couplings between the nucleons apparently are such as to make the lowest state the one for which $\mathcal{I} = i$. This is readily explained if one views the third nucleon as coupling to the $(l_i^2, 0)$ parent term. Thus in the case of the $d_{\frac{5}{2}}{}^3$ configuration, assumption 3 implies that the $\mathcal{I} = \frac{5}{2}$ substate will be more stable than the allowed $\mathcal{I} = \frac{3}{2}$ and $\mathcal{I} = \frac{9}{2}$ substates. The few cases of disagreement between the observed and the predicted nuclear momentum are believed to be due to a breakdown of this assumption.

Four equivalent nucleons complete the $(n,l_{\frac{3}{2}})$ nuclear orbitals and thus can give rise only to a zero value for $\mathcal{I}$. For higher orbitals the $\mathcal{I} = 0$ state is assumed to be the most stable, presumably because of the pairing tendencies for equivalent nucleons. Proceeding in this manner it should become apparent that assumptions 2 and 3 have a simple physical basis.

The fourth assumption suggests that the pairing energy is greater for larger values of i and has the consequence that, when we have closely competing nuclear orbitals, pairs will tend to accumulate in the state having the greatest $\mathcal{I}$ value. For example, if the $3s_{\frac{1}{2}}$ level is slightly lower than the $1h_{\frac{11}{2}}$, then in a nucleus with 69 neutrons the 69th neutron will tend to go into the $3s_{\frac{1}{2}}$ state, giving rise to $\mathcal{I}_\nu = \frac{1}{2}$. However, because of the stronger pairing tendency in the $1h_{\frac{11}{2}}$ state, in a nucleus with 70 neutrons the 69th and 70th neutrons will probably go into the $1h_{\frac{11}{2}}$ state, giving $\mathcal{I}_\nu = 0$. In an $N = 71$ nucleus the 71st neutron will then tend to go into the $3s_{\frac{1}{2}}$ state, giving $\mathcal{I}_\nu = \frac{1}{2}$. However, in an $N = 72$ nucleus the 71st and 72d neutrons will tend to go into the $1h_{\frac{11}{2}}$ state, giving $\mathcal{I}_\nu = 0$, etc. Accordingly, because of this pairing effect, the value $\mathcal{I}_\nu = \frac{11}{2}$ tends to "hide" from the stable state, although it would be expected to appear in a low-lying excited state.

The empirical evidence concerning the nuclear angular momenta has been obtained from studies of hyperfine structure and various types of magnetic resonance experiments. The experiments give only the values of I, the net nuclear angular-momentum quantum number, which is frequently called by the ambiguous name "nuclear spin." The experiments confirm the fact that all EE types have zero I values, which is consistent with the spin-orbit model. The model also predicts that the total I value of the EO or OE types of nuclei will be the i value of the odd nucleon. Of the known I values for odd mass number (about 70 values), two are not consistent with this model. The first $Na^{23}(12,11)$, which should have a $d_{\frac{5}{2}}{}^3$ proton configuration with $I = \frac{5}{2}$, actually has $I = \frac{3}{2}$. The second discrepancy, in connection with $Mn^{55}(30,25)$, corresponds to a similar situation. Mayer[15] suggests that these two discrepancies may be a result of the breakdown of rule 3.

The efficacy of rule 5 for odd-odd nuclei has recently been investigated using techniques developed for the study of atomic spectra. By assuming that a simple mixture of a strong ordinary force and a weak spin-spin force acts between the neutrons and protons outside of closed subshells, Schwartz[37] has shown that it is possible to account for the spins of nearly all odd-odd nuclei. The results, however, do not always conform with the fifth rule, which suggests that this rule is an oversimplification.

There are no precise direct methods for measuring nuclear orbital angular momenta (*i.e.*, the l values). However, on the basis of observations of nuclear magnetic moments and studies of β decay, internal conversion, isomerism, and other nuclear transitions, it is possible to infer the l values of nuclear energy states. These inferred l values may be used to provide a more detailed check of Mayer's model. Conversely, we may predict the l values, magnetic moments, and selection rules on the basis of this spin-orbit model and thereby test this model, as well as other aspects of nuclear theory, on the basis of the agreement between the experimental results and the predictions. We shall adopt this second approach, since it provides a convenient and remarkably successful scaffold to organize the experimental facts.

11-7. Magnetic Moments. Although we still do not understand why the neutron and the proton have their observed magnetic moments, it is perhaps not completely unreasonable to hope that a successful explanation of the magnetic moments of complex nuclei may be given in terms of the observed properties of these two fundamental particles. In recent years data on magnetic moments have been accumulating at an exceedingly rapid pace, and excellent compilations[20–22] are now available. We shall now compare the magnetic-moment predictions based upon the spin-orbit model with these experimental data.

In the atomic case the magnetic energy of a single valence electron in a magnetic field is

$$W_m = (\mathbf{l} \cdot \mathbf{H} + 2\,\mathbf{s} \cdot \mathbf{H})\mu_B \hbar^{-1} \tag{11-52}$$

where μ_B is the Bohr magneton. For the case of a proton in a nuclear orbital it is reasonable to assume a similar expression for the energy in a magnetic field, except that we must replace the Bohr magneton by the nuclear magneton $\mu_N = e\hbar/2m_pc$. However, it is known that the proton has an anomalous spin moment which is 2.7935 times greater than the moment would be if the proton were a Dirac-type particle. The neutron also possesses an anomalous moment -1.9135, although no moment would be expected if it were a simple Dirac particle. Thus in the presence of a magnetic field we must consider these anomalous magnetic moments in calculating the magnetic energy of a collection of neutrons and protons. In order to use a single treatment for both types of particles, it is convenient to assume that the magnetic energy of either a neutron or a proton has the form

$$W_m = (g_l \mathbf{l} \cdot \mathbf{H} + g_s \mathbf{s} \cdot \mathbf{H})\mu_N \hbar^{-1} \tag{11-52a}$$

where

$$g_{l\pi} = 1 \qquad g_{s\pi} = 2\mu_\pi = 5.5870 \tag{11-53}$$

and

$$g_{l\nu} = 0 \qquad g_{s\nu} = 2\mu_\nu = -3.8270 \tag{11-54}$$

Let us now make the assumption that for odd-mass nuclei the odd nucleon will contribute the entire magnetic energy or moment just as it contributed the entire mechanical moment ($i = \mathcal{I} = I$). We shall justify this assumption below. Consequently Eq. (11-52a) gives the magnetic energy of the odd nucleon in a magnetic field. Since this energy is exceedingly small compared to the spin-orbit interaction energy, we may expect that a calculation based on the vector model will give results in agreement with a strict quantum-mechanical calculation. Using the chain rule to evaluate the expectation value of the scalar products, we have (see Fig. 11-11)

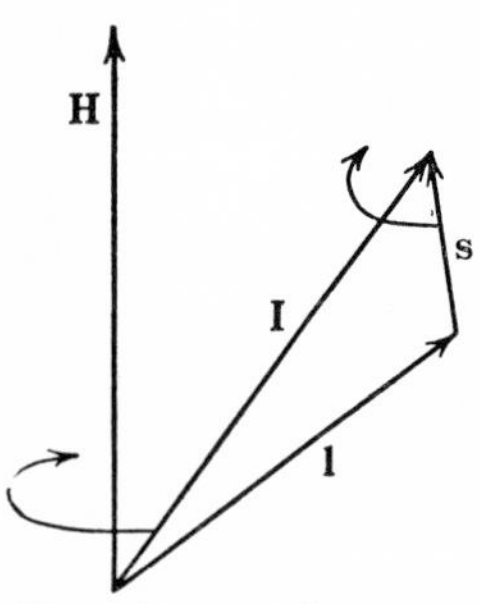

FIG. 11-11. Diagram showing coupling of a single odd nucleon in a magnetic field.

$$\langle W_m \rangle = \frac{g_l \mathbf{l} \cdot \mathbf{I} + g_s \mathbf{s} \cdot \mathbf{I}}{\mathbf{I} \cdot \mathbf{I}} \mathbf{I} \cdot \mathbf{H} \frac{\mu_N}{\hbar} \tag{11-55}$$

The values of $\mathbf{l} \cdot \mathbf{I}$ and $\mathbf{s} \cdot \mathbf{I}$ for a given (l,s,I) state can be computed using the Landé formulas. The result may be placed in the form

$$\langle W_m \rangle = \left[\frac{g_l + g_s}{2} + \frac{g_l - g_s}{2} \frac{l(l+1) - \frac{3}{4}}{I(I+1)}\right] M_I \mu_N H \tag{11-56}$$

If we follow the convention of defining the magnetic moment (in units of μ_N) as the effective moment of the nucleus in the state $M_I = I$, we obtain

$$\mu = \left[\frac{g_l + g_s}{2} + \frac{g_l - g_s}{2} \frac{l(l+1) - \frac{3}{4}}{I(I+1)}\right] I \tag{11-57}$$

For an odd-mass nucleus with a given value of I there are thus two possible values for the magnetic moment corresponding to the possible values $l = I + \frac{1}{2}$ and $l = I - \frac{1}{2}$. Letting $\mu_{\pi\nu}$ denote μ_π or μ_ν, we may simplify Eq. (11-57) to the form

$$\mu(I = l + \tfrac{1}{2}) = \mu_{\pi\nu} + \frac{g_l}{2}(2I - 1) \tag{11-58}$$

and

$$\mu(I = l - \tfrac{1}{2}) = -\mu_{\pi\nu} \frac{I}{I+1} + \frac{g_l}{2} \frac{2I+3}{I+1} I \tag{11-59}$$

The two functions $\mu(I = l \pm \frac{1}{2})$ are referred to as the Schmidt lines. If an extreme one-particle model of the type proposed by Mayer were completely reliable, it should predict the magnetic moment for any odd-mass nucleus and the experimental magnetic moments should lie along the Schmidt lines (see Figs. 11-12*a* and 11-12*b*). Actually for each I value the experimental magnetic moments fall into two groups, one group quite close to the line corresponding to $l = I + \frac{1}{2}$ and the other tending from the middle to the line corresponding to $l = I - \frac{1}{2}$. Mayer used only those magnetic moments which were close to the Schmidt lines to infer the experimental l values which were used to test her system of orbitals. Of the l values so obtained from 46 magnetic moments of odd-mass nuclei, only one is in serious disagreement with the theory. This discrepancy is $Eu^{153}(90,63)$, whose magnetic moment indicates an $f_{\frac{5}{2}}$ orbital instead of the expected $d_{\frac{5}{2}}$.

The fact that many magnetic moments of odd-mass nuclei deviate from the Schmidt limits probably indicates that the single-particle model in a central field is an oversimplification. It is rather puzzling to find that the magnetic moments for nuclei which have one particle more or less than that required to complete a closed shell do not fit the Schmidt lines any better than the others. One might expect that the single-particle model would have the greatest validity in these cases. Attempts to resolve these discrepancies have been made by Klinkenberg,[20] who uses adjusted g factors, DeShalit,[23] and others.

When we have two equivalent outer nucleons, the magnetic energy is

$$W_m = \sum_{i=1}^{2} (g_l \mathbf{l}_i \cdot \mathbf{H} + g_s \mathbf{s}_i \cdot \mathbf{H}) \frac{\mu_N}{\hbar} \tag{11-60}$$

Assuming $(i,i)\mathcal{I}$ coupling, it follows, exactly as in the analysis of the Zeeman effect for $(j,j)_J$ coupling in atomic physics, that the magnetic energy is

$$\langle W_m \rangle = g_I \mu_N M_I H \tag{11-61}$$

where

$$g_I = g_I(g_s, g_l, i, \mathcal{I}) \tag{11-62}$$

For the ground nuclear state $\mathcal{I} = 0$, and consequently M_I also vanishes. Accordingly we would expect that all EE nuclei will have zero magnetic moments. The experimental observations do not reveal any exceptions to this conclusion. This same analysis gives the physical bases for the

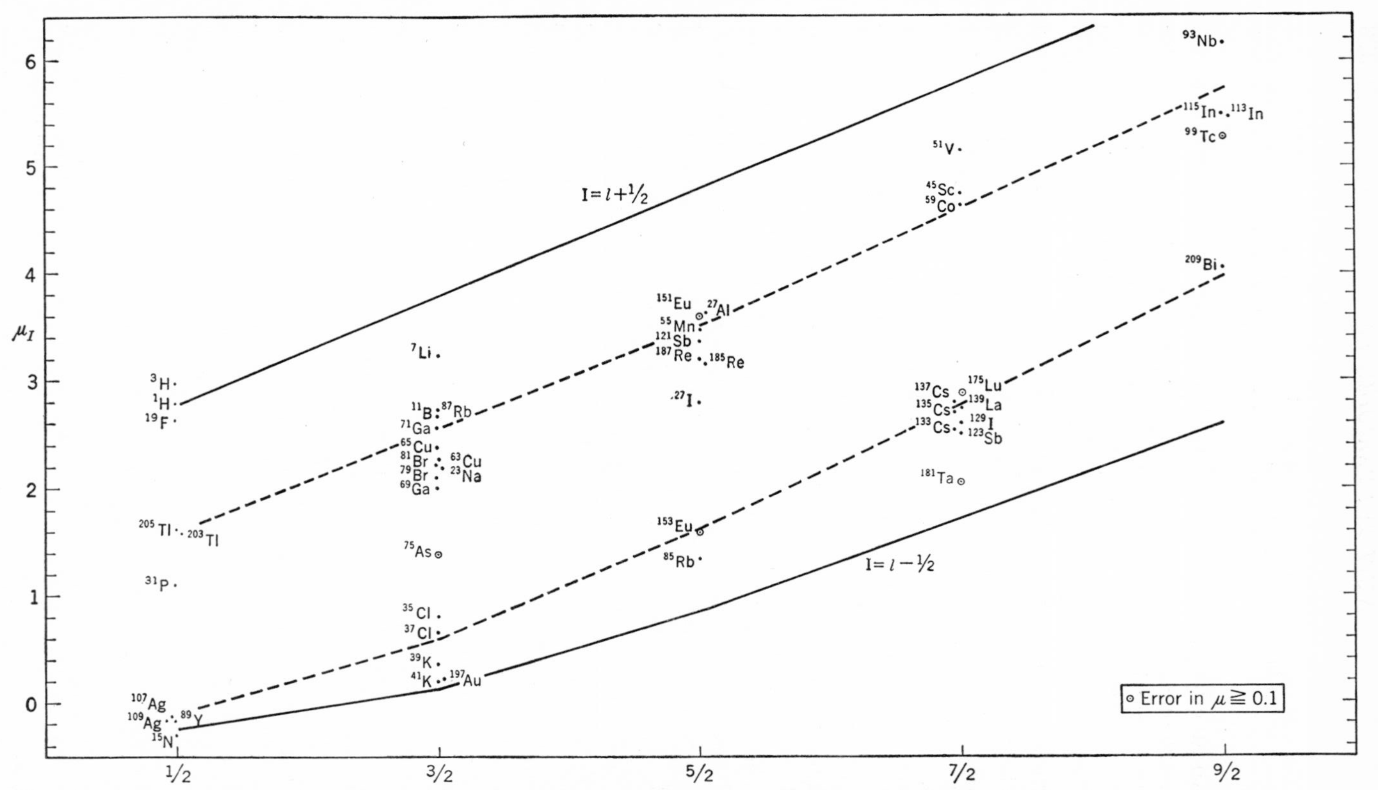

FIG. 11-12*a*. μ_I vs. I for odd-proton nuclei. Upper solid curve corresponds to Schmidt line for $I = i = l + \frac{1}{2}$. Lower solid curve corresponds to Schmidt line with $I = i = l - \frac{1}{2}$. The upper and lower dotted lines correspond to the Schmidt lines $I = i = l \pm \frac{1}{2}$ based upon adjusted g factors. (*From Klinkenberg, Ref.* 20.)

assumption that the odd nucleon contributes the entire magnetic moment of nuclei with odd A values.

Other interesting predictions which we may make on the basis of the cancellation of the magnetic and angular momenta of pairs of equivalent

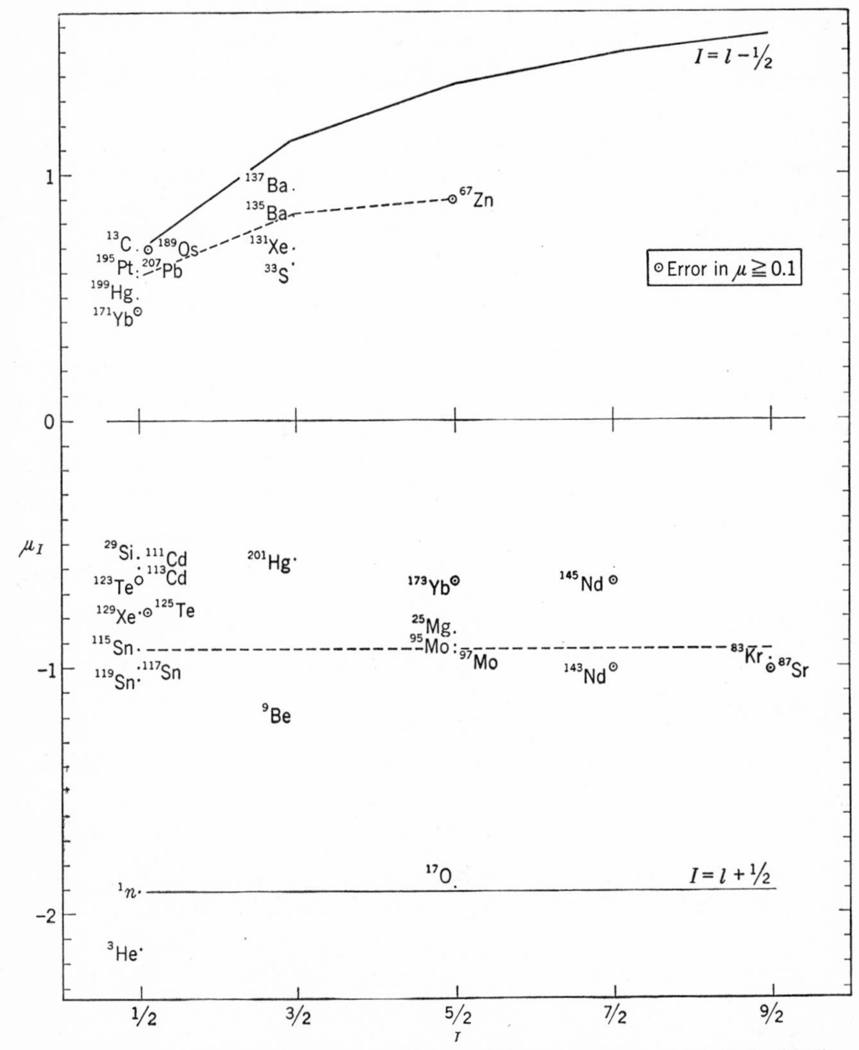

FIG. 11-12b. μ_I vs. I for odd-neutron nuclei. Solid curves correspond to Schmidt lines for free-nucleon g factors, and the dotted curves to Schmidt lines for adjusted g factors. (*From Klinkenberg, Ref.* 20.)

nucleons are that odd-A and odd-Z isotopes as well as odd-A and odd-N isotones should have identical mechanical and magnetic moments. In the former case the isotopes can differ only by pairs of neutrons; in the latter case the isotones can differ only by pairs of protons. The two simple examples of these rules are the proton-tritium similarity and the neutron-He^3 similarity. The moments of these pairs are in fact quite close, and it appears that these rules are generally satisfied quite well. On the basis of the third assumption of Mayer we would also expect similarities in the mechanical and magnetic moments of a sequence of odd-mass nuclei which differ by even units of A, but which need not be isotones or isotopes providing that the last protons (or neutrons) occupy the same orbital.

The stable odd-odd nuclides ${}_1H^2$, ${}_3Li^6$, ${}_5B^{10}$, and ${}_7N^{14}$ and the long-lived odd-odd nuclide ${}_{11}Na^{22}$ comprise another nuclear type which can be handled very simply. In all of these, the last proton and the last neutron occupy identical orbitals. It is therefore not unreasonable to expect a strong interaction between the odd neutron and the odd proton. In each of these cases the net nuclear angular momentum is observed to be an odd integer. This is probably a consequence of a coupling between the odd nucleons which prefers odd-I states. It is possible, however, that a general type of exclusion principle is working which forbids even-I values.

The magnetic moments expected for these odd-odd nuclei may readily be calculated in terms of the observed quantum numbers by the use of the vector model. The total magnetic energy is now

$$W_m = (g_{l\pi}\, \mathbf{l}_\pi \cdot \mathbf{H} + g_{s\pi}\, \mathbf{s}_\pi \cdot \mathbf{H} + g_{s\nu}\, \mathbf{s}_\nu \cdot \mathbf{H})\mu_N \hbar^{-1} \tag{11-63}$$

This may be simplified if we use

$$l_\pi = l_\nu = l \qquad s_\pi = s_\nu = s \qquad i_\pi = i_\nu = i \qquad g_{l\pi} = 1$$

We then obtain

$$W_m = (\mathbf{l} \cdot \mathbf{H} + 2\mu_d{}^\circ\, \mathbf{s} \cdot \mathbf{H})\,\frac{\mu_N}{\hbar} \tag{11-64}$$

where

$$\mu_d{}^\circ = \mu_\pi + \mu_\nu = 0.880 \tag{11-65}$$

The reason for choosing the symbol $\mu_d{}^\circ$ will be obvious shortly. Using the chain rule for $\mathbf{l} \cdot \mathbf{H}$ and $\mathbf{s} \cdot \mathbf{H}$, we have immediately (see Fig. 11-13)

$$\langle W_m \rangle = \frac{\mathbf{l} \cdot \mathbf{i} + 2\mu_d{}^\circ\, \mathbf{s} \cdot \mathbf{i}}{\mathbf{i} \cdot \mathbf{i}}\,\frac{\mathbf{i} \cdot \mathbf{I}}{\mathbf{I} \cdot \mathbf{I}}\, M_I H \mu_N \tag{11-66}$$

Using the Landé formulas, this becomes

$$\langle W_m \rangle = \left[\mu_d{}^\circ + \tfrac{1}{2} - (\mu_d{}^\circ - \tfrac{1}{2})\,\frac{l(l+1) - \frac{3}{4}}{i(i+1)}\right]\frac{M_I}{2}\, H\mu_N \tag{11-67}$$

Letting $M_I = I$, we obtain for the magnetic moment

$$\mu = \frac{I}{2}\left[\mu_d{}^\circ + \tfrac{1}{2} - (\mu_d{}^\circ - \tfrac{1}{2})\,\frac{l(l+1) - \frac{3}{4}}{i(i+1)}\right] \tag{11-68}$$

Consequently

$$\mu(i = l + \tfrac{1}{2}) = \frac{I}{2}\left(1 + \frac{\mu_d{}^\circ - \frac{1}{2}}{i}\right) \tag{11-69}$$

and

$$\mu(i = l - \tfrac{1}{2}) = \frac{I}{2}\left(1 + \frac{\mu_d{}^\circ - \frac{1}{2}}{i + 1}\right) \tag{11-70}$$

In Table 11-3 we give the data for the first five odd-odd nuclei. The agreement between theory and experiment must be characterized as excellent.

TABLE 11-3. μ_I VALUES FOR ODD-ODD NUCLIDES†

Nucleus	Orbital	I	μ_I (exptl.)	μ_I (calc.)
$_1H^2$	$1s_{\frac{1}{2}}$	1	0.8565	0.880
$_3Li^6$	$1p_{\frac{3}{2}}$	1	0.82	0.63
$_5B^{10}$	$1p_{\frac{3}{2}}$	3	1.80	1.88
$_7N^{14}$	$1p_{\frac{1}{2}}$	1	0.40	0.37
$_{11}Na^{22}$	$1d_{\frac{5}{2}}$	3	1.75	1.73

† From Feenberg, Ref. 9.

The thoughtful reader may be puzzled at the inclusion of the deuteron in our discussion. We are here considering a model in which each of the two odd nucleons is held in an effective central field presumably caused by the remaining nucleons. The source of this central field in the case of the deuteron, however, is even more obscure than in the usual case. We have included the deuteron in our discussion to provoke the reader into extra thought concerning this highly important nuclear system.

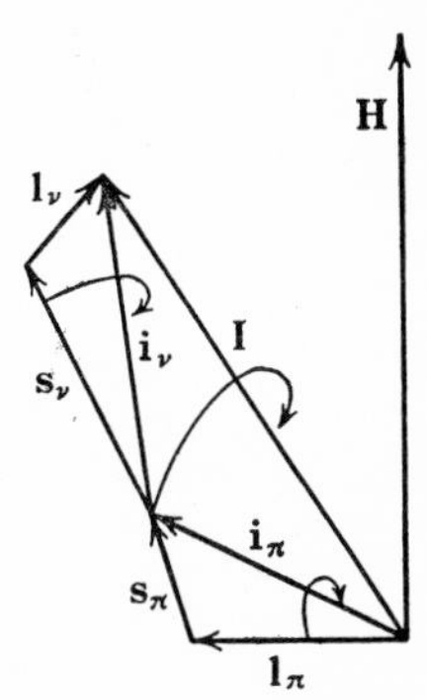

FIG. 11-13. Coupling of odd-odd nucleons in identical orbitals.

11-8. Quadrupole Moments and the Collective Model. Quadrupole moments of nuclei are also apparently related to shell structure, since large fluctuations in Q seem to occur at N and Z values related to the magic numbers (see Fig. 11-14). The independent-particle model suggests an immediate explanation for the existence of nuclear quadrupole moments and for their sensitivity to magic numbers. Since p, d, f, . . . states correspond to aspherical wave functions and hence to aspherical distributions, we would expect nuclei which have an odd proton in p, d, f, . . . states to possess a quadrupole moment. Unfortunately the magnitudes of the quadrupole moments computed on the basis of the independent-particle model are usually too small to account for the experimentally observed quadrupole moments. An additional discrepancy arises in that the predicted moments are always negative, whereas positive moments arise frequently.

The magnitude of experimental quadrupole moments suggests that 20 or 30 nucleons somehow share the nuclear angular momentum. To improve the agreement with experiment, Rainwater,[25] A. Bohr,[26] and others have explored the assumption that the average nuclear field in which the individual nucleons move itself possesses spherical symmetry.

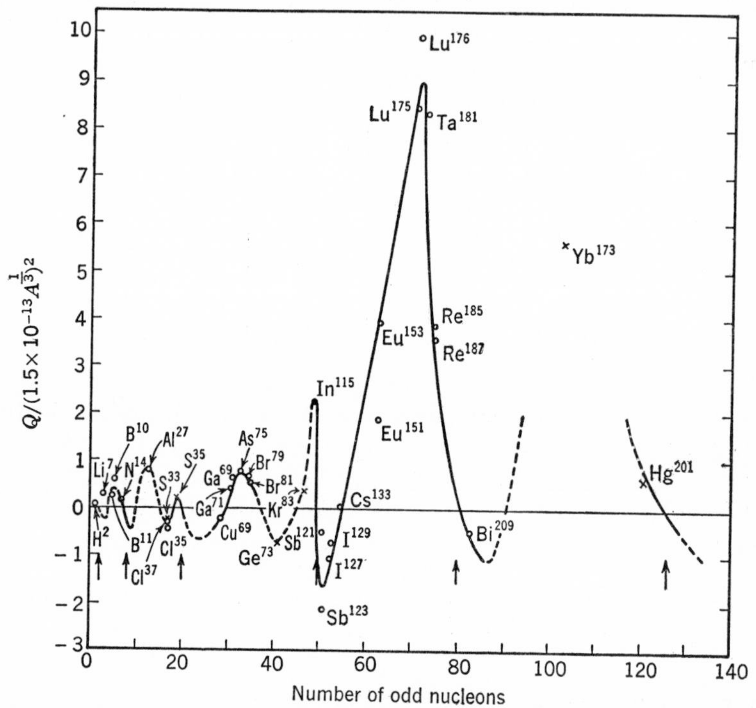

FIG. 11-14. Nuclear quadrupole moments divided by the square of the nuclear radius $(1.5 \times 10^{-13}A^{\frac{1}{3}})^2$. Known moments of odd-proton nuclei and odd-proton–odd-neutron nuclei (excepting Li^6 and Cl^{36}) are plotted as circles against the number of protons. Arrows indicate closing of major nucleon shells. Solid curve represents regions where quadrupole-moment behavior seems established; dashed curve indicates more doubtful regions. (*From Townes, Foley, and Low, Ref.* 24.)

With this assumption it is possible to account for the observed quadrupole moments and at the same time retain the essential features of the single-particle model. Bohr further notes that such an asymmetric model improves the agreement between the theoretical and empirical data on nuclear magnetic moments.

The question naturally arises as to why the average nuclear field should be asymmetrical and why this asymmetry, which involves the distributions of many nucleons, should be regulated by independent-particle shell closings. The answer to this question seems to require some compromise between the independent-particle model and a cooperative model such as the classical liquid-drop model. A model known as the collective model, which combines the features of the independent-particle model and the liquid-drop model, has been proposed by A. Bohr[27,38] and by Hill and Wheeler.[10] According to this model it is possible to interpret the sum of the individual energies and interaction energies of a complex system of particles as a surface energy, which comprises a surface vibration energy, a surface rotation energy, and a surface potential energy. Changes in the totality of individual particle states give rise to different surface energies. One might describe the result of the individual-particle wave functions as giving rise to a rapidly varying membranelike nuclear surface. When the nucleus is somewhat removed from major closed shells, this surface can undergo oscillation like a conventional liquid droplet and also can be distorted into a nonspherical shape by free nucleons in higher l states. The distortion reacts back on the individual particle states, so that in effect the coupling of each particle to the surface causes a strong indirect interparticle coupling. This indirect interparticle coupling results in collective permanent states of distortion and consequently in large quadrupole moments. Because of the strong interparticle coupling, low-lying excited states of the nucleus are collective motions which appear as surface vibrations and rotations.

In addition to the collective properties which are reminiscent of a classical liquid droplet, one might expect to observe the individual-particle states particularly when the nucleus is in the immediate vicinity of major closed shells. Then the spherical shape of the core is highly stable so that the couplings of the extra nucleons to the surface are rather ineffective. Accordingly the motions of the extra particles and the surface motion are independent. In these situations the predictions based upon the individual-particle model are expected to be reliable. Since the particles move approximately in a central field, they are expected to produce only small quadrupole moments, which is in accord with experience. As additional particles accumulate beyond a closed-shell core, the strong coupling situation develops.

Many qualitative observations and some quantitative observations point to the success of this particular marriage of the independent-particle and liquid-drop models. However, it is still too early to say whether this model represents the final answer.

11-9. Shell Effects among Excited States.[28,29] On the basis of the independent-particle model the lowest-lying excited states of nuclei may be interpreted in a manner analogous to that used in the study of fine structure in atomic spectroscopy. These lowest-lying states generally are those belonging to the same configuration as the ground state. For example, the lowest-lying states of an EE, EO, or OE nucleus might correspond to the allowed values of I other than zero connected with a pair of nucleons. If cosine coupling exists between the spins, the energies are presumably given by an equation analogous to Eq. (11-51a). Higher-lying states are expected to correspond to states in which one of the outer nucleons is raised to a higher orbital. In the 0th approximation the added energy of an excited state of the complex nucleus is simply the additional configuration and spin-orbit energy of this last nucleon. The fine structure of this state would depend upon the nature of the other couplings between the outer nucleons. Because we do not have a detailed knowledge of nucleon-nucleon interactions, the independent-particle model thus far has not been developed to the point that quantitative predictions of nuclear energy levels can be made. Instead the successes of the independent-particle model have been confined mainly to the classification (I- and l-value assignments) of experimentally observed levels. Using the spin-orbit coupling model, M. Goldhaber and R. Hill[(30)] have assigned l and I values to all known isomeric states of nuclei. These assignments have been tested by means of experimental data dealing with gamma-ray transitions, internal conversion, and beta decay. The authors find that the shell-model assignments provide an amazingly consistent basis for interpreting the experimental data. The results appear to be much better than might be expected from this over-simplified model, and M. Goldhaber and R. Hill venture the opinion that these assignments will stand the test of time even if the model is modified.

On the basis of the shell-model quantum-number assignments M. Goldhaber and Sunyar[(31)] have proposed the rule that the first excited states of EE nuclei have $I = 2$ and even parity (see next chapter). This is to be expected if we assume that in the first excited state one of the pairs couples into the $I = 2$ state with both particles still remaining in the ground-state configuration. G. Scharff-Goldhaber[(29)] has recently shown that this rule is compatible with experimental results for 66 out of 68 nuclei investigated. The two exceptions, O^{16} and Ge^{72}, also find a ready explanation. Thus in 0^{16} the neutron and proton shells are both filled; hence the state $I = 2$ is forbidden to either an outer pair of neutrons or an outer pair of protons.

For the second excited state of even-even nuclei, $I = 2$ or 4 and even parity appear to be preferred; however, about one-third of the cases investigated have other I values. The variation of energies of first excited states presents a striking picture in support of the shell-model interpretation. This is shown in Fig. 11-15.

Recent studies clearly indicate that the independent particle–spherical well model in its literal form is not capable of explaining quantitatively the location of all observed nuclear energy levels. Apart from the difficulties with quadrupole moments, several other discrepancies suggest that the model is an oversimplification. Several examples of isomeric states have been observed whose lifetimes are too short to be explained on the basis of the independent-particle model. To account for these

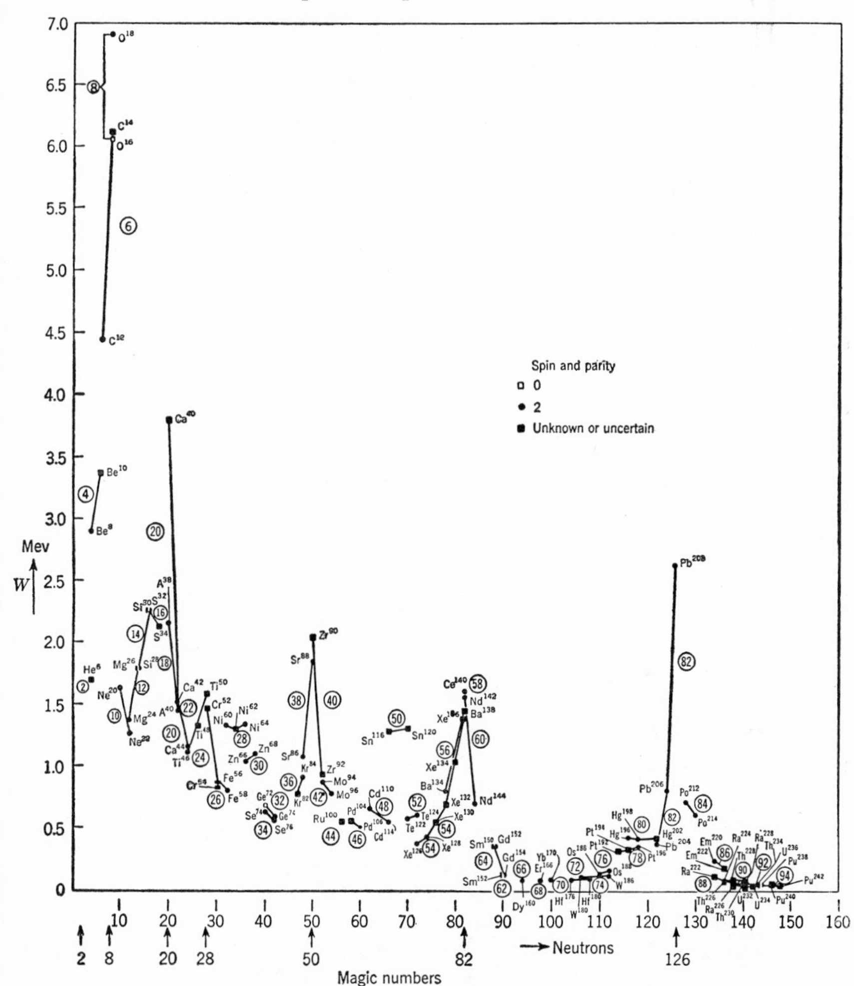

FIG. 11-15. Energies of first excited states of even-even nuclei plotted against number of neutrons. Points for isotopes of same element are connected with straight lines. The corresponding proton number, encircled, appears next to the connecting lines. (*From Scharff-Goldhaber, Ref.* 29.)

states, A. Bohr[32,38] suggests the use of the collective model in which excited states may be identified with coupled oscillations between nuclear-surface and single-particle motions. According to this collective model the low-lying states may in some cases be due to the change in particle levels with the accompanying readjustment of the surface. In other cases excitation of the surface may occur without a change in particle quantum numbers. Among such surface excitations the rotational levels are particularly interesting. The collective model suggests that the moment of inertia associated with these motions is determined by the departures from spherical symmetry and in consequence is much smaller than the moment of inertia for a rigid sphere. These low-lying rotational levels are expected to occur far away from shell edges, whereas particle excitation is expected to occur near shell edges. A. Bohr points to several data in support of this interpretation. Recently Asaro and Perlman[33] have discovered a remarkable regularity among the first three excited states of very heavy EE nuclei. They find a tendency for these levels to be proportional to $I(I + 1)$ with I restricted to 0, 2, 4, $\cdots$ quantum numbers which are predicted by Bohr. From the positions of the energy levels the effective moments of inertia are found to be much smaller than that for rigid nuclear rotation.

Ford[28] has shown that the collective model predicts the order and spacing of the levels of EE nuclei and that the calculated energies of first excited states are in qualitative agreement with experiment (see Fig. 11-15). However, the collective model applied rigorously appears to lead to unreasonable nuclear distortions.

We now turn our attention to the study of gamma, alpha, and beta decay, subjects which have witnessed remarkable advances in recent years by virtue of the application of the spin-orbit model.

PROBLEMS

***11-1.** Using the Wigner model, derive (*a*) an equation for the line of beta stability of odd-mass nuclides, (*b*) an expression for the masses of nuclides lying along the line of beta stability, and (*c*) expressions for the mass differences between odd-mass and even-mass isobars.

11-2. Use the Fermi gas formulas to estimate the wavelength, propagation constant, and total kinetic energy for the last neutron in a nuclide with $A \approx 100$. What is a reasonable estimate of the potential energy of this neutron?

11-3. What are the Wigner Ξ's for the ground states of ${}_2He^6$, ${}_3Li^6$, and ${}_4Be^6$?

11-4. Assuming a_{ss} is a constant, show that the pairing energy given by Eq. (11-51*a*) favors the $1h_{\frac{11}{2}}$ state over the $3s_{\frac{1}{2}}$ state.

11-5. To what g values do the dotted lines in Figs. 11-11 and 11-12 correspond?

***11-6.** The derivations of Eqs. (11-58) and (11-59) ignore the orbital angular momentum of the core and the associated contribution to the moment. What are the corrections introduced by this effect?

11-7. Use the shell-model rules to assign the orbital of the odd nucleon in the following β-active nuclides and their products: ${}_{16}S^{35}(\beta^-)$, ${}_{16}S^{37}(\beta^-)$, ${}_{36}Kr^{87}(\beta^-)$, ${}_{29}Cu^{67}(\beta^-)$, ${}_{30}Zn^{63}(\beta^-)$, ${}_{29}Cu^{61}(\beta^+)$.

11-8. On the basis of the shell-model rules determine the orbitals occupied by the outermost pair of nucleons and the net I values for the following β-active nuclides and their residuals: ${}_5B^{12}(\beta^-)$, ${}_{15}P^{34}(\beta^-)$, ${}_{17}Cl^{38}(\beta^-)$, ${}_{17}Cl^{36}(\beta^-)$, ${}_7N^{12}(\beta^+)$.

11-9. Use Fig. 11–9 to infer the proton and neutron numbers and configurations for stable nuclides with $A = 50$, 100, 150, 200, and 250. To what extent are these assignments consistent with experiment?

REFERENCES

1. Bohr, N., and P. Kalckar: *Kgl. Danske Videnskab. Selskab, Mat.-fys. Medd.*, **14**(10) (1936).
2. Gronblom, B., and R. Marshak: *Phys. Rev.*, **55,** 229 (1939).
3. Dee, P., and C. Gilbert: *Proc. Roy. Soc. (London)*, **A163,** 265 (1937).
4. Dennison, D.: *Phys. Rev.*, **57,** 454 (1940).
5. Inglis, D. R.: *Revs. Mod. Phys.*, **25,** 390 (1953).
6. Haefner, R. R.: *Revs. Mod. Phys.*, **23,** 228 (1951).
7. Hafstad, L., and E. Teller: *Phys. Rev.*, **54,** 681 (1938).
8. Wigner, E. P.: *Phys. Rev.*, **51,** 106 (1937); **51,** 947 (1937).
9. Feenberg, E.: *Revs. Mod. Phys.*, **19,** 239 (1947).
10. Hill, D. L., and J. A. Wheeler: *Phys. Rev.*, **89,** 1102 (1953).
11. Barkas, W. H.: *Phys. Rev.*, **55,** 691 (1939).
12. Elsasser, W. M.: *J. phys. radium*, **4,** 549 (1933).
13. Feenberg, E.: *Phys. Rev.*, **77,** 6 (1950).
14. Swiatecki, N. J.: *Proc. Phys. Soc. (London)*, **63,** 1208 (1950).
15. Mayer, M. G.: *Phys. Rev.*, **74,** 235 (1948); **78,** 16 (1950).
16. Haxel, O., J. H. D. Jensen, and H. E. Suess: *Z. Physik*, **128,** 295 (1950).
17. Malenka, B. J.: *Phys. Rev.*, **86,** 68 (1952).
18. Condon, E. U., and G. H. Shortley: "The Theory of Atomic Spectra," Cambridge University Press, New York, 1935.
19. Nordheim, L. W.: *Revs. Mod. Phys.*, **23,** 322 (1951).
20. Klinkenberg, P. F. A.: *Revs. Mod. Phys.*, **24,** 63 (1952).
21. Ramsey, N. F.: *Exptl. Nuclear Phys.*, **1,** 385 (1953).
22. Mack, J. E.: *Revs. Mod. Phys.*, **22,** 64 (1950).
23. DeShalit, A.: *Phys. Rev.*, **90,** 83 (1953).
24. Townes, C. H., H. M. Foley, and W. Low: *Phys. Rev.*, **76,** 1415 (1950).
25. Rainwater, J.: *Phys. Rev.*, **79,** 432 (1950).
26. Bohr, A.: *Phys. Rev.*, **81,** 134 (1950).
27. Bohr, A.: *Kgl. Danske Videnskab. Selskab, Mat.-fys. Medd.*, **26**(14) (1952).
28. Ford, K. W.: *Phys. Rev.*, **90,** 29 (1953).
29. Scharff-Goldhaber, G.: *Phys. Rev.*, **90,** 589 (1953).
30. Goldhaber, M., and R. D. Hill: *Revs. Mod. Phys.*, **24,** 179 (1952).
31. Goldhaber, M., and A. W. Sunyar: *Phys. Rev.*, **83,** 906 (1951).
32. Bohr, A.: *Phys. Rev.*, **89,** 316 (1953).
33. Asaro, F., and I. Perlman: *Phys. Rev.*, **91,** 763 (1953).
34. Frisch, D. H.: *Phys. Rev.*, **84,** 1169 (1951).
35. Weinberg, I. G., and J. M. Blatt: *Am. J. Phys.*, **21,** 124 (1953).
36. Green, A. E. S.: unpublished.
37. Schwartz, C.: *Phys. Rev.*, **94,** 95 (1954).
38. Bohr, A., and B. R. Mottelson: *Kgl. Danske Videnskab. Selskab, Mat.-fys. Medd.*, **27**(17) (1953).

CHAPTER 12

NUCLEAR DECAY

In this chapter we shall discuss the decay of excited nuclides and radionuclides. By radionuclides we mean nuclides which, although they are in their ground state, nevertheless decay with a measurable lifetime by the emission of alpha particles or beta particles or by orbital-electron capture. These nuclides are to be contrasted with stable nuclides which do not decay or which decay with lifetimes too long to be measured. By excited nuclides we mean nuclides, stable or radioactive, which possess additional energy beyond the inherent ground-state energy of the particular combination of nucleons. Such nuclides usually decay by gamma emission or by internal conversion. We shall confine our major attention to transitions between low-lying states, transitions in which the quantization of energy is most evident.

To assist in the visualization of the matter under discussion, let us refer back to our complete picture of nuclear energy in which the characteristic excitation energies as well as the ground-state masses are represented at each grid point on an N-Z or D-A grid by markers on vertical posts. Gamma radiation and internal conversion, the simplest modes of decay, take a point representing the energy of the system of nucleons straight downward along a particular vertical post. The energy released in such a process appears as the gamma-ray energy

$$E_\gamma = W_i^* - W_f \tag{12-1}$$

or as the kinetic energy of the internal-conversion electron

$$T_c = W_i^* - W_f - W_c \tag{12-2}$$

where W_c is the critical energy of the atomic level. The next simplest modes of decay, $\beta^\pm$ emission and K capture, take the point representing the nuclear energy of the system from one post to a neighboring isobar. The energy released appears as the sum of the kinetic and rest energies of the electron and neutrino or, in the case of K capture, the X ray and neutrino; these energies are:

$$\beta^-\colon W_i^* + M_i^* - (W_f + M_f) = T_{\beta^-} + E_\eta = T_{\beta^-,\max} \tag{12-3}$$

$$\beta^+\colon W_i^* + M_i^* - (W_f + M_f) = T_{\beta^+} + 2mc^2 + E_\eta = T_{\beta^+,\max} + 2mc^2 \tag{12-4}$$

$$K\colon W_i^* + M_i^* - (W_f + M_f) = W_c + E_\eta \tag{12-5}$$

These processes may take place between ground states of nuclei (W_i^* and/or $W_f = 0$) as well as excited states providing the right sides of these equations are positive.

In decay by alpha-particle emission the point representing the energy of the system splits, so that the (4,0) and ($A - 4$, D^*) grid points are required to represent the final energy. The energy of the decay, which appears as the kinetic energies of the alpha particle and the residual nucleus, is

$$W_i^* + M_i^* - (W_f + M_f) - M_\alpha = T \tag{12-6}$$

These processes may take place between the ground states of nuclei providing the right side of this equation is positive. For beta-stable nuclides this condition is usually satisfied by heavy nuclides with $A \gtrsim 150$.

The emission of gamma radiation by excited nuclides has been given the greatest theoretical attention, since the concepts used are extensions of the highly developed classical and quantum theories of electromagnetic radiation. Since these concepts are important not only to the study of gamma radiation but also to interpretation of all types of nuclear transitions, we shall now present briefly some important aspects of the classical and quantum theories of radiation.

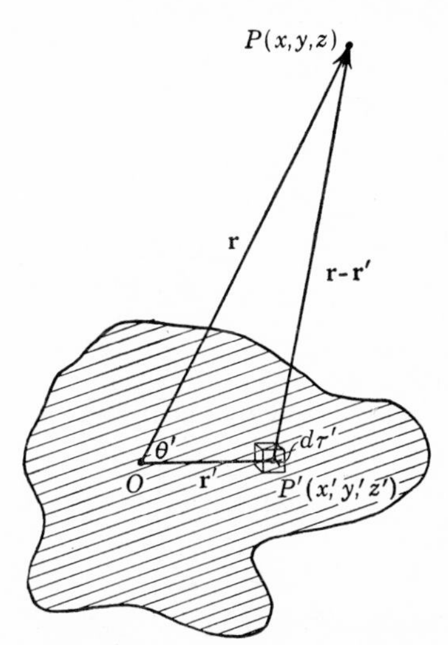

FIG. 12-1. Diagram illustrating the calculation of the electrostatic potential at a point outside of a charge distribution.

12-1. Radiation from a System of Moving Charges.[1] A development of the classical theory of radiation which has proved suitable for generalization to quantum theory is based upon the classical theory of retarded potentials. It is well known from electrostatic theory that the scalar electrostatic potential ϕ at a point $P(x,y,z)$ outside of a region which contains a static distribution of charge may be obtained by adding (the superposition principle) the contributions due to the charge in each volume element. Since

$$d\phi = \frac{\rho(x',y',z')\, d\tau'}{|\mathbf{r} - \mathbf{r}'|} \tag{12-7}$$

where $|\mathbf{r} - \mathbf{r}'|$ is the distance from the point (x',y',z') within the distribution to the point (x,y,z) and $\rho(x',y',z')$ is the charge density in the volume element $d\tau'$, it follows that

$$\phi(x,y,z) = \iiint_{\tau'} \frac{\rho(x',y',z')\, d\tau'}{|\mathbf{r} - \mathbf{r}'|} \tag{12-8}$$

In Fig. 12-1 we indicate the points $P(x,y,z)$ and $P'(x',y',z')$ in relation to an origin O. We note that the distance between these two points is given by

$$|\mathbf{r} - \mathbf{r}'| = (r^2 + r'^2 - 2rr' \cos \theta')^{\frac{1}{2}} \tag{12-9}$$

If the charge distribution varies with time, the corresponding potential outside the region will also vary with time. The classical theory of the electromagnetic field then gives for the scalar potential†

$$\Phi(x,y,z,t) = \iiint \frac{\rho(x',y',z',t^*)}{|\mathbf{r} - \mathbf{r}'|}\, d\tau' \tag{12-10}$$

where

$$t^* = t - \frac{|\mathbf{r} - \mathbf{r}'|}{c} \tag{12-11}$$

This equation has the following physical interpretation. The scalar field at the point (x,y,z) and the instant t contributed by the volume element $d\tau'$ is the field due to the charge $\rho(x',y',z',t^*)\, d\tau'$, which was in $d\tau'$ at a time prior to t by $|\mathbf{r} - \mathbf{r}'|/c$. This, of course, is the time required for the field to traverse the distance from the source to the point of interest.

The special case in which the charge density varies harmonically with time has particular interest in our study. This case may be conveniently investigated by assuming that $\rho(x',y',z',t^*)$ is the real part of

$$\begin{aligned}\rho(x',y',z') \exp (i\omega t^*) &= \rho(x',y',z') \exp \left[i\omega \left(t - \frac{|\mathbf{r} - \mathbf{r}'|}{c} \right) \right] \\ &= [\exp (i\omega t)]\rho(x',y',z') \exp (-ik\, |\mathbf{r} - \mathbf{r}'|) \end{aligned} \tag{12-12}$$

where $\rho(x',y',z')$ may be a complex function. The corresponding potential is now the real part of

$$\Phi(x,y,z,t) = \exp (i\omega t) \iiint \frac{\rho(x',y',z') \exp (-ik|\mathbf{r} - \mathbf{r}'|)}{|\mathbf{r} - \mathbf{r}'|}\, d\tau' \tag{12-13}$$

The explicit evaluation of Eq. (12-13) is complicated very greatly by the dependence of $|\mathbf{r} - \mathbf{r}'|$ upon r' and $\cos \theta'$. It is customary therefore to make certain approximations which are justified for the investigation of atomic and nuclear radiation. In the denominator of Eq. (12-13) we use $|\mathbf{r} - \mathbf{r}'| \approx r$; however, in the exponential term, which is more sensitive, we use the better approximation

$$|\mathbf{r} - \mathbf{r}'| \approx r - r' \cos \theta' \tag{12-14}$$

Both approximations are adequate whenever $r \gg r'$, that is, when the charge distribution is confined to a region which is very small compared to the distance from the origin to the point (x,y,z). Since the r values

† In our discussions in Sec. 12-1, the time dependence of wave functions is indicated by the use of capital letters so that boldface symbols may be reserved for vectors.

of interest correspond to macroscopic distances from an atom or nucleus, whereas the r' values are important only for atomic or nuclear distances, these approximations are well justified. Equation (12-13) therefore becomes

$$\Phi(x,y,z,t) = \frac{\exp\,[i(\omega t - kr)]}{r} \iiint \rho(x',y',z') \exp\,(i\mathbf{k} \cdot \mathbf{r}')\, d\tau' \qquad (12\text{-}15)$$

where

$$\mathbf{k} = \frac{\mathbf{r}}{r}\, k \qquad (12\text{-}16)$$

For usual atomic and nuclear spectra the wavelengths are much greater than the radial extension of the atom or nucleus, *i.e.*,

$$kr' = \frac{2\pi r'}{\lambda} \ll 1 \qquad (12\text{-}17)$$

Hence in applications of radiation theory to atomic and nuclear physics we may simplify the computations by making use of the expansion

$$\exp\,(i\mathbf{k} \cdot \mathbf{r}') = 1 + i\mathbf{k} \cdot \mathbf{r}' + \cdots + \frac{(i\mathbf{k} \cdot \mathbf{r}')^{l-1}}{(l-1)!} + \cdots \qquad (12\text{-}18)$$

The resulting electrostatic radiation field therefore takes the approximate form

$$\begin{aligned}\Phi(x,y,z,t) = \frac{\exp i(\omega t - kr)}{r} \Big[&\iiint \rho(x',y',z')\, d\tau' \\ &+ ik \iiint (\cos\theta') r' \rho(x',y',z')\, d\tau' \\ &- k^2 \iiint (\cos^2\theta') r'^2 \rho(x',y',z')\, d\tau' + \cdots \Big] \end{aligned} \qquad (12\text{-}19)$$

Since the successive terms in this expansion generally decrease rapidly, in actual applications to atomic and nuclear physics we generally use only the first, nonvanishing term.

Now it is possible to give the terms in the above expansion simple interpretations similar to those given in Sec. 2-7 for a static distribution of charge. One notes that, if a physical system with a harmonically varying point charge exists at the origin, it will, according to the theory of retarded potentials, produce the field at (x,y,z) which is the real part of

$$\Phi(x,y,z,t) = q\, \frac{\exp i(\omega t - kr)}{r} \qquad (12\text{-}20)$$

An array of two harmonically varying opposite charges (see Fig. 2-4) displaced from the origin along the z axis at $\pm s/2$ produces at (x,y,z) the field

$$\Phi(x,y,z,t) = \frac{q \exp i(\omega t - kr_1)}{r_1} - \frac{q \exp i(\omega t - kr_2)}{r_2} \qquad (12\text{-}21)$$

Using reasonable approximations, it follows that the long-range Φ is the real part of

$$\Phi = i \frac{\mathbf{P} \cdot \mathbf{k} \exp i(\omega t - kr)}{r} \tag{12-22}$$

where **P** is the vector moment of the dipole and **k** is given by Eq. (12-16). In a similar way an electric quadrupole consisting of two harmonically varying oppositely charged dipoles whose centers are displaced $\pm s'/2$ from the origin (see Fig. 2-5) will produce a characteristic harmonically varying field at a long distance. It is now possible to regard the successive terms in Eq. (12-19) as the scalar radiation field set up by a point charge, a dipole, a quadrupole, an octopole, etc., the moments of which are all varying harmonically with time. We are thus replacing the charge distribution, in so far as its effect at great distances is concerned, by equivalent simple localized objects. The magnitudes of these equivalent moments and the characteristic angles associated with them (in relation to the direction of **k**), of course, will depend upon the intrinsic nature of the charge distribution. We note that the general characterization of an electric monopole moment requires the specification only of a charge; a dipole moment requires a charge and a vector distance; a quadrupole moment, a charge and two distance vectors; an octopole moment, a charge and three distance vectors; etc. The complexity involved in treating the field set up by various moments thus increases very rapidly.

We have so far considered only the scalar field set up by a distribution of charges. For a complete study of electromagnetic radiation we must consider also the effects of the current distribution connected with the moving charges as well as the magnetic effects of intrinsic magnetic moments. The field due to a current distribution $\mathbf{j}(x',y',z',t^*)$ is most conveniently characterized by a vector potential which is given by

$$\mathbf{A}(x,y,z,t) = \iiint \frac{\mathbf{j}(x',y',z',t^*)}{|\mathbf{r} - \mathbf{r}'|} \, d\tau' \tag{12-23}$$

The radiation vector potential for harmonically varying distributions of currents and intrinsic magnetic moments may be developed using the theory of retarded potentials in a fashion analogous to that used in treatment of the scalar radiation potential. We must note that the scalar and vector potentials are not completely independent, since the charge and current distributions are related by the conservation equation

$$\frac{d\rho}{dt} + \operatorname{div} \mathbf{j} = 0 \tag{12-24}$$

Once obtained, the scalar and vector potentials may be used to determine the electric and magnetic field strengths by the use of the well-known formulas

$$\mathcal{E} = -\nabla\Phi - \frac{1}{c}\frac{\partial \mathbf{A}}{\partial t} \tag{12-25}$$

and

$$\mathbf{H} = \nabla \times \mathbf{A} \tag{12-26}$$

The Poynting's vector

$$\mathbf{S} = \frac{c}{4\pi}(\mathcal{E} \times \mathbf{H}) \tag{12-27}$$

then gives the instantaneous energy per unit time flowing in the direction of $\mathcal{E} \times \mathbf{H}$. The total power radiated is given by

$$\Omega = \int \mathbf{S} \cdot d\mathbf{A} \tag{12-28}$$

where $d\mathbf{A}$ represents the elements of area of a large sphere surrounding the radiating system.

Since the further pursuit of the theory and methods indicated above would take us beyond the scope of this book, we shall confine ourselves simply to the presentation of the main results of such a study. It turns out that we may replace an isolated system of harmonically varying charge, current, and magnetic-dipole distributions by an equivalent system consisting of an electric dipole, an electric quadrupole, an electric octopole, etc., and a magnetic dipole, magnetic quadrupole, etc., all varying harmonically. This equivalent system gives rise to the identical radiation at long ranges as the original system. Monopole electromagnetic radiation may be excluded, since conservation of charge precludes the possibility of an isolated system having a varying effective charge and classical theory does not admit the existence of magnetic poles. The classical theory gives finally[(2)] for the total power radiated by an electric dipole and a magnetic dipole

$$\Omega_E = \frac{16\pi^4\nu^4P^2}{3c^3} \tag{12-29}$$

$$\Omega_M = \frac{16\pi^4\nu^4M^2}{3c^3} \tag{12-30}$$

where P and M are the magnitudes of the electric dipole moment and magnetic dipole moment, respectively. To establish the plausibility of these results, we shall give an elementary derivation[(3)] of Eq. (12-29).

According to classical electromagnetic theory, an accelerating electron radiates energy at the rate

$$\Omega = \frac{2e^2a^2}{3c^3} \tag{12-31}$$

where a here denotes the magnitude of the acceleration. Let us assume that we have a linear oscillator consisting of an electron held to its equilibrium position by a potential of the form

$$V = \tfrac{1}{2}kx^2 \tag{12-32}$$

Assuming only very small damping, the motion may be approximately described by the equation

$$x = s \sin 2\pi\nu t \tag{12-33}$$

where s may be treated as a constant for a time no longer than several periods of oscillation. We have therefore

$$a = \ddot{x} = -(2\pi\nu)^2 s \sin 2\pi\nu t \tag{12-34}$$

and consequently

$$\Omega = \frac{32\pi^4\nu^4e^2s^2}{3c^3} \sin^2 2\pi\nu t \tag{12-35}$$

Since the time average of $\sin^2 2\pi\nu t$ over a complete cycle is $\frac{1}{2}$, the average energy radiated per unit time is

$$\bar{\Omega} = \frac{16\pi^4\nu^4e^2s^2}{3c^3} \tag{12-36}$$

If we let $P = es$, we obtain exactly Eq. (12-29).

12-2. Generalization to Quantum Theory. The transition from classical theory to a quantum theory has been taken in several steps. The earliest step, due essentially to Einstein,[(4)] is to regard

$$A = \frac{\Omega}{h\nu} \tag{12-37}$$

as the number of photons emitted per second, or alternatively as a transition probability per unit time for the emission of the quantum $h\nu$. In a similar way one may interpret $(S/h\nu)r^2\, d\Omega$ as the number of photons per second emitted into a solid angle $d\Omega$, or the transition probability per unit time for radiation into the solid angle $d\Omega$.

Spectroscopists recognized very early that the frequencies of spectral lines do not conform to the predictions of classical theory, but instead seem to correspond to the difference between natural terms associated with the atomic system (the Ritz law of combinations). The corresponding Einstein-Bohr frequency relation is

$$\nu_{if} = \frac{W_i - W_f}{h} \tag{12-38}$$

Bohr's theory of the hydrogen atom was the first quantitatively successful theory to yield such a result. In connection with this study Bohr[(5)]

in 1919 noted the asymptotic agreement between frequencies associated with transitions for large quantum numbers and the fundamentals and harmonics of the classical radiation from the system. He enlarged upon these limiting equalities in his famous correspondence principle, which states:

In the asymptotic limit of transitions between states having large quantum numbers, the frequency, angular distribution of intensity, and polarization approach those predicted by classical theory. For transitions between small quantum numbers the frequency is given by Eq. (12-38), *and the angular distribution of intensity and polarization correspond to a classical oscillator having a dipole moment, a quadrupole moment, a magnetic dipole moment, etc., which are the "averages" of those associated with the two states.*

Heisenberg[6] in 1925 took the next important step by sharpening the meaning of the word "averages" in Bohr's correspondence principle. By so doing he arrived at matrix mechanics, the first form of modern quantum mechanics. In terms of Schroedinger's theory Heisenberg essentially proposed that the average of any dynamical variable α between two states be computed by the use of

$$\langle\alpha\rangle_{if} = \iiint \Psi_i^*(x,y,z,t)\alpha_{op}\Psi_f(x,y,z,t)\,dx\,dy\,dz \qquad (12\text{-}39)$$

In view of the time dependence of the initial and final wave functions, this average may be written in the form [see Eqs. (10–19) and (12–38)]

$$\langle\alpha\rangle_{if} = \langle i|\alpha|f\rangle \exp 2\pi i\nu_{if}t \qquad (12\text{-}40)$$

where

$$\langle i|\alpha|f\rangle = \iiint \Psi_i^*(x,y,z)\alpha_{op}\Psi_f(x,y,z)\,dx\,dy\,dz \qquad (12\text{-}41)$$

is the so-called matrix element for the transition. We observe that this particular average varies harmonically with time precisely at the frequency of the spectral line emitted during the transition between the two energy states. Accordingly it would appear quite plausible to use this average obtained from quantum-mechanical considerations in place of the equivalent classical oscillating variable. In connection with the radiation from an electric or magnetic dipole, Heisenberg essentially proposed that, in the classical expressions for the power radiated and the angular distribution of intensity, we use the vector moments

$$\mathbf{P} = 2\langle i|\mathbf{P}|f\rangle \exp 2\pi i\nu_{if}t \qquad (12\text{-}42)$$

$$\mathbf{M} = 2\langle i|\mathbf{M}|f\rangle \exp 2\pi i\nu_{if}t \qquad (12\text{-}43)$$

The factor 2 in these moments stems essentially from the use of complex current and charge distribution functions in the quantum treatment.

Using now Eqs. (12-29), (12-30), and (12-37), we find the transition probabilities per unit time corresponding to these moments to be

$$A_{if} = \frac{64\pi^4 \nu_{if}^3 \langle i|\mathbf{P}|f\rangle^2}{3c^3 h} \tag{12-44}$$

for electric dipole emission and

$$A_{if} = \frac{64\pi^4 \nu_{if}^3 \langle i|\mathbf{M}|f\rangle^2}{3c^3 h} \tag{12-45}$$

for magnetic dipole emission.

The generalization of these formulas to the case of an arbitrary electric or magnetic multipole has been carried out in recent years by several authors.[7,8] The general result may be placed in the form

$$A_l = \frac{8\pi}{l} \frac{(l+1)k^{2l+1}Q_l^2}{[1\cdot3\cdot5 \cdot\cdot\cdot (2l+1)]^2\hbar} \tag{12-46}$$

where Q_l denotes the matrix element associated with the 2^l electric or magnetic moment. All theoretical estimates of transition probabilities in atomic and nuclear physics may be based upon Eq. (12-46).

12-3. Matrix Elements. To apply Eq. (12-46) to a particular case, we must evaluate a matrix element which has the form

$$Q_l = \iiint \Psi_i^* Q_{l,op} \Psi_f \, dx \, dy \, dz \tag{12-47}$$

This matrix element may be regarded as the "average" value of the 2^l-pole moment between the two states involved in the transition. Since the wave functions are finite only over a distance roughly equal to the size of the atom or nucleus, we would expect the matrix element associated with the 2^l electric moment to be of the order of magnitude of a classical multipole whose extension is about the size of the atom or nucleus and whose charge is of the order of e. Accordingly we may, in the atomic case, write

$$Q_{E,l}^{at} = e a_B^l \eta_{E,l} \tag{12-48}$$

where $a_B = \hbar^2/m_e e^2$ is the first Bohr radius and $\eta_{E,l}$ is a dimensionless constant which we might expect to be of the order of unity. Using Eqs. (12-48) and (12-46), we find that the ratio of the transition probabilities associated with an electric quadrupole moment and an electric dipole moment is given by

$$\frac{A_{E,2}^{at}}{A_{E,1}^{at}} = \frac{3}{100} k^2 a_B^2 \frac{\eta_{E,2}^2}{\eta_{E,1}^2} \approx \frac{3R_\infty^2 a_B^2}{100} = \frac{3}{100}\left(\frac{e^2}{c\hbar}\right)^2 \frac{1}{(4\pi)^2} \approx 10^{-8} \tag{12-49}$$

where for a typical case we have let $\eta_{E,l} \approx 1$ and have used $k \approx R_\infty$, the Rydberg constant, as an estimate of a typical atomic propagation constant.

Since a typical atomic magnetic dipole moment is of the order of a Bohr magneton ($\mu_B = e\hbar/2m_ec$ when e is in electrostatic units), we might expect an atomic magnetic quadrupole moment to run of the order of $a_B\mu_B$ and in general that

$$Q_{M,l}^{at} = \eta_{M,l}a_B^{l-1}\mu_B = \frac{\eta_{M,l}}{\eta_{E,l}}\frac{\mu_B}{ea_B}Q_{E,l}^{at} = \frac{\eta_{M,l}}{\eta_{E,l}}\frac{e^2}{2\hbar c}Q_{E,l}^{at} \tag{12-50}$$

where $\eta_{M,l}$ again is a dimensionless constant of the order of magnitude of unity. Accepting $\eta_{M,l} \approx \eta_{E,l}$, we see in view of Eq. (12-46) that the ratio of dipole transition probabilities is

$$\frac{A_{M,l}^{at}}{A_{E,l}^{at}} = \frac{\eta_{M,l}^2}{\eta_{E,l}^2}\left(\frac{e^2}{2\hbar c}\right)^2 \approx \frac{1}{4}\left(\frac{1}{137}\right)^2 \approx 10^{-5} \tag{12-51}$$

In view of the dominance of the transition probabilities connected with electric dipole transition, we can in atomic physics ignore other types of transitions except in rare instances when the electric dipole transition probability between two states vanishes identically (forbidden transitions). In such cases magnetic dipole transitions become important.

In the nuclear case we may use $R = bA^{\frac{1}{3}}$ as a measure of the extension of the nucleus and $\mu_N = e\hbar/2m_pc$ as a measure of magnetic moments. Accordingly we set

$$Q_{E,l} = eR^l\eta_{E,l} \tag{12-52}$$

and

$$Q_{M,l} = \mu_N R^{l-1}\eta_{M,l} = \frac{\eta_{M,l}}{\eta_{E,l}}\frac{\mu_N}{eR}Q_{E,l} \tag{12-53}$$

where again $\eta_{E,l}$ and $\eta_{M,l}$ are expected to be dimensionless factors of the order of unity. Substituting Eqs. (12-52) and (12-53) into Eq. (12-46), we find in the nuclear case that

$$A_{E,l} = \eta_{E,l}^2\,\frac{8\pi(l+1)}{l}\,\frac{e^2k(Rk)^{2l}}{[1\cdot 3\cdot 5\cdots(2l+1)]^2\hbar} \tag{12-54}$$

and

$$A_{M,l} = \frac{\eta_{M,l}^2}{\eta_{E,l}^2}\left(\frac{\mu_N}{eR}\right)^2 A_{E,l} \tag{12-55}$$

Here the ratio of the transition probabilities associated with the electric and magnetic 2^l moments is, in a typical case ($A \approx 100$),

$$\frac{A_{M,l}}{A_{E,l}} = \left(\frac{\eta_{M,l}}{\eta_{E,l}}\right)^2\left(\frac{\mu_N}{eR}\right)^2 = \left(\frac{\eta_{M,l}}{\eta_{E,l}}\right)^2\left(\frac{\hbar}{2m_pcR}\right)^2 \approx 10^{-3} \tag{12-56}$$

The ratio of transition probabilities of the electric 2^{l+1} moment to the electric 2^l moment for a typical case ($E_\gamma \approx 1$ Mev, $A \approx 100$) is

$$\frac{A_{E,\,l+1}}{A_{E,l}} = \frac{\eta_{E,\,l+1}^2}{\eta_{E,l}^2}\,\frac{l(l+2)}{(2l+3)^2}\,\frac{(kR)^2}{(l+1)^2} \approx 10^{-4} \tag{12-57}$$

It has been assumed frequently in the literature that the above two ratios may be regarded as about the same, so that we may roughly regard the transition probability associated with the 2^l magnetic moment to be of the same order of magnitude as the transition probability associated with the 2^{l+1} electric moment. However, Weisskopf[8] maintains that the transition probability associated with the 2^l magnetic moment is significantly larger than the 2^{l+1} electric transition probability. The experimental evidence[9] appears to support this contention.

To make a more precise estimate of the transition probabilities, we must determine the matrix elements given by Eq. (12-47), or, what is essentially the same thing, we must determine the dimensionless factors $\eta_{E,l}$ and $\eta_{M,l}$. To carry out such computations, we must know the wave functions which characterize the initial and final states. Unfortunately nuclear wave functions to a major extent are still matters of conjecture. We might arrive at nuclear wave functions on the basis of a particular model of the nucleus, such as the liquid-drop model or the independent-particle model. Using wave functions so calculated in conjunction with the appropriate operators which represent the various multipole moments, it is possible to place some limits on the dimensionless factors which we have introduced. For example, several authors have evaluated electric matrix elements on the basis of the liquid-drop model. Their results may be expressed as[10]

$$\begin{aligned} \eta_{E,l} &= \left(\frac{3l\hbar Z^2}{32\pi kcm_pAR^2}\right)^{\frac{1}{2}} && \text{for } l \geq 2 \\ &= 0 && \text{for } l = 1 \end{aligned} \tag{12-58}$$

The fact that the electric dipole transition probability vanishes, according to the liquid-drop model, is due to the absence of the $l = 1$ mode of oscillation. Such a nuclear distortion of a homogeneous fluid of protons and neutrons would imply a shifting of the center of mass of the droplet as a whole and is ruled out by conservation of momentum.

Using the independent-particle model, Weisskopf[8] arrives at an approximate estimate for the matrix element associated with a multipole electric transition which is equivalent to setting

$$\eta_{E,l} = \frac{3}{(4\pi)^{\frac{1}{2}}(l+3)} \tag{12-59}$$

For magnetic transitions Weisskopf[8] uses qualitative considerations to arrive at

$$\eta_{M,l} = 2(10)^{\frac{1}{2}}\eta_{E,l} \tag{12-60}$$

These estimates are rough upper limits based upon the assumption that the wave functions of the two states overlap to a large degree. Actual values may run considerably smaller than these estimates. Using these values of η, we may now predict the transition probabilities associated with various electric and magnetic multipole moments. Because of the extreme sensitivity of the transition probability to the value of l, we might expect the radiation associated with the lowest value of l to mask the radiation connected with the higher values of l. Expressing it differently, we might say that, if a transition can proceed by electric dipole radiation, it will do so almost exclusively, since the transition probability for magnetic dipole, quadrupole, etc., radiation or for electric quadrupole, octopole, etc., radiation is so small on a relative scale that it may be ignored. This fact is illustrated in Table 12-1, in which we give the

TABLE 12-1. AVERAGE LIFETIME (IN SECONDS) FOR $A = 100$

E, Mev	$E1$	$M1$	$E2$	$M2$	$E3$	$M3$	$E4$	$M4$	$E5$	$M5$
0.01	4×10^{-10}	4×10^{-8}	2×10^{-2}	2	10^{8}	10^{10}	10^{17}	10^{19}	10^{26}	10^{28}
0.1	4×10^{-13}	4×10^{-11}	10^{-6}	10^{-4}	10	10^{3}	10^{8}	10^{10}	10^{15}	10^{17}
1	6×10^{-16}	6×10^{-14}	10^{-11}	10^{-9}	10^{-6}	10^{-4}	10^{-1}	10	10^{4}	10^{6}
10	4×10^{-19}	4×10^{-17}	10^{-16}	10^{-4}	10^{-13}	10^{-11}	10^{-10}	10^{-8}	10^{-7}	10^{-5}

average lifetime of the first excited state decaying to the ground state for several values of E_γ and $A = 100$ computed on the basis of the Weisskopf equations for various electric and magnetic multipoles.

If a decay takes place from the first excited state to the ground state, the transition probability is simply the decay constant of this excited state, or the reciprocal of the average lifetime for the excited state. According to Table 12-1 we would expect these lifetimes to be exceedingly small when $l = 1$. While most lifetimes of first excited or low-lying excited states are nonmeasurable ($<10^{-10}$ sec), we frequently encounter low-lying nuclear states which have measurable lifetimes, and indeed we have encountered isomers with lifetimes ranging up to minutes or hours. A glance at Table 12-1 indicates that such a lifetime would result only for l values of the order of 3 or 4, when the energy is small. To account for the long lifetimes of isomeric states, Weiszäcker(11) has suggested that isomeric transitions correspond to highly forbidden transitions in which the lower multipole moments all vanish identically. The question as to when the transition probabilities associated with various multipole moments vanish has been given considerable study both in atomic and nuclear physics. The results of these studies may be formulated into a concise set of rules, which are known as selection rules.

12-4. Selection Rules. In atomic spectroscopy both general rules and highly specialized rules have been developed which tell when various matrix elements vanish or can be nonvanishing. The theoretical explanation for these rules in the atomic case is based upon a more detailed knowledge of wave functions than is available in the nuclear case. At the present time only the most general rules have been formulated for nuclear spectroscopy.

The principle of conservation of angular momentum provides the basis for the strongest selection rule. Heitler[12] has shown that the radiation emitted by an electric or magnetic multipole of order 2^l has an angular momentum $\mathbf{l}$ with respect to the origin to which the multipole is referred. Conservation of momentum therefore requires that the angular momenta $\mathbf{I}_i$ and $\mathbf{I}_f$ of the initial and final states and the angular momentum $\mathbf{l}$ emitted by a 2^l electric or magnetic multipole must satisfy

$$\mathbf{I}_i = \mathbf{I}_f + \mathbf{l} \tag{12-61}$$

If I_i and I_f are given, it follows that

$$l \doteq |I_f - I_i|, |I_f - I_i + 1|, \ . \ . \ . \ , |I_f + I_i| \tag{12-62}$$

In view of the extremely rapid decrease of transition probability with l, the multipole character of a transition will almost always be the smallest value

$$l_{\min} = |I_f - I_i| = \Delta I \tag{12-63}$$

Since the $2^{\Delta I}$ electric transition probability is usually much greater than the $2^{\Delta I}$-pole magnetic transition probability, the transition would be expected always to have the character of a $2^{\Delta I}$-pole electric transition. However, experimental observations indicate that the radiation for a transition between two states frequently has the character of $2^{\Delta I}$-pole magnetic transition. An adequate explanation for these cases can be given if consideration is given to the concept of parity.

The parity of a state is determined by the change in the value of the wave function which characterizes the state when the spatial coordinates of all the particles are inverted. If the wave function satisfies

$$\Psi(\mathbf{r}_1,\mathbf{r}_2, \ . \ . \ . \ ,\mathbf{r}_n) = \Psi(-\mathbf{r}_1,-\mathbf{r}_2, \ . \ . \ . \ ,-\mathbf{r}_n) \tag{12-64}$$

the state is said to have even parity. On the other hand if

$$\Psi(\mathbf{r}_1,\mathbf{r}_2, \ . \ . \ . \ ,\mathbf{r}_n) = -\Psi(-\mathbf{r}_1,-\mathbf{r}_2, \ . \ . \ . \ ,-\mathbf{r}_n) \tag{12-65}$$

the wave function is said to have odd parity. In central-field problems the spatial wave function associated with a single particle in spherical polar coordinates has the form

$$\Psi(\mathbf{r}) = C_{nlm_l} R_n{}^l(r) \Theta_l{}^{|m_l|}(\cos\theta) e^{im_l\varphi} \tag{12-66}$$

The interchange of the vectors $\mathbf{r}$ and $-\mathbf{r}$ is equivalent to replacing the spherical coordinates r, θ, and φ by r, $\pi - \theta$, and $\pi + \varphi$ (see Fig. 12-2). The form of the function of φ gives

$$e^{im_l(\pi+\varphi)} = (-1)^{m_l} e^{im_l\varphi} \tag{12-67}$$

Recalling that

$$\Theta_l^{|m_l|} = C_{lm_l} P_l^{m_l}(z) \sin^{|m_l|} \theta \tag{12-68}$$

we have

$$\Theta_l^{|m_l|}(\pi - \theta) = C_{lm_l} P_l^{m_l}(-z) \sin^{|m_l|} (\pi - \theta) \tag{12-69}$$

where we have let $z = \cos \theta$ and $-z = \cos (\pi - \theta)$. The sine function is unchanged by the replacement; however, $P_l^{m_l}$ is an even polymonial in z if $m_l + l$ is even and an odd polynomial if $m_l + l$ is odd. Consequently it follows that

$$\Theta_l^{|m|}(\pi - \theta) = (-1)^{m_l+l} \Theta_l^{|m_l|} (\theta) \tag{12-70}$$

Since the radial wave function is unaltered, it follows finally that

$$\Psi_{nlm_l}(\mathbf{r}) = (-1)^l \Psi_{nlm_l}(-\mathbf{r}) \tag{12-71}$$

Thus the parity of the central-field eigenfunction is even or odd according to the evenness or oddness of the quantum number l. For a system of independent particles in a central field we obviously have

$$\Psi(\mathbf{r}_1,\mathbf{r}_2, \ldots ,\mathbf{r}_n) = (-1)^{l_1+l_2+ \cdots +l_n} \cdot \Psi(-\mathbf{r}_1,-\mathbf{r}_2, \ldots ,-\mathbf{r}_n) \tag{12-72}$$

i.e., the parity depends upon the oddness or evenness of the sum of the orbital angular-momentum quantum numbers. It is customary to indicate the parity of a state by a superscript + for even parity and a superscript − for odd parity.

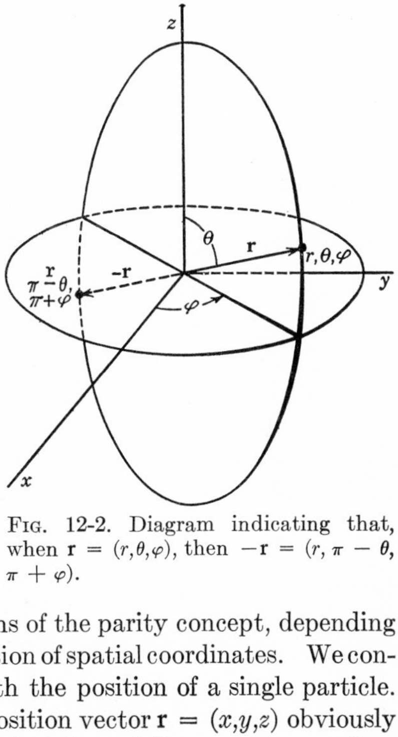

FIG. 12-2. Diagram indicating that, when $\mathbf{r} = (r,\theta,\varphi)$, then $-\mathbf{r} = (r, \pi - \theta, \pi + \varphi)$.

Operators representing dynamical variables may also be classified in terms of the parity concept, depending upon how they are affected by an inversion of spatial coordinates. We consider first the operators connected with the position of a single particle. The components of position and the position vector $\mathbf{r} = (x,y,z)$ obviously have odd parity. On the other hand, functions of distance alone such as

$$F(r) = F[(x^2 + y^2 + z^2)^{\frac{1}{2}}] \tag{12-73}$$

are unchanged by spatial reflections. The operators representing components of momentum have odd parity, since

$$\frac{\partial}{\partial(-x)} = -\frac{\partial}{\partial x} \qquad \text{etc.} \tag{12-74}$$

where we consider operators to be equal if, when applied to an arbitrary function, they yield identical functions. Thus the operators representing p_x, p_y, and p_z and $\mathbf{p}$ have odd parity. On the other hand since

$$\frac{\partial}{\partial(-x)}\frac{\partial}{\partial(-x)}\Psi = \frac{\partial^2\Psi}{\partial x^2} \qquad \text{etc.} \tag{12-75}$$

it is apparent that the operators representing p_x^2, p_y^2, and p_z^2 and $\mathbf{p}\cdot\mathbf{p}$ have even parity.

The mathematical property which we ultimately appeal to in formulating selection rules which depend upon parity is that an integral of an odd function between symmetric limits automatically vanishes. For example, the vector matrix element $\langle i|\mathbf{r}|f\rangle$ which must be evaluated in electric dipole emission is a combination of matrix elements given by

$$\langle i|\mathbf{r}|f\rangle = \mathbf{i}\langle i|x|f\rangle + \mathbf{j}\langle i|y|f\rangle + \mathbf{k}\langle i|z|f\rangle \tag{12-76}$$

where

$$\langle i|x|f\rangle = \iiint \Psi_i^* x \Psi_f \, dx\, dy\, dz \tag{12-77}$$

and $\mathbf{i}$, $\mathbf{j}$, and $\mathbf{k}$ are unit vectors along the x, y, and z axes. For these parity considerations it is convenient to use rectangular coordinates in order to take advantage of the fact that an even (odd) function of the position vector is also an even (odd) function of the components.

If Ψ_i and Ψ_f are both even functions, *i.e.*, if they have even parity, the three matrix elements in Eq. (12-76) vanish upon integration on x, since x and consequently the entire integrand are odd. Similarly the second and third matrix elements in Eq. (12-76) vanish upon integration upon y and z. In view of the odd parity of the operator in electric dipole transitions we can obtain a nonvanishing matrix element only if Ψ_i and Ψ_f have opposite parity. On the other hand the matrix elements for electric quadrupole radiation involve bilinear combinations of the components of position such as xy, y^2, etc., each of which has even parity. Hence, to have a nonvanishing quadrupole matrix element, the two wave functions or states must have the same parity. By a simple extension of this argument we arrive at the following selection rules for 2^l-pole electric transitions. The word "yes" means that the parity of the two states involved in a transition must change if the matrix element is to be nonvanishing. The word "no" means that the parity of the two states must not change. The parity changes for electric transitions are:

Multipole.........	Dipole	Quad.	Oct.	16-pole	32-pole	64-pole
Parity change.....	yes	no	yes	no	yes	no

The operators involved in the matrix elements for magnetic dipole transitions depend either upon the spin angular momentum of the particles or the orbital angular momentum $\mathbf{r}\times\mathbf{p}$. In either event the operator has even parity, and hence to have nonvanishing matrix elements for magnetic dipole emission requires no change in parity. The operators for magnetic quadrupole moments have odd parity, since they are more or less combinations of the dipole operators together with a length. Hence the parity must change for a magnetic quadrupole emission. In general the parity selection rules for magnetic transitions are:

Multipole.	Dipole	Quad.	Oct.	16-pole	32-pole	64-pole
Parity change.	no	yes	no	yes	no	yes

These tables may be summarized briefly by stating that the parity change must satisfy

$$(-1)^l \text{ for } E,l \text{ and } (-1)^{l+1} \text{ for } M,l \tag{12-78}$$

where a minus sign indicates "yes" (parity must change) and a plus sign indicates "no" (parity must not change). The angular-momentum and parity selection rules, together with the approximate expressions Eqs. (12-59) and (12-60) and Eqs. (12-54) and (12-55) for the transition probabilities, determine almost uniquely the character of the transition between two states. If the states have the angular momenta I_i and I_f, the multipole character will be $2^{\Delta I}$. If the parity change conforms to $(-1)^{\Delta I}$, the electric transition will occur. In this case the transition is called parity-favored. On the other hand if the parity change conforms to $(-1)^{\Delta I+1}$, the transition is called parity-unfavored and will usually proceed by the $2^{\Delta I}$ magnetic transition. A parity-unfavored transition could also proceed by the $2^{\Delta I+1}$ electric transition, although recent experimental evidence suggests that this type of radiation is usually small compared to the $2^{\Delta I}$-pole magnetic transition.

In view of the foregoing discussion we might replace the value of l in Eq. (12-54) by ΔI. Combining Eqs. (12-59) and (12-54), we find for parity-favored transitions

$$A_{E,l} = \frac{4.4(\Delta I + 1)}{\Delta I[1 \cdot 3 \cdots (2\,\Delta I + 1)]^2} \left(\frac{3}{\Delta I + 3}\right)^2 \left(\frac{E_\gamma}{197 \text{ Mev}}\right)^{2\,\Delta I+1} \times (1.5A^{\frac{1}{3}})^{2\,\Delta I} \times 10^{21} \quad \text{sec}^{-1} \tag{12-79}$$

Combining Eqs. (12-60), (12-55), and (12-54), we find for parity-unfavored transitions

$$A_{M,l} = \frac{1.9(\Delta I + 1)}{\Delta I[1 \cdot 3 \cdots (2\,\Delta I + 1)]^2} \left(\frac{3}{\Delta I + 3}\right)^2 \left(\frac{E_\gamma}{197 \text{ Mev}}\right)^{2\,\Delta I+1} \times (1.5A^{\frac{1}{3}})^{2\,\Delta I-2} \times 10^{21} \quad \text{sec}^{-1} \tag{12-80}$$

The foregoing theory of gamma-ray transitions may be subjected to various experimental tests. For example, measurements of lifetimes and energy values in cases of nuclear isomerism might be used in conjunction with Eqs. (12-79) and (12-80) to assign the ΔI value for a transition. A check on the theory would follow if ΔI is close to an integer and if the level scheme based upon the inferred value of ΔI is consistent with other data. To make such a quantitative comparison, however, we must first correct for the effect of internal-conversion processes upon the lifetime of isomeric states.[35]

12-5. Internal Conversion. The interpretation currently given to internal conversion is that the field set up by atomic electrons induces a transition in which the total system, in an excited nuclear state and a ground atomic state, jumps to the ground nuclear state and an excited atomic state. The electron carries off the remaining energy. According to this interpretation the total decay constant and lifetime of an isomeric state is given by

$$\lambda = \frac{1}{\tau} = \lambda_\gamma + \lambda_e = \lambda_\gamma(1 + \alpha) \tag{12-81}$$

where λ_e is the additional transition probability induced by the electron and α is the internal-conversion coefficient ($\alpha = N_e/N_\gamma$).

In the actual calculations we assume that the electromagnetic field of the nuclear multipole at the origin induces K, L, . . . atomic electrons to undergo transitions to continuum states of ionization. The time-dependent perturbation theory is used. The theoretical ratio $\alpha = \lambda_e/\lambda_\gamma$ depends primarily upon the atomic matrix elements. Since these atomic wave functions are known quite well, the matrix elements may be reliably evaluated. The calculations, however, are complicated, and generally explicit formulas are available only for certain limiting cases. For example, Dancoff and Morrison[13] arrive at the simplified formula for the K-shell internal-conversion coefficient due to a nuclear electric 2^l moment:

$$\alpha_K(l) = Z^3 \left(\frac{e^2}{\hbar c}\right)^4 \frac{l}{l+1} \left(\frac{2m_ec^2}{E_\gamma}\right)^{l+\frac{5}{2}} \tag{12-82}$$

The conditions for the validity of this formula are

$$W_K \ll T_e \ll m_ec^2 \tag{12-83}$$

where W_K is the K-shell excitation energy and T_e is the kinetic energy of the ejected electron. This formula is more complicated when the above conditions are not fulfilled. Fortunately numerical tables calculated by Rose *et al.*[14] are now available, giving K- and L-shell conversion coefficients for a wide range of energies.

The theory of internal conversion gives the internal-conversion coefficients as functions of the total transition energy, the charge of the nucleus, and the multipole nature of the transition. Experimentally one may determine with accuracy Z, E_γ, τ, N_K/N_L, and roughly N_K and N_L. The comparison between the complete theory and the experimental results frequently enables one to infer uniquely the type of transition, the I value, and the parity of the excited state relative to the ground state. Using the value of the conversion coefficient, one may then correct the experimentally observed lifetimes to obtain the decay constant associated with gamma-ray emission alone.

12-6. Experimental Confirmation and Nuclear Isomerism. Spectacular advances have been made during the past few years by applying the theory of gamma-ray transitions and the independent-particle model of the nucleus to the study of nuclear isomers. Improving upon the earlier classification of Axel and Dancoff,[(15)] Goldhaber and Sunyar[(16)] have identified numerous multipole transitions on the basis of K-conversion coefficients and K/L ratios. These classifications are in excellent agreement with expectations based upon the angular-momentum and parity assignments of the independent-particle model. Goldhaber and Hill[(17)] used the results of the shell model and the experimental classification based upon conversion coefficients, together with certain results of beta-decay theory, to assign I and parity values to all known isomeric states. Figure 6-11 shows examples taken from this extensive work. Although adequate for the purposes of classification of transitions, the Weisskopf formulas for gamma-ray transition probabilities have been found to give results which deviate significantly from the experimental results. The ratio of the experimental to theoretical (Weisskopf formula) transition probabilities may be regarded as a dimensionless factor (sometimes called an empirical squared matrix element) which will change the theoretical squared matrix elements to the correct ones. Goldhaber and Sunyar find that for electric transitions these correction factors frequently run of the order of 10^{-3}, indicating that the Weisskopf results are considerably larger than the experimental results. The correction factors for magnetic transition probabilities are quite close to unity, indicating an approximate agreement with Weisskopf's formula. Moszkowski,[(18)] using the independent-particle model, has recently made more careful calculations of matrix elements than those represented by Eqs. (12-79) and (12-80). Again good agreement is found for magnetic transition probabilities, but the theoretical electric transition probabilities are generally of the order of 1000 times greater than the experimental values. One might summarize the present status of the work on gamma radiation by stating that, while the theory is still incomplete, a considerable degree of success has already been achieved. Particularly remarkable has been the success of the shell model in giving I and parity assignments which are consistent with the observed multipole character of gamma-ray transitions.

12-7. Alpha Decay. We shall consider now the theory of Gamow[19] and Condon and Gurney[20] which underlies the decay constant–energy relationship for alpha decay [Eq. (6-56)]. This study was the earliest successful application of quantum mechanics to the nucleus. In Fig. 12-3 we indicate the energy relationships which govern the ground-to-ground-state alpha decay of a radioactive nucleus. The zero coordinate is taken as the sum of the ground-state masses of the daughter and alpha particle. The difference between M^* and $M + M_\alpha$ represents the energy Q_α available for the decay. This energy manifests itself experimentally as T, the sum of the kinetic energies of the alpha particle and the daugh-

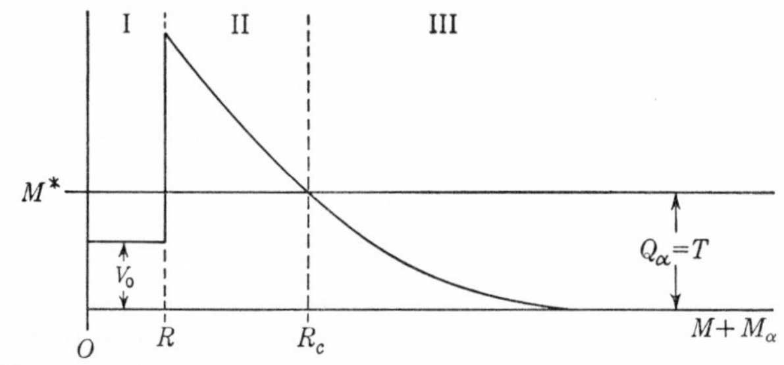

FIG. 12-3. Diagram showing energy relationships involved in alpha decay. The potential energy is drawn under the assumption that a nuclear force sets in abruptly at $R = bA^{\frac{1}{3}}$.

ter nucleus. We shall assume a potential energy of interaction exists between the alpha particle and the daughter which is given by

$$\begin{aligned} V &= V_0 \qquad && 0 < r < R = bA^{\frac{1}{3}} \\ &= \frac{2Ze^2}{r} && r > R = bA^{\frac{1}{3}} \end{aligned} \tag{12-84}$$

Throughout this discussion we shall assume that the radius of the alpha particle is also embodied in the expression $R = bA^{\frac{1}{3}}$. The potential function V is also indicated in Fig. 12-3. The difference between the total energy $Q_\alpha = T$ and the potential-energy curve represents the classical kinetic energy of the alpha particle at any particular distance from the nucleus. For the potential shown in Fig. 12-3 this difference vanishes at $r = R$ and at

$$r = R_c = \frac{2Ze^2}{Q_\alpha} = \frac{2Ze^2}{T} \tag{12-85}$$

According to classical physics only positive values of kinetic energy can occur; hence the alpha particle may exist in the region from 0 to R (region I) and from R_c to ∞ (region III) but cannot exist in the region from R to R_c (region II). Therefore, according to classical theory, an alpha particle with energy below the barrier height cannot traverse the region II outward or inward. As we have already pointed out, this contradicts direct experimental observations of alpha-induced reactions and alpha decay.

The quantum-mechanical theory of alpha decay does not place definite limits upon the location of the alpha particle. Instead the alpha particle is characterized by a wave function $\boldsymbol{\Psi}(\mathbf{r},t)$ which satisfies the equation

$$\left[-\frac{\hbar^2}{2m_r}\Delta + V(r) - i\hbar\frac{\partial}{\partial t}\right]\boldsymbol{\Psi}(\mathbf{r},t) = 0 \qquad (12\text{-}86)$$

The fact that an alpha particle can exist within a heavy nucleus for long periods of time suggests that the spatial wave function characterizing the alpha particle is large only in the region which we may identify with the nucleus. One may view the ground state and the low-lying excited states of an alpha emitter as the characteristic energy levels of a particle "virtually" bound inside the nucleus by a barrier which prevents its escape to the lower energy state at infinity. To a good approximation a virtual state may be characterized by the usual type of harmonically varying function of time. However, to a better approximation we may assume that

$$\boldsymbol{\Psi}(\mathbf{r},t) = \Psi(\mathbf{r})\exp\left(-\frac{iWt}{\hbar}\right)\exp\left(-\frac{\lambda t}{2}\right) \qquad (12\text{-}87)$$

Inserting this into the general Schroedinger wave equation and following through with the separation-of-variables procedure, we are led to the usual differential equations for Θ and Φ. The radial wave equation for $G = rR(r)$, however, is now

$$\frac{d^2G}{dr^2} + \frac{2m_r}{\hbar^2}\left[W - \frac{i\hbar\lambda}{2} - V(r) - \frac{\hbar^2}{2m_r}\frac{l(l+1)}{r^2}\right]G(r) = 0 \qquad (12\text{-}88)$$

For the type of real potential we are assuming, the centrifugal-force term in this equation may be treated as a small perturbation which is equivalent to an effective "centrifugal" barrier. We shall, for the 0th approximation, ignore it. If we knew the shape of the true nuclear potential for alpha particles, it might be possible to find the solutions of this equation which have appropriate boundary conditions and find, perhaps, a set of W and λ values. Our poor understanding of nuclear forces, however, makes it impossible to carry out such a complete study. Since $W = Q_\alpha = T$ values and λ values associated with α decay from the ground state of the parent are known and apparently related, one may attempt to verify the quantum theory partially by studying the explicit relationships between T and λ which are implicitly contained in the radial wave equation. In particular the theoretical relationship between T and λ is of interest for comparison with the Geiger-Nuttall law. Thus in principle we may solve Eq. (12-88) to determine G for the ground state in terms of the parameters characterizing the well, λ, and T. Substituting this solution back into Eq. (12-88) then gives a λ vs. T relationship. In actuality, to find the radial wave function requires advanced approximation methods which are quite complicated and very delicate, and the practical procedure for relating λ to T is quite different. We shall, therefore, confine ourselves here to a simplified derivation which will serve to bring out the gross features of the λ vs. T relationship for transitions between ground states.

Because decay constants are very small, we may as an approximation ignore λ in Eq. (12-88) and seek the well-behaved solutions of the radial wave function in a manner similar to that previously used for stationary-state problems (see Sec. 10-7). The fact that the potential well slopes downward and ultimately falls below the value of T has as a concomitant effect a small leakage of probability to a region far removed from the nucleus. At long distances $V(r)$ vanishes, and Eq. (12-88) has the general asymptotic solution

$$\vec{G} = A_\infty \exp(i\epsilon_W \rho) + B_\infty \exp(-i\epsilon_W \rho) \tag{12-89}$$

where $\rho = r/R$ and

$$\epsilon_W = k_W R = \left(\frac{Q_\alpha}{\hbar^2/2m_r R^2}\right)^{\frac{1}{2}} = \left(\frac{T}{\hbar^2/2m_r R^2}\right)^{\frac{1}{2}} \tag{12-90}$$

If we append to $\vec{G}$ the approximation time dependence $e^{-iTt/\hbar}$ and the factor $1/r$, we have for the complete wave function

$$\vec{\Psi} = \frac{A_\infty \exp[i(k_W r - \omega t)]}{r} + \frac{B_\infty \exp[-i(k_W r + \omega t)]}{r} \tag{12-91}$$

where $\omega = T/\hbar$ and we have ignored the dependence upon θ and φ. The two terms of Eq. (12-91) represent outgoing and ingoing spherical waves. On physical grounds we may set $B_\infty = 0$, since in the alpha-decay phenomena we have no ingoing particles. Using the resulting wave function, we find the probability of finding a particle in the volume element $r^2\,dr \sin\theta\,d\theta\,d\varphi$ at a long distance from the nucleus is given by

$$P\,dV = \vec{\Psi}^*\vec{\Psi}\,dV = \vec{G}^*\vec{G}\,dr \sin\theta\,d\theta\,d\varphi = A_\infty^* A_\infty\,dr \sin\theta\,d\theta\,d\varphi \tag{12-92}$$

Since particles in this volume element are moving radially outward with the velocity $v = dr/dt$, the flow of probability per unit time into the solid angle $d\Omega = \sin\theta\,d\theta\,d\varphi$ (see Fig. 12-4) is

$$\frac{P\,dV}{dt} = v\vec{G}^*\vec{G}\,d\Omega = vA_\infty^* A_\infty\,d\Omega \tag{12-93}$$

Since this is independent of direction, we may readily integrate the probability flux over the entire solid angle. We find that the total probability per unit time for a particle to escape to great distances from the nucleus is

$$\lambda = 4\pi v \vec{G}^* \vec{G} = 4\pi v A_\infty^* A_\infty \tag{12-94}$$

We see therefore that, to determine the dependence of λ upon T, we must find the dependence of $\vec{G}$ upon T. To do this, we must calculate the lowest eigenfunction of the Schroedinger time-independent wave equation everywhere and examine this solution in the limit of large r.

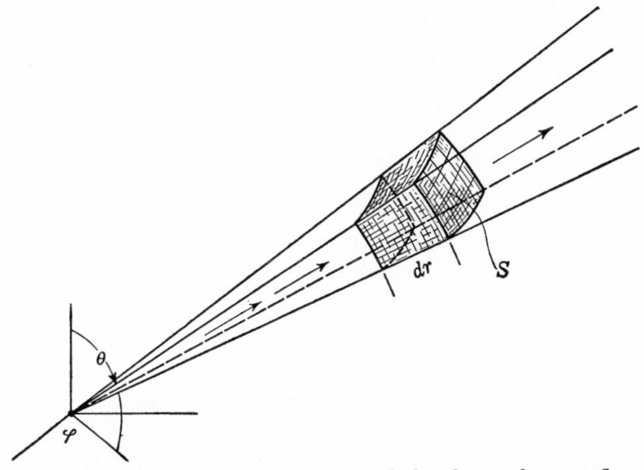

FIG. 12-4. The probability contained in the shaded volume element flows through S in a time $dt = dr/v$.

12-8. Approximate Solution of the Wave Equation. The factor $(2m_r/\hbar^2)[W - V(r)]$ in the wave equation changes its value and character in the three regions indicated in Fig. 12-3. To accommodate this change, we define the positive, definite dimensionless quantities ($T = W$)

$$\epsilon_{\text{I}}^2 = \frac{2m_rR^2}{\hbar^2}(T - V_0) \tag{12-95}$$

$$\epsilon_{\text{II}}^2 = \frac{2m_rR^2}{\hbar^2}\left(\frac{2Ze^2}{r} - T\right) = \epsilon_{\text{II}}^2(\rho) \tag{12-96}$$

$$\epsilon_{\text{III}}^2 = \frac{2m_rR^2}{\hbar^2}\left(T - \frac{2Ze^2}{r}\right) = \epsilon_{\text{III}}^2(\rho) \tag{12-97}$$

The radial wave equations for the three regions become

$$G_{\text{I}}'' + \epsilon_{\text{I}}^2 G_{\text{I}} = 0 \tag{12-98}$$

$$G_{\text{II}}'' - \epsilon_{\text{II}}^2 G_{\text{II}} = 0 \tag{12-99}$$

$$G_{\text{III}}'' + \epsilon_{\text{III}}^2 G_{\text{III}} = 0 \tag{12-100}$$

The solution in region I which is well-behaved at the origin is

$$G_{\mathrm{I}} = A_{\mathrm{I}} \sin \epsilon_{\mathrm{I}}\rho \tag{12-101}$$

If the barrier at $r = R$ or $\rho = 1$ were infinitely high, as it is in the spherical-box problem, the lowest energy state would correspond to a wave function for which

$$\epsilon_{\mathrm{I}} = \left[\frac{2m_rR^2}{\hbar^2}(T - V_0)\right]^{\frac{1}{2}} = \pi \tag{12-102}$$

The wave function would then vanish at the inner barrier. In the finite-well problem Eq. (12-102) is not quite true, and in consequence the wave function has a small but finite value at $\rho = 1$ ($r = R$). This same modification of the interior wave function might be expected to apply to the problem we are now considering. We recall that in the infinite-barrier case the normalization constant is equivalent to

$$A_{\mathrm{I}} = (2\pi R)^{-\frac{1}{2}} \tag{12-103}$$

Assuming that in the actual case there is very little leakage beyond $\rho = 1$, we may as an approximation use the same normalization constant.

If ϵ_{II} were constant in Eq. (12-99) as it is in the finite-well problem, the general solution for this region would be a linear combination of $\exp(-\epsilon_{\mathrm{II}}\rho)$ and $\exp(\epsilon_{\mathrm{II}}\rho)$. We recall that in the finite well we rejected $\exp(\epsilon\rho)$ on the grounds that it blows up at infinity. By joining $\sin(\epsilon_{\mathrm{I}}\rho)$ smoothly to $\exp(-\epsilon_{\mathrm{II}}\rho)$, we found a well-behaved solution and the energy eigenvalue corresponding to that solution. The fact that ϵ_{II} varies in this case complicates the problem considerably. Fortunately, however, since ϵ_{II} is relatively slow-varying, we may make use of a method of approximation which is known as the Wentzel-Kramers-Brillouin method. We assumed that G_{II} is given by

$$G_{\mathrm{II}} = e^{S(\rho)} \tag{12-104}$$

Substituting this into the radial wave equation, it follows that

$$S'' + S'^2 - \epsilon_{\mathrm{II}}{}^2 = 0 \tag{12-105}$$

In the zero-order approximation of the Wentzel-Kramers-Brillouin method we assume that

$$S'' \ll S'^2 \tag{12-106}$$

an equation which can be shown to be justified when $\epsilon_{\mathrm{II}}(\rho)$ is slowly varying. It follows therefore as a 0th approximation that

$$S' = \pm\epsilon_{\mathrm{II}}(\rho) \tag{12-107}$$

and hence

$$S = \pm \int_{\rho}^{\rho_0} \epsilon_{\mathrm{II}}(\rho)\, d\rho \tag{12-108}$$

where

$$\rho_c = \frac{R_c}{R} \tag{12-109}$$

In Eq. (12-108) we effectively choose our constant of integration so that $S(\rho)$ vanishes at the same point ρ_c at which $\epsilon(\rho)$ vanishes. The positive and negative exponential functions provide an approximate general solution for Eq. (12-99) which has the form

$$G_{\text{II}} = A_{\text{II}} \exp\left[\int_\rho^{\rho_c} \epsilon_{\text{II}}(\rho)\,d\rho\right] + B_{\text{II}} \exp\left[-\int_\rho^{\rho_c} \epsilon_{\text{II}}(\rho)\,d\rho\right] \tag{12-110}$$

The first term on the right is a decreasing function of ρ and is analogous to the exp $(-\epsilon\rho)$ of the finite-well problem, whereas the second term is an increasing function of ρ and compares with the exp $(\epsilon\rho)$ of the finite-well problem. By analogy with the finite-well problem we might expect B to be negligibly small. Ignoring B, we may evaluate A_{II} by equating first derivatives of G_{I} and G_{II} at $\rho = 1$. We find, using Eqs. (12-101) and (12-103), that

$$\frac{1}{(2\pi R)^{\frac{1}{2}}} \epsilon_{\text{I}} \cos \epsilon_{\text{I}} = -A_{\text{II}}\epsilon_{\text{II}}(1) \exp\left[\int_1^{\rho_c} \epsilon_{\text{II}}(\rho)\,d\rho\right] \tag{12-111}$$

In view of Eq. (12-102), $\cos \epsilon_{\text{I}} \approx -1$, and hence

$$A_{\text{II}} = \frac{1}{(2\pi R)^{\frac{1}{2}}} \frac{\epsilon_{\text{I}}}{\epsilon_{\text{II}}(1)} \exp\left[-\int_1^{\rho_c} \epsilon_{\text{II}}(\rho)\,d\rho\right] \tag{12-112}$$

We may also use the Wentzel-Kramers-Brillouin method for region III. Assuming an equation analogous to Eq. (12-104) and ignoring S''_{III}, we obtain

$$S'_{\text{III}} = \pm i\epsilon_{\text{III}}(\rho) \tag{12-113}$$

and hence

$$S_{\text{III}} = \pm i \int_{\rho_c}^{\rho} \epsilon_{\text{III}}(\rho)\,d\rho \tag{12-114}$$

where again we have effectively chosen a constant of integration such that $S(\rho)$ vanishes when $\epsilon_{\text{III}}(\rho)$ vanishes. The general 0th-order solution in region III is thus

$$G_{\text{III}} = A_{\text{III}} \exp\left[i \int_{\rho_c}^{\rho} \epsilon_{\text{III}}(\rho)\,d\rho\right] + B_{\text{III}} \exp\left[-i \int_{\rho_c}^{\rho} \epsilon_{\text{III}}(\rho)\,d\rho\right] \tag{12-115}$$

At long ranges the first term on the right approaches a form with the factor exp $(ik_W r)$ = exp $(i\epsilon_\infty \rho)$ and hence represents outgoing waves. The second term approaches a form with the factor exp $(-ik_W r)$ and hence represents ingoing waves. On the physical ground discussed previously we may set $B_{\text{III}} = 0$. An examination of G_{II} and G_{III} then shows that both functions and their first derivatives match at $\rho = \rho_c$ providing $A_{\text{II}} = A_{\text{III}}$. Using Eq. (12-112), we therefore have

$$G_{\text{III}}(\infty) = \frac{1}{(2\pi R)^{\frac{1}{2}}} \frac{\epsilon_{\text{I}}}{\epsilon_{\text{II}}(1)} \exp\left[-\int_1^{\rho_c} \epsilon_{\text{II}}(\rho)\, d\rho\right] \exp\left[i \int_{\rho_c}^{\infty} \epsilon_{\text{III}}(\rho)\, d\rho\right] \tag{12-116}$$

Inserting this into Eq. (12-94), we obtain finally for the decay constant

$$\lambda = \frac{2v}{R} \frac{\epsilon_{\text{I}}^2}{\epsilon_{\text{II}}^2(1)} \exp\left[-2 \int_1^{\rho_c} \epsilon_{\text{II}}(\rho)\, d\rho\right] \tag{12-117}$$

or

$$\lambda = C(v,R,Z) \exp - \mathcal{G} \tag{12-118}$$

where

$$\mathcal{G} = 2 \int_1^{\rho_c} \epsilon_{\text{II}}(\rho)\, d\rho = \frac{2\sqrt{2m_r}}{\hbar} \int_R^{R_c} \left(\frac{2Ze^2}{r} - T\right)^{\frac{1}{2}} dr \tag{12-119}$$

and $C(v,R,Z)$ is a slowly varying function which may be inferred from Eq. (12-117). Equation (12-119) can be integrated without difficulty if we introduce the variable and constant defined by

$$\cos u = \sqrt{\frac{r}{R_c}} \qquad \text{and} \qquad \cos u_0 = \sqrt{\frac{R}{R_c}} \tag{12-120}$$

We find by straightforward integration that

$$\mathcal{G} = \frac{4e^2 Z}{\hbar(2T/m_r)^{\frac{1}{2}}} (2u_0 - \sin 2u_0) \tag{12-121}$$

Since $\cos u_0$ is generally small for heavy nuclei, u_0 may be expanded about $\pi/2$. The first two terms of the series expression for $\mathcal{G}$ obtained in this way are

$$\mathcal{G} = \frac{4\pi e^2 Z}{\hbar(2T/m_r)^{\frac{1}{2}}} - \frac{8e(m_r Z R)^{\frac{1}{2}}}{\hbar} \tag{12-122}$$

The factor $\exp - \mathcal{G}$ arises in many quantum-mechanical problems which are concerned with the leakage or penetration of charged particles through potential barriers. This factor is present in its identical form even when a more refined treatment of the problem is given. We shall call this factor the probability of penetration, or the transparency of the coulomb barrier.

The coefficient represented in Eq. (12-118) is quite sensitive to the approximations and assumptions used in the derivation of Eq. (12-117), and we hold no brief for the result of the crude treatment used here. The factor $v/R \approx 10^{21}$ sec^{-1} suggests that we may interpret C to be proportional to the frequency with which the alpha particle strikes the barrier. We may now say that the probability of emission per unit time is proportional to the frequency of striking the barrier multiplied by the probability of penetration.

The fact that the alpha particle as such may not actually exist inside the parent has long been recognized as a serious weakness of the Gamow-Condon-Gurney theory. Bethe[21] has suggested a many-body theory in which the coefficient of the transparency factor is taken as the probability of formation of the alpha particle. Bethe estimates this factor to be about 10^{15} sec^{-1}. The current trend in interpretation is somewhat intermediate between the one-body model and the many-body model. The coefficient multiplying the transparency is now viewed as the product of a term representing the frequency of striking the barrier and a term which characterizes the probability of assembly of the two protons and two neutrons. Since the exact form of the coefficient is not well understood and since a variation of this coefficient has a very small effect as compared to the variation of $\mathcal{G}$, we may accept for the standard alpha-decay formula

$$\lambda = c \exp - \mathcal{G} \tag{12-123}$$

where c is a constant to be adjusted to experimental data. Accordingly we may write the decay-constant formula in the form

$$\log_{10} \lambda = \log_{10} c - \frac{4\pi e^2 Z}{\hbar 2.303} \left(\frac{m_r}{2T}\right)^{\frac{1}{2}} + \frac{8e}{\hbar} \frac{(m_r Z R)^{\frac{1}{2}}}{2.303} \tag{12-124}$$

To simplify the application of this equation to heavy nuclides, we shall let $m_r \approx m_\alpha/(1 + \frac{4}{220})$, $\mathbf{Z} = Z/100$, $\mathbf{A} = A/100$, and

$$R = \rho_b 1.50 A^{\frac{1}{3}} \times 10^{-13}$$

The factor ρ_b corrects the coefficient of the radius from the nominal value 1.50. Equation (12-124) becomes, when T is in Mev,

$$\log_{10} \lambda = \log_{10} c - 170.37 \frac{\mathbf{Z}}{T^{\frac{1}{2}}} + 33.730(\mathbf{Z}\rho_b \mathbf{A}^{\frac{1}{3}})^{\frac{1}{2}} \tag{12-125}$$

or

$$\log_{10} \lambda = C - 170.37\mathbf{Z}T^{-\frac{1}{2}} = C - 1.7037ZT^{-\frac{1}{2}} \tag{12-126}$$

where for most purposes

$$C = \log_{10} c + 33.730(\mathbf{Z}\rho_b \mathbf{A}^{\frac{1}{3}})^{\frac{1}{2}} \tag{12-127}$$

may be treated as a constant. In Chap. 6 we showed that this relationship conforms to the data for even-even alpha emitters if C is adjusted to experimental data.

12-9. Anomalies. While Eq. (12-126) gives the correct order of magnitude for decay constants, the experimental decay constants for many radioactive nuclides depart quite significantly from the theoretical values. Although these anomalies have been studied extensively and many attempts have been made to account for them, nevertheless the exact cause or causes of them are still not completely understood. These deviations have been attributed to three secondary effects: angular momentum, formation prohibition, and noncentral interactions. The effect of angular momentum may be investigated by giving consideration to the centrifugal-force term in Eq. (12-88) by usual perturbation methods. The corrections to $\mathcal{G}$ and to $\log_{10} \lambda$ due to the centrifugal barrier are[34]

$$\Delta \mathcal{G} = \frac{\hbar l(l+1)}{(m_r R Z e^2)^{\frac{1}{2}}} \tag{12-128}$$

$$\Delta \log_{10} \lambda = -\frac{\hbar l(l+1)}{(m_r R Z e^2)^{\frac{1}{2}} 2.303} = -\frac{0.0447 l(l+1)}{(\mathbf{Z} \rho \mathbf{A})^{\frac{1}{2}}} \tag{12-129}$$

It follows that for a given T the transparency is greatest when l is smallest. Angular-momentum effects are thought to become significant when the I values of the ground states of the parent and daughter differ. The alpha particle must then carry away the orbital angular momentum

$$\mathbf{l} = \mathbf{I}^* - \mathbf{I} \tag{12-130}$$

According to the usual relations the quantum numbers must satisfy

$$|I^* + I| \geq l \geq |I^* - I| \tag{12-131}$$

We may expect l to take on the least allowed value for the two states, since the centrifugal barrier is then lowest.

The concept of "formation" prohibition is discussed in a paper by Perlman, Ghiorso, and Seaborg.[22] They find it possible to attain quantitative agreement between the experimental data and the theory indicated above only for even-even nuclides. For these nuclides the radius $R = 1.48 A^{\frac{1}{3}} \times 10^{-13}$ cm leads to good agreement between the theory and experiment over a wide range of even Z and A values which are not too close to the doubly magic region around Pb^{208}. However, the experimental half-lives for odd-even, even-odd, and odd-odd nuclides invariably exceed those predicted by the Gamow formula. To explain these anomalies, the authors suggest that consideration should be given to the probability of formation of the alpha particle in the parent nucleus (see also Ref. 21). It is to be expected that the odd nucleon, which presumably is in the highest quantum state, is a component of the emitted alpha particle. Consequently this nucleon must pair with a low-lying nucleon of antiparallel spin, and perhaps, in addition, one or more of the remaining nucleons may have to change quantum state. Since these processes probably require appreciable time, we see the basis for forbidden decay in nuclei with odd nucleons. While the exact theory of this effect has not yet been worked out, the relationships of the decay-constant curves for even-even, odd-even, even-odd, and odd-odd clearly conform to this interpretation.

Preston,[23] following a suggestion originally due to Gamow, has investigated the effect of a noncentral electrostatic interaction between the alpha particle outside the nucleus and the unsymmetrically distributed protons in the product nucleus. This can also alter the decay constant from that given by the standard formula, since such a coupling provides a means for the alpha particle to exchange energy with the daughter nucleus and thereby modify the barrier transparency. Preston finds that this effect may be of considerable importance in connection with the formation-prohibited transitions.

The recent evidence in favor of the smaller coulomb radius constant ($b \approx 1.22 \times 10^{-13}$ cm) has a significant bearing upon alpha-decay theory. It appears that this change in itself would lead to a poorer fit of the theory to the experiment. However, recent evidence also suggests that nuclear boundaries are fuzzy rather than sharp as was generally assumed in alpha-decay theory. These two changes may compensate each other At this time the theory of alpha decay has not been refined to the extent that the differences between the observed and computed decay constants may be apportioned to the various small effects just described.

12-10. Alpha Fine Structure. The three above-mentioned secondary effects have also been invoked to explain the alpha fine structure associated with transitions to excited states of the daughters. The alpha-particle energies for a decay to an excited state of the daughter are given by $T = Q_\alpha - W$. In most cases which have been investigated the accompanying γ-ray energies are consistent with the level scheme inferred from the alpha-particle energies. A measurement of the half-life of the parent (or its total decay constant) and the relative intensities of the various alpha components enables one to assign partial decay constants for transitions to the various states of the daughter.

The great sensitivity of barrier transparency to T, according to the standard formula, suggests that the transition to the ground state will be the most probable. However, the experimental partial decay constants frequently show the largest transition probabilities to correspond to decay to an excited state of the daughter. In one attempt to explain the observed preference for excited states a large spin difference is assumed to exist between the parent and the ground state of the daughter. In consequence, the least angular momentum the alpha particle must carry away is that associated with $l = |I^* - I| = \Delta I$. If, however, a low-lying excited state of the daughter exists whose I value is significantly closer to I^*, the extra transparency due to the smaller centrifugal barrier may more than counteract the loss in transparency associated with the smaller value of T.

Perlman, Ghiorso, and Seaborg[22] note, however, that a spin change of about 5 units must be postulated to explain an alpha decay which is abnormally long by a factor of 10 [see Eq. (12-129)]. In the case of U^{235} a spin change of 10 units is needed to account for the decay constant, whereas a change of only 1 or 2 units is indicated by experiment. To account for the phenomena of alpha fine structure, they suggest, in attune with their ideas on formation prohibition, that the ejected alpha particle from nuclei with odd outer nucleons is formed from low-lying nucleons. These are more likely to be paired and consequently not so prohibited in their assembly into an alpha particle. The daughter nucleus in such a case will, of course, be in an excited state. Preston suggests that, should the direct transition to the ground state of the daughter nucleus be forbidden (formation prohibition), then noncentral interaction may have a large effect upon the partial decay constants. The quantitative resolution of all these questions has yet to be made.

12-11. Elementary Theory of Beta Decay. According to the Pauli neutrino hypothesis, which was put forth to explain the continuous nature of the β spectrum, the basic transformations in beta decay are

$$n \rightarrow p + \beta^- + \eta$$
$$p \rightarrow n + \beta^+ + \eta$$
$$p + e^- \rightarrow n + \eta$$

Fermi[24] has incorporated these transformations into a detailed theory in which a beta transition is analogous to a gamma transition with the electron-neutrino field acting in place of the electromagnetic field. Since no classical theory is available upon which to base an elementary treatment, we must develop beta-decay theory strictly with quantum-mechanical methods.

Using the basic result of time-dependent perturbation theory [Eq. (10-172)], we may compute the probability per unit time for the emission of a beta particle within the momentum range p to $p + dp$. Writing $I(p)\,dp$ in place of w, we have

$$I(p)\,dp = \frac{2\pi}{\hbar}\left|\int \Psi_i^* H_{op} \Psi_f \, d\tau\right|^2 \frac{d\mathfrak{N}}{dE_\beta} \tag{12-132}$$

where Ψ_i and Ψ_f characterize the initial and final states of the nuclear system. The elementary theory of beta decay is essentially based upon the choice of the perturbation energy

$$H = g\varphi_\beta \phi_\eta \tag{12-133}$$

where g is a constant analogous to electric charge and φ_β and ϕ_η are the time-independent wave functions which characterize the electron and the neutrino fields. This interaction is similar to the static interaction energy between a charged particle and an electrostatic field

$$V = e\phi \qquad (12\text{-}134)$$

where ϕ is the wave function which characterizes the electrostatic field (*i.e.*, the electrostatic potential). Since the neutrino interacts weakly with nucleons, it is reasonable to use for the neutrinos a time-independent wave function, normalized for one particle per unit volume, which characterizes a free particle with the propagation constant $q = p_\eta/\hbar$, namely,

$$\phi_\eta = \exp\,(i\,\mathbf{q}\cdot\mathbf{r}) \qquad (12\text{-}135)$$

For high-velocity electrons one may ignore the electrostatic effect of the nucleus upon the ejected electron and use the wave function ($k = p_\beta/\hbar$)

$$\varphi_\beta = \exp\,(i\,\mathbf{k}\cdot\mathbf{r}) \qquad (12\text{-}136)$$

From Eqs. (12-132) and (12-133) we find that the probability per unit time for the emission of a beta particle within the range p to $p + dp$ is

$$I(p)\,dp = \frac{2\pi}{\hbar}\,g^2\,\frac{d\mathfrak{N}}{dE_\beta}\left|\int \Psi_i^*\,\Psi_f \exp\,[i(\mathbf{k}+\mathbf{q})\cdot\mathbf{r}]\,d\tau\right|^2 \qquad (12\text{-}137)$$

The exponential term may be expanded into the power series

$$\exp\,[i(\mathbf{k}+\mathbf{q})\cdot\mathbf{r}] = 1 + i(\mathbf{k}+\mathbf{q})\cdot\mathbf{r} - \frac{[(\mathbf{k}+\mathbf{q})\cdot\mathbf{r}]^2}{2} + \cdots \qquad (12\text{-}138)$$

Since the nuclear wave functions have appreciable values only in regions of the order of nuclear dimensions, the significant values of r are no greater than the nuclear radius ($R = bA^{\frac{1}{3}}$). For most beta decays the electron kinetic energies are of the order of 1 Mev ($\gamma = [1 - (v^2/c^2)]^{-\frac{1}{2}}$ is of the order of 3), and hence electron momenta as well as the neutrino momenta are of the order of a few mc units, where m denotes the electron mass. Neutrino momenta are also usually a small number of mc units. Consequently

$$(\mathbf{k}+\mathbf{q})\cdot\mathbf{r} = \frac{(\mathbf{p}_\beta + \mathbf{p}_\eta)\cdot\mathbf{r}}{\hbar} \approx 3\,\frac{mc}{\hbar}\,bA^{\frac{1}{3}} \approx \frac{1}{10} \qquad (12\text{-}139)$$

This small value suggests that we need retain only the highest term (the constant unity) in the power series given by Eq. (12-138). Let us proceed tentatively on the basis that, when this term is inserted into Eq. (12-137), the matrix element is nonvanishing. We obtain

$$I(p)\,dp = \frac{2\pi}{\hbar}\,g^2\,\frac{d\mathfrak{N}}{dE_\beta}\,|M|^2 \qquad (12\text{-}140)$$

where

$$M = \int \Psi_i^* \Psi_f \, d\tau \tag{12-141}$$

is no longer dependent upon the energies or momenta of the light particles. The evaluation of the matrix element is a problem which cannot be carried out completely because nuclear wave functions are not known. The greatest interest, therefore, centers upon the conditions which might cause M to vanish. Before studying these conditions, let us consider the statistical factor $d\mathfrak{N}/dE_\beta$.

The number of neutrino waves per unit volume in the propagation-constant interval q to $q + dq$ and the number of electron waves per unit volume in the interval k to $k + dk$ are [see Eq. (11-13)]

$$dn_\eta = \frac{q^2 \, dq}{2\pi^2} \tag{12-142}$$

and

$$dn_\beta = \frac{k^2 \, dk}{2\pi^2} \tag{12-143}$$

Therefore the total number of waves per unit volume in the composite interval q to $q + dq$ and k to $k + dk$ if the two propagation constants were independent is

$$d\mathfrak{N} = \frac{k^2 \, dk \, q^2 \, dq}{4\pi^4} \tag{12-144}$$

However, because of conservation of energy the propagation constants k and q are not independent but instead must satisfy (assuming that the neutrino has zero rest mass and hence that $E_\eta = cp_\eta$)

$$E_\beta + E_\eta = E_{\text{max}} \tag{12-145}$$

or

$$(m^2c^4 + \hbar^2k^2c^2)^{\frac{1}{2}} + c\hbar q = (m^2c^4 + \hbar^2 k_{\text{max}}{}^2 c^2)^{\frac{1}{2}} \tag{12-146}$$

Consequently,

$$dE\eta = c\hbar \, dq = -dE_\beta \tag{12-147}$$

Using this and Eq. (12-145) to eliminate dq and q in Eq. (12-144), we obtain (ignoring the negative sign)

$$\frac{d\mathfrak{N}}{dE_\beta} = \frac{k^2 \, dk \, q^2}{4\pi^4 c\hbar} = \frac{p^2 \, dp \, E_\eta{}^2}{4\pi^4 c^3 \hbar^6} = \frac{p^2(E_{\text{max}} - E_\beta)^2 \, dp}{4\pi^4 c^3 \hbar^6} \tag{12-148}$$

Inserting this statistical factor into Eq. (12-140), we get as the result of the theory

$$I(p) \, dp = \frac{g^2 |M|^2}{2\pi^3 c^3 \hbar^7} (E_{\text{max}} - E_\beta)^2 p^2 \, dp \tag{12-149}$$

A partial test of the theory now may be made to see whether the experimental relationships between intensity and momentum conform to this equation. A convenient method for testing the agreement or disagreement is based upon the observation that the function $(I/p^2)^{\frac{1}{2}}$ is linear in the kinetic energy, *i.e.*, that

$$\left[\frac{I(p)}{p^2}\right]^{\frac{1}{2}} = C(E_{\max} - E_\beta) = C(T_{\max} - T_\beta) \qquad (12\text{-}150)$$

where $T_{\max}$ refers to the maximum beta kinetic energy and

$$C = \frac{g|M|}{(2\pi^3 c^3 \hbar^7)^{\frac{1}{2}}} \qquad (12\text{-}151)$$

A plot of $(I/p^2)^{\frac{1}{2}}$ vs. T prepared from the experimental momentum distribution is known as a Kurie plot. Assuming the neutrino rest energy to be negligible, the theory predicts that this function is a straight line which intersects the T axis at $T_{\max}$.

In early efforts to test the theory by means of Kurie plots of the energy spectrum, serious deviations from a straight line were noted, particularly in the neighborhood of low energies. Some of these deviations are now accounted for by giving consideration to the distortion of the β-particle wave function [Eq. (12-136)] at low energies due to the coulomb charge of the nucleus. An appropriate correction for this effect for small Z may be made by multiplying the right side of Eq. (12-149) by the factor

$$F(Z,p) = \frac{2\pi\delta}{1 - e^{-2\pi\delta}} \qquad (12\text{-}152)$$

where

$$\delta = \pm \frac{Ze^2 E_{\max}}{\hbar c^2 p} \qquad (12\text{-}153)$$

and Z is the charge of the daughter nucleus. The upper sign is for electron emission and the lower sign for positron emission. For heavy nuclei the coulomb field of the nucleus causes a still stronger distortion of the electron wave function, and more complicated $F(Z,p)$ functions must be used. These functions have been calculated and are available in graphical and tabular form.[36] When consideration is given to this effect, Eq. (12-149) becomes

$$I(p)\,dp = \frac{g^2|M|^2}{2\pi^3 c^3 \hbar^7} F(Z,p)(T_{\max} - T)^2 p^2\,dp \qquad (12\text{-}154)$$

and hence

$$\left[\frac{I(p)}{F(Z,p)p^2}\right]^{\frac{1}{2}} = C(T_{\max} - T) \qquad (12\text{-}155)$$

Even after this correction was made to the early data, significant deviations of the experimental Kurie plots from straight lines were noted, particularly at low energies. However, with the development of thin backing material for supporting radioactive materials in beta-ray spectroscopes, the deviations were found in most cases to be due to experimental difficulties rather than to errors in the theory. The most recent experiments indicate many instances of beta spectra which conform to the Kurie plots from the highest electron energies down to energies in the neighborhood of 10 kev. In Figs. 12-5 and 12-6 we show Kurie plots for the decay of tritium. In Fig. 12-7 we show a Kurie plot for the decay of F^{20}. Despite the extreme differences in energies and lifetimes these two spectra have similar Kurie plots. The deviations at the low-energy side are probably instrumental in origin.

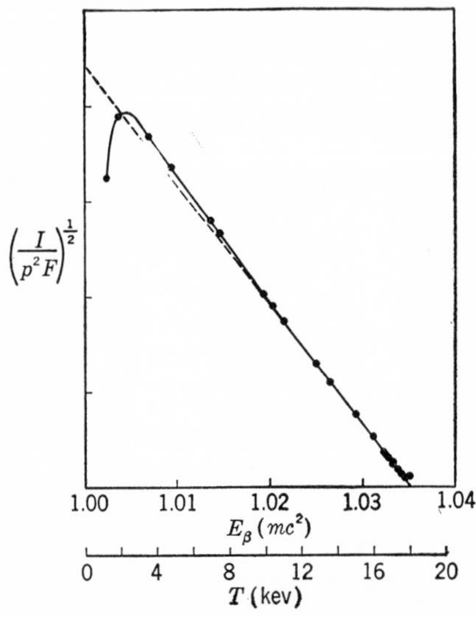

FIG. 12-5. Kurie plot of tritium spectrum data obtained with a source which was grounded by a 2 $\mu g/cm^2$ Cu deposit on the backing. The upper scale represents total electron energies in units of the electron rest energy. The lower scale represents electron kinetic energies. (*From Langer and Moffat, Ref.* 25.)

12-12. Lifetime of Beta Decay. Equation (12-154) gives the probability per second for the emission of an electron with the momentum p to $p + dp$. Consequently, the probability per second for an electron to be ejected with any momentum between 0 and $p_{\max}$ is

$$\lambda = \frac{1}{\tau} = \frac{g^2|M|^2m^5c^4}{2\pi^3\hbar^7} f(Z,T_{\max}) \tag{12-156}$$

where

$$f(Z,T_{\max}) = \int_0^{p_{\max}/mc} F(Z,p)\left(\frac{T_{\max} - T}{mc^2}\right)^2\left(\frac{p}{mc}\right)^2\frac{dp}{mc} \tag{12-157}$$

When $p_{\max}/mc \gg 1$ or $T_{\max}/mc^2 \gg 1$ and when $F(Z,p) \approx 1$, we can show

$$f(Z,T_{\max}) \approx \text{constant} \times T_{\max}{}^5 \tag{12-158}$$

Accordingly for high energies

$$\lambda = \frac{1}{\tau} \approx T_{\max}{}^5 \tag{12-159}$$

This relationship is known as the fifth-power law and is obeyed in some cases, particularly by the positron spectra of light nuclei. To the extent that Eq. (12-159) is satisfied, a plot of $\log_{10} \lambda$ vs. $\log_{10} T_{max}$ for various beta-active substances is expected to yield a straight line with the slope 5.

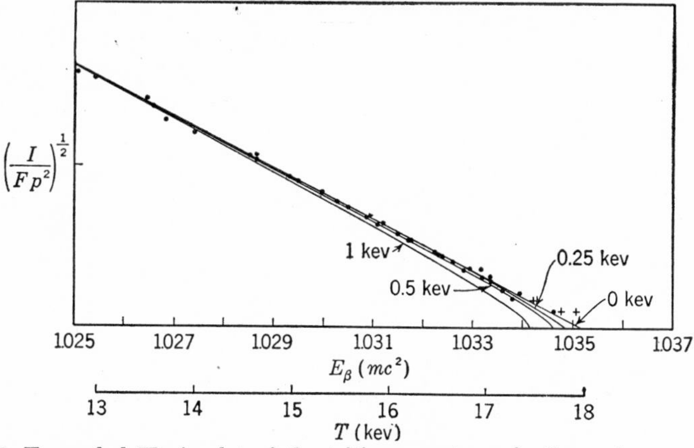

FIG. 12-6. Expanded Kurie plot of the tritium spectrum in the region near the end point. The curves are the theoretical plots expected for the indicated rest mass (in kev) of the neutrino. (*From Langer and Moffat, Ref.* 25.)

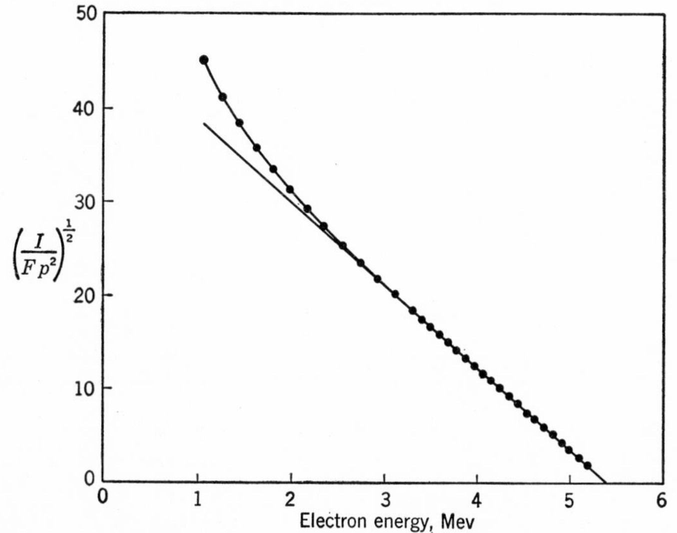

FIG. 12-7. Kurie plot for the decay of F^{20}. (*From Alburger, Ref.* 26.)

This theoretical behavior is roughly confirmed by the Sargent plots referred to in Sec. 6-4.

For heavy nuclei the distortion due to the coulomb field is more effective, and there is no simple analytical expression for $f(Z,T_{max})$. However, tables and graphs of $f(Z,T_{max})$ are available.[36]

In the study of lifetimes in β decay the so-called ft product, or comparative half-life, provides a useful criterion for inferring facts about nuclear matrix elements. The f factor in Eq. (12-156) essentially corrects for the energy of the transition and the nuclear charge. The product of this theoretical f factor and the experimental half-life ($t = \tau \ln 2$) should depend solely upon the nuclear matrix element, *i.e.*, upon

$$ft = \frac{2\pi^3\hbar^7 \ln 2}{g^2 m^5 c^4 |M|^2} = \frac{\text{constant}}{|M|^2} \tag{12-160}$$

Compilations of $\log_{10} ft$ values for β decay have been made in an effort to study the factors which affect these matrix elements. These $\log_{10} ft$ values usually range from about 3.5 to 10, although a few exceptional cases lie outside this range. Since the smaller the matrix element, the larger the log ft value, one may view this parameter associated with a decay as a measure of the degree of forbiddenness of a β transition. In view of the simple nature of the matrix M which is obtained when only the constant term in the expansion of $\exp [i(\mathbf{k} + \mathbf{q}) \cdot \mathbf{r}]$ is used, we can readily conclude by an extension of the arguments for electric gamma transitions that nonzero values result only when the I values characterizing the two states are identical and the parities of the two states are identical. Expressed symbolically, the selection rules for these "allowed" transitions are

$$\Delta I = 0 \qquad \text{"no"} \tag{12-161}$$

For transitions which satisfy these selection rules the nonzero values of M may vary over rather wide limits, depending upon the degree of overlap or similarity of the initial and final wave functions. In the transformations between mirror nuclei such as H^3 and He^3 in

$${}_1^2H^3 \rightarrow \beta^- + {}_2^1He^3 \tag{12-162}$$

the wave functions characterizing the states are expected to be almost identical, since in this type of transformation the nucleon in the last proton orbital goes over into the identical neutron orbital. The integral is expected to be close to unity in these cases. Experiment confirms this conclusion, since most of the $\log_{10} ft$ values between 3 and 4 correspond to these so-called allowed "favored" transitions. Thus, despite the great range in lifetimes, experiments indicate that the $\log_{10} ft$ values for image transitions cluster quite close together around 3.55. This fact tends to support the underlying theory if we accept the constant $g \approx 3.5 \times 10^{-49}$ erg-cm^3 (Ref. 25). For allowed transitions corresponding to two nuclei which are not mirror nuclei, the matrix elements are expected to be smaller than 1 and to tend to grow smaller as A increases, since the neutron and proton wave functions become more dissimilar. Values of $\log_{10} ft$ of 4 to 6 appear to correspond to these transitions.

Many cases of beta decay have been studied which give rise to the allowed spectrum [Eq. (12-154)] and an allowed $\log_{10} ft$ value but nevertheless violate the allowed selection rule [Eq. (12-161)]. A historic example is

$$ {}_2^4\mathrm{He}^6\ (I = 0) \rightarrow \beta^- + {}_3^3\mathrm{Li}^6\ (I = 1) \qquad \log ft = 2.74 \qquad (12\text{-}163) $$

This case and many other instances of selection-rule violations are regarded as results of a nuclear interaction which differs from that [Eq. (12-133)] proposed by Fermi. To account for these transitions, Gamow and Teller[27] have proposed an interaction Hamiltonian which includes an operator depending upon the spins of the nucleons involved in the transition. Even if the electron and neutrino carry away no orbital angular momentum, as is the case for the field which corresponds to the first term in the power-series expansion, they may still cause a change in the net I value. For example, the electron and neutron, which are both spin $\frac{1}{2}$ particles, may carry away the net spin angular momentum 0 or 1. In the latter case the change in I value from the parent to the daughter may be ± 1 or 0. In the former case it can be only zero. Since the dependence upon spin angular momentum does not alter the dependence upon linear and orbital angular momentum, we can readily account for the cases of allowed spectra which violate the angular-momentum selection rule for the Fermi interaction. The condition for nonvanishing matrix elements according to the Gamow-Teller theory is

$$ \Delta I = 0, \pm 1 \text{ (not } 0 \rightarrow 0) \qquad \text{“no”} \qquad (12\text{-}164) $$

12-13. Forbidden Beta Decay.[28] Numerous instances of beta decay have been observed which violate both the Fermi and the Gamow-Teller selection rules for allowed transitions and which correspond to $\log_{10} ft$ values greater than 6. As in the interpretation of forbidden gamma radiation, these cases of beta decay are thought to correspond to instances in which the lowest-order matrix element vanishes identically. Since the magnitude of the second term in Eq. (12-138), $(\mathbf{k} + \mathbf{q}) \cdot \mathbf{r}$, is of the order of one-tenth the first term, the squared matrix element of a first-forbidden transition should be about one-hundredth of the usual allowed transitions. Accordingly the $\log_{10} ft$ values should range from about 6 to 8. The matrix element now depends upon the electron momenta, so we may expect the beta energy spectrum to be altered from the allowed spectrum [Eq. (12-154)]. Unfortunately, one cannot go to this approximation without considering relativistic interactions, which are expected to give rise to squared matrix elements of the order of v^2/c^2, where v is the velocity of the nucleons. Since $v/c \approx \frac{1}{10}$, transitions associated with these relativistic effects also may be regarded as first-forbidden spectra.

The theoretical shape of the first-forbidden spectra depends upon whether the transition is identified with the term $(\mathbf{k} + \mathbf{q}) \cdot \mathbf{r}$ in the elementary theory or with a relativistic interaction. It turns out that some relativistic matrix elements are independent of the electron momenta, so that an allowed spectrum may nevertheless go with a first-forbidden decay. Certain forbidden spectra are thought to correspond to mixtures of various types of relativistic interactions in addition to the first-forbidden beta radiation associated with the elementary Fermi or Gamow-Teller interaction. Because of the variety of complex interaction combinations which may account for forbidden beta spectra, the theory is so complicated as to preclude an elementary discussion. However, according to the theory of forbidden spectra, transitions which satisfy $\Delta I = 2$, "yes," have the special property that a unique energy dependence is predicted which differs from the allowed spectrum. Shull and Feenberg(29) have shown that for this group the values of $\log_{10} [(E_{max}/mc^2)^2 - 1] ft$ are expected to be homogeneous rather than the $\log_{10} ft$ values. Since 1949 about 25 cases of this type of first-forbidden spectrum have been reported.

Several observations have been made of beta spectra which are known to be second or higher forbidden. Neither the Fermi interaction nor the Gamow-Teller interaction, even when a strictly relativistic treatment is employed, seems capable of explaining the observations. The exact disposition of these cases is still uncertain.

Because the $\log_{10} ft$ values associated with different degrees of forbiddenness are expected to be sufficiently distinct (*i.e.*, to differ by about 2 units), we would expect experimental $\log_{10} ft$ values to fall into distinct groups. However, a distribution function prepared from all known decays in which the number of decays is plotted against the $\log_{10} ft$ values does not show any clear grouping of decays. Hence from this viewpoint the entire theory of forbidden beta decay looks rather unconvincing. However, a study of all known beta transitions by Mayer, Moszkowski, and Nordheim(30) from an entirely different viewpoint appears to confirm the fundamental notions underlying beta-decay theory. These authors essentially use the theory of nuclear shell structure in conjunction with measured spins and magnetic moments to assign I values and l values to the ground states of all odd-A nuclei. The parity of a state is assigned on the same basis as for a single particle in the orbital (+ for l even, − for l odd). Using these spin and parity assignments, they group together the decays which correspond to the same degree of forbiddenness. Strikingly enough, they find that the $\log_{10} ft$ values within these groups are rather homogeneous and have mean values which conform with expectations on the basis of beta-decay theory. Specifically, in considering transitions which, on the basis of the spin and parity assignments of the shell model, correspond to the allowed group $\Delta l = 0$, $\Delta I = 0,1$, "no," Mayer, Moszkowski, and Nordheim observe that the majority of such transitions are contained in a $\log_{10} ft$ band 5.0 ± 0.3. No general fine trends in ft values within the group are apparent. The absence of a recognizable distinction between $\Delta I = 0$ and $\Delta I = 1$ transitions indicates that the Gamow-Teller selection rules prevail. A small group with assignments $\Delta l = 2$, "no," and $\Delta I = 1$ lead to $\log_{10} ft$ values which are somewhat larger ($\sim$6.0) than expected for allowed transitions. This suggests the workings of a weak selection rule which pertains to orbital angular momentum apart from that included in the parity rule.

All members of the first-forbidden group $\Delta l = 1$, "yes," $\Delta I = 0,1$ give $\log_{10} ft$ values between 6 and 8 with clusterings around 6.2 and 7.2. The $\Delta l = 1$, $\Delta I = 2$ first-forbidden group, which has a uniquely defined shape, gives a somewhat homogeneous set of comparative half-lives averaging about 8.8.

A final group consisting of second- and higher-forbidden transitions contains $\log_{10} ft$ values from 12 to 17.7. The more advanced theory of beta decay suggests that the $\log_{10} ft$ values of the last two groups should depend somewhat upon the beta energy, and the data (particularly for the $\Delta l = 1$, $\Delta I = 2$ group) do reveal this dependence.

Nordheim[31] has extended these interpretations of beta decay according to shell structure to the even nuclei. He assumes that the even-even nuclide involved in the decay always has zero spin and even parity. The parity and I value of the odd-odd nuclide are assigned on the basis of the orbitals given by the shell model and certain simple assumptions regarding the coupling between the last neutron and proton. On the basis of these assumptions he arranges the known $\log_{10} ft$ values of even-A nuclides into the same groups used to analyze the odd-A nuclides. Apart from a few exceptions the $\log_{10} ft$ values within these groups are quite homogeneous and in accord with the expectations of the theory of beta decay and the theory of shell structure.

12-14. Electron Capture. The interpretation currently given to orbital-electron capture is that the electron density in the neighborhood of the nucleus perturbs the parent and induces it to undergo a transition to the daughter state by capturing a K- or L-shell electron. An unobservable neutrino is ejected with the definite energy

$$E_\eta = {}_ZM - {}_{Z-1}M - W_c \qquad (12\text{-}165)$$

where ${}_ZM$ and ${}_{Z-1}M$ are the neutral atomic masses of the parent and daughter and W_c is the critical K or L energy of the daughter. Since we do not have to deal with a continuous spectrum, the transition probability per unit time here corresponds directly to the decay constant for orbital-electron capture. Consequently we may set

$$w = \lambda = \tau^{-1} = \frac{2\pi}{\hbar}\left|\int \Psi_i^* H_{op}\Psi_f \, d\tau\right|^2 \frac{d\mathfrak{N}}{dE_\eta} \tag{12-166}$$

According to the Fermi theory the interaction energy which induces the transition is given by Eq. (12-133). The neutrino wave function given by Eq. (12-135) for the positive energy state

$$E_\eta = c\hbar q \tag{12-167}$$

may again be used. However, the electron wave function must now characterize the bound state of the initial system. To a good approximation we may use for the K electron the 1s wave function of a hydrogenic system with the charge number of the parent nuclide. This wave function is

$$\varphi_{1s} = \frac{1}{\pi^{\frac{1}{2}}}\left(\frac{Z}{a_B}\right)^{\frac{3}{2}} e^{-Zr/a_B} \tag{12-168}$$

Again we may take advantage of the fact that the nuclear wave functions are appreciable over only a small distance, *i.e.*, small compared to $|q|^{-1}$ or a_B/Z. Hence we may expand the neutrino and electron wave functions about $r = 0$ and retain only the constant terms. With these approximations Eq. (12-166) becomes

$$\lambda_K = \tau_K^{-1} = \frac{2}{\hbar} g^2|M|^2\left(\frac{Z}{a_B}\right)^3 \frac{d\mathfrak{N}}{dE_\eta} \tag{12-169}$$

where M is given by Eq. (12-141). Since the electron state is a discrete state, it makes no contribution to the statistical factor $d\mathfrak{N}/dE_\eta$. Consequently this factor refers simply to the energy density of neutrino waves in the neighborhood of the positive energy state E_η. This is given by [see Eqs. (12-167) and (12-142)]

$$\frac{d\mathfrak{N}}{dE_\eta} = \frac{d\mathfrak{N}}{dq}\frac{dq}{dE_\eta} = \frac{q^2}{2\pi^2\hbar c} = \frac{E_\eta^{\ 2}}{2\pi^2\hbar^3c^3} \tag{12-170}$$

Inserting this into Eq. (12-169), we obtain finally

$$\lambda_K = \frac{g^2m^3}{\pi^2\hbar^7}\left(\frac{e^2}{\hbar c}\right)^3 |M|^2Z^3E_\eta^{\ 2} \tag{12-171}$$

where we have used Eq. (1-42) for the Bohr radius.

The interesting aspect of this equation is its dependence upon Z, which indicates that decay constants should become large (τ_K small) for the heavy elements. The opposite trend occurs for positron-decay constants by virtue of the fact that a large Z tends to push out the positron wave function from the nucleus. Since the mass difference between isobars tends to become smaller and smaller as A increases, the positron threshold $2mc^2$ is fulfilled only by nuclides rather far on the neutron-deficient side of the line of beta stability. These three effects provide a simple explanation for the fact that K capture is the more important adjustment process for neutron-deficient heavy nuclei.

The study of radioactive nuclides which are K-capture- and β^+-active provides a check on some aspects of the theory of beta decay. From Eqs. (12-171) and (12-156) we see that the ratio of the number of K-capture events to positron emissions is

$$\frac{N_K}{N_{\beta^+}} = \frac{\lambda_K}{\lambda_{\beta^+}} = \frac{1}{2\pi}\left(\frac{e^2}{\hbar c}\right)^3 \frac{E_\eta{}^2}{m^2c^4}\frac{Z^3}{f(Z,T_{\max})} \tag{12-172}$$

The experimental ratios of K capture to positron emission tend to support this type of expression.

The capture of an L-orbital electron is also a possible adjustment process for a neutron-deficient nucleus, although in general the probability is considerably smaller because the L-electron wave functions have a smaller concentration in the neighborhood of the nucleus. Of the L-shell electrons the $2s$ electron has the highest density in the neighborhood of the nucleus. The wave function for this state is approximately

$$\begin{aligned} \varphi_{2s} &= \frac{1}{2(2\pi)^{\frac{1}{2}}}\left(\frac{Z'}{a_B}\right)^{\frac{3}{2}}\left(1 - \frac{Z'r}{2a_B}\right)e^{-Z'r/a_B} \\ &\approx \frac{1}{2(2\pi)^{\frac{1}{2}}}\left(\frac{Z'}{a_B}\right)^{\frac{3}{2}}\left(1 - \frac{3}{2}\frac{Z'r}{a_B} + \cdots\right) \end{aligned} \tag{12-173}$$

where Z' here denotes the effective charge experienced by a $2s$ electron in the parent. This charge differs from Z because of the screening effect of the inner electrons. Carrying through the analysis with this wave function, we find that

$$\frac{N_L}{N_K} = \frac{\lambda_L}{\lambda_K} = \frac{1}{8}\left(\frac{Z'}{Z}\right)^3\left(\frac{E_{\eta L}}{E_{\eta K}}\right)^2 \tag{12-174}$$

Assuming the mass difference is relatively large compared to the critical X-ray energies so that $E_{\eta L} \approx E_{\eta K}$, we would expect L-capture events to occur of the order of 10 per cent of the time. On the other hand, if the mass difference is very small, the relative number of L captures to K captures would be expected to be much larger, and should the mass difference lie below the K-capture threshold, then L capture would be expected to occur exclusively.

Unfortunately it is rather difficult to detect K and L capture because, apart from the energetic but nonobservable neutrinos, the radiations emitted have very low energies. These radiations are the X-ray quanta which follow after the readjustment of the daughter nucleus to its ground state. The K_α line of the daughter nucleus with energy $W_K - W_L$ is thus one of the principal signals for the observation of K capture, and the L_α line with the energy $W_L - W_M$ serves for the observation of L capture. The emission of Auger electrons with energy approximately $W_K - 2W_L$ provides another mechanism for detecting K capture. Improvements of particle-detection and absolute-counting techniques in this low range of energies would greatly enhance the value of research dealing with orbital capture.

The acceleration of the electron toward the nucleus in the K-capture process may also result in the emission of gamma rays. The theory of this so-called "inner Bremsstrahlung" has been worked out for K capture by Morrison and Schiff.(32) The theory predicts a continuous distribution of gamma rays ranging in energy from zero to the maximum $E_{\gamma,\max}$ available for the decay [which equals the E_η given by Eq. (12-165)]. The expression for the probability per unit time for the emission of a gamma ray whose momentum lies within the range p_γ to $p_\gamma + dp_\gamma$ is analogous to Eq. (12-132):

$$I(p_\gamma)\, dp_\gamma = \frac{2\pi}{\hbar} H_{if} \frac{d\mathfrak{N}}{dE_\gamma} \tag{12-175}$$

where H_{if} is a matrix element which involves not only the coupling between the nuclear particles and the electron-neutrino field [Eq. (12-133)] but also the coupling between the electron and the electromagnetic field. Because of the division of the energy between the gamma ray and the neutrino the statistical factor in this case has the form of Eq. (12-148) with β replaced by γ. The treatment of the matrix element H_{if} is quite involved. However, it has been shown that except at low energies the ratio $I(p_\gamma)\, dp_\gamma/\lambda_K$, where λ_K is given by Eq. (12-171), has the simple form

$$\frac{I(p_\gamma)\, dp_\gamma}{\lambda_K} = \frac{1}{\pi} \frac{e^2}{\hbar c} \left(1 - \frac{E_\gamma}{E_{\gamma,\max}}\right)^2 \frac{E_\gamma}{(mc^2)^2}\, dE_\gamma \tag{12-176}$$

For a given emitter, λ_K is fixed; hence if we plot $[I(p_\gamma)/E_\gamma]^{\frac{1}{2}}$ against E_γ, we would expect a straight line intersecting the axis at $E_{\gamma,\max}$. In practice one simply looks for the zero intercept of a plot of $[N_\gamma(E_\gamma)/E_\gamma]^{\frac{1}{2}}$ against E_γ, where $N_\gamma(E_\gamma)$ is the observed number of gamma counts per unit energy interval.

A number of recent investigations have been made with scintillation spectrometers applying this linear plot analysis. These studies indicate fair agreement with the theory, particularly in the neighborhood of the maximum energy. Indeed, several precise determinations of the mass differences involved in the K capture have been made recently in this way (see Refs. 24 to 26, Chap. 6).

The total radioactive emission probability per K capture, obtained by integrating Eq. (12-176) from 0 to $E_{\gamma,\max}$, is simply

$$\frac{\lambda_\gamma}{\lambda_K} = \frac{N_\gamma}{N_K} = \frac{1}{12\pi}\frac{e^2}{\hbar c}\left(\frac{E_{\gamma,\max}}{mc^2}\right)^2 \tag{12-177}$$

where N_γ here is the total gamma activity.

PROBLEMS

12-1. What are the expected types of gamma-ray transitions between the following states of odd-A nuclei: $g_{\frac{9}{2}} \rightarrow p_{\frac{1}{2}}$, $f_{\frac{5}{2}} \rightarrow p_{\frac{3}{2}}$, $h_{\frac{11}{2}} \rightarrow d_{\frac{5}{2}}$, $h_{\frac{11}{2}} \rightarrow d_{\frac{3}{2}}$?

12-2. What are the expected types of gamma-ray transitions between the following states of even-A nuclei: $4^+ \rightarrow 2^+$, $5^- \rightarrow 2^+$, $5^- \rightarrow 1^+$, $2^+ \rightarrow 2^-$, $2^+ \rightarrow 2^+$?

12-3. The ground state and the 0.134-Mev and 0.299-Mev excited states of $_{80}\mathrm{Hg}^{197}$ have been classified as $p_{\frac{1}{2}}$, $f_{\frac{5}{2}}$, and $i_{\frac{13}{2}}$ states, respectively. What types of transitions are expected between these states and what are the theoretical gamma decay constants?

†**12-4.** Use Eq. (12-126) with $C = 55.5$, together with alpha-decay data for even-odd, odd-even, and odd-odd nuclides, to find the departures between experimental and theoretical values of $\log_{10} \lambda$ (when no branching occurs).

12-5. A typical run on an H^3 β^- spectrum with a 40-cm magnetic spectrometer yields the data tabulated below in the columns entitled BR (in gauss-centimeters) and n (in counts per minute). The corresponding theoretical values of $F(Z,p)$ are also listed. The momentum interval for each field setting is proportional to BR; hence n/BR is expected to be proportional to the function $I(p)$. Prepare a Kurie plot of the tritium spectrum. (Data kindly provided by Prof. L. M. Langer.)

BR	n	$F(Z,p)$	BR	n	$F(Z,p)$
134.8	498	1.680	410.7	563	1.212
177.7	1008	1.495	409.8	459	1.207
209.0	1321	1.420	417.1	353	1.204
234.5	1558	1.376	422.4	277	1.202
292.8	1771	1.300	427.2	225	1.201
295.2	1728	1.298	432.5	136	1.200
319.3	1669	1.275	436.3	107	1.198
364.1	1180	1.241	440.2	63	1.197
373.7	1041	1.230	444.0	54	1.195
386.7	819	1.223	446.9	16	1.194

12-6. Derive the correct statistical factor $d\mathfrak{N}/dE_\beta$ which would be appropriate in place of Eq. (12-148) if the neutrino had a small but finite ($\leq 0.01\ m_e$) rest mass.

12-7. According to tables, $f(Z,T_{\max}) = 2.58 \times 10^{-6}$ for $T_{\max} = 18.0$ kev and $Z = 1$. The half-life of tritium is 12.5 years. What are the values of ft (in seconds) and $\log_{10} ft$?

12-8. Which of the β transitions in Probs. 11-7 and 11-8 are allowed?

†**12-9.** Prepare a Sargent diagram for light positron emitters for which parent and daughter are mirror nuclides, that is, have $(N,Z) = (Z - 1, Z)$ and

$$(N',Z') = (Z, Z - 1)$$

REFERENCES

1. Stratton, J. A.: "Electromagnetic Theory," p. 428, McGraw-Hill Book Company, Inc., New York, 1941.
2. Condon, E. U., and G. H. Shortley: "The Theory of Atomic Spectra," Cambridge University Press, New York, 1935.
3. F. K. Richtmyer and E. H. Kennard: "Introduction to Modern Physics," 4th ed., McGraw-Hill Book Company, Inc., New York, 1947.
4. Einstein, A.: *Physik. Z.*, **18,** 121 (1917).
5. Bohr, N.: quoted in Ref. 2.
6. Heisenberg, W.: *Z. Physik*, **33,** 879 (1925).
7. Fierz, M.: *Helv. Phys. Acta*, **22,** 489 (1949).
8. Weisskopf, V.: *Phys. Rev.*, **83,** 1073 (1951).
9. Hill, R. D.: *Phys. Rev.*, **81,** 470 (1951).
10. Fierz, M.: *Helv. Phys. Acta*, **16,** 365 (1943).
11. Weiszäcker, C. F. von: *Naturwiss.*, **24,** 813 (1936).
12. Heitler, W.: *Proc. Cambridge Phil. Soc.*, **32,** 112 (1936).
13. Dancoff, S. M., and P. Morrison: *Phys. Rev.*, **55,** 122 (1939).
14. Rose, M. E., G. H. Goetzel, B. I. Spinrad, J. Harr, and P. Strong: *Phys. Rev.*, **83,** 79 (1951).
15. Axel, P., and S. M. Dancoff: *Phys. Rev.*, **76,** 892 (1949).
16. Goldhaber, M., and A. W. Sunyar: *Phys. Rev.*, **83,** 906 (1951).
17. Goldhaber, M., and R. D. Hill: *Revs. Mod. Phys.*, **24,** 179 (1952).
18. Moszkowski, S. A.: *Phys. Rev.*, **89,** 48 (1953).
19. Gamow, G.: *Z. Physik*, **51,** 204 (1928).
20. Condon, E. U., and R. W. Gurney: *Nature*, **122,** 439 (1928).
21. Bethe, H. A.: *Revs. Mod. Phys.*, **9,** 161 (1937).
22. Perlman, I., A. Ghiorso, and G. T. Seaborg: *Phys. Rev.*, **77,** 45 (1950).
23. Preston, M. A.: *Phys. Rev.*, **82,** 551 (1951).
24. Fermi, E.: *Z. Physik*, **88,** 161 (1934).
25. Langer, L. M., and R. J. D. Moffat: *Phys. Rev.*, **88,** 693 (1952).
26. Alburger, D. E.: *Phys. Rev.*, **88,** 1260 (1952).
27. Gamow, G., and E. Teller: *Phys. Rev.*, **49,** 895 (1936).
28. Konopinski, E. J., and L. M. Langer: *Ann. Rev. Nuclear Sci.*, **2,** 261 (1953).
29. Shull, F. B., and E. Feenberg: *Phys. Rev.*, **75,** 1768 (1949).
30. Mayer, M. G., S. A. Moszkowski, and L. W. Nordheim: *Revs. Mod. Phys.*, **23,** 315 (1951).
31. Nordheim, L. W.: *Revs. Mod. Phys.*, **23,** 322 (1951).
32. Morrison, P., and L. I. Schiff: *Phys. Rev.*, **58,** 24 (1940).
33. Jauch, J. M., *U.S. Atomic Energy Comm. Rept. ORNL* 1102, 1951.
34. Gamow, G., and C. L. Critchfield: "Atomic Nucleus and Nuclear Energy Sources," Oxford University Press, New York, 1949.
35. Segrè, E., and A. C. Helmholz, *Revs. Mod. Phys.*, **21,** 271 (1949).
36. "Tables for the Analysis of Beta Spectra," *National Bureau of Standards Applied Mathematics Series*, No. 13, 1952.

CHAPTER 13

THEORY OF NUCLEAR REACTIONS

In this chapter we shall discuss the important theoretical interpretations of the cross sections associated with various types of bombardment reactions. Underlying all these theories is the assumption that the incident beam may be represented by a plane wave whose wavelength is the de Broglie wavelength of the incident particle in the center-of-mass system. For massive particles such as neutrons, protons, etc., the propagation constant for particles having the energy T_l in the laboratory system is

$$k = \left(\frac{2m_rT}{\hbar^2}\right)^{\frac{1}{2}} = \frac{(2mT_l)^{\frac{1}{2}}}{[1 + (m/M)\hbar} = 2.20\,\frac{(aT_l)^{\frac{1}{2}}}{1 + (a/A)} \times 10^{12}\ \text{cm}^{-1} \qquad (13\text{-}1)$$

where m and M are the masses of the incident and target nuclides, a and A in the last expression are the corresponding mass numbers, and T_l is the kinetic energy in Mev. The reciprocal of the propagation constant is frequently introduced in scattering discussions. It is given by

$$\lambda\!\!\!^{-} = k^{-1} = \frac{\lambda}{2\pi} = 0.455\,\frac{1 + (a/A)}{(aT_l)^{\frac{1}{2}}} \times 10^{-12} \qquad \text{cm} \qquad (13\text{-}2)$$

In the wave analysis the nucleus is regarded as a highly refractive and/or absorptive region which distorts the incident plane waves, causing some outgoing waves which are not in the direction of the incident beam. We identify these outgoing waves with the scattered particles. If these particles are of the same type as the incident particles and have the same energy, we characterize the reaction as an elastic scattering. If the outgoing particles are identical with the incident particles but have a different energy, we refer to the process as inelastic scattering. If the outgoing particles are different from the incoming particles, we refer to the process as a nuclear reaction.

Within the category of elastic scattering we may distinguish two types of processes, namely, potential scattering and resonant scattering. In potential scattering the target nucleus establishes a region of force characterized by a potential which refracts the incident waves, giving rise to interference effects. The scattering cross sections for this process may be computed using Schroedinger's time-independent wave equation. Although interference maxima and minima arise, the variation of the cross section with energy in potential scattering is generally smooth.

On the other hand the interpretation of resonance elastic scattering (and also resonance inelastic scattering and resonance nuclear reactions) seems to require the acceptance of the concept of a compound nucleus as an intermediate step in a bombardment type of reaction. We recall that, according to this picture, the incident and target nuclei coalesce for a period of time which is long compared to the time it would take the incident nuclear particle to traverse a distance equal to the diameter of the target nucleus ($\sim 10^{-21}$ sec for a 1-Mev neutron). Presumably the incident particle upon striking the target nucleus quickly shares its energy with the other nucleons. Then for a long period of time (compared to R/v) the energy is continuously redistributed in a complicated manner until finally all or a large part of it accidentally concentrates on one particle, which is then emitted.

We shall first discuss the theory of potential elastic scattering, particularly with reference to the scattering of neutrons. This picture of neutron scattering is concordant with the independent-particle model of the nucleus.

13-1. Quantum-mechanical Treatment of Potential Elastic Scattering. The quantum-mechanical calculation of the potential-elastic-scattering cross sections is based upon the solution of the Schroedinger time-independent wave equation for the state of the equivalent one-body dynamical system having the total energy

$$W = T = \frac{p^2}{2m_r} = \frac{\hbar^2 k^2}{2m_r} \tag{13-3}$$

The wave function describing the entire continuous scattering process must satisfy the Schroedinger amplitude equation

$$\left[\Delta + \frac{2m_r}{\hbar^2}(W - V)\right]\Psi(\mathbf{r}) = 0 \tag{13-4}$$

The mathematical problem now is quite different from that involved in the solution of Schroedinger's equation for discrete energy states of binding. In previous problems we sought the solution of the Schroedinger amplitude equation which contained an initially unknown energy parameter. The allowed values of the parameter and the corresponding energy eigenfunctions were found by appealing to the requirement that the wave functions be well-behaved. In the scattering problems the energy constant in the Schroedinger equation is given at the outset, and the problem is to find the solution of this equation which, at long ranges, has a certain specific form [Eq. (13-16)]. When we find the exact solution everywhere, then a factor $f(\theta,\varphi)$ in the asymptotic form of this solution yields $\sigma(\theta,\varphi)$, the quantity of interest. This type of mathematical problem closely resembles the numerous boundary-value problems which arise in studies of other types of wave phenomena, particularly the scattering of light and sound. Accordingly it is not surprising to find that most of the mathematical methods of solution for this present problem are the counterparts of the methods used in earlier wave studies.

In the quantum-mechanical treatment of scattering we assume that at great distances from the scatterer a monoergic beam of incident particles may be represented by a complex wave function corresponding to monochromatic waves traveling in the z direction, *i.e.*,

$$\Psi_i(r,t) = A \exp [i(kz - \omega t)] \tag{13-5}$$

where

$$k = \frac{p}{\hbar} = \frac{m_r v}{\hbar} \tag{13-6}$$

$$\omega = \frac{W}{\hbar} \tag{13-7}$$

and A is the amplitude of the complex wave. We also assume that at great distances from the scatterer the outgoing scattered particles are described by a wave function of the type

$$\Psi_s(r,t) = \frac{Af(\theta,\varphi)}{r} \exp [i(kr - \omega t)] \tag{13-8}$$

where the amplitude $Af(\theta,\varphi)$ now depends upon the direction of the scattered waves. We have inserted the explicit factor $(1/r)$ because the scattered probability density $\Psi_s^*\Psi_s$ in any direction decreases as $1/r^2$ (the inverse-square law). Since the scattering is elastic, the frequencies (energies) and wavelengths of the incoming and scattered waves are the same. Using the general interpretive postulate for wave functions, we observe that the probability for finding an incident particle in any element of volume of the beam at great distances from the scatterer is

$$P_i\, d\tau = \Psi_i^*\Psi_i\, d\tau = A^*A\, dx\, dy\, dz \tag{13-9}$$

This probability flows a distance dz through the area $dx\, dy$ in the time $dt = dz/v$, where v is the velocity of the particles in the incident beam (we assume probability flows at the velocity of the associated particles). Consequently the probability current per unit area, or the incident flux density, is

$$\frac{P_i d\tau}{dx\, dy\, dt} = vA^*A \tag{13-10}$$

The probability of finding a scattered particle in the volume element

$$d\tau' = r^2 \sin\theta \, d\varphi \, d\theta \, dr = r^2 \, d\Omega \, dr \tag{13-11}$$

is

$$P_s \, d\tau' = A^*Af^*(\theta,\varphi)f(\theta,\varphi) \, d\Omega \, dr \tag{13-12}$$

Thus the probability current at the point (r,θ,φ) due to the scattered particles moving radially outward with the velocity v into the solid angle $d\Omega$ is (letting $dt = dr/v$)

$$\frac{P_s \, d\tau'}{dt} = vA^*Af^*(\theta,\varphi)f(\theta,\varphi) \, d\Omega \tag{13-13}$$

Using the basic definition for the differential cross section

$$\sigma(\theta,\varphi) \, d\Omega = \frac{\text{probability current into solid angle } d\Omega}{\text{incident probability-current density}} \tag{13-14}$$

we obtain finally for the differential cross section per unit solid angle

$$\sigma(\theta,\varphi) = f^*(\theta,\varphi)f(\theta,\varphi) = |f(\theta,\varphi)|^2 \tag{13-15}$$

The quantum-mechanical treatment of elastic scattering is based upon the requirement that the complete time-independent wave function describing the equivalent one-body dynamical system in the energy state $W = T$ have the asymptotic form (for convenience we let $A = 1$ since this normalization factor does not affect the results)

$$\overrightarrow{\Psi}(r,\theta,\varphi) = \exp(ikr\cos\theta) + r^{-1}f(\theta,\varphi)\exp ikr \tag{13-16}$$

where we may identify the two parts of this wave function with the incident and scattered waves. The basic quantum-mechanical procedure for obtaining the differential cross section is thus (1) to solve Schroedinger's equation [Eq. (13-4)] for the given energy [Eq. (13-3)] to obtain an exact solution which has this asymptotic form and (2) to investigate the asymptotic form in order to identify the function $f(\theta,\varphi)$. $\sigma(\theta,\varphi)$ is then obtained from Eq. (13-15). From Eq. (13-16) we see that, if $\Psi(r,\theta,\varphi)$ is known, then

$$f(\theta,\varphi) = \lim_{r\to\infty} [\Psi(r,\theta,\varphi) - \exp(ikr\cos\theta)]r\exp(-ikr) \tag{13-17}$$

Alternatively we may view the fact that both sides of Eq. (13-17) must be independent of r as the formal expression of the boundary condition upon the exact solution of Schroedinger's wave equation.

The exact solution of Schroedinger's equation can be carried out only in a few special cases. Accordingly we must usually resort to some approximation method. The method used will depend mostly upon the nature of the potential and the (average) magnitude of the potential energy of the incident particles relative to their kinetic energy. We shall now consider a method that is particularly suited to nuclear physics.

13-2. Method of Partial Waves.[1,2] The method of partial waves is based upon the assumption that the desired exact solution of Schroedinger's wave equation in the absence of interaction (*i.e.*, for an unscattered plane wave) and the desired exact solution of Schroedinger's equation when the potential energy is not zero may be expressed as

$$\begin{aligned}\Psi_i &= \exp(ikr\cos\theta) \\ &= (kr)^{-1}\sum_{l=0}^{\infty}(2l+1)e^{i\pi l/2}P_l(\cos\theta)J_l(kr)\end{aligned} \qquad (13\text{-}18)$$

and

$$\Psi(r,\theta,\varphi) = (kr)^{-1}\sum_{l=0}^{\infty}(2l+1)e^{i\pi l/2}P_l(\cos\theta)G_l(kr) \qquad (13\text{-}19)$$

where $P_l(\cos\theta)$ are the Legendre polynomials. It is well known from studies of Bessel functions[3] that the first expansion is valid if

$$J_l(kr) = \left(\frac{kr\pi}{2}\right)^{\frac{1}{2}} \mathfrak{J}_{l+\frac{1}{2}}(kr) \qquad (13\text{-}20)$$

where $\mathfrak{J}_{l+\frac{1}{2}}(kr)$ are the usual Bessel functions. In order that the second expansion be a solution of the wave equation, $G_l(kr)$ must satisfy the radial wave equation for the lth partial wave. If we introduce the dimensionless coordinate $\rho = r/a$, the dimensionless total-energy parameter

$$\epsilon_k = ka = \left(\frac{T}{\hbar^2/2m_ra^2}\right)^{\frac{1}{2}} = \left(\frac{T}{E_0}\right)^{\frac{1}{2}} \qquad (13\text{-}21)$$

and the dimensionless potential-energy parameter

$$\epsilon(\rho) = \left[-\frac{V(r)}{E_0}\right]^{\frac{1}{2}} \qquad (13\text{-}22)$$

then the radial wave equation for the lth partial wave is

$$G_l'' + \left[\epsilon_k^2 + \epsilon^2(\rho) - \frac{l(l+1)}{\rho^2}\right]G_l = 0 \qquad (13\text{-}23)$$

Having found the well-behaved solution of this equation for each l, we may, using Eq. (13-17), deduce the function $f(\theta,\varphi)$ by means of

$$f(\theta,\varphi) = k^{-1}\sum_{l=0}^{\infty}(2l+1)P_l(\cos\theta)D_l \qquad (13\text{-}24)$$

where

$$D_l = \lim_{\rho\to\infty} e^{i\pi l/2}(G_l - J_l)e^{-i\epsilon_k\rho} \qquad (13\text{-}25)$$

Since $f(\theta,\varphi)$ is independent of ρ, we must find the solutions of the radial wave equations whose asymptotic forms are such that each D_l is a constant independent of ρ. Having found these solutions, then the differential and total cross sections may be expressed in terms of these constants.

It is well known from the theory of Bessel functions that

$$\lim_{\rho\to\infty} J_l(\epsilon_k\rho) = \sin\left(\epsilon_k\rho - \frac{\pi l}{2}\right) \tag{13-26}$$

The fact that $J_l(\epsilon_k\rho)$ is a sine function follows immediately from the appropriate radial wave equation for J_l. This may be obtained from Eq. (13-23) by setting $\epsilon^2(\rho) = 0$ and replacing G_l by J_l. The specific value of the phase factor in Eq. (13-26) must be determined in connection with the detailed verification of Eq. (13-18), which we have here taken for granted. Since the phase factor vanishes for $l = 0$, the nonvanishing phase factor for $l \neq 0$ in the Bessel function may be viewed as the cumulative effect, at long ranges, of the "centrifugal-force" term in the radial wave equation for J_l. It is reasonable to expect, therefore, that the effect of $\epsilon^2(\rho)$ upon the asymptotic form of $G_l(\rho)$ at most will cause an additional phase change and an altered amplitude. Accordingly we shall let

$$\lim_{\rho\to\infty} G_l(\rho) = A_l \sin\left(\epsilon_k\rho - \frac{l\pi}{2} + \delta^l\right) \tag{13-27}$$

where A_l is the asymptotic amplitude and δ^l the additional nuclear phase shift associated with the lth partial wave. Since D_l in Eq. (13-25) must be independent of ρ, it is readily seen, upon inserting Eqs. (13-26) and (13-27) and making use of the well-known identity

$$\sin\alpha = \frac{\exp i\alpha - \exp(-i\alpha)}{2i} \tag{13-28}$$

that the term in D_l with the factor $\exp(-i2\epsilon_k\rho)$ will vanish only if

$$A_l = e^{i\delta^l} \tag{13-29}$$

Using this amplitude, it follows from Eq. (13-25) that

$$D_l = e^{i\delta^l}\sin\delta^l \tag{13-30}$$

In view of Eqs. (13-24) and (13-15) the differential cross section per unit solid angle is

$$\sigma(\theta,\varphi) = \lambda\!\!\!^{-2}\left|\sum_{l=0}^{\infty}(2l+1)P_l(\cos\theta)\,e^{i\delta^l}\sin\delta^l\right|^2 \tag{13-31}$$

By integration the total cross section is

$$\sigma = 4\pi\lambda\!\!\!^{-2} \sum_{l=0}^{\infty} (2l + 1) \sin^2 \delta^l \tag{13-32}$$

where we have used the well-known formula

$$\begin{aligned} \int_0^\pi P_l(\cos\theta)P_{l'}(\cos\theta)\sin\theta\, d\theta &= \frac{2}{2l+1} \qquad \text{when } l' = l \\ &= 0 \qquad \text{when } l' \neq l \end{aligned} \tag{13-33}$$

The final results for both the differential and total cross sections are thus given in terms of the phase shifts δ_l, which must be obtained from the exact solutions of the radial wave equations.

We may write Eq. (13-32) in the form

$$\sigma = \sum_{l=0}^{\infty} \sigma^l \tag{13-34}$$

where

$$\sigma^l = (2l + 1)\pi a^2 \frac{4 \sin^2 \delta^l}{\epsilon_k{}^2} \tag{13-35}$$

The energy dependence of the total cross section manifests itself through the factor $4 \sin^2 \delta^l/\epsilon_k{}^2$. The factor $2l + 1$ may be regarded as the statistical weight of the lth partial wave and πa^2 as the geometric cross section of the scatterer.

13-3. Physical Interpretation of Partial Waves. In view of the identity of the angular dependent factor $P_l(\cos\theta)$ with the $m_l = 0$ spherical harmonic which arose in the bound-state central-field problem (see Chap. 10), we may assume that an orbital angular momentum $[l(l + 1)]^{\frac{1}{2}}\hbar$ and a vanishing z component of orbital angular momentum are associated with the lth partial wave. It is customary to designate the wave functions as follows: that associated with $l = 0$ is the S wave; that with $l = 1$ is the P wave; with $l = 2$, the D wave; etc. The interpretation in terms of angular momentum brings to mind a classical picture, which may be used with profit if one develops dexterity in switching from a wave interpretation to a particle interpretation. Suppose we consider an incident particle moving with the momentum p and directed relative to the center of mass so as to have an impact parameter b and hence the angular momentum pb. Using this expression, we may identify an impact parameter with each partial wave by

$$|\mathbf{l}| = [l(l + 1)]^{\frac{1}{2}}\hbar = b_l p = b_l \hbar k \tag{13-36}$$

Thus the effective impact parameter for the lth partial wave is

$$b_l = [l(l + 1)]^{\frac{1}{2}} k^{-1} \tag{13-37}$$

Note that the impact parameter assigned to S waves is zero. If the forces which cause the scattering have a distinct range a beyond which these forces are negligible, then the lth partial wave will not be scattered if

$$b_l \gg a$$

or

$$[l(l+1)]^{\frac{1}{2}} = kb_l \gg ka = \epsilon_k = \left(\frac{T}{E_0}\right)^{\frac{1}{2}} \tag{13-38}$$

Accordingly, as a rough criterion we may ignore the scattering of the lth partial wave if

$$T \ll l(l+1)E_0 \tag{13-39}$$

At low energies, relative to E_0, when the method of partial waves is particularly useful, the phase shifts decrease rapidly with l so that the contributions of the P, D, E, . . . waves to the total cross section decrease rapidly. The higher partial waves may nevertheless manifest themselves in the differential cross section through the cross-product terms with the lower partial waves[4] [see Eq. (13-31)]. For example, suppose that only δ^0 and δ^1 differ significantly from zero and that $\delta^0 \gg \delta^1$. The total cross section is then

$$\sigma = 4\pi\lambda\!\!\!^{-2}(\sin^2 \delta^0 + 3 \sin^2 \delta^1) \tag{13-40}$$

It is obvious that the P wave contributes very little to the result. On the other hand the differential cross section for this case is

$$\sigma(\theta,\varphi) = \lambda\!\!\!^{-2}[\sin^2 \delta^0 + 6 \sin \delta^0 \sin \delta^1 \cos (\delta^1 - \delta^0) \cos \theta + 9 \sin^2 \delta^1 \cos^2 \theta] \tag{13-41}$$

While the $\cos^2 \theta$ term may be negligible, the $\cos \theta$ cross-product term may appreciably change the angular distribution from the spherically symmetric distribution which is expected for S waves alone.

13-4. Calculation of S-wave Phase Shift for Square Spherical Well. To calculate the phase shifts, we must solve the radial wave equations for the important values of l. The nature of solutions of these equations depends upon the potential-energy function. For certain well types explicit analytic solutions of these equations can be found. However, for most well types analytical solutions are not available, and we must resort to numerical or approximate methods of solution. The square well is a great favorite of the physicist because the solutions of the radial wave equation can be given in terms of known functions, and the problem of extracting the phase shifts from the solutions is particularly simple. We shall consider here in detail the calculations of the S-wave phase shift for the square-well potential. We refer the reader to the quantum-mechanical literature[2,4] for the calculation of phase shifts for other partial waves and for other types of well shapes.

The S-wave radial wave equation for the square well is

$$G_i'' + (\epsilon_k^2 + \epsilon_0^2)G_i = 0 \qquad \text{for } \rho < 1 \tag{13-42}$$

$$G_e'' + \epsilon_k^2 G_e = 0 \qquad \text{for } \rho > 1 \tag{13-43}$$

The interior solution which satisfies the condition $G_i(0) = 0$ is

$$G_i = C_i \sin [(\epsilon_0^2 + \epsilon_k^2)^{\frac{1}{2}}\rho] \tag{13-44}$$

The general exterior solution may be accepted as (letting $\delta^0 = \delta$)

$$G_e = C_e \sin (\epsilon_k\rho + \delta) \tag{13-45}$$

Since this already is in the form of the asymptotic solution, we do not have to make an analysis of the limit of this function to extract the phase shift. The other requirements on wave functions are that, for all values of ρ, G must be continuous and have a continuous first derivative. If we equate the value of G_i and G_e and G_e' and G_i' at $\rho = 1$, we find that, even after the normalization constants C_i and C_e are adjusted for the continuity of G, both equations can be satisfied simultaneously only if δ is related to ϵ_k and ϵ_0 in a certain way. The relation can be obtained most simply without evaluating the normalization constants by insisting that

$$\frac{G_i'}{G_i} = \frac{G_e'}{G_e} \qquad \text{at } \rho = 1 \tag{13-46}$$

We obtain immediately

$$(\epsilon_k^2 + \epsilon_0^2)^{\frac{1}{2}} \cot (\epsilon_k^2 + \epsilon_0^2)^{\frac{1}{2}} = \epsilon_k \cot (\epsilon_k + \delta) \tag{13-47}$$

or

$$\tan (\epsilon_k + \delta) = \frac{\epsilon_k}{(\epsilon_k^2 + \epsilon_0^2)^{\frac{1}{2}}} \tan (\epsilon_k^2 + \epsilon_0^2)^{\frac{1}{2}} \tag{13-48}$$

Consequently the phase shift is given by

$$\delta = \left[\tan^{-1} \frac{\epsilon_k \tan (\epsilon_k^2 + \epsilon_0^2)^{\frac{1}{2}}}{(\epsilon_k^2 + \epsilon_0^2)^{\frac{1}{2}}}\right] - \epsilon_k \tag{13-49}$$

For a given ϵ_0 we can use this equation to evaluate δ for every value of ϵ_k. The corresponding S-wave cross section is then given by

$$\sigma^0 = \pi a^2 \left(\frac{4 \sin^2 \delta}{\epsilon_k^2}\right) \tag{13-50}$$

The variation of the S-wave cross section with energy (through δ and through ϵ_k) takes on an interesting variety of forms according to the value of ϵ_0. The straightforward method for generating these curves is by means of Eqs. (13-49) and (13-50). However, explicit formulas for σ^0 may be developed for special cases.

Let us consider the variation with ϵ_k when $0 \approx \epsilon_k \ll \epsilon_0$. We may then set

$$(\epsilon_0^2 + \epsilon_k^2)^{\frac{1}{2}} \approx \epsilon_0 + \frac{1}{2}\frac{\epsilon_k^2}{\epsilon_0} \tag{13-51}$$

and

$$\tan(\epsilon_0^2 + \epsilon_k^2)^{\frac{1}{2}} \approx \frac{(\tan \epsilon_0) + (\epsilon_k^2/2\epsilon_0)}{1 - (\epsilon_k^2/2\epsilon_0)\tan \epsilon_0} \tag{13-52}$$

As long as ϵ_0 is appreciably different from the critical values $\pi/2$, $3\pi/2$, $5\pi/2$, . . . , the argument of the arc tangent in Eq. (13-49) will be small.

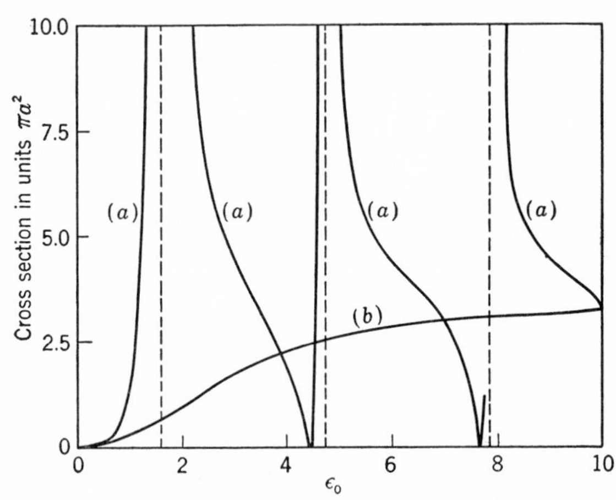

FIG. 13-1. Variation with ϵ_0 of low-velocity-limit S-wave cross section (a) for square well and (b) for square barrier. (*From Mott and Massey, Ref.* 2.)

Consequently, ignoring terms of the order of ϵ_k^2, we find

$$\delta = \epsilon_k \left(\frac{\tan \epsilon_0}{\epsilon_0} - 1\right) \tag{13-53}$$

The total S-wave cross section is thus finite and tends in this low-velocity limit to the constant value [replacing sin δ by δ in Eq. (13-50)]

$$\sigma^0(0) = \pi a^2 \left[4\left(\frac{\tan \epsilon_0}{\epsilon_0} - 1\right)^2\right] \tag{13-54}$$

In view of this result the low-velocity cross section may be expected to be zero whenever $\tan \epsilon_0 = \epsilon_0$. The ϵ_0 values which satisfy this equation are slightly smaller than the critical values $3\pi/2$, $5\pi/2$, $7\pi/2$, ... The values of the total cross section at low velocities when ϵ_0 is close to one of the critical values require more careful investigation, since we may no longer assume that δ is small. It is not difficult to show, however, that the zero-velocity total cross section is infinite, as we would expect from Eq. (13-54). In Fig. 13-1 we show the variation of the low-velocity-limit cross section with ϵ_0. In Fig. 13-2 we indicate the variation of the S, P, and D total cross sections with ϵ_k for several fixed values of ϵ_0. The fact that, for extremely large values of ϵ_k, the S-wave cross section vanishes follows immediately from Eq. (13-48). Since ϵ_0 may be ignored, it is obvious that $\delta = 0$. Of course, the cross sections for the P, D, F, . . . waves become important at large values of ϵ_k.

The minima that occur in the total cross section for certain large values of ϵ_0 correspond to the Ramsauer-Townsend[(2)] effect of atomic physics.

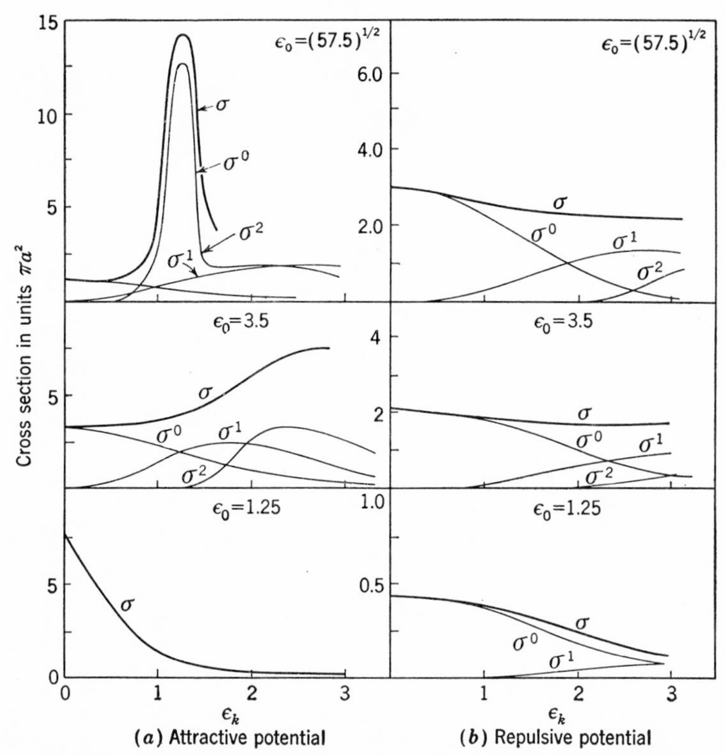

FIG. 13-2. Variation of S, P, and D total cross sections with ϵ_k for several fixed values of ϵ_0 (*a*) for square well, (*b*) for square barrier.

These minima arise for deep wells at particular low energies when the S-wave phase shift is π, 2π, 3π, . . . [see Eq. (13-50)]. One may describe the effect as one in which the S waves are altered by one-half, three-halves, five-halves, etc., wavelengths within the well. The outside waves are basically unaltered as far as observations can detect. If such phase shifts occur for small values of ϵ_k, when the P- and D-wave cross sections are negligible, then the total cross section will vanish and the substance will be transparent to the incident particles at these energies.

13-5. Spherical Barrier. The maxima and minima which we have noted in the S-wave cross section for the spherical well do not arise if the potential function corresponds to a repulsive field. For example, let us consider the S-wave scattering caused by the potential barrier

$$\begin{aligned} V &= V_0 \qquad \text{for } r < a \\ &= 0 \qquad \text{for } r > a \end{aligned} \tag{13-55}$$

We here define the well-strength parameter by

$$\begin{aligned} \epsilon^2(\rho) &= \epsilon_0{}^2 = \frac{V_0}{E_0} \qquad \text{for } \rho < 1 \\ &= 0 \qquad \text{for } \rho > 1 \end{aligned} \tag{13-56}$$

The interior radial wave equation is

$$G_i'' + (\epsilon_k{}^2 - \epsilon_0{}^2)G_i = 0 \tag{13-57}$$

and the exterior wave equation is identical with Eq. (13-43). The interior solution which vanishes at the origin may now have either the form

$$G_i = C_i \sinh [(\epsilon_0{}^2 - \epsilon_k{}^2)^{\frac{1}{2}}\rho] \qquad \text{if } \epsilon_0 > \epsilon_k \tag{13-58}$$

or the form

$$G_i = C_i \sin [(\epsilon_k{}^2 - \epsilon_0{}^2)^{\frac{1}{2}}\rho] \qquad \text{if } \epsilon_k > \epsilon_0 \tag{13-59}$$

At low energies the first solution is appropriate, and the continuity condition gives as the equation for the S-wave phase shift

$$\tan (\epsilon_k + \delta) = \frac{\epsilon_k \tanh (\epsilon_0{}^2 - \epsilon_k{}^2)^{\frac{1}{2}}}{(\epsilon_0{}^2 - \epsilon_k{}^2)^{\frac{1}{2}}} \tag{13-60}$$

The S-wave phase shift always tends to zero in the low-velocity limit, and the S-wave cross section now has a finite value for any value of ϵ_0. The low-velocity-limit cross section is

$$\sigma^0(0) = 4\pi a^2 \left(\frac{\tanh \epsilon_0}{\epsilon_0} - 1\right)^2 \tag{13-61}$$

For a fixed nonzero value of ϵ_0 the S-wave cross section invariably decreases in a regular manner as ϵ_k or k increases (see Fig. 13-2).

The limiting case for which V_0 is infinite, *i.e.*, the impenetrable sphere, is particularly interesting by reason of its simplicity. (In nuclear physics the words potential scattering are frequently taken as synonymous with scattering by an impenetrable sphere.) We may find the low-velocity cross section by using the equations above for the square barrier and a limiting process in which V_0 is made to approach infinity. However, it is much simpler simply to recognize that the internal wave function must vanish identically. The external S wave function, which vanishes at $r = a$, is obviously

$$G_e = C_e \sin [\epsilon_k(\rho - 1)] = C_e \sin [k(r - a)] \tag{13-62}$$

The S-wave phase shift therefore is simply given by

$$-\delta^0 = ka = \epsilon_k \tag{13-63}$$

The S-wave cross section in the low-velocity limit is

$$\sigma^0 = 4\pi a^2 \tag{13-64}$$

The determination of the P- and D-wave phase shifts is somewhat more complicated. The results are[5]

$$-\delta^1 = ka - \frac{\pi}{2} + \cot^{-1} ka \approx \frac{\epsilon_k{}^3}{3} \tag{13-65}$$

$$-\delta^2 = ka - \pi + \cot^{-1} \frac{(k^2a^2 - 3)}{3ka} \approx \frac{\epsilon_k{}^5}{45} \tag{13-66}$$

where the expressions to the right are useful approximations when $\epsilon_k \ll 1$. In the other extreme (*i.e.*, when $\epsilon_k \gg 1$), the method of partial waves becomes less useful since all the phase shifts must be calculated and the series of partial-wave cross sections must be summed. This problem has been treated by Massey and Mohr,[6] who show that in the high-energy limit the total cross section for an impenetrable sphere approaches

$$\sigma = 2\pi a^2 \tag{13-67}$$

This limiting value is just twice the geometrical cross section, an apparently paradoxical result, which can be shown to be caused by diffraction effects at small angles.

13-6. Scattering of Charged Particles. The method of partial waves may be applied to the theoretical study of the scattering caused by a coulomb field. The radial wave equation in this case is

$$G_l'' + \left[\epsilon_k{}^2 - \frac{2d}{\rho} - \frac{l(l+1)}{\rho^2}\right] G_l = 0 \tag{13-68}$$

where

$$d = \frac{m_r z Z e^2 a}{\hbar^2} \tag{13-69}$$

Certain complications arise in the solution of these equations because of the slow variation with radial distance of the coulomb force. In effect the coulomb field distorts the parts of the total wave functions which are identified with the incident and scattered particles, even at infinite ranges. If one accepts the asymptotic solution

$$\overrightarrow{G_l} = A_l \sin\left(\epsilon_k\rho - \frac{l\pi}{2} + \delta_c{}^l\right) \tag{13-70}$$

one finds for the coulomb phase shifts

$$\delta_c{}^l = \gamma^l - \frac{d}{\epsilon_k} \ln 2\epsilon_k\rho \tag{13-71}$$

where

$$\gamma^l = \arg \Gamma\left(i\frac{d}{\epsilon_k} + l + 1\right) \tag{13-72}$$

Γ here denotes the gamma function. Although the problem is mathematically complicated, nevertheless, the fact that the exact solutions of Eq. (13-68) may be expressed in terms of confluent hypergeometric functions enables one to find analytic expressions for all the phase shifts. It is further possible to sum the series of partial waves to obtain the solution of Schroedinger's equation in closed form. The function $f(\theta,\varphi)$ may be extracted from the asymptotic form of this solution and the square of its magnitude determined. In this way one obtains for the differential cross section per unit solid angle

$$\sigma(\theta,\varphi) = \left(\frac{d}{2k^2a}\right)^2 \csc^4\frac{\theta}{2} = \left(\frac{zZe^2}{4T}\right)^2 \csc^4\frac{\theta}{2} \tag{13-73}$$

which is exactly the Rutherford scattering formula.

Although this result can also be obtained by simpler quantum-mechanical methods, the method of partial waves is particularly useful for studying the effects of nuclear fields which may cause departures from Rutherford scattering.

When an additional nuclear potential is present, the radial wave equation for the lth partial wave is

$$G_l'' + \left[\epsilon_k{}^2 + \epsilon^2(\rho) - \frac{2d}{\rho} - \frac{l(l+1)}{\rho^2}\right] G_l = 0 \tag{13-74}$$

The asymptotic solution is assumed to have the form

$$\overrightarrow{G_l} = B_l \sin\left(\epsilon_k\rho - \frac{l\pi}{2} + \delta_c{}^l + \delta^l\right) \tag{13-75}$$

where δ^l is an additional phase shift due to the departure of the potential energy from the coulomb field. This additional phase shift may be found by solving the radial wave equation and comparing the asymptotic form of the solution with the asymptotic form of the solution of the radial wave equation for the pure coulomb field. Having obtained the additional phase shift for each partial wave in this way, it can be shown that

$$f(\theta,\varphi) = f_c(\theta,\varphi) + k^{-1} \sum_{l=0}^{\infty} (2l+1)e^{i(2\gamma^l+\delta^l)} \sin \delta^l\, P_l \cos\theta \tag{13-76}$$

Just as in the case of pure nuclear scattering, the additional phase shifts and the corresponding anomalies in the scattering cross section here also decrease with l at low and moderate energies. Consequently it is necessary only to consider the anomalies caused by the first few partial waves. In the low-velocity case the interference terms which arise between coulomb scattering and nuclear scattering provide information as to the sign of δ^0, information which cannot be obtained in the case of purely nuclear scattering. For example, at low energies the differential cross section per unit solid angle in the center-of-mass system is

$$\sigma(\theta,\varphi) = \left(\frac{zZe^2}{4T}\right)^2 \left(\csc^4 \frac{\theta}{2}\right) + \frac{\sin^2 \delta^0}{k^2} - \frac{zZe^2}{2Tk} \csc^2 \frac{\theta}{2} \sin \delta^0 \cos \left[\frac{zZe^2k}{2T} \ln \left(\sin^2 \frac{\theta}{2}\right) + \delta^0\right] \tag{13-77}$$

The fact that the cross-product term is not quadratic in $\sin \delta^0$ enables one to determine whether the nuclear force in the S state is attractive or repulsive, since an attractive force causes a positive phase shift and repulsive force a negative phase shift. Since the factors with $zZe^2/4T$ in Eq. (13-77) become smaller at high energies, the purely nuclear scattering dominates at very high energies at angles somewhat removed from $\theta = 0$.

13-7. Angular Momenta and Scattering. In nuclear scattering problems the angular momenta of the particles involved have a significant influence upon the scattering cross section. This influence may manifest itself if the effective-potential-energy function is sensitive to the relative orientation of the spins $\mathbf{s}$ and $\mathbf{I}$ of the incident and target nuclei, or if the effective potential energy has a dependence upon the orbital angular momentum $\mathbf{l}$ which is apart from that implicit in the centrifugal-force term. In resonant scattering, angular-momentum effects are particularly important, appearing both in connection with statistical-weight factors and as important parameters in the "selection rules." Although the strict quantum-mechanical methods for treating angular momenta in nuclear reactions are quite complicated, it is fortunately possible to give a reasonable interpretation to the results in terms of the semiclassical model for angular momenta. If we introduce

$$\mathbf{I}^* = \mathbf{l} + \mathbf{s} + \mathbf{I} \tag{13-78}$$

then conservation of angular momenta and the rules for combining angular momenta restrict the possible values of I^*. By considering the allowed z components of these angular momenta, we find the totality of possible states to number $(2s + 1)(2l + 1)(2I + 1)$. The statistical weight of one allowed I^* state therefore is

$$g_{I^*} = \frac{2I^* + 1}{(2s + 1)(2l + 1)(2I + 1)} \tag{13-79}$$

For a given l, s, and I the partial cross sections due to the scattering associated with various I^*, when these states of angular momentum scatter independently, are given by

$$\sigma^l = \sum_{I^*} g_{I^*} \sigma_{I^*}{}^l \tag{13-80}$$

To give a simple but important illustration of this result, we may consider the case of slow-neutron scattering by protons, where $l = 0$, $s = \frac{1}{2}$, $I = \frac{1}{2}$, and $I^* = 0$ or 1. Therefore

$$\sigma^0 = \tfrac{1}{4}\sigma_0{}^0 + \tfrac{3}{4}\sigma_1{}^0 \tag{13-81}$$

where

$$\sigma_{I^*}{}^0 = 4\pi\lambda\!\!\!^{-2} \sin^2 \delta_{I^*}{}^0 \tag{13-82}$$

If the effective potential energy does not depend upon I^*, the phase shifts and hence the S-wave cross sections for the $I^* = 0$ and $I^* = 1$ states are identical, and in consequence the sum of the two cross sections is just the result obtained for S waves when spin is not considered.

13-8. Applications to Nuclear Physics. The foregoing theory of potential scattering finds several special and broad applications in nuclear physics. Applications to neutron-proton scattering and proton-proton scattering will be discussed in the next chapter. Let us here consider the application of the theory to elastic scattering by massive nuclei.

The successes of the independent-particle model of the nucleus when applied to states of binding suggest that this model may also be successful for the positive energy states which arise in scattering problems. According to this model a nucleon within the nucleus experiences at any point an effective central potential which is the average effect of the short-range interactions with the other nucleons in the vicinity of that point. This effective potential is expected to be dependent upon the density of nuclear matter at the point. Since the density of nuclear matter is thought to be approximately constant within any nucleus and from nucleus to nucleus, it is reasonable to accept a universal potential energy $-V_0$ for nuclear matter. We might also reasonably assume that this potential energy extends over a radius given by $R = bA^{\frac{1}{3}}$. The natural energy unit E_0 for any problem consequently depends upon the mass number and is given by

$$E_0 = \frac{\hbar^2}{2m_r R^2} = \frac{\hbar^2}{2m_r b^2 A^{\frac{2}{3}}} \approx \frac{10}{A^{\frac{2}{3}}} \quad \text{Mev} \tag{13-83}$$

where in the last expression we have used $b = 1.45 \times 10^{-13}$ cm and $m_r = 1$ MU. The well-strength parameter also depends upon mass number and is given by

$$\epsilon_0 = \left(\frac{V_0}{E_0}\right)^{\frac{1}{2}} = \left(\frac{2m_r b^2 V_0}{\hbar^2}\right)^{\frac{1}{2}} A^{\frac{1}{3}} \approx 2A^{\frac{1}{3}} \tag{13-84}$$

where in the last expression we have introduced the reasonable value[7] $V_0 = 40$ Mev. Since ϵ_0 ranges up to about 13, a range which includes the critical values $\pi/2$, $3\pi/2$, $5\pi/2$, and $7\pi/2$ and approaches the value $9\pi/2$, we should expect to see several minima and maxima in the scattering-cross-section surface $\sigma(T,A)$. Since the natural energy unit E_0 varies from about 10 Mev to 0.2 Mev, we should expect P, D, F, . . . waves to be scattered at moderate energies, particularly for the medium and heavy elements. Consequently we should observe substantial departures from spherical symmetry in the angular distributions.

The recent experimental work of Barschall[8] reveals the existence of maxima and minima in the total-cross-section surface (see Fig. 7-14) and departures from spherical symmetry (Fig. 7-16) in the angular distributions. However, it does not appear that the adjustment of V_0 and b, the only parameters at our disposal, will permit a quantitative fit of the theory to the experiment. This lack of detailed agreement is not unexpected, since the foregoing theory neglects other processes which contribute to the total cross section and the differential cross sections. Foremost among these are the resonant-scattering and reaction processes which occur via the intermediate formation of the compound nucleus. We shall next consider these processes.

13-9. Compound Nucleus and Its Decay. To explain resonant scattering and nuclear reactions, it appears that we must view the scattering as a two-step process which is indicated symbolically by

$$x + X \rightarrow X^* \rightarrow x' + X' \tag{13-85}$$

where X^* denotes the compound nucleus. The compound nucleus is formed with the excitation energy W^* given by (see Chap. 7)

$$T + B_x^* = W^* = T' + B_{x'}^* + W' \tag{13-86}$$

If the incident kinetic energy is small, the compound nucleus still has the excitation energy B_x^*. Estimates of these binding energies are given in Table 7-1. This table indicates that, with the exception of alpha particles in heavy nuclides, the compound nucleus formed in the first step of a reaction is usually in a highly excited state. Let us therefore consider the concepts which have been introduced in the literature to account for phenomena associated with decay from highly excited states.

In our study of gamma radiation we identified with the ith excited nuclear state a transition probability per unit time A_{if} for decay to the fth lower state of the same nucleus. More generally, we identify with an excited state of a nucleus a transition probability per unit time A_{xif} for other energetically permissible modes of decay, where the subscript x denotes the emitted particle and the subscript f now denotes the final state of the daughter. The particles that are of interest here as emitted particles are gamma rays, neutrons, protons, alpha particles, and, to a much less extent, deuterons, tritons, and He^3. Beta decay has a rather special position in nuclear physics (partly because of the long lifetimes when compared with other processes) and need not be considered here. The decay constant, or the total probability for a transition from the ith excited state, as well as the lifetime of this state, may be obtained from the transition probabilities by the use of the equations

$$\lambda_i = \sum_f \sum_x A_{xif} = \tau_i^{-1} \tag{13-87}$$

The justification for these equations may be given very simply. If N_i is the number of nuclei in the state i at time t, then

$$dN_i = -N_i \sum_{fx} A_{xif}\, dt = -N_i \lambda_i\, dt \tag{13-88}$$

is the change in N_i during the time interval dt, where we use Eq. (13-87) to define λ_i and τ_i. By integration we find that the number of nuclei in the ith state at an arbitrary time is

$$N_i = N_{i,0} \exp(-\lambda_i t) = N_{i,0} \exp\left(-\frac{t}{\tau_i}\right) \tag{13-89}$$

The exponential form of the last expression justifies the use of the word lifetime for the constant τ_i.

Equation (13-89), which is applicable whenever we have a great number of identical decaying systems, expresses the statistical significance of the decay constant and the lifetime. According to current interpretations of quantum mechanics, these constants are actually embodied in the wave functions which characterize the states of an individual system. We recall (Sec. 10-13) that wave functions for decaying states have the form

$$\boldsymbol{\Psi}_i(\mathbf{r},t) = \Psi_i(\mathbf{r}) \exp\left[-i\left(W_i - i\frac{\Gamma_i}{2}\right)\frac{t}{\hbar}\right] \tag{13-90}$$

where

$$\Gamma_i = \hbar\lambda_i = \frac{\hbar}{\tau_i} \tag{13-91}$$

is the energy width of the level. The fact that energy levels are not perfectly sharp implies that a gamma ray or a nuclear particle resulting from a transition between two states also has a natural energy width. One may be tempted to identify $\hbar A_{xif}$ as the energy width of a spectral line or nuclear particle. This surmise would be incorrect. The energy width of the emitted proton or particle depends upon the sum of the total widths of the two states. A correspondence argument which bears out this relation follows if we use damped wave functions rather than undamped wave functions in the Heisenberg "average" between states. This "average" then takes the form

$$\langle \alpha \rangle_{if} = \langle i|\alpha|f\rangle \exp(-i\nu_{if}t) \exp\left[-(\Gamma_i + \Gamma_f)\frac{t}{2\hbar}\right] \qquad (13\text{-}92)$$

The total damping factor associated with a transition therefore is $(\Gamma_i + \Gamma_f)/\hbar$. The significance of this quantity as the line width follows immediately from a Fourier inversion of Eq. (13-92).

Estimates of the natural widths of typical spectral lines in atomic physics indicate that this spread is usually too small to be detected by direct spectroscopic methods. Other physical effects generally make much larger contributions to the width of spectral lines, namely, the Doppler effect due to the random thermal velocities of the emitting atoms, collision damping due to the sudden radiation phase changes associated with atomic collisions, and pressure broadening due to the electric polarization of radiating atoms by the neighboring atoms. In nuclear transitions, however, the more interesting phenomenon of natural line width is detectable in many cases.

In addition to the width Γ_i of an excited state we may identify with a state a constant D_i, which is the average level spacing in the neighborhood of the ith excited state (see Sec. 8-9). Sometimes D_i will refer specifically to the average level spacing of states with the same I value and parity. When $D_i \gg \Gamma_i$, the concept of a quantum state has a clear meaning. However, when $D_i \lesssim \Gamma_i$, the quantum-state concept breaks down, and we may expect on the basis of the Bohr correspondence principle that a classical or statistical description may become appropriate. Γ_i increases rapidly with energy, since more modes of decay become available. On the other hand, D_i generally decreases with excitation energy; accordingly quantum states tend to fuse together at very high excitation energies.

Quantum-mechanical studies using the time-dependent perturbation theory suggest that the partial width

$$\Gamma_{xif} = \hbar A_{xif} \qquad (13\text{-}93)$$

for the ejection of a heavy nuclear particle can be written in the form

$$\Gamma_{xif} = 2k\mathcal{P}_l\gamma_{xif}^2 \qquad (13\text{-}94)$$

where γ_{xif}^2 is the "reduced" width, $\mathcal{P}_l$ is the penetrability factor for the particular particle, and k is the propagation constant for the emitted particle. For neutrons the penetrability factor is simply that associated with the centrifugal barrier. For small l, these are[9] ($\epsilon_k = kR = kbA^{\frac{1}{3}}$)

$$\mathcal{P}_0 = 1 \tag{13-95}$$

$$\mathcal{P}_1 = \frac{\epsilon_k^2}{1 + \epsilon_k^2} \tag{13-96}$$

and

$$\mathcal{P}_2 = \frac{\epsilon_k^4}{9 + \epsilon_k^2 + \epsilon_k^4} \tag{13-97}$$

For protons and other charged particles the penetrability is the coulomb-barrier factor which arises in the theory of alpha decay. The factors k and $\mathcal{P}_l$ in the formula for the partial width are due to effects which are essentially external to the nucleus, whereas the reduced width depends upon the wave functions of the nuclear states involved in the transition. In fact, γ_{xif}^2 is proportional to the square of the matrix element for the transition. An interesting relationship first pointed out by Bethe[10] is the proportionality of the reduced width γ^2 to the spacing D between levels, *i.e.*,

$$\gamma^2 \simeq C_n D \tag{13-98}$$

The experimental data[11] support this conclusion and indicate that, despite the fact that the widths vary by a factor of the order of 10^6, the variation of the ratio γ^2/D is relatively small. These residual fluctuations of the ratio γ^2/D are quite irregular, and very little can be said about them except that they probably reflect the characteristics of individual nuclei.

In connection with their schematic interpretation of neutron resonances, Feshbach, Peaslee, and Weisskopf[12] propose a still more explicit relation between the width for neutron emission to the ground state of the residual nucleus and the distance between levels of the same spin and parity. Their proposed result for the region of excitation of the compound nucleus formed when a neutron is captured is

$$\Gamma_n = \frac{2}{\pi}\frac{k}{K} D\mathcal{P}_l \tag{13-99}$$

where

$$K = (K_0^2 + k^2)^{\frac{1}{2}} \tag{13-100}$$

with

$$K_0 \approx 1 \times 10^{13}\ \mathrm{cm}^{-1} \tag{13-101}$$

Since $k/K_0 \ll 1$, the neutron-emission width at low neutron energies is small compared to the level spacing. This schematic theory essentially gives

$$\gamma^2 = \frac{D}{\pi K} \tag{13-102}$$

Since K is not very sensitive to k for the usual range of neutron energies, this relation is consistent with observations of the approximate constancy of γ^2/D.

We may estimate the order of magnitude of the partial widths for charged particles by assuming [Eq. (13-98)] that

$$\gamma_x^2 = C_x D \tag{13-103}$$

where the C_x for the proton is about the same as that for the neutron but is somewhat smaller for the alpha particle and deuteron. The coulomb penetrability factor, of course, drastically reduces the partial widths Γ_x for the emission of charged particles relative to the neutron partial width [see Eq. (13-94)].

In many cases the transition probability for one particular mode of decay far exceeds all others. We may then replace the total width of the level by the partial width for that mode of decay. An important example of this situation arises in the study of neutron resonances induced by moderately fast neutrons; here the total width of the compound state may be taken approximately equal to the partial width for the decay to the ground state by the emission of a neutron (resonant elastic scattering).

For the treatment of gamma radiation from moderately high states of excitation and for the emission of massive particles from highly excited states, we may define the *integrated* partial width for the emission of a certain type of particle by

$$\Gamma_x = \sum_f \Gamma_{xif} \tag{13-104}$$

This concept is useful whenever the partial widths for decay to excited states of the residual nucleus are of the same magnitude as the partial width to the ground state.

In the studies of nuclear reactions the integrated gamma width is usually large compared to the partial gamma width for decay to the ground state; hence the integrated width Γ_γ is the important quantity characterizing the gamma decay of the excited state. Theoretical and experimental estimates of the integrated radiation widths for levels in the neighborhood of 5 to 10 Mev indicate that these widths range from about 10 ev in very light nuclei to about 0.1 ev in heavy[13] nuclei. For all but the very low states the radiation width is rather insensitive to the excitation energy and not very sensitive to the mass of the nuclide. This contrasts greatly with the partial and integrated widths for particle emission, which are exceedingly sensitive to these factors.

We have thus far concerned ourselves with the partial, integrated, and total widths associated with the individual excited states of nuclides.

The excitation of the individual states of the compound nucleus during the bombardment reaction is possible only when the level spacing is large compared to the energy width of the incident beam. In many actual experiments this condition is not satisfied; *e.g.*, in the bombardment of heavy nuclides by fast neutrons the energy spread is usually so large compared to the level spacing of the compound nucleus that many states of the compound nucleus are excited. Under these circumstances one can give only statistical meaning to concepts such as excitation energy, integrated widths, total widths, and level spacings. A theoretical study of the widths and level spacing in the regions of high excitation requires several concepts from statistical mechanics and thermodynamics. To avoid a lengthy digression, we shall, when the occasion arises, simply quote the results of such studies and refer the interested reader to original sources.

13-10. Resonant Scattering and Reactions. A resonance occurs in a nuclear reaction with monoergic incident particles when the total kinetic energy in the center-of-mass system is such as to give rise to an excitation energy which is equal to an energy level of the compound nucleus, *i.e.*, when

$$W^* = W_r^* = T_r + B_x^* \tag{13-105}$$

where the subscript r denotes resonance.

The theory of nuclear resonance developed by Breit and Wigner[14] is quite analogous to the Ladenburg-Kramers-Heisenberg theory of resonance optical dispersion. Many of the concepts and much of the mathematical treatment used in both nuclear and optical resonance theory have appeared in radio engineering work.[11]

A simple extension of our discussion of potential scattering may be used to obtain a qualitative picture of the occurrence of nuclear resonances. The interior wave function for potential scattering [see Eq. (13-44)] may be written in the form

$$G_i = \frac{A}{2i} \{\exp [i(\epsilon_0^2 + \epsilon_k^2)^{\frac{1}{2}}\rho] - \exp [-i(\epsilon_0^2 + \epsilon_k^2)^{\frac{1}{2}}\rho]\} \tag{13-106}$$

This latter form suggests that, within the nucleus, interference occurs between ingoing and outgoing waves having equal amplitude whose phases are such as to give rise to a node at $\rho = 0$. Let us now suppose that the complex interactions of the waves within the nucleus are such as to produce a phase shift of the interior wave function so that near the nuclear boundary the interior wave function has the form

$$G_i = A_i \sin [(\epsilon_0^2 + \epsilon_k^2)^{\frac{1}{2}}\rho + \delta_i(\epsilon_k)] \tag{13-107}$$

where $\delta_i(\epsilon_k)$ is the interior phase shift associated with the complex nuclear interactions. We have indicated that this interior phase shift depends upon energy. A nuclear "resonance" would be expected to correspond to a condition in which the interior wave function is quite large. Since the wave function must join smoothly to the exterior wave function, we might expect that the greatest interior stimulation would correspond to the case for which the amplitude of the interior sine function is equal to that of the exterior sine function [Eq. (13-45)]. Since the sine functions must also join smoothly, resonance would correspond to the case for which the arguments of both sine functions are equal to the critical values $\pi/2$, $3\pi/2$, $5\pi/2$, . . . , *i.e.*, to the case when, at $\rho = 1$,

$$\epsilon_{kr} + \delta_r = (\epsilon_{kr}^2 + \epsilon_0^2)^{\frac{1}{2}} + \delta_i(\epsilon_{kr}) = (v + \tfrac{1}{2})\pi \qquad (13\text{-}108)$$

where $v \doteq 0, 1, 2, \ldots$.

Unfortunately we can make little use of this equation unless we know the explicit function $\delta_i(\epsilon_k)$. For each nucleus, $\delta_i(\epsilon_k)$ must be a function such that each critical value $(v + \frac{1}{2})\pi$ corresponds to an energy state of the compound nucleus. Since we do not yet have a theory which can predict energy levels, little can be said about this function at this time. However, an investigation of the shape of the cross-section curve in the neighborhood of a resonance, under the simple assumption that $\delta_i(\epsilon_k)$ is a smooth function, leads to resonance patterns similar to the frequency-response curves of radio circuits and optical media.

The theoretical literature concerned with the detailed investigation of nuclear resonances is very extensive and quite complicated. The theory is incomplete in the sense that it is not capable of predicting detailed resonance shapes and the positions of resonances. Instead, the theory merely attempts to characterize complete resonance curves by means of universal functions which embody a few parameters which must be determined from experiment.

According to the theory of Breit and Wigner, the lth-partial-wave resonance-reaction cross section associated with a compound state with angular momentum I^* is given by[14]

$$\sigma_{x,x'}{}^l = \frac{\pi\lambda\!\!\!^{-2}(2l + 1)g_{I^*}\Gamma_x\Gamma_{x'}}{(T - T_r)^2 + (\Gamma^2/4)} \qquad (13\text{-}109)$$

where Γ_x and $\Gamma_{x'}$ are the partial widths connecting the compound state to the $x + X$ and $x' + X'$ states, respectively, Γ is the total width of the excited state, and

$$g_{I^*} = \frac{2I^* + 1}{(2s + 1)(2I + 1)(2l + 1)} \qquad (13\text{-}110)$$

is the statistical weight of the compound state. To go further with the discussion of the Breit-Wigner formula, we must specialize our discussion to be applicable to the particular cases which arise in practice. Let us first consider the case of neutron-induced processes.

13-11. Neutron-induced Resonant Processes. In Table 13-1 we indicate the predominant and secondary processes which appear to account for neutron cross sections in the various energy and nuclide regions. As noted in the table, the total cross section in the medium-fast region for light and medium nuclides can be explained largely in terms of elastic scattering. The resonant regions are particularly interesting because of

TABLE 13-1. IMPORTANT NEUTRON-INDUCED PROCESSES†

Neutron energy region	Light nuclides	Medium nuclides	Heavy nuclides
Slow	γ, α_r, n_r	γ, n_r	γ
Medium-fast	n_r	n_r	n
Fast	n_r, n', p_r, α_r	$n, n', 2n, p, \alpha$	$n', \gamma, 2n, \alpha, n, f$

† γ denotes the (n,γ) radiative capture process; n denotes elastic neutron scattering; n' denotes inelastic neutron scattering; α, p, $2n$, and f denote the (n,α), (n,p), $(n,2n)$, and neutron-induced fission reactions. The subscript r indicates that resonances are observed in the cross sections.

the detailed information which they yield concerning the resonance levels of the compound nucleus. In this region it is a good approximation to let

$$\Gamma \approx \Gamma_n \tag{13-111}$$

where Γ_n is the partial width for neutron reemission; then Eq. (13-109) becomes

$$\sigma_{n,n}{}^l = \frac{\pi \lambda\!\!\!^{-2}(2l + 1)g_{I^*}\Gamma^2}{(T - T_r)^2 + (\Gamma^2/4)} \tag{13-112}$$

In the neighborhood of an isolated resonance the Breit-Wigner formula gives the familiar type of resonance curve with the half width Γ and $\sigma_{\max} = g_{I^*}(2l + 1)4\pi\lambda\!\!\!^{-2}$. The experimental shapes for elastic neutron resonance, however, frequently deviate from that predicted by the Breit-Wigner formula just presented. These deviations are attributed to the interference between the potential and resonance scattering associated with the lth partial wave. When consideration is given to this phenomenon, the Breit-Wigner formula becomes[15]

$$\sigma_{n,n}{}^l = 4\pi\lambda\!\!\!^{-2}(2l + 1)g_{I^*}\left|\frac{\Gamma/2}{T - T_r - (i\Gamma/2)} - (\exp i\delta^l)\sin\delta^l\right|^2 + \sigma_p{}^l \tag{13-113}$$

where $\sigma_p{}^l$, which represents the balance of the potential scattering, is given by

$$\sigma_p{}^l = 4\pi\lambda\!\!\!^{-2}\sum_{l'\neq l}(2l' + 1)\sin^2\delta^{l'} + 4\pi\lambda\!\!\!^{-2}(1 - g_{I^*})(2l + 1)\sin^2\delta^l \tag{13-114}$$

The general characteristics of this cross-section formula may now be investigated quite readily. Far away from a resonance, *i.e.*, when $|T - T_r| > \Gamma/2$, resonant scattering becomes insignificant and we obtain just the usual potential scattering. On the other hand in the neighborhood of a resonance and when the δ^l are all small, just the resonance term is important. When the resonance and potential terms are comparable, the interference effects associated with the cross-product term in Eq. (13-113) result in a variety of resonant shapes depending upon the values of T_r, Γ, δ^l, and g_{I^*}. Some of these shapes are apparent in Fig. 7-13, which shows the neutron cross sections of S^{32}.

The theoretical cross sections all correspond to the case of a monoergic beam. A spread in energy will, of course, affect the shape of the observed line. To a certain extent this effect can be allowed for; however, the analysis is rather complicated, so that it is simpler, when studying resonances, to work with data corresponding to energy spreads which are small compared to the level widths.

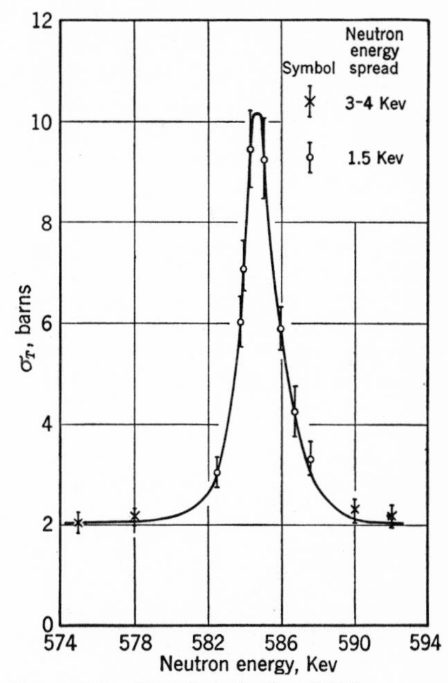

FIG. 13-3. Details of the 585-kev resonance of S^{32}. (*From Peterson, Barschall, and Bockelman, Ref.* 16.)

In Fig. 13-3 we indicate the details of the 585-kev resonance of S^{32}. This resonance has been analyzed by Feld, Feshbach, Goldberger, Goldstein, and Weisskopf,[15] who assign the quantum numbers $I^* = \frac{3}{2}$, $l = 1$, and the resonance parameters $\Gamma = 2$ kev and $\sigma_{\max} = 10.6$ barns. The reader is referred to this report for the results of their analysis of other resonances of S^{32} and the resonances associated with other nuclides.

For slow-neutron resonance ($\ll$100 ev), the S-wave ($l = 0$) radiative capture process is generally the most important process; hence in this region

$$\Gamma \approx \Gamma_\gamma \tag{13-115}$$

Since the partial width for neutron emission is proportional to the propagation constant of the neutron, we may in view of Eq. (13-94) set

$$\Gamma_n = \frac{k}{k_r}\,\Gamma_{nr} = \frac{\lambda\!\!\!^-_r}{\lambda\!\!\!^-}\,\Gamma_{nr} = \left(\frac{T}{T_r}\right)^{\frac{1}{2}}\Gamma_{nr} \tag{13-116}$$

where k_r and Γ_{nr} are the propagation constant and neutron width at resonance. According to the general Breit-Wigner formula, the S-wave radiative capture cross section for this case is

$$\sigma_{n,\gamma}{}^0 = \frac{g_{I^*}\pi\lambda\!\!\!^{-}\lambda\!\!\!^{-}_r\Gamma_{nr}\Gamma_\gamma}{(T - T_r)^2 + (\Gamma^2/4)} = \sigma_r\left(\frac{T_r}{T}\right)^{\frac{1}{2}}\left[\frac{\Gamma^2/4}{(T - T_r)^2 + (\Gamma^2/4)}\right] \tag{13-117}$$

where σ_r, the (n,γ) cross section at resonance, is equal to

$$\sigma_r = \frac{4\pi\lambda\!\!\!^{-}_r{}^2 g_{I^*}\Gamma_{nr}\Gamma_\gamma}{\Gamma^2} \tag{13-118}$$

In Fig. 13-4 we show the fit of the Breit-Wigner formula to a slow-neutron resonance in rhodium. On the lower side of a resonance, *i.e.*, when

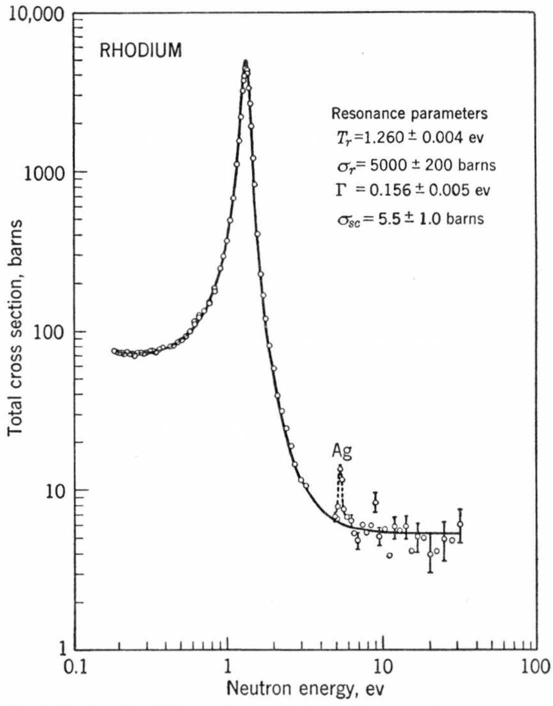

FIG. 13-4. The fit of the Breit-Wigner formula to a slow-neutron resonance in rhodium. The curve corresponds to the resonance parameters $T_r = 1.260$ ev, $\sigma_r = 5000$ barns, $\Gamma = 0.156$ ev, and $\sigma_{sc} = 5.5$ barns due to free-atom scattering. (*From Sailor, Ref.* 17.)

$T \ll T_r$, the denominator in the last factor of Eq. (13-117) may be treated as a constant; then the cross section varies simply as a constant times $T^{-\frac{1}{2}}$. Since $T^{-\frac{1}{2}} \sim 1/v$, this variation of the radiative capture cross section is referred to as the $1/v$ law.

Fast-neutron cross sections may usually be identified with processes in which the compound nucleus decays by the emission of a neutron with less energy than that of the incident neutron (*i.e.*, the residual nucleus is left in an excited state). This mode of decay generally becomes important when the level spacing is comparable with the level width, so that resonance effects are not observable. Since for fast neutrons there are many final states to decay by neutron emission, the total width of the compound state is large compared to the partial width Γ_n for neutron emission to the ground state of the residual. Elastic scattering consequently represents only a small fraction of the total cross section.

Except in the case of light nuclides the ejection of charged particles by fast neutrons is a rather unimportant process, even though this mode of decay is energetically possible. This fact is simply explained in terms of the coulomb penetrability factor in the formula for the partial width for charged-particle emission. When very fast neutrons are used, the number of energy states of the compound nucleus which are excited is usually so large that a statistical treatment is necessary.

13-12. Resonant Processes Induced by Charged Particles. The observations of the reactions induced by charged particles may be interpreted in a manner which is quite similar to the interpretation of neutron-induced reactions with the exception that the effect of the inward penetration of the coulomb barrier must be taken into account. These effects may be subdivided into two parts, (1) a modification of the probability of penetration into the nucleus because of the coulomb barrier and (2) a modification of the nuclear potential scattering by virtue of the coulomb (Rutherford) scattering. Resonant proton-induced processes have been detected in the (p,α) and (p,γ) processes for light nuclei. All of these reactions may be interpreted in terms of the Breit-Wigner formula by assigning appropriate total widths to the levels of the compound nucleus. When consideration is given to the coulomb penetrability, the partial widths for charged-particle emission are compatible with the known neutron partial widths in the same region of excitation. Because of the extreme sensitivity of the coulomb penetrability factor to energy, the variations of the cross sections with energy, particularly at lower kinetic energies, are due mostly to the coulomb penetrability factor.

Resonances have also been detected in several (d,p) and (d,n) reactions. Since the excitation of the compound nucleus formed after the capture of a deuteron is very high, it is unlikely that a resonance can be associated with the capture of the deuteron as a whole. Instead, according to the interpretation given to these resonances by Oppenheimer and Phillips,[18] the neutron or the proton alone is stripped from the deuteron and captured by the target nucleus. Accordingly the resonances are essentially those associated with the excited state formed by neutron or proton capture. The angular distributions of the particles resulting from these reactions also are consistent with the stripping interpretation.

Butler[19] has shown that these angular distributions can be used to infer the spin and parity of the final nucleus.

The interference effects between resonance scattering and Rutherford scattering have been studied in connection with the scattering of charged particles. For a discussion of these effects we refer the reader to early works of Bethe[20] and Devons[21] as well as the more recent studies of Crichtfield and Dodder[22] and Jackson and Galonsky.[23]

13-13. Reciprocity Theorem. One of the more powerful approaches to the theory of nuclear reactions makes use of the time-dependent perturbation theory. To apply this theory to nuclear reactions, we must evaluate the factor $d\mathfrak{N}/dT$. We recall that the number of states per unit propagation-constant range per unit volume of real space is

$$\frac{d\mathfrak{N}}{dk} = \frac{k^2}{2\pi^2} \tag{13-119}$$

If the propagation constants correspond to matter waves, we have

$$T = \frac{\hbar^2 k^2}{2m_r} \qquad \text{and} \qquad \frac{dT}{dk} = \frac{\hbar^2 k}{m_r} \tag{13-120}$$

Consequently the energy density of states per unit volume of real space is

$$\frac{d\mathfrak{N}}{dT} = \frac{d\mathfrak{N}/dk}{dT/dk} = \frac{m_r k}{2\pi^2\hbar^2} \tag{13-121}$$

If the waves corresponding to these states are streaming homogeneously in all directions, the number of states per unit volume whose propagation constants correspond to waves streaming into a unit solid angle $d\Omega$ in the direction $\mathbf{k}$ is

$$\mathfrak{N}(\mathbf{k}) = \mathfrak{N}\frac{d\Omega}{4\pi} = \frac{k^3}{24\pi^3}\,d\Omega \tag{13-122}$$

The number per unit propagation-constant interval and the number per unit energy therefore are

$$\frac{d\mathfrak{N}(\mathbf{k})}{dk} = \frac{k^2\,d\Omega}{8\pi^3} \tag{13-123}$$

and

$$\frac{d\mathfrak{N}(\mathbf{k})}{dT} = \frac{m_r k\,d\Omega}{8\pi^3\hbar^2} \tag{13-124}$$

The equation for the transition probability per unit time assumes many different aspects depending upon the detail with which one characterizes the initial and final states in a particular problem. For example, if we consider the probability per unit time for a system to jump into a state with the emission of a particle with the kinetic energy T, we use the

$d\mathfrak{N}/dT$ corresponding to a free particle having an arbitrary direction in space. Consequently for this case we have

$$w = \frac{2\pi}{\hbar} \left| \int \Psi_i^* H_{op} \Psi_f \, d\tau \right|^2 \frac{m_r k}{2\pi^2 \hbar^2} \tag{13-125}$$

On the other hand if we wish to calculate the probability of transition into a state in which the outgoing particle goes into a particular solid angle $d\Omega$, we use for the final state a wave function corresponding to a wave propagating in a particular direction $\mathbf{k}$, and for $d\mathfrak{N}/dT$ we use Eq. (13-124). The transition probability or the probability per unit time for emission into $d\Omega$ therefore is

$$w = \frac{2\pi}{\hbar} \left| \int \Psi_i^* H_{op} \Psi_f \, d\tau \right|^2 \frac{m_r k \, d\Omega}{8\pi^3 \hbar^2} \tag{13-126}$$

When there is one particle per unit volume, the incident flux is

$$\frac{\text{Incident probability}}{\text{Area} \times \text{time}} = v = \frac{\hbar k}{m_r} \tag{13-127}$$

Consequently, using Eq. (7-55), we obtain for the differential cross section

$$\sigma(\theta,\varphi) \, d\Omega = \frac{m_r m_r' k'}{4\pi^2 \hbar^4 k} \left| \int \Psi_i^* H_{op} \Psi_f \, d\tau \right|^2 d\Omega \tag{13-128}$$

where the primes are used to refer to the outgoing particles. The dependence of this cross section upon the "external" factors is quite revealing. Assuming the wave functions are independent of the angle, the formula for the total cross section of an $X(x,x')X'$ reaction may be written as

$$\sigma_{x,x'} = \frac{m_r m_r' k'}{\pi \hbar^4 k} \left| \int \Psi_i^* H_{op} \Psi_f \, d\tau \right|^2 \tag{13-129}$$

If we consider now the inverse reaction $X'(x',x)X$, we find

$$\sigma_{x',x} = \frac{m_r m_r' k}{\pi \hbar^4 k'} \left| \int \Psi_f^* H_{op} \Psi_i \, d\tau \right|^2 \tag{13-130}$$

Since the squared matrix elements are equal, we find, upon dividing Eq. (13-129) by Eq. (13-130),

$$\frac{\sigma_{x,x'}}{\sigma_{x',x}} = \frac{k'^2}{k^2} = \frac{p'^2}{p^2} \tag{13-131}$$

This result is known as the reciprocity theorem. It is very useful for inferring information about a reaction when the cross sections for the inverse reaction are known.

The quantitative dependence of transition probabilities per unit time and cross sections upon the matrix elements for the transition cannot be investigated in nuclear physics today, because relatively little is known about nuclear wave functions. Consequently, most considerations of these matrix elements have been limited to the study and the formulation of the conditions for which matrix elements vanish or do not vanish. These selection rules are first being unraveled in the research going on at this time, so that we refer the reader to the current literature for their description.

13-14. Statistical Theory. The concept of a compound state whose existence and decay are independent of its mode of formation has a strict quantum-mechanical significance only when a single excited state of the compound nucleus is involved in the reaction. When the incident beam of particles has an energy spread which is greater than the level spacing in the region of excitation of the compound nucleus, then several compound levels may be excited simultaneously. For a limited region of energies one must use a sum of wave functions in which there exist definite relations between the phases and amplitudes of the wave functions describing distinct energy levels. These phase relations and amplitudes will depend upon the nature of the excitation process. Consequently in this region the compound nucleus will "remember" in part its mode of formation. However, as we increase the incident energy as well as the energy spread, the number of excited compound levels becomes very large. We may then treat the phases as random or the superposition as incoherent. Again we arrive at a condition for which the compound nucleus forgets its mode of formation. Under these circumstances we can give meaning only to average values of the energies, the level widths, and the level spacings. The cross section for a particular process can be obtained by summing the Breit-Wigner formula over all the levels of the compound nucleus with an appropriate weight factor which depends upon the energy definition and the distribution of energy levels. As usual, the neutron-induced processes have been given the greatest attention.

Breit and Wigner[14] and Wigner[11] give for the average neutron-absorption cross section when many levels are involved

$$\bar{\sigma} = 2\pi\lambda\!\!\!^{-2}\,\frac{\bar{\Gamma}_a}{D}\,\frac{(1 + R/\lambda\!\!\!^{-})^2}{1 + (\lambda\!\!\!^{-}\bar{\Gamma}_a/2\gamma_n{}^2)} \qquad (13\text{-}132)$$

where $\bar{\Gamma}_a$ is the integrated width for absorption and the factor $\lambda\!\!\!^{-}\bar{\Gamma}_a/2\gamma_n{}^2$ in the denominator is generally small compared to 1. The above relation is valid up to about 300 kev in the heavy elements and to 1 Mev for light elements. At higher energies inelastic scattering becomes important and occasions a decrease in the cross sections.

A formula for any reaction cross section due to Bohr, Peierls, and

Placzek,[24] which is found by summations over many resonances and which is valid when $kR \ll 1$, is

$$\bar{\sigma}_{x,x'} = 2\pi^2\lambda\!\!\!^{-2} \frac{\bar{\Gamma}_x \bar{\Gamma}_{x'}}{\bar{D}^* \bar{\Gamma}^*} \tag{13-133}$$

where $\bar{\Gamma}_x$ and $\bar{\Gamma}_{x'}$ are the average integrated widths for emission of the particles x and x', and $\bar{D}^*$ and $\bar{\Gamma}^*$ are the average level spacing and total width associated with the compound nucleus. On the other hand, when $kR \gg 1$, these statistical methods give simply

$$\bar{\sigma}_{x,x'} = \pi R^2 \frac{\bar{\Gamma}_{x'}}{\bar{\Gamma}^*} \tag{13-134}$$

Equations (13-132) to (13-134) can all be placed in the form

$$\bar{\sigma}_{x,x'}(T) = \sigma_x(T)\eta_{x'}(W^*) \tag{13-135}$$

where $\sigma_x(T)$ is the cross section for the capture of the incident particle and

$$\eta_{x'} = \frac{\bar{\Gamma}_{x'}}{\bar{\Gamma}^*} \tag{13-136}$$

is the probability for the decay of the compound nucleus by the emission of x'. The remaining factors in these equations may be identified with $\sigma_x(T)$. We refer the reader back to Sec. 9-13 for a discussion of the application of these formulas. In Fig. 9-15 we have shown estimates of the integrated widths as functions of the excitation energy. At excitation energies higher than those indicated on this diagram, the partial width for decay by the emission of two neutrons becomes important. The partial width for the emission of protons is negligible in heavy elements because of the coulomb barrier. For light elements, decay by proton emission is competitive with decay by neutron emission at energies above the thresholds. However, the proton yield drops off rapidly after $Z = 30$ and may be ignored beyond $Z = 50$. At high excitations of medium-weight elements, decay by simultaneous proton and neutron emission is important and competitive with decay by neutron emission alone.

Feshbach, Peaslee, and Weisskopf[25] have proposed a continuum theory of neutron reactions which has been given considerable attention in the literature. According to this theory the neutron waves which penetrate into the nucleus are absorbed so rapidly that they do not return to interfere with incoming waves. Accordingly these authors assume that the interior wave in the neighborhood of the nuclear boundary is represented by

$$G_i = \exp\left[-i(\epsilon_0^2 + \epsilon_k^2)^{\frac{1}{2}}\rho\right] = \exp\left[-i(k^2 + K_0^2)^{\frac{1}{2}}r\right] \tag{13-137}$$

where

$$K_0 = \frac{\epsilon_0}{R} \approx 1 \times 10^{13} \tag{13-138}$$

The ratio G_i'/G_i at the nuclear boundary ($\rho = 1$ or $r = R$) has the value

$$\frac{G_i'}{G_i} = -i(\epsilon_0^2 + \epsilon_k^2)^{\frac{1}{2}} = -i(K_0^2 + k^2)^{\frac{1}{2}}R \tag{13-139}$$

This universal relation for all ϵ_k and for all nuclei is the fundamental assumption of the Feshbach-Peaslee-Weisskopf continuum theory of nuclear reactions. If we proceed to equate this ratio to the external ratio in the usual fashion of wave analysis, we are led for the case of S waves to

$$\epsilon_k \cot (\epsilon_k + \delta) = -i(\epsilon_0^2 + \epsilon_k^2)^{\frac{1}{2}} \tag{13-140}$$

a transcendental equation which leads to complex phase shifts. The significance of complex phase shifts is obvious from Eq. (13-29). In the case of pure potential scattering the amplitude A_l is a complex quantity whose magnitude is unity. However, when absorption occurs, the amplitude is a complex quantity whose magnitude is smaller than unity by virtue of the imaginary component of the phase shift. It can be shown in this case that the number of incoming particles exceeds the number of outgoing particles. The remaining flux corresponds to the ingoing particles which are absorbed in the formation of the compound nucleus. We refer the reader to Blatt and Weisskopf[9] for a comprehensive treatment of the Feshbach-Peaslee-Weisskopf theory. For our purposes here we might arrive at the major result of this continuum theory by certain elementary considerations.

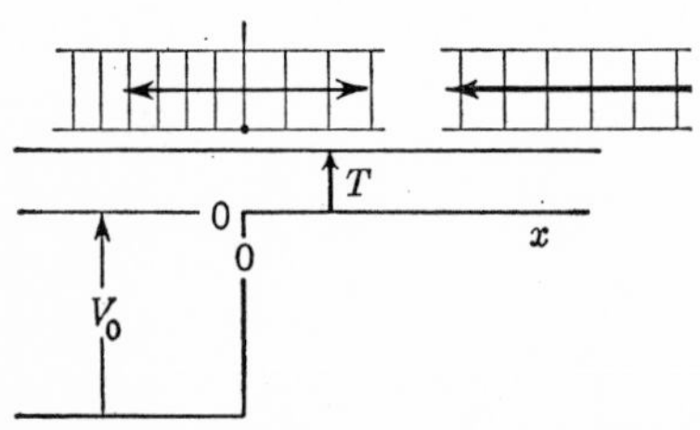

FIG. 13-5. Diagram illustrating an incident wave with energy T impinging upon a potential discontinuity and the reflected and transmitted waves.

Let us consider a problem in which particles coming from the right impinge upon a potential discontinuity characterized by (see Fig. 13-5)

$$\begin{aligned} V &= -V_0 \qquad \text{for } x < 0 \\ &= 0 \qquad \text{for } x > 0 \end{aligned} \tag{13-141}$$

Some of the particles will pass the potential discontinuity and be transmitted into the left region. Others will be reflected back by the discontinuity. The transmission coefficient, namely, the ratio of the number of transmitted particles to the number of incident particles, can be obtained from the ratio of the intensities of the transmitted wave to the incident wave. The reflection coefficient, which is the ratio of the number of reflected particles to the number of incident particles, follows from the ratio of the reflected to the incident intensity.

Using the dimensionless variable $\rho = x/a$, the wave equation is

$$\Psi'' + (\epsilon_0^2 + \epsilon_k^2)\Psi = 0 \qquad \text{for } \rho < 0 \tag{13-142}$$

and

$$\Psi'' + \epsilon_k^2\Psi = 0 \qquad \text{for } \rho > 0 \tag{13-143}$$

We may take as the right and left solutions for these equations

$$\Psi_r = A \exp(-i\epsilon_k\rho) + B \exp(i\epsilon_k\rho) \tag{13-144}$$

$$\Psi_l = C \exp[-i(\epsilon_k^2 + \epsilon_0^2)^{\frac{1}{2}}\rho] \tag{13-145}$$

where A, B, and C represent the amplitudes of the incident, reflected, and transmitted waves, respectively. Matching Ψ'/Ψ at $\rho = 0$, we find

$$\frac{A - B}{A + B} = \frac{\epsilon_0^2 + \epsilon_k^2}{\epsilon_k^2} \tag{13-146}$$

Solving for the reflection coefficient, we obtain

$$\mathcal{R} = \frac{B^2}{A^2} = \frac{[\epsilon_k - (\epsilon_0^2 + \epsilon_k^2)^{\frac{1}{2}}]^2}{[\epsilon_k + (\epsilon_0^2 + \epsilon_k^2)^{\frac{1}{2}}]^2} \tag{13-147}$$

Thus the reflected wave obviously grows smaller as ϵ_k becomes larger. Conservation of flux leads to the condition $A^2 = B^2 + C^2$. Hence the transmission coefficient is

$$\mathfrak{I} = \frac{C^2}{A^2} = 1 - \mathcal{R} = \frac{4\epsilon_k(\epsilon_k^2 + \epsilon_0^2)^{\frac{1}{2}}}{[\epsilon_k + (\epsilon_k^2 + \epsilon_0^2)^{\frac{1}{2}}]^2} = \frac{4k(k^2 + K_0^2)^{\frac{1}{2}}}{[k + (k^2 + K_0^2)^{\frac{1}{2}}]^2} \tag{13-148}$$

One may now arrive at the result of the Feshbach-Peaslee-Weisskopf continuum theory by assuming that the neutron-absorption cross section is the product of the transmission coefficient and the effective area presented to the neutrons by the target nuclei. In view of the lack of definition of the neutron beam over a distance equal to the wavelength, we may accept $\pi(R + ƛ)^2$ for the effective area. Consequently the absorption cross section is

$$\sigma_a = \pi(R + ƛ)^2 \frac{4k(k^2 + K_0^2)^{\frac{1}{2}}}{[k + (k^2 + K_0^2)^{\frac{1}{2}}]^2} \tag{13-149}$$

To obtain the total cross section, we must add the elastic-scattering cross section, which results from waves reflected at the potential discontinuity and at the centrifugal barrier outside the nucleus. When this result is added to σ_a, a total cross section is obtained which should compare with the experimental total cross sections as measured by absorption experiments. The Feshbach-Peaslee-Weisskopf theory leads to total cross sections which decrease monotonically with increasing energy according to

$$\sigma_t = \frac{4\pi}{k(k^2 + K_0^2)^{\frac{1}{2}}} \qquad \lambdabar \gg R \tag{13-150}$$

and

$$\sigma_t = 2\pi(R + \lambdabar)^2 \qquad \lambdabar \ll R \tag{13-151}$$

Contradicting the general nature of these functions, the experimental work of Barschall and others reveals minima and maxima which are more suggestive of the potential-scattering picture which we have previously discussed. In view of this recent experimental evidence Feshbach, Porter, and Weisskopf[27] have considered a compromise between the potential-scattering picture and the compound-nucleus picture which is heavily weighted with respect to the former description. Following the optical model of Fernbach, Serber, and Taylor,[26] they assume a complex potential

$$\begin{aligned} V(r) &= -V_0(1 + i\zeta) \qquad && \text{for } r < R \\ &= 0 && \text{for } r > R \end{aligned} \tag{13-152}$$

The factor ζ characterizes the absorption of neutrons in nuclear matter, in the sense that

$$d = \zeta^{-1}(k^2 + K_0^2)^{-\frac{1}{2}} \tag{13-153}$$

is the distance within nuclear matter in which the neutron intensity reduces by $1/e$. To fit the experimental observations, Feshbach, Porter, and Weisskopf choose

$$V_0 = 19 \text{ Mev} \qquad R = 1.45 \times 10^{-13} A^{\frac{1}{3}} \qquad \zeta = 0.05$$

This last parameter corresponds to a free path of 2×10^{-12} cm, which is considerably larger than the value intrinsic to the Feshbach-Peaslee-Weisskopf continuum theory. This larger mean free path in nuclear matter is probably the effect of the exclusion principle, which lessens the interaction of the incident neutron with nucleons in the fully occupied low-lying states.

The theoretical total cross sections based upon Eq. (13-152) are quite promising. They are indicated in Fig. 13-6 alongside the experimental results. The same complex potential also leads to angular distributions that may be compatible with angular distributions experimentally measured by Walt and Barschall at 1 Mev (see Fig. 7-16) and by Snowdon and Whitehead[40] at 3.7 Mev. However, it is still an open question as to how quantitatively and how completely this simple phenomenological theory can account for the experimental data. Adair[7] has suggested the use of a potential well depth of 40 Mev instead of 19 Mev in Eq. (13-152). This deeper well would serve to identify a low-velocity resonance in the total cross section at $A = 150$ with the critical value $\epsilon_0 = 7\pi/2$ [see Eq. (13-84)], whereas the 19-Mev well depth identifies it with the $\epsilon_0 = 5\pi/2$ resonance. The 40-Mev well depth seems necessary to account for bound levels of heavy nuclei as described by the shell model. It appears likely that this deeper well will not invalidate the successes of this so-called "cloudy crystal ball" model of the nucleus.[41]

13-15. Photonuclear Cross Sections.[9,28–30] The photonuclear effect may be interpreted as a radiative transition from the ground state of

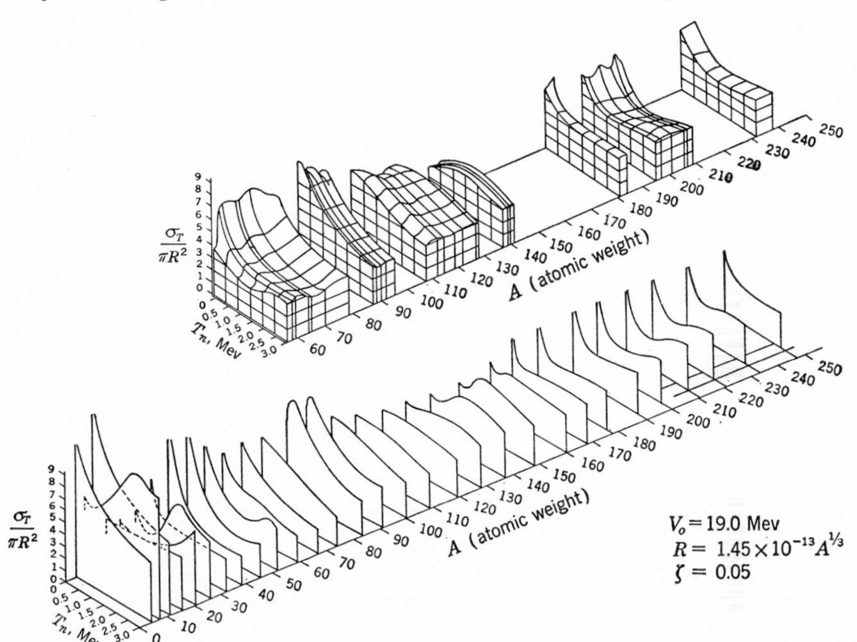

FIG. 13-6. Total neutron cross section as a function of energy and atomic number. Upper profile: experimental results. (*From Barschall, Ref.* 8.) Lower profile: theoretical results, with the constants as indicated. (*From Feshbach, Porter, and Weisskopf, Ref.* 27.)

the target to a final state which consists of the residual nucleus and one or more ejected particles. Since the incident-gamma-ray energy usually spans many levels, the assumption of the intermediate formation of a compound or excited nucleus in the statistical sense would appear to be particularly justified here. According to the statistical theory the photonuclear cross section is

$$\sigma_{\gamma,x}(E_\gamma) = \sigma_\gamma(E_\gamma)\eta_x(W^*) \qquad (13\text{-}154)$$

where $\sigma_\gamma(E_\gamma)$ is the total cross section for the capture of a photon and $\eta_x(W^*)$ is the probability for the ejection of x. Of course, in this case

$$W^* = E_\gamma \qquad (13\text{-}155)$$

i.e., the excitation energy of the excited or compound nucleus in the case of gamma-induced processes is simply the energy of the gamma ray. Theoretical estimates of capture cross sections have been made on the basis of the inverse of the theory of radiative transitions. Such a study can be carried out in a general way without reference to a particular model for the absorption mechanism. The results of such a qualitative study by Blatt and Weisskopf(31) are shown in Fig. 13-7, in which the contributions to the formation of the excited nucleus by means of vari-

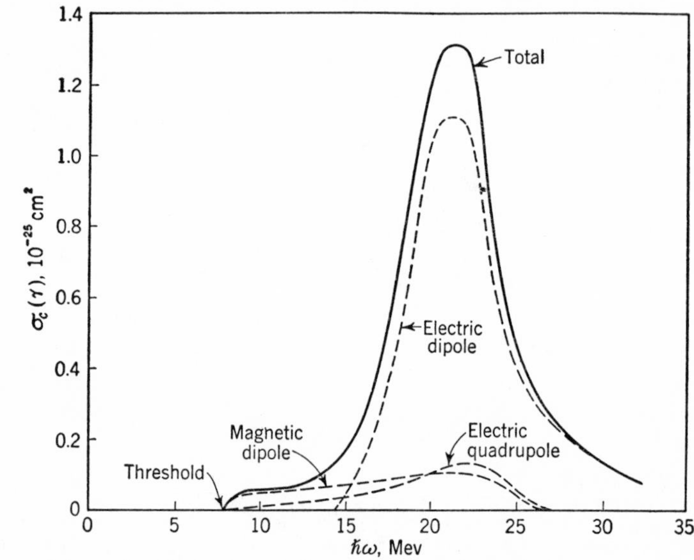

FIG. 13-7. Schematic illustration of the qualitative theoretical expectation regarding the cross section $\sigma_c(\gamma)$ for the formation of an excited nucleus by gamma-ray absorption. The contributions from electric dipole, magnetic dipole, and electric quadrupole radiation are shown separately. The figure is drawn for an intermediate nucleus. (*From Blatt and Weisskopf, Ref.* 31.)

ous gamma-ray absorption processes are shown. We note that the bulk of the cross section is contributed by electric dipole absorption.

The cross sections for various photonuclear processes to be expected on the basis of the statistical model follow readily from Eq. (13-154) if we use the calculated $\sigma_\gamma(E_\gamma)$ in conjunction with $\eta_x = \bar{\Gamma}_x/\bar{\Gamma}^*$ (see Fig. 9-15). Experimental tests of the theoretical predictions may be made in various ways. Since the total gamma-absorption cross section is

$$\sigma_{\gamma t} = \sum_x \sigma_{\gamma,x} = \sigma_\gamma \sum_x \eta_x = \sigma_\gamma \qquad (13\text{-}156)$$

we see that the total absorption cross section is simply equal to the photon-capture cross section. In view of the coulomb barrier against the emission of charged particles, one would expect that neutrons would predominate as the ejected particles.

In Fig. 13-8 we indicate the general shape of the observed photoneutron-production cross section for a typical nuclide as measured by neutron-detecting technique. A "giant" resonance rising to the neighborhood of 100 millibarns occurs at about 6 or 7 Mev above the (γ,n) threshold. The total photonuclear cross section falls off abruptly above the giant resonance and then, according to Jones and Terwilliger,[29] rises slowly up to about half the resonance peak at 320 Mev. The giant resonance is mainly associated with the (γ,n) reaction. Katz *et al.*[28] report that the location of $E_{\max}$ (see Fig. 13-8) past $A \approx 100$ varies as $A^{-\frac{1}{6}}$, with fluctuations of about 2 Mev from this A dependence. The width of the resonance ranges from about 2 Mev for light nuclei to 6 Mev for $A \approx 50$, then slowly back to 5 Mev for $A \approx 200$.

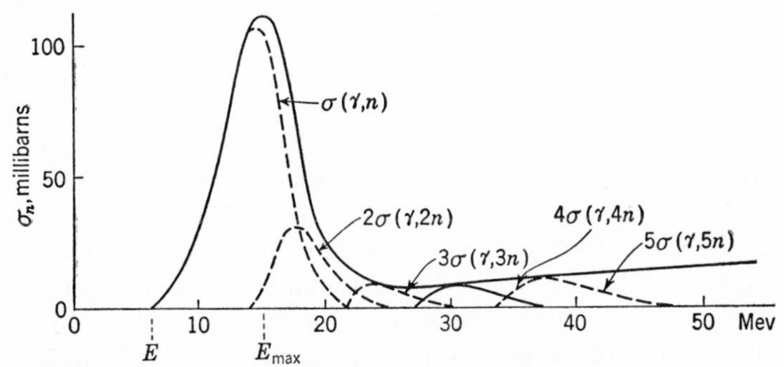

FIG. 13-8. Schematic illustration of photoneutron-production cross section, showing qualitatively the contributions of (γ,n), $(\gamma,2n)$, and $(\gamma,3n)$ processes.

The $(\gamma,2n)$, $(\gamma,3n)$, . . . processes make appreciable contributions to the photoneutron-production cross section above their respective thresholds. If we assume that the cross sections for the production of charged particles, because of the coulomb barrier, are much smaller than the cross sections for neutron production, then we may interpret the curve shown in Fig. 13-8 as the photocapture cross section multiplied by the average number of neutrons emitted per event. The contributions of the individual reactions to σ_n in Fig. 13-8 are indicated schematically.

Various workers[32-34] have observed that at low energies the photoejected particles have a spherically symmetrical distribution. This is in conformity with the expectation on the basis of the statistical model, since the compound nucleus should not remember the direction of the incident gamma ray. On the other hand some of the experiments on the photonuclear effect appear to disagree with the statistical model. Among these are experiments which indicate that high-energy protons from (γ,p) reactions are not spherically symmetrical. Stephens[32] reports striking differences in the distributions of photoprotons ejected by 24-Mev *Bremsstrahlung* for indium, cerium, and bismuth. The proton distribution has a peak at about 60 Mev for indium, rises very slightly in the backward direction for cerium, and rises markedly in the forward direction for bismuth. Cameron,[32] using gamma rays obtained from an electron synchrotron operated at 25, 40, and 60 Mev, finds forward peaking for aluminum photoprotons but an asymmetry for tantalum of the form $a + b \sin^2 \theta$. In the energy region above 150 Mev, Wattenberg *et al.*[32] find the carbon photoprotons to be peaked in the forward direction with the asymmetry becoming greater with increased energy. Feld,[32] using a result of the study of the atomic photoeffect, finds that the distributions obtained by Wattenberg may be represented by

$$\sigma(\theta,\varphi) = \frac{a + b \sin^2 \theta}{[1 - (v/c) \cos \theta]^4} \tag{13-157}$$

with $b/a \approx 3$ for 190-Mev protons and somewhat less for higher-energy protons.

It has been noted by several physicists that the number of photoprotons relative to the number of photoneutrons is frequently too great to be explained by the statistical theory. In addition, the spectrum of photoprotons noted by Stephens[32] does not conform to the expectations of the statistical model, there being too many high-energy particles. Anisotropy in photofission fragments recently observed at 16 Mev by Winhold[32] also would appear to contradict the statistical model.

Several attempts have been made to resolve the contradictions between experiment and the statistical model. To account for the large numbers of photoprotons, Courant[35] has suggested the occurrence of a direct photoprotonic effect analogous to the atomic photoelectric effect. Goldhaber and Teller[36] have proposed a special model in which the high-energy gamma-ray absorption, particularly the giant resonance, is caused by nuclear dipole vibrations in which protons are induced to move one way and neutrons in the opposite direction. Steinwedel and Jensen[37] have shown that this model accounts for the general variation of E_{max} with A as well as for the magnitude and dependence upon A of the integrated cross sections. The integrated cross section for absorption of a photon is defined as

$$I_\sigma = \int \sigma_\gamma(E_\gamma)\, dE_\gamma \tag{13-158}$$

and is measured in Mev-barns. Experimentally it is obtained from the area under the curve for the total absorption cross section when the assumption is made that the high-energy tail of the curve declines rapidly to zero.

In a theoretical study which is based upon rather general sum rules and is not dependent upon any special mechanism for photoabsorption,

Levinger and Bethe[38] have calculated the integrated cross section for the dipole absorption of a photon. They obtain

$$\int_0^\infty \sigma_\gamma(E_\gamma)\, dE_\gamma = 0.060 \frac{NZ}{A} (1 + 0.8x) \tag{13-159}$$

where x is the fraction of the exchange force in the neutron-proton interaction. The experimental evidence for all but the light nuclei appears to bear out this theoretical formula. Eyges[39] obtains from his data for $_{73}Ta^{181}$

$$\int \sigma_\gamma\, dE_\gamma = 3.77 \text{ Mev-barns} \tag{13-160}$$

This corresponds to $x = 0.56$, which is in reasonable agreement with the theory and other experimental results. Katz[32] also notes agreement of Eq. (13-159) with experiment for all but light nuclei. For light nuclei, the experimental values appear to be smaller than those calculated from the Bethe-Levinger theory. On the other hand Halpern[32] and Jones and Terwilliger,[29] in a study of yields of photoreactions using 320-Mev *Bremsstrahlung,* find integrated cross sections somewhat larger than expected from Eq. (13-159). Halpern notes that the photoreaction cross sections beyond 150 Mev are mostly connected with photomeson production.

The independent particle model has been explored as an opposite extreme to the classical model of Goldhaber and Teller. This model, however, fails in the following ways: (1) the calculated cross sections for direct ejection of photoneutrons are too small; (2) the predicted values of E_{max} are too low; and (3) absorption is expected to occur appreciably below the (γ,n) threshold.

Present thinking seems to favor a model intermediate between the two extremes. This intermediate model may take a form in which some small group of nucleons plays the important part in the absorption of gamma rays. In the collective model of A. Bohr the nucleons beyond a closed shell would serve as such a group. Serious consideration has also been given to a model in which the subunit is a quasi-deuteron consisting of a proton and neutron which happen to be close together. The quasi-deuteron model appears to be useful in the high-energy region, although its significance in the 10- to 20-Mev region is not yet clear.

Whatever the final interpretation of photoinduced processes turns out to be, it would appear that work in this field has proved to be far more interesting and fruitful than had originally been expected.

PROBLEMS

***13-1.** Plot the S-wave phase shifts and the S-wave cross sections (in units of πa^2) as functions of ϵ_k for the square well when (a) $\epsilon_0 = 5\pi/2$ and (b) $\epsilon_0 = 8$.

***13-2.** Plot the S-wave phase shifts and cross sections (in units of πa^2) as functions of ϵ_k for the square barrier when (a) $\epsilon_0 = 5\pi/2$, (b) $\epsilon_0 = 8$.

***13-3.** Plot the S-wave phase shifts and S-wave cross sections (in units of πa^2) as functions of ϵ_0 for the square well for (a) $\epsilon_k = 0$, (b) $\epsilon_k = 0.25$, and (c) $\epsilon_k = 1$.

***13-4.** Plot the S-wave phase shifts and S-wave cross sections (in units of πa^2) for the square barrier as functions of ϵ_0 for (a) $\epsilon_k = 0$, (b) $\epsilon_k = 0.25$, and (c) $\epsilon_k = 1$.

13-5. Verify Eqs. (13-29) and (13-30).

***13-6.** The 0- to 2-Mev scattering of neutrons by deuterons in the center-of-mass system may be characterized by the function $\sigma(\theta,\varphi) = \lambda\!\!\!^{-2}(A + B\cos\theta + C\cos^2\theta)$. Assuming independent scattering in the quartet and doublet states, derive a formula for A, B, and C in terms of the ^2S, ^2P, ^4S, and ^4P phase shifts. An analysis indicates that at 1-Mev bombarding energies $\delta(^2S) = -65°$, $\delta(^4S) = -22°$, $\delta(^2P) = -6°$, and $\delta(^4P) = 10°$. What is the total cross section? Plot the differential cross section per unit solid angle.

***13-7.** Estimate the natural widths associated with the 115-, 375-, and 700-kev resonances of S^{32} under the assumptions (a) that they are S-wave resonances, (b) that $\delta^\circ = -kR$, where $R = 1.5A^{\frac{1}{3}} \times 10^{-13}$, and (c) that $\sigma_p{}^0$ may be ignored. Compare the theoretical resonance shapes with the observed shapes.

***13-8.** Plot the theoretical curve for the 585-kev resonance of S^{32} on the basis of the resonance parameters assigned by Feld *et al.*[15]

REFERENCES

1. Faxen, H., and J. Holtsmark: *Z. Physik*, **45**, 307 (1927).
2. Mott, N. F., and H. S. W. Massey: "The Theory of Atomic Collisions," 2d ed., Oxford University Press, New York, 1949.
3. Watson, G. N.: "Theory of Bessel Functions," p. 128, The Macmillan Company, New York, 1944.
4. Schiff, L. I.: "Quantum Mechanics," p. 114, McGraw-Hill Book Company, Inc., New York, 1949.
5. Schiff, L. I.: *ibid.*, p. 110.
6. Massey, H. S. W., and C. B. H. Mohr: *Proc. Roy. Soc.* (*London*), **A141,** 434 (1933).
7. Adair, R. K.: *Phys. Rev.*, **94,** 737 (1954).
8. Barschall, H. H.: *Phys. Rev.*, **86,** 431 (1952).
9. Blatt, J., and V. Weisskopf: "Theoretical Nuclear Physics," p. 361, John Wiley & Sons, Inc., New York, 1952.
10. Bethe, H. A.: *Revs. Mod. Phys.*, **9,** 75 (1937).
11. Wigner, E. P.: *Am. J. Phys.*, **17,** 99 (1949).
12. Feshbach, H., D. C. Peaslee, and V. Weisskopf: *Phys. Rev.*, **71,** 145 (1947).
13. Adair, R. K.: *Revs. Mod. Phys.*, **22,** 254 (1950).
14. Breit, G., and E. P. Wigner: *Phys. Rev.*, **49,** 519 (1936).
15. Feld, B. T., H. Feshbach, M. L. Goldberger, H. Goldstein, and V. F. Weisskopf: *U.S. Atomic Energy Comm. NYO* 636 (1951).
16. Peterson, R. E., H. H. Barschall, and C. K. Bockelman: *Phys. Rev.*, **79,** 593 (1950).
17. Sailor, V. L.: *Phys. Rev.*, **91,** 55 (1953).
18. Oppenheimer, J. R., and M. Phillips: *Phys. Rev.*, **48,** 500 (1935).
19. Butler, S. T.: *Proc. Roy. Soc.* (*London*), **A208,** 559 (1951).
20. Bethe, H. A.: *Revs. Mod. Phys.*, **9,** 174 (1937).
21. Devons, S.: *Proc. Roy. Soc.* (*London*), **A172,** 127, 559 (1939).
22. Crichtfield, C. L., and D. C. Dodder: *Phys. Rev.*, **76,** 602 (1949).
23. Jackson, H. L., and A. Galonsky: *Phys. Rev.*, **84,** 401 (1951).

24. Bohr, A., R. E. Peierls, and G. Placzek: *Nature,* **144,** 200 (1939).
25. Feshbach, H., D. C. Peaslee, and V. F. Weisskopf: *Phys. Rev.,* **71,** 145 (1947).
26. Fernbach, S., R. Serber, and T. B. Taylor: *Phys. Rev.,* **75,** 1352 (1949).
27. Feshbach, H., C. E. Porter, and V. F. Weisskopf: *Phys. Rev.,* **90,** 166 (1953).
28. Montalbetti, R., L. Katz, and J. Goldenberg: *Phys. Rev.,* **91,** 659 (1953).
29. Jones, L. W., and K. M. Terwilliger: *Phys. Rev.,* **91,** 699 (1953).
30. Templeton, D. H.: *Ann. Rev. Nuclear Sci.,* **2,** 93 (1953).
31. Blatt, J., and V. Weisskopf: "Theoretical Nuclear Physics," p. 656, John Wiley & Sons, Inc., New York, 1952.
32. Report of M.I.T. Conference on Photonuclear Physics, May 4–5, 1953.
33. Kerst, D. W., and G. A. Price: *Phys. Rev.,* **79,** 725 (1950).
34. Diven, B. C., and G. M. Almy: *Phys. Rev.,* **80,** 407 (1950).
35. Courant, E. D.: *Phys. Rev.,* **82,** 703 (1951).
36. Goldhaber, M., and E. Teller: *Phys. Rev.,* **74,** 1046 (1948).
37. Steinwedel, H., and J. H. D. Jensen: *Z. Naturforsch.,* **69,** 217 (1951).
38. Levinger, J. S., and H. A. Bethe: *Phys. Rev.,* **78,** 115 (1950).
39. Eyges, L.: *Phys. Rev.,* **86,** 325 (1952).
40. Snowdon, S. C., and W. D. Whitehead: *Phys. Rev.,* **94,** 1267 (1954).
41. Feshbach, H., C. E. Porter, and V. F. Weisskopf: *Phys. Rev.,* **96,** 1267 (1954). See also Barschall, H. H.: *Am. J. Phys.,* **22,** 517 (1954).

CHAPTER 14

NUCLEAR FORCES

All the material which we have discussed thus far, of course, bears directly upon the question of the basic nature of nuclear forces. Thus the systematics of nuclear masses, binding energies, magnetic moments, quadrupole moments, energy levels, scattering cross sections, and transition probabilities reveal important nuclear tendencies, which should be useful in efforts to find a suitable theory of nuclear interactions. We have already inferred the following tendencies: (1) strong forces, (2) saturation, (3) incompressibility, (4) charge symmetry, (5) pairing, and (6) spin-orbit coupling. A successful theory of nuclear forces must account for these tendencies.

Although complex systems provide valuable information, the multiplicity of coordinates needed usually complicates the analysis so much that the basic interactions are obscured. There are also indications that many-body forces may arise in complex systems, forces which cannot be handled with present methods of calculation. Accordingly we might look to simple systems for guidance as to the nature of nuclear forces. The simplest of these are the basic two-body problems of nuclear physics, the neutron-proton system, the proton-proton system, and the neutron-neutron system.

14-1. Low- and Moderate-energy Data. Of the three possible nucleon-nucleon systems, only the neutron-proton system is known to exist in a stable state of binding (*i.e.*, the deuteron). The facts that He^2 and the bineutron are not stable are in themselves revealing clues concerning nuclear forces. We shall now present the major facts obtained from low- and moderate-energy experiments (0 to 10 Mev) which are thought to bear upon the nature of nuclear forces in the neutron-proton system and the proton-proton system. Little as yet is known about the neutron-neutron system. Efforts to interpret these facts will be described in the later sections.

Listed below are several important static properties of the deuteron which have been established by experiment:

Binding energy: $B = 2.226 \pm 0.003$ Mev
Spin moment: $I = 1$
Magnetic moment: $\mu = 0.8573$
Quadrupole moment: $Q = 2.74$ millibarns

The deuteron binding energy quoted above has been obtained from experimental investigations of the $H^1(n,\gamma)H^2$, $H^2(p,n)2p$, and $H^2(\gamma,n)H^1$ reactions. The moments listed above have been obtained from molecular-beam experiments.

The photodisintegration cross sections of the deuteron at various energies above the threshold (2.226 Mev) are shown in Fig. 14-1. The differential cross sections in the center-of-mass system are consistent with the formula

$$\sigma(\theta,\varphi) = a + b(1 + \kappa \cos \theta) \sin^2 \theta \tag{14-1}$$

where $\kappa \approx 0$ for low gamma energies (<5 Mev). Experimental values[2] of the ratio a/b for gamma-ray energies slightly in excess of the photo-

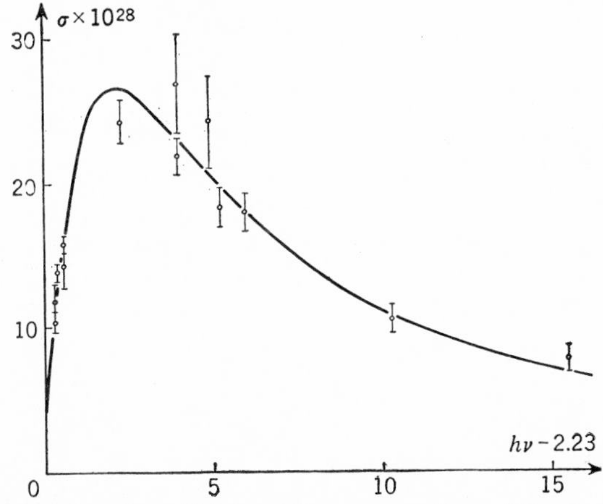

FIG. 14-1. Graph showing photodisintegration cross sections of the deuteron at energies above the threshold. The smooth curve corresponds to a theoretical result based upon a Yukawa potential. (*From Hulthén and Nagel, Ref.* 1.)

disintegration threshold are about 0.4; they fall to about 0.2 at 0.5 Mev and about 0.1 at 4 Mev. For gamma-ray energies of 10 Mev or more, Fuller[3] finds the photoprotons to have a slight asymmetry relative to $\theta = 90°$, there being more forward protons. At 6 and 7 Mev, Goldhaber[4] finds that $a/b \approx 0.09$ and 0.17, respectively, and $\kappa \approx 0.4$. Between 18 and 22 Mev, Weinstock and Halpern[5] find $a/b \approx 0.19$ and $\kappa \approx 0.2$.

Experimental data on the total neutron cross section of hydrogen as a function of energy are shown in Fig. 14-2. The slow-neutron cross section (1 to 10 ev) approaches the value 20.36 barns.[7] In the thermal range ($\ll$1 ev) the scattering of neutrons is sensitive in several ways to the molecular binding of the proton. Of particular interest is the scattering of protons by molecular hydrogen in the ortho and para forms. For 20°K neutrons (0.00173 ev) Sutton *et al.*[8] obtain the cross sections

124 barns for orthohydrogen and 3.97 barns for parahydrogen. The differential neutron-proton cross section indicates isotropy in the center-of-mass system for energies less than 15 Mev.

The low-energy experimental cross sections for the $H^1(n,\gamma)H^2$ reaction appear to follow the theoretically predicted $1/v$ law, *i.e.*,

$$\sigma_c v = \text{constant} \tag{14-2}$$

Whitehouse and Graham[9] report the constant 6.81×10^{-20} cm³/sec. The weighted-mean thermal-neutron cross section ($\bar{T} \approx 0.025$ ev, $\bar{v} \approx 2.2 \times 10^5$ cm/sec) is given by Hornyak *et al.*[2] as 0.316 barn.

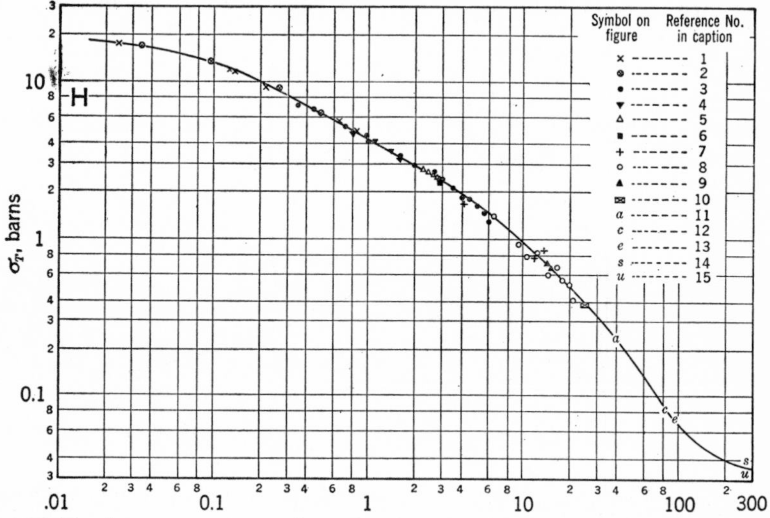

Fig. 14-2. Total neutron cross sections of hydrogen as a function of the neutron kinetic energy (in Mev). See Ref. 6 for the sources of the experimental points. (*From Adair, Ref.* 6.)

Proton-proton scattering has been the subject of many precise experiments starting with the early work of Tuve, Heydenburg and Hafstad[10] and Herb, Kerst, Parkinson, and Plain.[11] The recent work, in the 1- to 5-Mev range, by Worthington, Findley, and McGruer[12] at Wisconsin under the supervision of R. G. Herb and, in the 18-Mev range, by Yntema and White[13] at Princeton is probably the most precise now available. The data and the analysis will be discussed in Sec. 14-6.

Although the $H^1(p,\beta^+)H^2$ reaction has been studied extensively, there is no direct experimental information on this reaction. This reaction is now thought to be very important in solar and stellar energy evolution.[2] The theoretical cross section is of the order of 10^{-35} barn at 1 Mev.

14-2. Interpretation with a Spin-independent Central Force. Almost every effort made thus far to interpret the experimental evidence bearing upon the neutron-proton, proton-proton and neutron-neutron interactions starts with the assumption of a particular type of interaction. Several experimental facts are then used to adjust some initially undetermined parameters which appear in the interaction function. The adjusted interaction function is then evaluated on the basis of the consistency with further experimental data of the deductions based upon it. The greater and broader the amount of experimental information, which is summarized by an interaction function containing only a few adjusted constants, the more useful and the more convincing it becomes.

For the purposes of our introductory discussion we shall first proceed on the assumption that the nucleon-nucleon interaction is spin-independent and is of the central-field type, *i.e.*, that

$$V = V(r, V_0, a, \text{shape})$$

Later we shall be more realistic and allow for the existence of spin-dependent and noncentral forces. Once the form (shape) of the potential function has been agreed upon, it is possible to characterize it uniquely by a depth parameter and a range parameter. The well shapes most frequently assumed in efforts to interpret the experimental data are the square well, the exponential well, the Gaussian well, and the Yukawa well. In each of these cases one may introduce a dimensionless "well strength" ϵ_0, which depends upon the well depth and well width by the relation

$$\epsilon_0 = \left(\frac{V_0}{\hbar^2/2m_r a^2}\right)^{\frac{1}{2}} = \left(\frac{V_0}{E_0}\right)^{\frac{1}{2}} \tag{14-3}$$

where E_0 is the natural energy unit. Since for nucleon-nucleon problems $m_r \approx m/2$, where $m \approx 1$ MU,

$$E_0 = \frac{\hbar^2}{2m_r a^2} \approx \frac{\hbar^2}{ma^2} \approx \frac{41.4}{\mathbf{a}^2} \quad \text{Mev} \tag{14-4}$$

where **a** is in units of 10^{-13} cm. The effect of the well in nucleon-nucleon scattering and bound-state problems enters primarily through the well-strength parameter ϵ_0.

The parameter α, defined by

$$\alpha = \left(\frac{2m_r|W|}{\hbar^2}\right)^{\frac{1}{2}} = \left(\frac{mB}{\hbar^2}\right)^{\frac{1}{2}} \tag{14-5}$$

where B is the binding energy of the deuteron, arises frequently in studies of the deuteron and in neutron-proton scattering. From Eq. (10-87) we see that this parameter determines the rate of decrease of the radial wave function at long ranges. The reciprocal of α is frequently referred to as the deuteron radius. If we accept the recent value $B = 2.226$ Mev, we find for the deuteron radius

$$\alpha^{-1} = 4.314 \times 10^{-13} \text{ cm} \tag{14-6}$$

In many problems the details of the deuteron ground-state wave function inside the well have little influence upon the physical process under study. For such problems one may sometimes replace the exact wave function everywhere by the asymptotic wave function. When this wave function is normalized, it becomes

$$\Psi = \left(\frac{\alpha}{2\pi}\right)^{\frac{1}{2}} \frac{e^{-\alpha r}}{r} \tag{14-7}$$

This wave function may be viewed as the ground-state wave function corresponding to the case for which the well depth is extremely large and the well range is extremely small. When application is made of this wave function, the results are referred to as the zero-range approximation.

The application of quantum mechanics to the deuteron problem has an aspect which is somewhat unusual in relation to problems which we have previously considered. We here know quite accurately the energy eigenvalue ($W = -2.226$ Mev), but we do not know the depth, width, and shape of the well. In studies of the deuteron problem we generally assume one of the usual well shapes and seek the well parameters which will give rise to the observed binding energy. The good-behavior requirement on wave functions leads to an eigenvalue relationship between ϵ_0 and $\epsilon_B = (B/E_0)^{\frac{1}{2}}$. Since B is here known, this eigenvalue equation may be viewed as a relationship between the well parameters V_0 and a. To illustrate this development, let us consider again the square well. We have already shown that the eigenvalue relation for S states is

$$\tan\, (\epsilon_0{}^2 - \epsilon_B{}^2)^{\frac{1}{2}} = -\frac{(\epsilon_0{}^2 - \epsilon_B{}^2)^{\frac{1}{2}}}{\epsilon_B} \tag{14-8}$$

The binding-energy parameter ϵ_B is given by

$$\epsilon_B = \left(\frac{B}{E_0}\right)^{\frac{1}{2}} = 0.232\mathbf{a} \tag{14-9}$$

We must now find a well-strength parameter ϵ_0 which, together with this ϵ_B, satisfies the energy-eigenvalue equation.

Since the deuteron has only one state of binding and since this binding energy is rather weak compared to the natural unit E_0 for any reasonable value of $\mathbf{a}$, we might expect to find ϵ_0 to be slightly in excess of $\pi/2$ (1.571). Looking in this vicinity, we find for $\mathbf{a} = 1$ by numerical solution of Eq. (14-8) that $\epsilon_0 = 1.692$. Accordingly the range $a = 1 \times 10^{-13}$ is consistent with $V_0 = 118$ Mev. By selecting other ranges and proceeding in this same way, we can find the functions $\epsilon_0(a)$ and $V_0(a)$ which will give rise to 2.226 Mev binding energy of the deuteron. These functions are shown in Fig. 14-3.

Having determined the function $V_0(a)$, we may now proceed to the analysis of neutron-proton scattering with the hope of uniquely determining the values of V_0 and a which will account for the properties of the deuteron and neutron-proton scattering cross sections. We recall from Chap. 13 that, for the low-velocity limit when ϵ_0 is somewhat removed from the critical value $\pi/2$,

$$\sigma^0(0) = 4\pi a^2 \left(\frac{\tan \epsilon_0}{\epsilon_0} - 1\right)^2 \qquad (14\text{-}10)$$

If we assume **a** = 1 and, in order to account for the deuteron binding, $\epsilon_0 = 1.692$, we obtain for the low-velocity-limit cross section

$$\sigma^0(0) = 4\pi \times 10^{-26} \left(\frac{\tan 1.692}{1.692} - 1\right)^2 = 4.3 \text{ barns} \qquad (14\text{-}11)$$

This result disagrees with the experimental value of 20.36 barns.

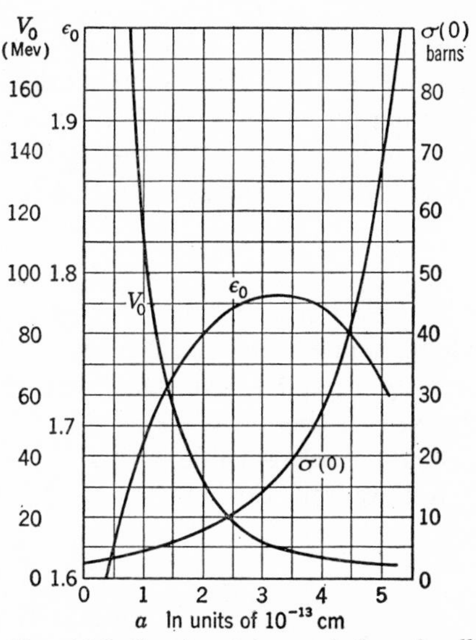

FIG. 14-3. Graphs giving variation of well depth, well strength, and low-velocity-limit cross section with well range on the assumption that the neutron-proton interaction is a spin-independent central force.

One might hope to bring agreement with experiment by an adjustment of the range constant. The effect of a range adjustment upon $\sigma^0(0)$ is also shown in Fig. 14-3. We see that a range of the order of 3.5 will bring approximate agreement. This corresponds to $\epsilon_0 \approx 1.785$ and $V_0 \approx 9$ Mev. Having found a unique set of well parameters to fit the deuteron binding energy and the zero-energy neutron-proton scattering cross section, we might, as a stringent test of the entire theory, compare the theoretical σ^0 vs. k relationship or σ^0 vs. T relationship with the experimental scattering cross section as a function of the propagation constant or energy. The theoretical cross sections may be calculated using

$$\sigma^0 = 4\pi a^2 \frac{\sin^2 \delta}{\epsilon_k{}^2} \qquad (14\text{-}12)$$

where $\epsilon_k = ka$ and the phase shifts δ are obtained from the solution of

$$\tan (\epsilon_k + \delta) = \epsilon_k \frac{\tan [(\epsilon_k{}^2 + \epsilon_0{}^2)^{\frac{1}{2}}]}{(\epsilon_k{}^2 + \epsilon_0{}^2)^{\frac{1}{2}}} \qquad (14\text{-}13)$$

The fit obtained by such a development is very poor and suggests that, for the square well at least, no choice of V_0 and a consistent with the deuteron binding energy will lead to agreement with the low-energy scattering data. We might be suspicious of our choice of well shape and be tempted to investigate a different well shape in an effort to secure agreement. However, Landau and Smorodinski[14] have called attention to the fact that the theoretical low-energy scattering results are quite insensitive to the shape of the well for any reasonable shape. Schwinger,[15] Bethe,[16] Blatt and Jackson,[17] and others have in fact developed a so-called shape-independent method of analysis for the interpretation of low-energy scattering which leads to an explicit $\sigma^0(k)$ function which is applicable to any reasonable well shape. According to this method the S-wave phase shifts may be characterized by the equation

$$k \cot \delta = -\frac{1}{d} + \frac{1}{2} r_0 k^2 \tag{14-14}$$

where r_0 and d are natural lengths. The lengths should be obtainable directly from the experimental data by determining the experimental shifts with the aid of Eq. (14-12). A plot of $k \cot \delta$ vs. k^2 should then indicate a straight line with slope equal to $r_0/2$ and the intercept $-d^{-1}$. It follows from Eqs. (14-12) and (14-14) that the cross section is given by

$$\sigma^0 = \frac{4\pi}{k^2 + (-d^{-1} + \frac{1}{2} r_0 k^2)^2} \tag{14-15}$$

The length r_0 is called the effective range of the well. Blatt and Jackson[17] give formulas and graphs which relate the effective range to the actual range and the well depth for the square well, the Gaussian well, the Yukawa well, and the exponential well. Their work indicates that r_0 depends mainly upon the well width a but that it also has a slight sensitivity to the well depth and the well shape. In the case of the square well it is quite close to the actual range constant a. Equation (14-15) indicates that, for $k = 0$,

$$\sigma^0 = 4\pi d^2 \tag{14-16}$$

so that the parameter d is a length associated with the low-velocity-limit cross section. This length is usually referred to as the Fermi scattering length. The theory indicates that the Fermi length is given by

$$d^{-1} = \alpha(1 - \tfrac{1}{2}\alpha r_0) \tag{14-17}$$

We may now try to fit the low-energy neutron-proton scattering data by attempting to find r_0 and d values which will make Eq. (14-15) (with $k^2 = Tm/\hbar^2$) fit the observed curve (see Fig. 14-2). However, any attempt to do this leads inevitably to the conclusion that no reasonable choice of r_0 and d satisfying Eq. (14-17) can be found. This verifies the conclusion for the case of the square well that no choice of V_0 and a consistent with the deuteron binding energy will lead to agreement with the low-energy scattering data. It is apparent therefore that the neutron-proton interaction cannot be represented as a simple function of the radial coordinate.

14-3. Spin Dependence of Neutron-Proton Interaction. In 1935 Wigner[18] suggested that, to remove the difficulty described in the preceding section, we must assume that the interaction for the spin singlet state of the neutron-proton system differs from the interaction in the spin triplet state. In neutron-proton scattering the statistical weight of the singlet system is $\frac{1}{4}$ as compared to the statistical weight $\frac{3}{4}$ of the triplet system. Hence the total neutron-proton cross section is given by

$$\sigma^0 = \tfrac{3}{4}\,{}^3\sigma^0 + \tfrac{1}{4}\,{}^1\sigma^0 \tag{14-18}$$

where ${}^3\sigma^0$ denotes the S-wave scattering cross section associated with the triplet state and ${}^1\sigma^0$ the S-wave scattering cross section associated with the singlet state. To calculate ${}^3\sigma^0$ and ${}^1\sigma^0$, we may make use of the formulas given in the preceding section, but we must now distinguish between triplet-state parameters such as ${}^3a$, ${}^3V_0$, ${}^3\epsilon_0$, ${}^3\alpha$, ${}^3d$, and ${}^3r_0$ and the singlet-state parameters such as ${}^1a$, ${}^1V_0$, ${}^1\epsilon_0$, ${}^1\alpha$, ${}^1d$, and ${}^1r_0$.

Experimentally it has been established that the ground state of the deuteron has the total angular-momentum quantum number $I = 1$. If a central force is operative, this state is expected to correspond to a state with zero orbital angular momentum, *i.e.*, an S state, and hence we must attribute the total spin to the sum of the neutron and proton spin angular momenta in the triplet state. If ${}^3\mathbf{a} = 1$, we might expect that for this ${}^3S$ state the value of ϵ_0 would be 1.692, and ${}^3\sigma^0(0)$ is of the order of 4.3 barns. It is now possible to obtain 20.34 barns for $\sigma^0(0)$ providing ${}^1\sigma^0(0)$ is extremely large ($\sim$68.4 barns). Such a large value of ${}^1\sigma^0(0)$ can occur only if the effective well-strength parameter ${}^1\epsilon_0$ is very close to the critical value $\pi/2$ [see Eq. (14-10)]. In the low-velocity limit for the ${}^1S$ state we have

$$68.4 \times 10^{-24}\ \text{cm}^2 = 4\pi({}^1a)^2\left(\frac{\tan {}^1\epsilon_0}{{}^1\epsilon_0} - 1\right)^2 \tag{14-19}$$

We may now calculate the well strength ${}^1\epsilon_0$ for any assumed singlet range constant. If, for example, we also let ${}^1\mathbf{a} = 1$, we may satisfy Eq. (14-19) with either ${}^1\epsilon_0 = 1.599$ or ${}^1\epsilon_0 = 1.544$. The former value corresponds to a singlet state which is just barely bound, whereas the latter value (since $1.544 < \pi/2$) corresponds to a virtual singlet state. Experiment (see next section) indicates that the singlet state is actually a virtual state. The singlet well depth for ${}^1\mathbf{a} = 1$ and ${}^1\epsilon_0 = 1.544$ corresponds to

$V_0 = 99$ Mev, and the binding energy for this case is of the order of -70 kev.

If we assume any other reasonable common range parameter for the triplet and singlet well, we will find that ${}^3\epsilon_0$ and ${}^1\epsilon_0$ will not change very much. Of course, the well depths ${}^3V_0$ and ${}^1V_0$ will be quite sensitive to the choice of the well range. Several of the early theoretical studies,[18] based upon early scattering data and the older values of the deuteron binding, arrived at the well parameters

$$ {}^3a = {}^1a \approx 2.8 \times 10^{-13} \text{ cm} \qquad {}^3V_0 \approx 21 \text{ Mev} \qquad {}^1V_0 \approx 12 \text{ Mev} $$

These well parameters still give a reasonable account of the low-energy neutron-proton scattering cross sections.

We have arrived at the important conclusion, due first to Wigner, that the forces between the neutron and proton are dependent upon the relative spin orientations of the two nucleons. The effective well is stronger when the proton and neutron spins are approximately parallel ($S = 1$) than when they are antiparallel ($S = 0$). The ratio ${}^1V_0/{}^3V_0$ is of the order of 5/9. This ratio is not very sensitive to the choice of the common range, and in fact it is rather insensitive to the choice of the well shape.[19]

If, in the light of recent theoretical methods and recent data, we wished to fix the best triplet and singlet central-force parameters to the total cross sections in the 0- to 5-Mev range, we would use the shape-independent result

$$ \sigma^0 = \frac{3\pi}{k^2 + [-({}^3d)^{-1} + \frac{1}{2}\,{}^3r_0k^2]^2} + \frac{\pi}{k^2 + [-({}^1d)^{-1} + \frac{1}{2}\,{}^1r_0k^2]^2} \tag{14-20} $$

Since the experimental value of ${}^3\alpha^{-1}$ imposes one relation between ${}^3d$ and ${}^3r_0$ [see Eq. (14-17)], we have at our disposal three adjustable parameters to fit the experimental neutron-proton scattering cross sections. It is gratifying that it is possible to find three parameters which will lead to agreement between experiment and the foregoing theory of low-energy scattering. This success of the theory in itself, however, must not be taken too seriously, since by using three adjustable parameters one might force a variety of functions to fit the same experimental data. In fact, the low-energy neutron-proton scattering data can be fitted by Eq. (14-20) with a range of choices of three parameters, a fact which has been somewhat disconcerting to experimentalists who have worked hard to accumulate precise data with the hope of learning the detailed nature of the neutron-proton interaction.

The theory takes on a more convincing aspect when consideration is given to the fact that ${}^1d$ and ${}^3d$ may be evaluated independently by thermal-energy-neutron scattering experiments with chemically bound protons. Recent values obtained from such experiments[20] (see next section) are

$$^{3}d = 5.388 \times 10^{-13} \text{ cm} \tag{14-21}$$

and

$$^{1}d = -23.68 \times 10^{-13} \text{ cm} \tag{14-22}$$

This value for ^{3}d and the experimental value for the deuteron radius lead to

$$^{3}r_0 = 1.72 \times 10^{-13} \text{ cm} \tag{14-23}$$

Accepting the above constants, consistency with the low-energy neutron-proton scattering data is obtained when the singlet effective range is chosen as[21]

$$^{1}r_0 = 2.47 \times 10^{-13} \text{ cm} \tag{14-24}$$

It would appear, although there is still some uncertainty, that the singlet well range is greater than the triplet well range.

14-4. Neutron Scattering by Bound Protons. The analysis of the neutron scattering cross section of ortho- and parahydrogen provides a very convincing confirmation of the spin dependence of the neutron-proton force. It is possible to infer from experiments with pure parahydrogen and mixed ortho- and parahydrogen the cross-section values for the pure forms. The results of Sutton *et al.*[8] at 20°K are 124 barns for orthohydrogen and 3.97 barns for parahydrogen.

To study the significance of these numbers, we shall employ a method of analysis which is an adaptation of one developed by Fermi and Marshall[22] for the study of thermal-neutron scattering by molecules. Because of the extremely large wavelengths of thermal neutrons, only S waves are involved in the scattering. For simplicity of notation, we shall here omit the superscript zero which we previously used to denote S-wave parameters. In this treatment we employ the Fermi length, which is partially defined by the equation

$$\sigma(0) = 4\pi d^2 \tag{14-25}$$

According to the Fermi theory a scattering length can be either positive or negative according to whether the last discrete state of the system consisting of the incident neutron and the scatterer is a real or virtual state. For neutron-proton scattering we may identify ^{3}d and ^{1}d with the two possible values (1 and 0) of $\mathbf{S} = \mathbf{s}_n + \mathbf{s}_p$. A useful identity due to Schwinger and Teller[23] is

$$d = \frac{3\,{}^{3}d + {}^{1}d}{4} + ({}^{3}d - {}^{1}d)\,\frac{\mathbf{s}_n \cdot \mathbf{s}_p}{\hbar^2} \tag{14-26}$$

The Landé formula for $\mathbf{s}_n \cdot \mathbf{s}_p/\hbar^2$ for the states $S = 1$ and 0 yields $\frac{1}{4}$ and $-\frac{3}{4}$, respectively. Hence it follows immediately that $d = {}^3d$ for $S = 1$ and $d = {}^1d$ for $S = 0$.

Equation (14-26) may be used to derive the formula for scattering by free protons. We have

$$\sigma_f = 4\pi\langle d^2\rangle = 4\pi \left\langle \frac{(3\,{}^3d + {}^1d)^2}{16} + \tfrac{1}{2}(3\,{}^3d + {}^1d)({}^3d - {}^1d)\,\frac{\mathbf{s}_n \cdot \mathbf{s}_p}{\hbar^2} + ({}^3d - {}^1d)^2\left(\frac{\mathbf{s}_n \cdot \mathbf{s}_p}{\hbar^2}\right)^2\right\rangle$$

$$= 4\pi\left[\frac{(3\,{}^3d + {}^1d)^2}{16} + \frac{3}{16}({}^3d - {}^1d)^2\right]$$

$$= 4\pi[\tfrac{3}{4}({}^3d)^2 + \tfrac{1}{4}({}^1d)^2] \tag{14-27}$$

In the above derivation we have used the weighted averages

$$\left\langle\frac{\mathbf{s}_n \cdot \mathbf{s}_p}{\hbar^2}\right\rangle = \frac{1}{4}\left(-\frac{3}{4}\right) + \frac{3}{4}\left(\frac{1}{4}\right) = 0$$

and

$$\left\langle\left(\frac{\mathbf{s}_n \cdot \mathbf{s}_p}{\hbar^2}\right)^2\right\rangle = \frac{1}{4}\left(-\frac{3}{4}\right)^2 + \frac{3}{4}\left(\frac{1}{4}\right)^2 = \frac{3}{16}$$

which are obtained by using the statistical weights $\frac{1}{4}$ and $\frac{3}{4}$ for the $S = 0$ and $S = 1$ states in conjunction with the values $-\frac{3}{4}$ and $\frac{1}{4}$ for $\mathbf{s}_n \cdot \mathbf{s}_p$ in these states. The final result follows much more simply from the direct application of Eqs. (14-25) and (14-18). However, the above illustrates a method of calculation which will be useful.

In very-low-energy scattering by ortho- and parahydrogen the wavelengths of the incident neutrons are large compared to the molecular separation. The waves scattered by the two protons in the molecules are thus in phase and add coherently. Accordingly, if we add the scattering lengths (for incoherent scattering we would add the scattering cross sections), we obtain for the sum of the scattering lengths [see Eq. (14-26)] for molecular hydrogen

$$d_{p1} + d_{p2} = \frac{3\,{}^3d + {}^1d}{2} + ({}^3d - {}^1d)\,\frac{\mathbf{s}_n \cdot \mathbf{S}_{\mathrm{H}_2}}{\hbar^2} \tag{14-28}$$

where

$$\mathbf{S}_{\mathrm{H}_2} = \mathbf{s}_{p_1} + \mathbf{s}_{p_2} \tag{14-29}$$

is the total spin of the hydrogen molecule. The molecular cross section and the molecular scattering length D are given by

$$\sigma_{\mathrm{H}_2} = 4\pi D^2 = \pi(3\,{}^3d + {}^1d)^2 + 4\pi(3\,{}^3d + {}^1d)({}^3d - {}^1d)\mathbf{s}_n \cdot \mathbf{S}_{\mathrm{H}_2}\hbar^{-2} + 4\pi({}^3d - {}^1d)^2(\mathbf{s}_n \cdot \mathbf{S}_{\mathrm{H}_2})^2\hbar^{-4} \tag{14-30}$$

Since the incident beam of neutrons is not polarized in relation to $\mathbf{S}_{H_2}$, we must evaluate the averages of the spin-dependent terms.

The quantum number S_{H_2} has the value 1 in the ortho state and 0 in the para state. For molecules in the $S_{H_2} = 0$ state, the instantaneous value and average value of $\mathbf{s}_n \cdot \mathbf{S}_{H_2}$ will certainly vanish, so that we have

$$\sigma_{\text{para}} = \pi(3\,{}^3d + {}^1d)^2 \tag{14-31}$$

and

$$D_{\text{para}} = \tfrac{1}{2}(3\,{}^3d + {}^1d) \tag{14-32}$$

On the other hand, for the ortho state the total-spin vector $\mathbf{S}_T = \mathbf{s}_n + \mathbf{S}_{H_2}$ may correspond to the quantum number $S_T = \frac{3}{2}$ or $\frac{1}{2}$. The former state has the statistical weight $\frac{4}{6}$, whereas the latter has the statistical weight $\frac{2}{6}$. According to the Landé formula the values of $\mathbf{s}_n \cdot \mathbf{S}_{H_2}\hbar^{-2}$ in the $S_T = \frac{3}{2}$ and $S_T = \frac{1}{2}$ states are $\frac{1}{2}$ and -1, respectively. Thus the average value of $\mathbf{s}_n \cdot \mathbf{S}_{H_2}\,\hbar^{-2}$ is

$$\left\langle \frac{\mathbf{s}_n \cdot \mathbf{S}_{H_2}}{\hbar^2} \right\rangle = \frac{4}{6}\left(\frac{1}{2}\right) + \frac{2}{6}(-1) = 0$$

However,

$$\left\langle \left(\frac{\mathbf{s}_n \cdot \mathbf{S}_{H_2}}{\hbar^2}\right)^2 \right\rangle = \frac{4}{6}\left(\frac{1}{2}\right)^2 + \frac{2}{6}(-1)^2 = \frac{1}{2}$$

We have thus for orthohydrogen

$$\sigma_{\text{ortho}} = \pi[(3\,{}^3d + {}^1d)^2 + 2({}^3d - {}^1d)^2] \tag{14-33}$$

Before drawing any conclusion from the data we must consider certain other effects besides those of spin. Our analysis of scattering was made in the center-of-mass system, in which the reduced mass was used in place of the mass of the incident neutron. In neutron-proton scattering by free protons we have $m_r = m/2$, where $m_n \approx m_p \approx m \approx 1$ MU. However, in the scattering of a neutron by a proton which is tightly bound by molecular forces in a molecule of mass number A, the appropriate reduced mass is $m_r' = [A/(A+1)]m = [2A/(A+1)]m_r$. Consequently, for scattering by the hydrogen molecule, it is necessary to correct the scattering length by the factor $\frac{4}{3}$. This correction introduces a factor $\frac{16}{9}$ into the cross sections given by Eqs. (14-31) and (14-33). At low energies we must also make a slight correction for the Doppler effect, arising from the random molecular motion, on the proton-neutron collisions, as well as a slight correction for the possibility of inelastic scattering, which results in the conversion of ortho- to parahydrogen. Finally, we must make a correction for the slight differences in phase of the scattered waves because the protons are a finite distance apart. When all these corrections are made, Sutton *et al.*[8] on the basis of the calculations of Hammermesh and Schwinger,[24] arrive at the formulas for 0.001723-ev neutrons:

$$\sigma_{\text{para}} = 6.423(3\,{}^3d + {}^1d)^2 \tag{14-34}$$
$$\sigma_{\text{ortho}} = 14.506({}^3d - {}^1d)^2 + 6.435(3\,{}^3d + {}^1d)^2 \tag{14-35}$$

Inserting their experimental results, they obtained

$$^3d = 5.20 \times 10^{-13}\text{ cm} \qquad \text{and} \qquad {}^1d = -23.4 \times 10^{-13}\text{ cm}$$

These values give rise to a free-proton cross section of 19.8 barns, which is in good agreement with the experimental value of Melkonian *et al.*[7] (20.36 barns). These results thus confirm Wigner's assumption of the spin dependence of nuclear forces, and show that the singlet state is virtual. It is obvious from Eqs. (14-34) and (14-35) that, were $^3d = {}^1d$, the ortho and para cross sections would almost be identical.

An important consequence of this study is the confirmation that the neutron spin is $\frac{1}{2}$. Schwinger[25] has studied this scattering problem under the assumption of an arbitrary value for the neutron spin. The corresponding analysis by Sutton for the hypothetical case of $\mathbf{s}_n = \frac{3}{2}$ would lead to a prĕdicted free-proton cross section of 7 barns, which is incompatible with the observed value.

Burgy, Ringo, and Hughes,[20] from the analysis of the coherent scattering of thermal neutrons by a hydrocarbon mirror, are able to arrive more directly at a precise value for the coherent-scattering length at low energies. Their result is

$$D_{\text{para}} = \tfrac{1}{2}(3\,{}^3d + {}^1d) = -3.76 \times 10^{-13}\text{ cm} \tag{14-36}$$

This, combined with Melkonian's free-proton cross section

$$\sigma_f = 4\pi[\tfrac{3}{4}({}^3d)^2 + \tfrac{1}{4}({}^1d)^2] = 20.36 \times 10^{-24}\text{ cm}^2 \tag{14-37}$$

leads to the values quoted in the previous section, namely,

$$^3d = 5.388 \times 10^{-13}\text{ cm} \qquad \text{and} \qquad {}^1d = -23.68 \times 10^{-13}\text{ cm}$$

14-5. The H(n,γ)D and D(γ,n)H Reactions. The H(n,γ)D reaction, which is significant only at very low energies, provides an additional mechanism for the study of the neutron-proton interaction. This process may be viewed as a transition from a continuous positive energy state of the neutron-proton system to the ^3S state of the deuteron. This transition, which involves the electromagnetic field associated with the gamma ray, may be studied with the aid of the time-dependent perturbation theory. Since at low energies only S wave functions of the continuum are appreciable, the transition does not involve a change in orbital angular momentum or parity of the system. This excludes the possibility that the transition has an electric dipole character but allows the transition to have a magnetic dipole character (see selection rules, Sec. 12-4). The magnetic dipole matrix element of a ^3S continuum state to the ^3S ground state can be shown to vanish identically. However, the matrix element of a ^1S continuum state to the ^3S deuteron state has a finite value and leads to a finite radiative-capture cross section. During a ^1S to ^3S process, the spins of the neutron and proton switch from the antiparallel orientation ($S = 0$) to the parallel orientation ($S = 1$).

For unpolarized incident neutrons the theory[26] indicates that $\sigma_c v$ should be insensitive to the neutron velocity (the $1/v$ law). The approximate result obtained, when use is made of the zero-range approximation, is[27]

$$\sigma_c v = 2\pi \frac{e^2}{\hbar c} c \left(\frac{\hbar}{mc}\right)^2 \left(\frac{^3B}{mc^2}\right)^{\frac{3}{2}} (1 - {}^3\alpha\, {}^1d)^2(\mu_n - \mu_p)^2 \qquad (14\text{-}38)$$

The numerical value for $\sigma_c v$ obtained by inserting experimental values for ^3B, $^3\alpha$, and ^1d is approximately equal to the experimental value. This agreement confirms the idea that the singlet state is virtual and the other assumptions underlying the derivation of Eq. (14-38).

The reaction D(γ,n)H is the inverse of the radiative-capture reaction and may be treated by analogous methods. Immediately above the threshold energy ($E_\gamma = 2.226$ Mev) the photodisintegration process occurs only by magnetic-dipole oscillations which induce transitions between the ^3S ground state and the virtual ^1S. The differential cross section for unpolarized incident photons is independent of the angle. In the zero-range approximation the total cross section is found to be[27]

$$\sigma_{M1}(\gamma,n) = \frac{2\pi}{3} \frac{e^2}{\hbar c} \left(\frac{\hbar}{mc}\right)^2 \frac{k\, {}^3\alpha(1 - {}^3\alpha\, {}^1d)^2}{[k^2 + ({}^3\alpha)^2][1 + k^2({}^1d)^2]} (\mu_n - \mu_p)^2 \qquad (14\text{-}39)$$

where k is the propagation constant which characterizes the outgoing waves.

Electric-dipole transitions to the ^3P state of the continuum become important very rapidly as the gamma-ray energy increases above the threshold and are completely dominant when the excess energy is of the order of several Mev. The differential cross section for this transition varies as $\sin^2 \theta$, and the total electric cross section is given approximately by[27]

$$\sigma_{E1}(\gamma,n) = \frac{8\pi}{3} \frac{e^2}{\hbar c} \frac{k\, {}^3\alpha}{[k^2 + ({}^3\alpha)^2]^3} \frac{1}{({}^3\alpha)^2(1 - {}^3\alpha\, {}^3r_0)} \qquad (14\text{-}40)$$

The experiments conducted thus far are in the main compatible with these simple results, although there are indications of a need for a refined analysis.[1] The slight asymmetry in the angular distribution observed by Goldhaber and others [Eq. (14-1)] is, perhaps, indicative of the existence of a noncentral force.

14-6. Proton-Proton Scattering.[28,29] Although the analysis of proton-proton scattering is complicated by the coulomb force and the effect of proton-proton exchange, nevertheless the analysis is simplified by the fact that in low-energy scattering only one strictly nuclear interaction is effective. It can be shown (see Sec. 14-7) that for S waves only singlet

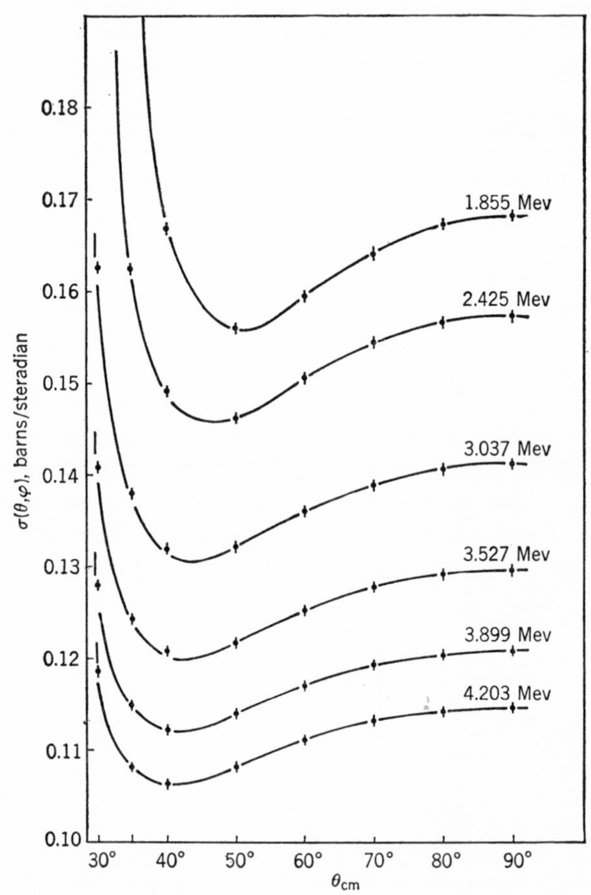

Fig. 14-4. Graphs showing the fits of the proton-proton differential cross sections based upon the assumption of S-wave nuclear scattering only. (*From Breit and Gluckstern, Ref.* 28.)

spin states of the two-proton system can exist. Thus the anomalies shown by low-energy proton-proton scattering should be explainable completely in terms of a single phase-shift function ${}^1\delta(T)$, whereas two functions ${}^3\delta(T)$ and ${}^1\delta(T)$ are needed to characterize the cross sections for low-energy neutron-proton scattering.

The analysis of the data on low- and medium-energy proton-proton scattering has been the subject of many theoretical studies. In Fig. 14-4 we show a comparison of recent experimental values of the differential cross section with curves based upon a pure S-wave anomaly. The curves from 90 to 180° are not shown, but because of the equivalence of the incident and recoil protons, the results are expected to be symmetrical relative to 90°. It is obvious that these calculated curves fit the results extremely well. Powell and Hall[30] find, however, that the inclusion of small P-wave scattering improves the fit even further.

Since the pioneer work of Breit, Condon, and Present[31] numerous attempts have been made to use the proton-proton-scattering data to infer nuclear-potential parameters. The essential conclusions of this early analysis of the low-energy data have not been changed by recent experimental and theoretical work. Again one finds that the data actually tell little about the nuclear-potential function. If one assumes a particular well shape, then the experimental data may be used to evaluate two parameters which characterize the well. Even with the high degree of accuracy possible in low-energy scattering experiments, it is difficult to draw any but the most general conclusions about the well shape.

To compare theory with experiment, it has proved expedient to utilize an intermediate quantity $f(T)$, which was first introduced by Breit, Condon, and Present. This quantity can be determined directly from the experimental data as well as from an assumed theoretical interaction. The function $f(T)$ is almost linear in the energy and is analogous to the expression $k \cot \delta$ in Eq. (14-14) of the shape-independent theory of neutron-proton scattering. Closely related quantities have been used by Bethe[16] and Blatt and Jackson[32] in their extensions of the effective-range formalism to proton-proton scattering. In Fig. 14-5 we show the comparison of Yovits *et al.*[33] between several theoretical f curves and the experimental counterparts. The authors note a trend toward agreement with the long-tailed Yukawa and exponential wells. The best fit for a square well corresponds to a range constant 2.58×10^{-13} cm and a well depth $V_0 = 13.5$ Mev.

Perhaps the most interesting result of studies of proton-proton scattering at low energies has been the apparent agreement between the singlet proton-proton and the singlet neutron-proton nuclear well depths and nuclear well ranges. The agreement suggests that the proper nuclear forces at low energies are essentially independent of charge character. This conclusion, known as the charge-independent hypothesis, has been applied widely and seems to be a rather good rule for low-energy studies.

14-7. Isobaric Spin and Generalized Exclusion Principle. For some time theorists have been attempting to find a nucleon-nucleon interaction function which accounts not only for the known properties of all nucleon-nucleon systems but also for the properties of complex nuclei. In such work theorists are, to a certain extent, guided by field-theory considerations which limit somewhat the type of interaction chosen for study. However, to a major extent experimental information has been the guide to the choice of nucleon-nucleon interactions. This approach is frequently referred to as the phenomenological approach to nuclear forces.

If the proper nuclear force is different or operates differently in the proton-neutron, the proton-proton, and the neutron-neutron systems, it

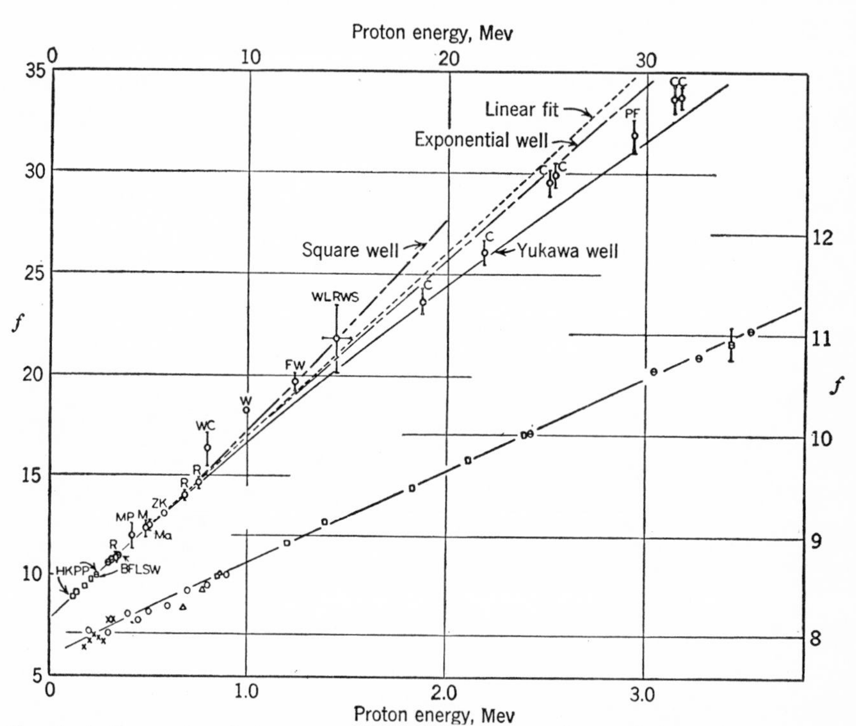

FIG. 14-5. Comparison between experimental f values and several theoretical f curves, for various proton kinetic energies. The lower curve, using scale on right and lower margins, shows best linear fit in conjunction with experimental points. The upper curves show best fit for several well shapes in conjunction with experimental points. See Ref. 33 for sources of data. (*From Yovits, Smith, Hull, Bengston, and Breit, Ref.* 33.)

would be desirable if these differences were embodied in a single interaction function rather than requiring three distinct interaction functions. Since this goal has not yet been reached, the purpose of this further discussion is simply to indicate the trend of current work rather than to present the details of this work. For the purposes of this discussion, we shall accept the conclusion that the gross properties of low-energy nucleon-nucleon phenomena can be accounted for in terms of central forces.

In the historical development of nuclear theory, great weight has been attached to the fact that nucleons may transform into one another. In his first paper on nuclear forces, Heisenberg[34] assumed that the neutron and proton are two possible isobaric states of a nucleon, analogous to the two spin states of a spin $\frac{1}{2}$ particle. In order to exploit the analogy fully, let us assign to a nucleon the charge-character value $\frac{1}{2}$ when it is a neutron and the charge-character value $-\frac{1}{2}$ when it is a proton. These two numbers may be viewed as the permissible values, in an abstract space, of the z component of a dimensionless isobaric-spin vector $\mathbf{t}$ (this vector is often referred to as the isotopic-spin vector). We introduce two quantum numbers t and m_t, which determine the magnitude and the z component of the isobaric-spin vector according to the equations

$$|\mathbf{t}| = [t(t+1)]^{\frac{1}{2}} \qquad \text{where } t \doteq \tfrac{1}{2} \tag{14-41}$$

and

$$t_z = m_t \qquad \text{where } m_t \doteq \tfrac{1}{2}\ (n),\ -\tfrac{1}{2}\ (p) \tag{14-42}$$

We may now assign to a system of two nucleons the derived total-isobaric-spin vector

$$\mathbf{T} = \mathbf{t}_1 + \mathbf{t}_2 \tag{14-43}$$

The same quantization rules which were previously used to determine the allowed values of total spin and z component of total spin here lead to

$$|\mathbf{T}| = [T(T+1)]^{\frac{1}{2}} \qquad \text{where } T \doteq 0, 1 \tag{14-44}$$

We see that, when $T = 0$, $T_z = M_T \doteq 0$, whereas when $T = 1$,

$$T_z = M_T \doteq 1, 0, -1$$

The $T = 1$ state is sometimes referred to as the isobaric-spin triplet state, and the $T = 0$ state is referred to as the isobaric-spin singlet state.

Since the z components of isobaric spin are additive, *i.e.*,

$$M_T = m_{t_1} + m_{t_2} \tag{14-45}$$

the $M_T = 1$ state can correspond only to a neutron-neutron $(\frac{1}{2},\frac{1}{2})$ physical system. On the other hand, the $M_T = -1$ state can correspond only to a proton-proton $(-\frac{1}{2},-\frac{1}{2})$ physical system. The $(T = 1, M_T = 0)$ and the $(T = 0, M_T = 0)$ states must both correspond to the neutron-proton $(\frac{1}{2},-\frac{1}{2})$ system. The experimental arrangement selects the $(T=1, M_T = 1)$ state in studies of neutron-neutron systems or the $(T = 1, M_T = -1)$ state in studies of proton-proton systems. However, in studies of neutron-proton systems we must appeal to a generalized exclusion principle to determine whether the system is in the $(T = 1, M_T = 0)$ state or the $(T = 0, M_T = 0)$ state. For application to two-body problems we may use a simple form of the generalized exclusion principle which can be shown to follow from general symmetry requirements upon the wave functions which characterize a system of nucleons. This form states that:

The sum of the quantum numbers L, S, and T which characterize the orbital angular momentum, the total spin angular momentum, and the total isobaric spin of a system of two nucleons must always be an odd number.

Alternately we may require that

$$(-1)^{L+S+T} = -1 \tag{14-46}$$

Since S and T can take on only the values 0 and 1, we can readily enumerate the most important cases which arise. In Table 14-1 we indicate the allowed combinations of L, S, and T; the notation for these states; and the physical systems in which these states may occur. Since the require-

TABLE 14-1. ALLOWED VALUES OF EXCHANGE OPERATORS

Physical system	Notation	L	S	T	B.†	H.†	M.†	W.†	$\boldsymbol{\sigma}_1 \cdot \boldsymbol{\sigma}_2$‡	$\boldsymbol{\tau}_1 \cdot \boldsymbol{\tau}_2$‡
p-p n-p n-n	^1S	0	0	1	1	1	−1	−1	−3	1
n-p	^3S	0	1	0	−1	−1	−1	−1	1	−3
n-p	^1P	1	0	0	1	−1	1	−1	−3	−3
p-p n-p n-n	^3P	1	1	1	−1	1	1	−1	1	1

† See Sec. 14-8.
‡ See Sec. 14-9.

ments upon S and T for a given value of L depend only upon the evenness or oddness of L rather than upon the specific numerical value, this table can readily be applied to $D, F, G, \ldots$ states. The entries in the last six columns will be explained in the next two sections.

If L and S are known, the exclusion principle or Table 14-1 uniquely determines whether a neutron-proton system is in the $T = 1$ or $T = 0$ state. For example, in the ^3S state of the deuteron, $T = 0$; whereas in the ^1S state, $T = 1$. Since $T = 1$ in the proton-proton system, S-wave protons ($L = 0$) can couple only into the ^1S state. We have already used this restriction in our discussion of proton-proton scattering.

14-8. Exchange Operators and Exchange Forces. The dynamical quantity

$$P_S = \frac{1}{2}\left(1 + \frac{4\,\mathbf{s}_1 \cdot \mathbf{s}_2}{\hbar^2}\right) \tag{14-47}$$

which is associated with two spin $\frac{1}{2}$ particles has the value +1 in the spin triplet ($S = 1$) and −1 in the spin singlet ($S = 0$) states, respectively. This statement readily follows from the Landé formulas, which give $\mathbf{s}_1 \cdot \mathbf{s}_2 = \hbar^2/4$ and $-3\hbar^2/4$ for these two states. In using this quantity, it is customary to define

$$\boldsymbol{\sigma} = \frac{2}{\hbar}\mathbf{s} \tag{14-48}$$

in which case Eq. (14-47) becomes

$$P_S = \tfrac{1}{2}(1 + \boldsymbol{\sigma}_1 \cdot \boldsymbol{\sigma}_2) \tag{14-49}$$

This dynamical quantity is known as the spin exchange operator. The values which this operator may take on are given by

$$P_S \doteq (-1)^{S+1} \tag{14-50}$$

Analogous to the above operator Heisenberg has introduced the isobaric-spin exchange operator

$$P_T = \tfrac{1}{2}(1 + \boldsymbol{\tau}_1 \cdot \boldsymbol{\tau}_2) \tag{14-51}$$

where

$$\boldsymbol{\tau} = 2\mathbf{t} \tag{14-52}$$

This quantity takes on two values $+1$ or -1 corresponding to the $T = 1$ and $T = 0$ isobaric-spin states. These allowed values are given by

$$P_T \doteq (-1)^{T+1} \tag{14-53}$$

A third operator P_L, called the space exchange operator, may be defined by imposing the requirement that

$$P_L \doteq (-1)^L \tag{14-54}$$

The earliest efforts to account for the saturation and incompressibility tendencies of nuclear forces were based upon various types of exchange forces. Bartlett[(35)] proposed a potential which depended directly upon the total spin according to

$$V_B = -P_S J(r) = (-1)^S J(r) \tag{14-55}$$

Heisenberg[(34)] suggested an isobaric-spin exchange force characterized by

$$V_H = P_T J(r) = (-1)^{T+1} J(r) \tag{14-56}$$

Majorana[(36)] suggested the space exchange potential

$$V_M = -P_L J(r) = (-1)^{L+1} J(r) \tag{14-57}$$

In early studies Wigner[(37)] gave consideration to a potential without exchange which has the simple form

$$V_W = -J(r) \tag{14-58}$$

In each of these expressions we shall assume that $J(r)$ is a positive, definite energy function.

While the Bartlett, Heisenberg, and Majorana forces depend directly upon S, T, and L, respectively, each of these has an indirect dependence upon the other two quantum numbers by virtue of the exclusion principle. This fact is illustrated in the columns of Table 14-1 which are labeled B., H., M., and W., in which the coefficients of $J(r)$ are given for the four types of forces. An examination of this table discloses that, although each of these forces is attractive in the ^3S state, none of the four forces can account for the observed difference between the depths of the ^1S and ^3S wells. However, we can easily arrange mixtures consisting mostly of Wigner or Majorana forces and partly of Heisenberg or Bartlett forces which give the approximate well-depth ratio needed when the singlet and triplet ranges are assumed to be identical.

Exchange forces have been given serious consideration in nuclear physics because the assumption of appropriate exchange forces affords the possibility of accounting for the observed saturation tendencies of nuclear forces. As a qualitative indication of the manner in which saturation may come about according to this idea, we note that at most four nucleons can exist in the 1s state (the two neutrons and two protons in He^4). The exclusion principle requires that the fifth nucleon go into the 1p state. The interaction between the 1p nucleon and each of the 1s nucleons may be identified with an $L_{12} = l_1 + l_2 = 1$. Consequently, the fifth particle would be repelled by the Majorana interaction with each of the 1s particles. This type of explanation may account for the known fact that there is no stable system with $A = 5$. Other exchange forces would act somewhat differently. Nevertheless, in a complex nucleus any type of exchange force would give rise to alternations between attractive and repulsive interactions and would tend to hold the nucleons apart. In contrast, an ordinary force which is attractive at all radii and between all pairs would tend to cause the complex system to collapse into a state of extremely high density.

14-9. Neutral, Charged, and Symmetric Potentials. Since the advent of the meson theory, the dependence of nuclear forces upon isobaric spin has been related to the existence of positive, negative, and neutral mesons. In the neutral theory the nuclear forces result from the interaction with the neutral meson field just as electronic forces result from the interactions with the neutral photon field (electromagnetic field). In the charged theory the forces are a consequence of the couplings of nucleons with positive and negative meson fields. In the symmetric theory the forces are connected with a particular mixture of positive, negative, and neutral meson fields. If the interaction based upon neutral-meson theory has the form (the subscript n here symbolizes neutral-meson theory rather than neutron)

$$V_n = -J(\mathbf{r},\mathbf{s}_1,\mathbf{s}_2) \tag{14-59}$$

which we here allow to depend upon the spin of the nucleons, then the corresponding charged theory leads to the interaction

$$V_c = \tfrac{1}{2}(1 + \boldsymbol{\tau}_1 \cdot \boldsymbol{\tau}_2)J(\mathbf{r},\mathbf{s}_1,\mathbf{s}_2) \tag{14-60}$$

and the symmetric theory yields

$$V_s = (\boldsymbol{\tau}_1 \cdot \boldsymbol{\tau}_2)J(\mathbf{r},\mathbf{s}_1,\mathbf{s}_2) \tag{14-61}$$

The last column of Table 14-1 contains the values of $\boldsymbol{\tau}_1 \cdot \boldsymbol{\tau}_2$ for various states.

Letting $J_1(r)$ and $J_2(r)$ denote two functions having identical form, an interaction based upon the neutral theory which may account for the gross properties of two-nucleon systems (ignoring the anomalous magnetic and quadrupole moments of the deuteron) is

$$V_n = -[J_1(r) + \boldsymbol{\sigma}_1 \cdot \boldsymbol{\sigma}_2 \, J_2(r)] \tag{14-62}$$

According to this interaction the forces between neutron-proton, proton-proton, and neutron-neutron systems are identical in states having the same values of L and S. The above interaction contains two adjustable well-depth parameters and two adjustable well-width parameters. In the spin triplet and spin singlet states these interactions are

$$^3V_n = -J_1 - J_2 \tag{14-63}$$

and

$$^1V_n = -J_1 + 3J_2 \tag{14-64}$$

To the extent that the two-nucleon data indicate that the neutron-proton and proton-proton forces are identical in ^1S states, this last interaction, of course, may be adjusted to fit the data. However, nothing is gained by this synthesis of the ^1V and ^3V interactions unless perhaps it is possible to reduce the number of adjusted parameters. Several years ago it was common to assume that the ranges in the singlet and triplet states were identical. For this case Eq. (14-62) may be written in the form

$$V_n = -(1 + c\,\boldsymbol{\sigma}_1 \cdot \boldsymbol{\sigma}_2)J(r) \tag{14-65}$$

which gives

$$^3V_n = -(1 + c)J(r) \tag{14-66}$$

and

$$^1V_n = -(1 - 3c)J(r) \tag{14-67}$$

We may here generate the ratio $^1V/^3V \approx 5/9$ needed, on the equal-range assumption, to account for the difference in binding energies of the ^1S and ^3S states of the deuteron simply by letting $c \approx \frac{1}{8}$. Accordingly, the neutral theory requires a strong ordinary attractive force, together with a weak spin-spin force, in order to be attractive in both ^1S and ^3S states and to have the appropriate ratio. To obtain saturation with ordinary forces, we must assume that the potential $J(r)$ is such that there is a repulsive force at short ranges.

The charged exchange interaction corresponding to Eq. (14-62) is

$$V_c = \tfrac{1}{2}(1 + \boldsymbol{\tau}_1 \cdot \boldsymbol{\tau}_2)[J_1(r) + \boldsymbol{\sigma}_1 \cdot \boldsymbol{\sigma}_2 \, J_2(r)] \tag{14-68}$$

This gives for the ^3S state of the neutron-proton system ($T = 0$)

$$^3V_c = -(J_1 + J_2) = -(1 + c)J(r) \tag{14-69}$$

and for the ^1S neutron-proton and proton-proton states ($T = 1$)

$$^1V_c = J_1 - 3J_2 = (1 - 3c)J(r) \tag{14-70}$$

where the forms on the right correspond to the case of equal ranges. If $c \approx \frac{2}{3}$, then the $^1V/^3V$ ratio is 0.60. Accordingly, the static and spin-spin terms must be comparable in a charged theory.

In the symmetrical theory we have, in correspondence with Eq. (14-61),

$$V_s = \boldsymbol{\tau}_1 \cdot \boldsymbol{\tau}_2[J_1(r) + \boldsymbol{\sigma}_1 \cdot \boldsymbol{\sigma}_2 \, J_2(r)] \tag{14-71}$$

Accordingly for S states

$$^3V_s = -3J + J_2 \tag{14-72}$$

$$^1V_s = J_1 - 3J_2 \tag{14-73}$$

For equal ranges we find

$$^3V_s = -3(1 + c)J(r) \tag{14-74}$$

$$^1V_s = (1 - 3c)J(r) \tag{14-75}$$

The constant $c \approx 2$ gives the desired ratio $^1V/^3V = 5/9$. Hence in the symmetric theory a strong static potential and a somewhat stronger spin-spin potential will account for the relative depths of the ^1S and ^3S wells of the deuteron. At the same time it is thought that such a potential would lead naturally to the saturation properties of nuclear forces.

14-10. Magnetic Moments of the Deuteron. If the deuteron wave function were a pure S state, we would not expect any contribution to the magnetic moment due to the orbital motion of the proton. Since the spins of the proton and neutron are parallel, the deuteron magnetic moment, when expressed in nuclear magnetons, should be

$$\mu_d{}^0 = \mu_p + \mu_n = 0.8798 \tag{14-76}$$

The experimental value is 0.8573. Accordingly we must explain the magnetic anomaly

$$\mu_d - \mu_d{}^0 = -0.0225 \tag{14-77}$$

This anomaly suggests that the ground state of the deuteron may actually be a mixture of an S state with other states of higher angular momentum. We know from experiment that the total angular-momentum quantum number of the ground state is $I = 1$. Since $\mathbf{L} + \mathbf{S} = \mathbf{I}$ implies $I = L + S, L + S - 1, \ldots, |L - S|$, we may arrive at the total spin I by various combinations of L and S. If, however, we accept the assumption that in the ground state the spins are rigidly coupled into the spin triplet state, then only the L values 0, 1, and 2, that is, S, P, and D states, can produce the total spin 1. Of these three states the $^3S_1$ and $^3D_1$ states have even parity, whereas the $^3P_1$ has odd parity.

In an effort to account simultaneously for the anomalous magnetic moment of deuteron and the small quadrupole moment of the deuteron, Rarita and Schwinger[38] have suggested that there exists a noncentral force in the neutron-proton interaction which couples the even-parity $^3S_1$ and $^3D_1$ states together so that the ground state contains a small $^3D_1$ admixture. The effect of this noncentral force must, of course, be small enough so as not to upset seriously the predictions based upon a central force, which do fairly adequately agree with the low-energy data

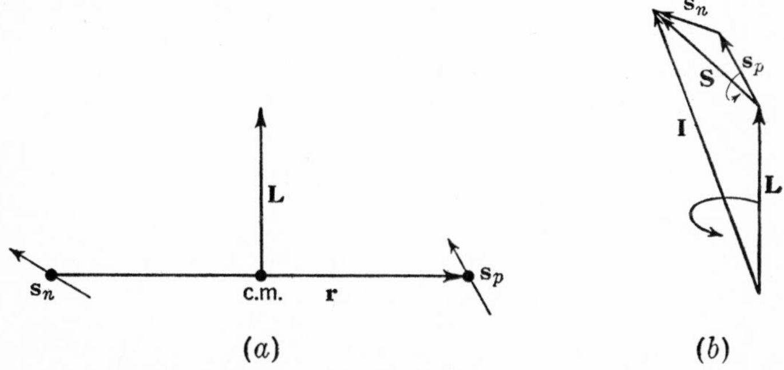

FIG. 14-6. (a) Diagram showing a physical picture of the deuteron, in which the position and angular-momentum vectors are shown schematically. (b) Vector diagram showing a possible combination of angular momenta.

for neutron-proton and proton-proton systems. To show how a small component may account for the magnetic anomaly, let us derive an expression for the magnetic moment of a hypothetical deuteron in a bound state of higher orbital angular momentum. In Fig. 14-6a we give a physical picture of such a system. From classical considerations it is obvious that, if the orbital angular momentum of the deuteron is $\mathbf{L}$, then $\mathbf{L}/2$ is the angular momentum of the proton about the center of mass and $\mathbf{L}/2$ is the angular momentum of the neutron about the center of mass. Since the proton is an entity with the net charge e, the proton orbital angular momentum gives rise to a magnetic moment $\mu_N\mathbf{L}/2\hbar$. The magnetic energy of a deuteron in a magnetic field consequently is

$$W_m = (\tfrac{1}{2}\,\mathbf{L}\cdot\mathbf{H} + 2\mu_p\,\mathbf{s}_p\cdot\mathbf{H} + 2\mu_n\,\mathbf{s}_n\cdot\mathbf{H})\mu_N\hbar^{-1} \qquad (14\text{-}78)$$

In Fig. 14-6b we indicate the vector diagram appropriate to the assumption that there exists a strong force which couples the spins of the neutron and proton into a spin triplet state and that the net spin and orbital angular momentum couple to form the total angular momentum $\mathbf{I}$. The expectation of these scalar products may be evaluated using the chain rule and the Landé formulas. We obtain

$$\langle W_m \rangle = \left(\tfrac{1}{2}\,\mathbf{L}\cdot\mathbf{I} + 2\mu_p \frac{\mathbf{s}_p\cdot\mathbf{S}}{\mathbf{S}\cdot\mathbf{S}}\,\mathbf{S}\cdot\mathbf{I} + 2\mu_n \frac{\mathbf{s}_n\cdot\mathbf{S}}{\mathbf{S}\cdot\mathbf{S}}\,\mathbf{S}\cdot\mathbf{I} \right) \frac{\mathbf{I}\cdot\mathbf{H}}{\mathbf{I}\cdot\mathbf{I}} \frac{\mu_N}{\hbar}$$

$$= \left(\tfrac{1}{2}\,\mathbf{L}\cdot\mathbf{I} + \mu_d{}^0\,\mathbf{S}\cdot\mathbf{I} \right) \frac{M_I H \mu_N}{I(I+1)\hbar^2} \tag{14-79}$$

where we have used the result that $\mathbf{s}\cdot\mathbf{S}/\mathbf{S}\cdot\mathbf{S} = \frac{1}{2}$. Using the Landé formulas and letting $M_I = I$, we arrive at the magnetic moment

$${}^{2S+1}\mu_I{}^L = \frac{I}{2}\left[\mu_d{}^0 + \frac{1}{2} - \left(\mu_d{}^0 - \frac{1}{2}\right) \frac{L(L+1) - S(S+1)}{I(I+1)} \right] \tag{14-80}$$

Inserting the L, S, I quantum numbers 0, 1, 1 into Eq. (14-80), we find, as is expected, that the magnetic moment for the ${}^3S_1$ state is just $\mu_d{}^0$. The set 2, 1, 1, which corresponds to the ${}^3D_1$ state, leads to

$${}^3\mu_1{}^2 = \frac{3}{4} - \frac{\mu_d{}^0}{2} = 0.3101 \tag{14-81}$$

Letting $\sin^2 w$ represent the ${}^3D_1$ probability, we find that the appropriate weight combination of the ${}^3S_1$ and ${}^3D_1$ moments is

$$\mu_d = \mu_d{}^0(1 - \sin^2 w) + (\sin^2 w)\left(\frac{3}{4} - \frac{\mu_d{}^0}{2}\right) \tag{14-82}$$

Accordingly

$$\mu_d - \mu_d{}^0 = -\tfrac{3}{2}(\mu_d{}^0 - \tfrac{1}{2}) \sin^2 w \tag{14-83}$$

Inserting the experimental value for the anomaly, we obtain for the fractional ${}^3D_1$ admixture in the ground state of the deuteron

$$\sin^2 w = 0.0393 \tag{14-84}$$

14-11. Quadrupole Moment of the Deuteron and the Tensor Force. The small admixture of ${}^3D_1$ state needed to account for the magnetic moment of the deuteron may also account for the quadrupole moment of the deuteron. The D-state wave function corresponds to a distribution of the protonic charge, which varies with θ and hence would be expected to give rise to an electric quadrupole moment. To determine this moment, we must calculate the radial parts of the ${}^3S_1$ and ${}^3D_1$ wave functions, a calculation which depends upon the detailed nature of the noncentral force which causes the small ${}^3D_1$ admixture. Rarita and Schwinger[(38)] have assumed that this noncentral force is the so-called tensor force which has the form

$$V_T = -S_{1,2}K(r) = -[3(\boldsymbol{\sigma}_n\cdot\mathbf{u})(\boldsymbol{\sigma}_p\cdot\mathbf{u}) - \boldsymbol{\sigma}_n\cdot\boldsymbol{\sigma}_p]K(r) \tag{14-85}$$

where

$$\mathbf{u} = \frac{\mathbf{r}_p - \mathbf{r}_n}{|\mathbf{r}_p - \mathbf{r}_n|} = \frac{\mathbf{r}}{r} \tag{14-86}$$

and $S_{1,2}$ is the so-called tensor-force operator. This tensor-force potential is analogous to the potential energy of two magnets or electrostatic dipoles.

In a two-nucleon system the net spin vector $\mathbf{S} = \mathbf{s}_1 + \mathbf{s}_2$ establishes an intrinsic direction in space, and the tensor force may act to concentrate the spatial distribution relative to this intrinsic direction. To obtain a physical insight into the effect of such a potential, let us consider its classical effect upon the deuteron. In the singlet spin state there is no net $\mathbf{S}$. Hence the $S_{1,2}$ operator may be set to zero, since the tensor force, of course, cannot act to alter the central-field distribution relative to a nonexistent preferred direction.

In discussing the spin triplet state let us, for convenience, take the $\mathbf{S}$ direction to be the z direction. In Fig. 14-7 we show the orientation of the two parallel spin vectors relative to the radial vector joining the two nucleons. Treating the σ's as unit vectors, the tensor potential in this classical case may be written as

$$V_T = -S_{1,2}K(r) = -[3(\cos^2\theta) - 1]K(r) \tag{14-87}$$

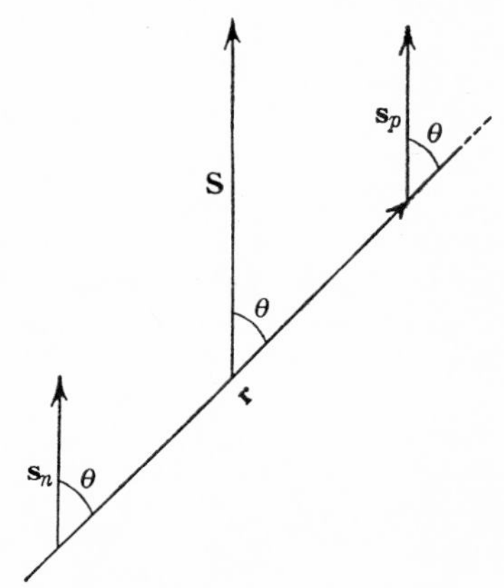

FIG. 14-7. Diagram showing orientation of parallel spin vectors relative to radial vector.

If $K(r)$ is a positive definite function, then for any r the potential energy will have the minima $-2K$ at $\theta = 0$ and $180°$ and the maxima K at $\theta = 90$ and $270°$. This potential will thus act to force the radial vector to lie along the resultant $\mathbf{S}$ vector. A combination of a large central force which has no preferred orientation and a small tensor force will tend to produce a distribution of the radial vector which is elongated along the line of the resultant spin $\mathbf{S}$. Such a cigarlike distribution will have associated with it an electric quadrupole moment.

It is a basic feature of quantum mechanics that asymmetrical angular distributions are correlated with states of higher angular momenta. The type of distribution caused by a tensor force can be shown by strict quantum-mechanical methods to correspond to the $L = 2$ states of orbital angular momentum. More specifically it can be shown that the tensor-force *operator* acting upon a ${}^3S_1$ wave function will convert it into a ${}^3D_1$ wave function. The ${}^3S_1$ and ${}^3D_1$ states are thereby coupled by the tensor force, and the state of minimum energy is a combination of these two states. This combination may be written in the form

$$\Psi = {}^3\Psi_1{}^0 \cos w + {}^3\Psi_1{}^2 \sin w \tag{14-88}$$

Rarita and Schwinger have shown, by an appropriate treatment of the angular and spin variables, that the radial wave functions ($G^l = rR^l$) for the $^3S_1$ and $^3D_1$ states must satisfy the simultaneous equations

$$\cos w \frac{d^2G^{(0)}}{dr^2} + \frac{2m_r}{\hbar^2}(W - {}^3V)G^{(0)} \cos w + \sqrt{8}\frac{2m_r}{\hbar^2} KG^{(2)} \sin w = 0 \tag{14-89}$$

and

$$\sin w \frac{d^2G^{(2)}}{dr^2} + \frac{2m_r}{\hbar^2}\left(W - {}^3V - \frac{6\hbar^2}{2m_r r^2} - 2K\right) G^{(2)} \sin w + \sqrt{8}\frac{2m_r}{\hbar^2} KG^{(0)} \cos w = 0 \tag{14-90}$$

Once the ^3V and K functions are chosen, it is possible by insisting upon the good-behavior requirements to find $G^{(0)}$ and $G^{(2)}$, the corresponding lowest energy eigenvalue W, and the value of the constant w. Having obtained these functions and these constants, the quadrupole moment may be calculated using[39]

$$Q = -\frac{\sqrt{2}}{10}\,\mathcal{R}\left(\int_0^\infty G^{*(0)}G^{(2)}r^2\,dr\right)\sin w \cos w - \frac{1}{20}\left(\int_0^\infty G^{*(2)}G^{(2)}r^2\,dr\right)\sin^2 w \tag{14-91}$$

where $\mathcal{R}$ means "the real part of." For a small admixture of ^3D state the major contribution to the quadrupole moment is due to the S-D cross terms in the angular distribution function rather than to the square of the D term.

In 1941 Rarita and Schwinger made use of the interaction function

$$V = -\mathcal{I}_{1,2}V_0(1 + c_\sigma \boldsymbol{\sigma}_1 \cdot \boldsymbol{\sigma}_2 + \gamma S_{1,2})\xi(r) \tag{14-92}$$

where

$$\begin{aligned} \xi(r) &= 1 \qquad 0 < r < a \\ &= 0 \qquad r > a \end{aligned} \tag{14-93}$$

and $\mathcal{I}_{1,2}$ is the neutral, charged, or symmetric isobaric-spin operator. They found it possible to account for the then available low-energy nucleon-nucleon data, including the magnetic and quadrupole moments of the deuteron, by using the parameters

$$\mathcal{I}_{1,2}V_0 = 13.5 \text{ Mev} \qquad a = 2.8 \times 10^{-13} \text{ cm} \qquad c_\sigma = 0.036 \qquad \gamma = 0.775$$

Hu and Massey,[40] using more recent data, have extended the investigation of interactions having the form of Eq. (14-92) to include the Gaussian, exponential, and Yukawa wells. Their theoretical study and other recent investigations indicate that, no matter what well shape is chosen, Eq. (14-92) is not sufficiently versatile to account for all the available low-energy nucleon-nucleon data. In recent studies somewhat better success has been achieved by introducing a fifth adjustable parameter, which usually is taken as the range of the tensor force. Pease and Feshbach[41] make use of

$$V = -V_0\left[\left(1 - \frac{1}{2}g + \frac{1}{2}g\, \boldsymbol{\sigma}_1 \cdot \boldsymbol{\sigma}_2\right) f\left(\frac{r}{a_c}\right) + \gamma S_{1,2} f\left(\frac{r}{a_t}\right)\right] \qquad (14\text{-}94)$$

where $f(x) = e^{-x}/x$. Using this form, they find moderate success in explaining not only the low-energy two-body data but also the properties of triton, when they use

$$V_0 = 46.96 \text{ Mev} \qquad g = 0.005 \qquad \gamma = 0.5085$$

$$a_t = 1.70 \times 10^{-13} \text{ cm} \qquad \frac{a_t}{a_c} = 1.44$$

The coulomb energy of He^3, however, is in error by 25 per cent according to this function. An interesting, although possibly fortuitous, aspect of this potential is that g may be set identically to zero without making an appreciable sacrifice of "fit." For this choice of g the central part of the singlet and triplet potentials are identical, and the tensor force alone accounts for the difference in the properties of the singlet and triplet states.

In summary, it appears possible, using a five-parameter or even possibly a four-parameter phenomenological interaction, to give a fair account of the following low-energy data: the deuteron binding energy (one number), ortho and para coherent-scattering lengths (two numbers), proton-proton scattering at low energies (two numbers), neutron-proton scattering at low energies (four numbers), the deuteron magnetic moment (one number), the deuteron quadrupole moment (one number), photodisintegration cross sections (two numbers), neutron-capture cross section (one number), triton properties (two numbers). Since several of these numbers are closely related, we see that the best phenomenological synthesis of nucleon-nucleon interactions now known does not have a very great "yield" of numbers in relation to the numbers planted. We must recognize, however, that the wavelengths of matter waves in this energy region are rather large compared to the range of nuclear forces. Hence we cannot really expect to "see" the fine details of the nucleon-nucleon interaction by low-energy experiments. Accordingly, the fact that we can interpret a great amount of raw experimental data in the low-energy region in terms of five or so numbers is more of a demonstration that the usual laws and methods of quantum mechanics are applicable than it is an indication of the reliability of the postulated interaction.

We would expect to learn more about the nucleon-nucleon interaction by investigations in the high-energy region where the De Broglie wavelengths are either comparable to or smaller than the range of nuclear forces. In the high-energy region, P, D, F, . . . waves should be scattered, so that we should learn from their phase shifts whether nuclear forces are attractive or repulsive in these states. In this way we might verify or contradict the exchange character of the assumed nucleon-nucleon interaction. The scattering should also reveal clearly whether the neutron-proton and proton-proton nuclear forces in like states are identical, as is expected according to the assumption of the charge independence of the nucleon-nucleon interaction.

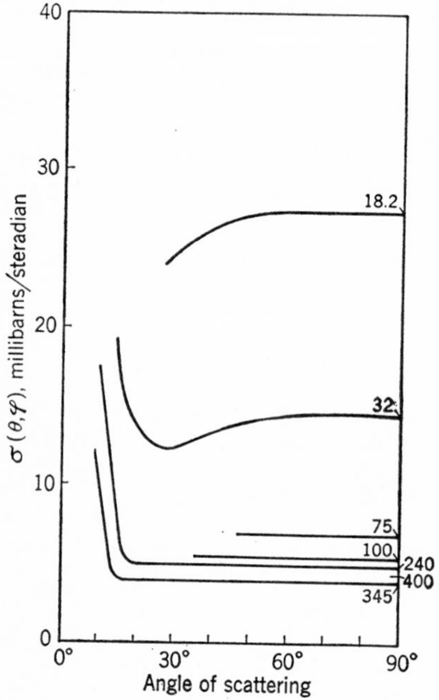

FIG. 14-8. Diagram showing general trends of experimental results on high-energy proton-proton differential scattering cross sections.

The predictions concerning high-energy experiments which have been made in the literature are quite varied, reflecting the numerous changes which have been made in the assumed nucleon-nucleon interaction. One of the common features of these predictions is that variations of the differential cross sections with angle should set in at energies of the order of 10 Mev and become quite appreciable as the energy builds up. Scattering in the forward direction is expected at high energies.

14-12. High-energy Nucleon-Nucleon Experiments. With the development of high-energy accelerators, data on neutron-proton and proton-proton scattering in the high-energy range have been accumulating quite rapidly. The pioneer work with the Berkeley 184-in. cyclotron(42) has now been supplemented by work at other laboratories, so that the overall nature of the results in the energy range up to about 450 Mev appears to be fairly well established. Some caution, however, must be exercised in the interpretation of the experimental data, since detection and energy-measuring techniques in this energy range are still rather crude. High-energy neutrons are obtained by indirect methods such as the stripping of high-energy deuterons by lithium, whereas protons are obtained by direct acceleration. In general, the energy spread of a neutron beam is somewhat larger (~5 per cent) than the energy spread of a high-energy proton beam (~3 per cent).

The general nature of the experimental measurements of the differential cross sections for proton-proton scattering is indicated in Fig. 14-8. The remarkable aspect of these results is the approximate constancy of

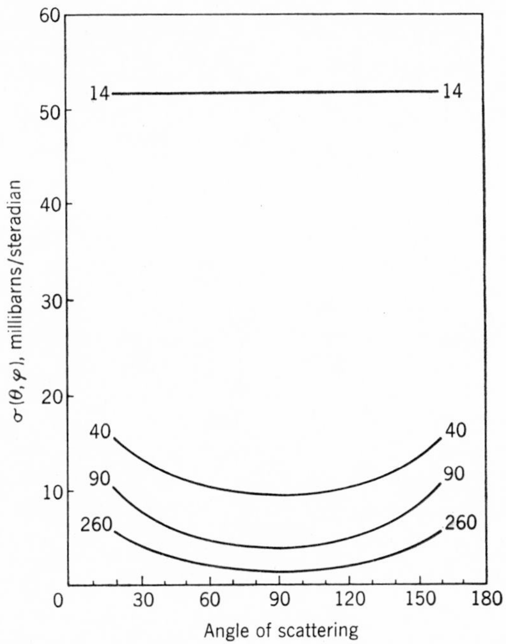

FIG. 14-9. Diagram showing general trends of experimental results on high-energy neutron-proton differential cross sections.

the observed cross section in the 20 to 90° region. In this region the coulomb scattering should be small, so that the differential cross sections reflect purely nuclear interactions. It is also observed that the differential cross section per unit solid angle at 90° is rather insensitive to the energy between 100 and 400 Mev, running around 4 millibarns/steradian.(42,43,64) In Fig. 14-9 we indicate the general nature of the experimental differential cross sections for neutron-proton scattering at several high energies.(44) We note a marked anisotropy of scattered particles with the suggestion of approximate symmetry about 90°. The differential cross section per unit solid angle at 90° appears somewhat more sensitive to the energy and is about 1.2 millibarns/steradian at 260 Mev.

The isotropy of the proton-proton scattering suggests that only S waves are scattered even at these very high energies. However, a simple analysis shows that the value of the cross section is too large to be explained by S scattering alone. On the other hand, the anisotropy of neutron-proton scattering and the approximate symmetry about 90° suggest that $D, G, \ldots$, and other, even L, partial waves are scattered, an observation which would appear to disprove the charge-independence hypothesis. In general, the high-energy results are so completely at variance with what was anticipated on the basis of low-energy nucleon-nucleon interactions as to break the phenomenological approach to the problem wide open.

The current literature contains numerous proposals and rebuttals concerning the nucleon-nucleon interactions which account for the high-energy data. Christian and Hart[45] have shown that the high-energy neutron-proton data can be accounted for fairly well on the basis of the exchange force proposed by Serber:

$$V = -\tfrac{1}{2}V_0(1 + P_L)\xi(r) \qquad (14\text{-}95)$$

This force is attractive for even L and vanishes for odd L and in consequence leads to differential cross sections which are symmetric about 90°. A serious objection to this exchange force is the fact that it does not produce the repulsions necessary to account for the saturation properties of nuclei. Christian and Noyes[46] suggest that, if we wish to fit the neutron-proton and proton-proton data by means of static potentials, we must give up the charge-independence hypothesis. To account for the proton-proton data, they use a combination of a central force and a singular (as r^{-1} and r^{-2}) tensor force. On the other hand Case and Pais[47] claim that charge independence can be retained if we introduce a rather singular spin-orbit force into the nucleon-nucleon interaction. With such a force they can qualitatively account for the relative and absolute magnitudes of the proton-proton and neutron-proton differential cross sections at 90° at 260 Mev. However, they have difficulty in fitting the data at other energies. If they make the neutron-proton cross section a minimum at 90°, they find that their spin-orbit force has the wrong sign for use in connection with the shell model.

Jastrow[48] has shown that it is possible to account for the qualitative features of the neutron-proton and proton-proton scattering data by assuming a potential with a repulsive core. Such short-range repulsion has long been considered as a possible explanation of nuclear saturation, which is an additional point in favor of Jastrow's suggestion. However, the radius of the core used to account for the scattering results is too small to account for the saturation properties of nuclei.

It should be clear from the foregoing discussion that the high-energy experimental data have been given a variety of interpretations, none of which has been established with finality. One general conclusion which appears to be common to all recent explanations is that a strong singularity exists in nucleon-nucleon interaction at small distances.

The unanticipated experimental observations which have been reported each year suggest that perhaps other types of nuclear interactions besides central, spin-orbit, and tensor should be explored which we have not yet considered. Wigner[49] and Eisenbud and Wigner[50] have tabulated a host of possible combinations of the vectors $\mathbf{r}$, $\boldsymbol{\sigma}_1$, $\boldsymbol{\sigma}_2$, $\mathbf{p}_1$, $\mathbf{p}_2$, $\boldsymbol{\tau}_1$, and $\boldsymbol{\tau}_2$ which satisfy certain basic invariance requirements. Unfortunately the number of possible interactions which may be arrived at in this way is so great as to preclude the systematic investigation of their effects singly and in combinations. For this reason theoretical physicists have sought a more definitive basis for limiting the nucleon-nucleon-interaction forms which require investigation. It has been hoped that meson field theory, a subject which properly belongs to fundamental-particle physics, would give some assistance in this direction.

14-13. Meson Theory of Nuclear Forces. Efforts to devise a field theory of nuclear forces along the lines of the successful field theory of electromagnetic forces (electrodynamics) extend back to the work of Heisenberg[34] in 1932. Field theories of forces between particles are based upon the idea that the interaction between particles takes place through the intermediary of a field. In applications of the field theory to the deduction of explicit interactions between particles the field enters as an intermediate, almost fictional, concept. On the other hand, in other physical situations, the field manifests itself as real particles as, for example, photons, which are the particle manifestations of the electromagnetic field. The characterizing aspect of the large number of theories which come under the heading of "meson theories" is that in these theories nucleons act as sources and sinks of fields which in real processes manifest themselves as mesons, particles which are intermediate in mass between the electron and proton. This foundation of the bulk of the theoretical speculation concerning the origin of nuclear forces was laid out in 1935 by Yukawa.[51] The discovery in 1936 by Anderson and Neddermeyer[52] of an unstable particle (the μ meson) with mass intermediate between an electron and a nucleon gave great impetus to the development of Yukawa's idea. Many of the leading theoreticians in the field of quantum electrodynamics, which to a great extent had been developed a few years earlier (1930 to 1933), redirected their efforts toward finding a specific quantum field theory for nuclear forces. We shall here present only the underlying ideas of this very complicated subject.

14-14. Wave Equations. The wave equation for the wave functions which characterize a field may be regarded as a basic statement of the laws governing the field, summarizing as it does the totality of possible motions or states of the system. A formal procedure is available for inferring wave equations from classical considerations which has proved remarkably successful in several important applications. The steps in this procedure are as follows:

1. Express the Hamiltonian or total energy of a system as a function of position and momentum variables, *i.e.*, let

$$H = H(x,y,z,p_x,p_y,p_z) \tag{14-96}$$

2. On the right replace the dynamical variables p_x, p_y, and p_z by the operators $-i\hbar\, \partial/\partial x$, $-i\hbar\, \partial/\partial y$, and $-i\hbar\, \partial/\partial z$.

3. On the left replace the dynamical variable H by the operator $i\hbar\, \partial/\partial t$.

4. Allow both sides to operate on the wave function $\Psi(\mathbf{r},t)$.

To illustrate this procedure, let us apply it to the "derivation" of the Schroedinger time-dependent wave equation for a particle in a potential field. In this case the Hamiltonian is

$$H = \frac{1}{2m}(p_x^2 + p_y^2 + p_z^2) + V(\mathbf{r}) \tag{14-97}$$

Substituting the appropriate operators and introducing the wave function, we find immediately

$$i\hbar \frac{\partial}{\partial t}\Psi(\mathbf{r},t) = \left[\frac{\hbar^2}{-2m}\left(\frac{\partial^2}{\partial x^2} + \frac{\partial^2}{\partial y^2} + \frac{\partial^2}{\partial z^2}\right) + V(\mathbf{r})\right]\Psi(\mathbf{r},t) \tag{14-98}$$

which is precisely the general Schroedinger wave equation.

In this equation $\Psi(\mathbf{r},t)$ is the amplitude of the "probability field" which characterizes the behavior of atomic particles at nonrelativistic velocities. For a free particle, $V(\mathbf{r}) = 0$; hence the Schroedinger wave equation is

$$\left(-\frac{\hbar^2}{2m}\Delta - i\hbar\frac{\partial}{\partial t}\right)\Psi(\mathbf{r},t) = 0 \tag{14-99}$$

Since the Newtonian dynamics, upon which Eqs. (14-97) to (14-99) are based, is known to break down for the motion of particles approaching the velocity of light, we may expect that this corresponding quantum-mechanical generalization will be inadequate for the description of high-energy motions. We might therefore attempt to base a wave equation for a free particle upon the strictly relativistic expression for the total energy

$$H = (m^2c^4 + p^2c^2)^{\frac{1}{2}} \tag{14-100}$$

Unfortunately the nonlinear operator which is generated on the right side by our procedure does not have a meaning in the usual sense, so that direct application of this formula has not proved fruitful. If, however, we apply the operator-substitution formalism to

$$H^2 = m^2c^4 + p^2c^2 \tag{14-101}$$

we obtain upon rearranging terms the relativistic Schroedinger[53] wave equation

$$\left(\Delta - \frac{1}{c^2}\frac{\partial^2}{\partial t^2} - \kappa^2\right)\boldsymbol{\Psi}(\mathbf{r},t) = 0 \tag{14-102}$$

where $\kappa = mc/\hbar$.

If the mass of the particle is allowed to vanish, Eq. (14-102) becomes

$$\left(\Delta - \frac{1}{c^2}\frac{\partial^2}{\partial t^2}\right)\boldsymbol{\Psi}(\mathbf{r},t) = 0 \tag{14-103}$$

This is identical with the wave equation satisfied by the electromagnetic wave functions in free space (Maxwell's wave equation). Thus our procedure also generates the wave equation for this basic field.

Dirac[54] overcame the difficulty with the nonlinear operator in another way. In essence, Dirac replaced the quadratic expression Eq. (14-101) by a linear relation

$$H = c(\alpha_x p_x + \alpha_y p_y + \alpha_z p_z) + \beta mc^2 \tag{14-104}$$

In order that Eq. (14-104) might contain Eq. (14-102), Dirac chose α_x, α_y, α_z, and β to be four-by-four matrices with certain special algebraic properties. Applying our operator-replacement procedure, we find that the wave equation is

$$i\hbar\frac{\partial}{\partial t}\boldsymbol{\Psi}^D(\mathbf{r},t) = (c\,\boldsymbol{\alpha}\cdot\mathbf{p} + \beta mc^2)\boldsymbol{\Psi}^D(\mathbf{r},t) \tag{14-105}$$

where $\boldsymbol{\Psi}^D$ is the Dirac wave function. This equation is the famous Dirac wave equation for the probability amplitude of a free electron. Because of the matrix operators which are present in this expression, the Dirac wave function consists of a set of four ordinary wave functions arranged in the form of a four-by-one matrix. It has been shown that this equation not only automatically endows the electron with the observed properties of spin but also predicts the existence of negative energy states for a free electron. According to the Dirac hole-theory interpretation[55] electrons in such states manifest themselves by their absence as antielectrons or, as they are usually called, positrons.

Since the Dirac wave equation is a part of quantum electrodynamics, we shall not be further concerned with it, beyond mentioning the fact that it is often assumed that the Dirac equation is satisfied by the probability amplitude of a free nucleon. This assumption leads one to expect that antiprotons and antineutrons may be created at sufficiently high energies.

In his first paper on the meson theory Yukawa chose the relativistic Schroedinger equation [Eq. (14-102)] as the wave equation for the meson field, and he assumed that the meson field is related to the forces between nucleons in a manner analogous to the relation between the photon and the forces between electrons. In view of the dependence of Yukawa's work upon earlier concepts in electromagnetic theory, let us present these concepts briefly.

By assuming the wave equation for the electromagnetic field to be independent of time, Eq. (14-103) for the electrostatic potential $\phi(r)$ becomes

$$\Delta\phi(\mathbf{r}) = 0 \tag{14-106}$$

This well-known Laplace's equation pertains to an empty field. In the presence of a distribution of charges this equation must be modified by adding on the right a function $4\pi q\rho(\mathbf{r})$, where q represents a coupling constant and $\rho(\mathbf{r})$ a density function. We then obtain Poisson's equation

$$\Delta\phi(\mathbf{r}) = 4\pi q\rho(\mathbf{r}) \tag{14-107}$$

It is well known in the theory of inhomogeneous differential equations associated with an equation of the type

$$\Omega_{op}\Psi = 4\pi q\rho(\mathbf{r}) \tag{14-108}$$

that there exists a symmetrical solution $G(\mathbf{r},\mathbf{r}')$ of the homogeneous equation such that every particular solution of Eq. (14-108) is given by

$$\Psi(\mathbf{r}) = q\int\rho(\mathbf{r}')G(\mathbf{r},\mathbf{r}')\,dV' \tag{14-109}$$

The function $G(\mathbf{r},\mathbf{r}')$ is known as the Green's function. In the case of the electrostatic field set up by a charge distribution, the Green's function is simply the coulomb electrostatic potential associated with a unit charge at each point $\mathbf{r}'$, that is,

$$G(\mathbf{r},\mathbf{r}') = \frac{1}{|\mathbf{r} - \mathbf{r}'|} \tag{14-110}$$

Equation (14-109) then becomes the usual formula for the coulomb potential at any point in the neighborhood of a distribution of charge.

The significance of the coulomb potential function in connection with a system of charged particles is well known. The electrostatic field is viewed as the intermediary through which charges influence each other. For example, an isolated pole with the strength q_1 located at $\mathbf{r}_1$ sets up the electrostatic potential

$$V = \frac{q_1}{|\mathbf{r} - \mathbf{r}_1|} \tag{14-111}$$

The energy of a second pole with the strength q_2 located at $\mathbf{r}_2$ is given by

$$V = q_2\phi(\mathbf{r}_2) = \frac{q_1q_2}{|\mathbf{r}_2 - \mathbf{r}_1|} = \frac{q_1q_2}{r} \tag{14-112}$$

where $r = |\mathbf{r}_2 - \mathbf{r}_1|$. We note that this last expression is completely symmetrical relative to the pole at $\mathbf{r}_1$ and the pole at $\mathbf{r}_2$. We may now view the right side of Eq. (14-112), which no longer has reference to the field, as the explicit energy of the system of two charges.

In his generalizations, Yukawa considered the static form of the relativistic Schroedinger wave equation in the presence of sources. He assumed the field to be coupled to a source density $\rho(\mathbf{r})$ via a coupling constant g, which is analogous to charge. The corresponding wave equation is

$$(\Delta - \kappa^2)\Psi = 4\pi g\rho(\mathbf{r}) \tag{14-113}$$

The Green's function connected with this equation is

$$G(\mathbf{r},\mathbf{r}') = \frac{\exp(-\kappa|\mathbf{r} - \mathbf{r}'|)}{|\mathbf{r} - \mathbf{r}'|} \tag{14-114}$$

Giving this function the meaning of a mesic potential, we find by analogy with Eq. (14-112) that the explicit potential energy of a system of two nucleons is

$$V = \frac{g^2 \exp(-\kappa|\mathbf{r}_2 - \mathbf{r}_1|)}{|\mathbf{r}_2 - \mathbf{r}_1|} = \frac{g^2 \exp(-\kappa r)}{r} \tag{14-115}$$

At separations small compared to κ^{-1} this potential energy varies with r just as the coulomb energy does. However, the potential energy declines very rapidly as r becomes large compared to κ^{-1}. Yukawa noted that such an interaction energy may account for the fact that nuclear forces act only over a short range. Yukawa therefore identified the approximately known experimental range of nuclear forces with

$$\kappa^{-1} = \frac{\hbar}{mc}$$

From the approximately known range of nuclear forces Yukawa estimated the mass of this new particle to be about $200m_e$. As we noted earlier, the discovery of the μ meson in 1936 was immediately thought to be a verification of Yukawa's hypothesis.

14-15. Forms of Meson Theory. The first task undertaken by the theoretical physicists who accepted the basic idea of Yukawa was to investigate various forms of meson theory in an effort to find a specific form which leads to an interaction function which could account for the detailed experimental observations of neutron-proton and proton-proton systems. These earliest studies of meson theory followed closely the methods which have proved successful in quantum electrodynamics and were based upon postulates which departed only slightly from the assumptions used in quantum electrodynamics. Now, within the general framework of meson theories which meet the requirements of relativistic invariance and which depart only slightly from quantum electrodynamics, there are several possible specific theories. These theories essentially depend upon the choice of (1) the tensoral character of the meson-field wave function, (2) the isobaric-spin character of the meson-field wave functions, (3) the intrinsic nature of the source-field coupling, and (4) the strength of the source-coupling constant.

The tensoral character of the meson field depends upon the number of component wave functions which are needed to characterize the field and upon the manner in which these wave functions are affected by a Lorentz transformation of coordinates. The components of a tensor in four-space (space-time) may be specified by appending indices to the wave functions, indices which denote the numbers 1, 2, 3, and 4. Wave functions with 1, 4, 16, 64, . . . components are indicated simply by ϕ, ϕ_α, $\phi_{\alpha\beta}$, $\phi_{\alpha\beta\gamma}$, ... These wave functions are known as scalar, vector, second-rank-tensor, third-rank-tensor, etc., wave functions. The tensoral types of wave functions which have received most serious attention in meson theory are the scalar, vector, pseudovector, and pseudoscalar. These last two are special kinds of third- and fourth-rank tensors which have the property of complete antisymmetry. This property ensures that all component wave functions with two or more identical indices vanish (for example, $\phi_{1,1,1} = \phi_{1,1,3} = \phi_{1,3,1} = 0$) and that component wave functions which differ only in the order of the indices are identical, apart from a possible factor of -1 (for example, $\phi_{1,2,3} = \phi_{3,1,2} = -\phi_{2,1,3} = -\phi_{1,3,2}$, etc.).

Since a completely antisymmetric third-rank tensor has only four independent components ($\phi_{1,2,3}$, $\phi_{2,3,4}$, $\phi_{3,4,1}$, and $\phi_{4,1,2}$), it may in most regards be handled as a vector, and for this reason it is called a pseudovector. A completely antisymmetric fourth-rank tensor having only one independent component ($\phi_{1,2,3,4}$) is analogous to a scalar and therefore is called a pseudoscalar. It has been shown theoretically that scalar and pseudoscalar fields materialize as particles with spin 0, whereas vector and pseudovector fields materialize as particles with spin 1.

The isobaric-spin character of a meson field is related to the charge of the mesons associated with the field. In the neutral theory, the field materializes as neutral mesons. In the charged theory, the field consists of two isobaric-spin components, one associated with positively charged mesons and one associated with negatively charged mesons. The charge-symmetric theory allows three field components, those associated with positive, negative, and neutral mesons. These components are not completely independent, since together they make up an abstract three-vector whose components satisfy certain algebraic relations. In relation to nuclear forces the effect of using a neutral, charged, or symmetrical theory is identical with that which we have described in our discussion of phenomenological theories.

Two types of source-field couplings have received the greatest attention, namely, pole-type couplings and dipole-type couplings. In pole-type coupling the interaction energy between the source and the field depends upon the meson-field wave function and a characteristic coupling constant g associated with the source itself. In dipole-type couplings this energy depends upon the first derivatives of the meson-field wave function and a characteristic dipole moment $\boldsymbol{\mu}$ associated with the source. A well-known classical example of a pole-type coupling is the interaction energy

$$V = e\phi \tag{14-116}$$

for a point charge in a field characterized by the electrostatic potential ϕ. On the other hand the interaction between a permanent electric dipole and an electric field characterized by a potential ϕ is given by

$$V = \boldsymbol{\mu} \cdot \nabla\phi \tag{14-117}$$

where $\boldsymbol{\mu}$ is the dipole moment, which dimensionally has the magnitude of a coupling constant times a length. Since the dipole moment is an intrinsic property of the source, it would seem proper in meson theory, despite common practice to the contrary, to accept for the nuclear moment a characteristic nucleon length, such as $\hbar/mc$, times a coupling constant, which we shall denote by f to distinguish it from the pole-type-coupling parameter. On the basis of the assumed field and the field-source coupling it is possible by classical or quantum field-theory methods to eliminate the field and deduce explicit interactions between sources. For example, in the electrostatic case, if we insert into Eq. (14-116) the potential due to another charge and into Eq. (14-117) the potential due to another dipole, the explicit interaction energies become

$$V_{PP} = e^2\left(\frac{1}{r}\right) \tag{14-118}$$

$$V_{DD} = (\boldsymbol{\mu} \cdot \nabla)(\boldsymbol{\mu} \cdot \nabla)\frac{1}{r} \tag{14-119}$$

Kemmer[56] has made a systematic study of theories which meet relativistic requirements and at the same time represent relatively small departures from quantum electrodynamics. For a neutral theory, when various relativistic and higher-order effects which are known to be small in the electrodynamic case are ignored, the results are[57]

$$V_{s,f} = V_{ps,f} = 0 \tag{14-120}$$

$$V_{v,g} = -V_{s,g} = J = g^2 \frac{e^{-\kappa r}}{r} \tag{14-121}$$

$$V_{v,f} = -V_{pv,f} = f^2 \left[2\, \boldsymbol{\sigma}_1 \cdot \boldsymbol{\sigma}_2\, a^2 \frac{(r^2 J')'}{3r^2} - S_{1,2} a^2 \frac{r(J'/r)'}{3} \right] \tag{14-122}$$

$$V_{ps,g} = -V_{pv,g} = g^2 \left[\boldsymbol{\sigma}_1 \cdot \boldsymbol{\sigma}_2\, a^2 \frac{(r^2 J')'}{3r^2} + S_{1,2} a^2 \frac{r(J'/r)'}{3} \right] \tag{14-123}$$

where s, v, pv, and ps refer to scalar, vector, pseudoscalar, and pseudovector, respectively, g and f to pole and dipole coupling, respectively, and a to the characteristic nucleon length.

The corresponding charged and charge-symmetric interactions are the same, except they are preceded by the isobaric-spin operators

$$\tfrac{1}{2}(1 + \boldsymbol{\tau}_1 \cdot \boldsymbol{\tau}_2)$$

and $\boldsymbol{\tau}_1 \cdot \boldsymbol{\tau}_2$, respectively. When consideration is given to the isobaric-spin effects, we have a large number of basic interaction forms to attempt to bring into consistency with experiment by adjustment of the coupling constant or dipole moment. Unfortunately none of these simple forms individually is capable of organizing the experimental data.

14-16. Theoretical Difficulties. Apart from the fact that none of the theoretical meson interactions is capable of explaining the experimental data, basic difficulties arise with these interactions because the space function associated with the tensor-force operator has an r^{-3} singularity. Such a high singularity is a bête noire when the deduced interaction is used in the ordinary Schroedinger equation. In fact, according to an exact mathematical analysis the binding energy of a system held together by an attractive force with such a strong singularity should have no limit, and the system should condense to an infinitesimal size.

Now it is well known that r^{-3} interactions arise among relativistic terms in electrodynamics. In principle the objections raised above are equally great in electrodynamics. However, in practical calculations it has proved possible to make use of the experimentally established facts that these interactions cause small effects. Accordingly somewhat questionable perturbation methods are used which suppress the apparently unreal effects associated with the r^{-3} singularity, yet at the same time bring out the small but real effects connected with the action of these forces at medium and long ranges. Unfortunately the evidence in meson theory indicates that the physical effects associated with these singular functions are relatively large, so that a perturbation method based upon the assumption that they are small is here much more questionable.

Another theoretical difficulty arises from the action of the field set up by a nucleon upon itself. The computation of this so-called self-energy depends upon the particular meson theory chosen and the treatment accorded to the sources of the field. However, in practically all forms of meson theory this nucleon self-energy is infinite. This difficulty also has been encountered both in classical electrodynamics and in quantum electrodynamics and has resisted resolution despite the most intensive study by many theoreticians. In electrodynamics it has been necessary to use the expedient of simply ignoring these infinite constants or, more recently, of systematically identifying them with known finite constants. However, these renormalization methods, although successful in quantum electrodynamics, have not yet proved adequate to cope with the difficulties in meson theory.

A difficulty of a closely connected nature is the lack of convergence of the perturbation methods used in meson field theory. Most of the practical perturbation methods in quantum electrodynamics are based upon power-series expansions in the dimensionless fine-structure constant:

$$\alpha = \frac{e^2}{\hbar c} = 0.0072973 = \frac{1}{137.04} \qquad (14\text{-}124)$$

The small magnitude of this parameter compared to unity provides theoretical justification for the neglect of higher-order terms in this power series. From the pragmatic viewpoint a more convincing justification lies in the consistency with experiment of the results obtained by neglecting higher-order terms. However, to account for the much greater strength of nuclear forces, it has been necessary to use mesonic fine-structure constants ($g^2/\hbar c$ or $f^2/\hbar c$) which have been variously estimated at from 0.1 to 10. The neglect of higher-order terms in a power series of a constant of the order of unity is certainly a questionable affair. Despite this, theoretical physicists, for want of a better perturbation method, have for the most part carried out the investigation of meson theory with the use of power-series methods.

In dealing with all of these difficulties the physicist has entered a realm which is closely related to the mathematical study of the evaluation of divergent series and integrals. It is known that the results of these calculations depend upon the rules used in the summation or integration procedure. If such calculations are used in a physical theory, we must regard the rules of summation and integration as a part of the postulatory basis of the theory. However, the elegance and convincing power of a theory are clearly lost when it is constantly necessary to introduce new rules of calculation at each point in the application of the theory.

In the main the fundamental difficulties which we have discussed above were recognized soon after meson theory was proposed, and despite intensive efforts toward their solution these difficulties are still with us. Because of the shaky and illusive nature of the foundations of meson theory and the widespread recognition of the logical inconsistency of the theory, the literature of this subject has developed in a most unusual manner for a natural science. One might characterize the major efforts to apply meson theory without reconstructing its foundations as "fashions," each of which has taken a position of prominence in the literature as a promising heuristic development and then has been dismissed as inefficacious.

Perhaps a very brief description of some of the main "fashions" is not out of place. One of the first attempts to apply meson theory was based upon the "cutoff" device suggested by Bethe(58) in 1940. In this theory singular functions such as r^{-1}, r^{-2}, and r^{-3} were replaced near $r = 0$ by finite functions, on the grounds that the future correct theory will effectively provide such a cutoff. Next came the "mixture" idea, proposed in a simple form by Møller and Rosenfeld(59) in 1940 and in a more elaborate form by Schwinger(60) in 1942. These were attempts to apply meson theory by combining two or more forms of meson fields so as to cancel the unmanageable infinities and singularities. More recently, attempts have been made in meson theory to use the "renormalization" methods developed for electrodynamics by Tomonaga,(61) Schwinger,(62) Feynman,(63) and others, to discriminate between the parts of the singularities and infinities which are real effects and the parts which have no physical significance.

While all of these approaches are objectionable in that they have failed to come to grips with the fundamental field-theory difficulties, the main reason for their decline from favor has been that they have not been able to give a reasonable account of existing information and that they have failed utterly to anticipate any of the subsequent experimental findings. The fashion from around 1950 to the time of this writing might perhaps be characterized as that of "despair and hope," despair at the difficulties which have been encountered in attempts to utilize conventional field-theory ideas and hope that the experiments with recently available very-high-energy machines will soon provide the key clues to the nature of nuclear forces. We are still in this period.

A description of the very recent experimental findings with artificially created mesons would require chapters and would probably be obsolete by the time of publication. One might also debate as to which of the very recent theoretical speculations are worthy of note and which have an ephemeral character. The host of unanticipated mesons which have been discovered in cosmic rays and which are now being studied more carefully in the laboratory certainly indicate that the mild projections of quantum electrodynamics into meson theory which have been given such widespread attention are inadequate to cope with the unfolding phenomena in the very-high-energy range. It would appear that the current situation demands a fundamentally new type of theory which accommodates many particles and which at the outset is devoid of the unphysical singularities and infinities. The theory must also account for the internal structure of nucleons and other fundamental particles as well as their interplay. Many exploratory proposals in this direction have been made, although which of these represent bold speculation and which represent wild speculation remain matters of opinion and matters to be settled by future experiments.

In concluding this book, we might remark that perhaps never before in history has nature presented so great a challenge to the human imagination as it is doing now in nuclear and field-particle physics. It should be a source of gratification to everyone working in these fields to know that there are great discoveries yet to be made.

PROBLEMS

***14-1.** Use the well parameters ${}^3a = {}^1a = 2.8 \times 10^{-13}$ cm, ${}^3V_0 = 21$ Mev, and ${}^1V_0 = 12$ Mev to compute the scattering cross section vs. kinetic energy for 0- to 10-Mev neutrons. How does this curve compare with the experimental curve (see Fig. 14-2)?

***14-2.** Use the effective-range parameters in Eqs. (14-21) to (14-24) to calculate the curve of cross section vs. kinetic energy for 0- to 10-Mev neutron-proton scattering. How does this compare with experiment?

14-3. What are the potential functions for the singlet S state according to Eqs. (14-92) and (14-94)?

14-4. Show that $J = e^{-\kappa r}/r$ satisfies $(\Delta - \kappa^2)J = 0$ when $r \neq 0$.

14-5. What are the explicit radial functions associated with the tensor and spin-spin force in Eqs. (14-122) and (14-123) and with $(\boldsymbol{\mu}_1 \cdot \nabla\, \boldsymbol{\mu}_2 \cdot \nabla)J(r)$ when $J(r) = 1/r$ and when $J(r) = e^{-\kappa r}/r$?

†14-6. Prepare a bibliography of articles which have appeared in the literature since 1952 on (*a*) 0- to 25-Mev nucleon-nucleon interactions, (*b*) high-energy nucleon-nucleon interactions, (*c*) meson theory of nuclear forces.

REFERENCES

1. Hulthén, L., and B. C. H. Nagel: *Phys. Rev.*, **90,** 66 (1953).
2. Hornyak, W. F., T. Lauritsen, P. Morrison, and W. A. Fowler: *Revs. Mod. Phys.*, **22,** 291 (1950).
3. Fuller, E. G.: *Phys. Rev.*, **79,** 303 (1950).
4. Goldhaber, G.: *Phys. Rev.*, **81,** 930 (1951).
5. Weinstock, E. V., and J. Halpern: *Phys. Rev.*, **91,** 461 (1953).
6. Adair, R. K.: *Revs. Mod. Phys.*, **22,** 254 (1950).
7. Melkonian, E., L. J. Rainwater, and W. W. Havens, Jr.: *Phys. Rev.*, **75,** 1295 (1949).
8. Sutton, R. B., T. Hall, E. E. Anderson, H. S. Bridge, J. W. DeWire, L. S. Lavatelli, E. A. Long, J. Snyder, and R. W. Williams: *Phys. Rev.*, **72,** 1147 (1947).

9. Whitehouse, W. J., and G. A. R. Graham: *Can. J. Research*, **A25**, 261 (1947).
10. Tuve, M. A., N. P. Heydenburg, and L. R. Hafstad: *Phys. Rev.*, **50**, 806 (1936); **53**, 239 (1938).
11. Herb, R., D. Kerst, D. Parkinson, and G. Plain: *Phys. Rev.*, **55**, 998 (1939).
12. Worthington, H. R., D. E. Findley, and J. N. McGruer: *Phys. Rev.*, **87**, 223 (1952).
13. Yntema, J. L., and M. G. White: *Phys. Rev.*, **87**, 223 (1952).
14. Landau, L., and J. Smorodinski: *J. Phys. (U.S.S.R.)*, **8**, 154 (1944).
15. Schwinger, J.: *Phys. Rev.*, **78**, 135 (1950).
16. Bethe, H. A.: *Phys. Rev.*, **76**, 38 (1949).
17. Blatt, J. D., and J. M. Jackson: *Phys. Rev.*, **76**, 18 (1949).
18. Wigner, E. P.: unpublished.
19. Rosenfeld, L.: "Nuclear Forces," p. 131, Interscience Publishers, Inc., New York, 1948.
20. Burgy, M. T., G. R. Ringo, and D. J. Hughes: *Phys. Rev.*, **84**, 1161 (1951).
21. Jastrow, R.: *Phys. Rev.*, **91**, 750 (1953).
22. Fermi, E., and L. Marshall: *Phys. Rev.*, **71**, 666 (1947).
23. Schwinger, J., and E. Teller: *Phys. Rev.*, **52**, 286, 1250 (1937).
24. Hammermesh, M., and J. Schwinger: *Phys. Rev.*, **71**, 678 (1947).
25. Schwinger, J.: *Phys. Rev.*, **52**, 1250 (1937).
26. Bethe, H. A.: *Revs. Mod. Phys.*, **8**, 137 (1936).
27. Blatt, J., and V. Weisskopf: "Theoretical Nuclear Physics," pp. 600–614, John Wiley & Sons, Inc., New York, 1952.
28. Breit, G., and R. L. Gluckstern: *Ann. Rev. Nuclear Sci.*, **2**, 393 (1953).
29. Breit, G., and M. H. Hull, Jr.: *Am. J. Phys.*, **21**, 184 (1953).
30. Powell, J. L., and H. H. Hall: *Phys. Rev.*, **87**, 223 (1952).
31. Breit, G., E. U. Condon, and R. D. Present: *Phys. Rev.*, **50**, 825 (1936).
32. Blatt, J. D., and J. M. Jackson: *Revs. Mod. Phys.*, **22**, 77 (1950).
33. Yovits, M. C., R. L. Smith, M. H. Hull, Jr., J. Bengston, and G. Breit: *Phys. Rev.*, **85**, 540 (1952).
34. Heisenberg, W.: *Z. Physik*, **77**, 1 (1932).
35. Bartlett, J. H., Jr.: *Phys. Rev.*, **49**, 102 (1936).
36. Majorana, E.: *Z. Physik*, **82**, 137 (1933).
37. Wigner, E. P.: *Phys. Rev.*, **43**, 252 (1933); *Z. Physik*, **83**, 253 (1933).
38. Rarita, W., and J. Schwinger: *Phys. Rev.*, **59**, 436, 556 (1941).
39. Rosenfeld, L.: Ref. 19, p. 92.
40. Hu, T., and H. S. W. Massey: *Proc. Roy. Soc. (London)*, **A196**, 135 (1949).
41. Pease, R., and H. Feshbach: *Phys. Rev.*, **81**, 142 (1951); **88**, 945 (1952).
42. Chamberlain, O., E. Segrè, and C. Wiegand: *Phys. Rev.*, **81**, 284 (1951).
43. Oxley, C. L., and R. D. Schamberger: *Phys. Rev.*, **85**, 416 (1952).
44. Christian, R. S.: *Repts. Progr. Phys.*, **15**, 137 (1952).
45. Christian, R., and E. Hart: *Phys. Rev.*, **77**, 441 (1950).
46. Christian, R., and H. Noyes: *Phys. Rev.*, **79**, 85 (1950).
47. Case, K. M., and A. Pais: *Phys. Rev.*, **79**, 185 (1950); **80**, 203 (1951).
48. Jastrow, R.: *Phys. Rev.*, **81**, 165 (1951).
49. Wigner, E. P.: *Phys. Rev.*, **51**, 106 (1937).
50. Eisenbud, L., and E. P. Wigner: *Proc. Natl. Acad. Sci. U.S.*, **27**, 281 (1941).
51. Yukawa, H.: *Proc. Phys.-Math. Soc. Japan*, **3**, 17, 18 (1935).
52. Anderson, C. A., and S. H. Neddermeyer: *Phys. Rev.*, **50**, 263 (1936).
53. Schroedinger, E.: *Ann. Physik*, **81**, 169 (1926).
54. Dirac, P. A. M.: *Proc. Roy. Soc. (London)*, **A117**, 610 (1928).
55. Dirac, P. A. M.: "The Principles of Quantum Mechanics," 3d ed., p. 272, Oxford University Press, New York, 1947.

56. Kemmer, N.: *Proc. Roy. Soc.* (*London*), **A166,** 127 (1938).
57. Green, A. E. S.: *Phys. Rev.*, **75,** 1926 (1949).
58. Bethe, H. A.: *Phys. Rev.*, **57,** 260 (1940).
59. Møller, C., and L. Rosenfeld: *Proc. Phys. Soc.* (*Copenhagen*), **17**(8) (1940).
60. Schwinger, J.: *Phys. Rev.*, **61,** 387 (1942).
61. Tomonaga, S.: *Progr. Theoret. Phys.* (*Japan*), **1,** 27 (1946).
62. Schwinger, J.: *Phys. Rev.*, **74,** 1439 (1948); **75,** 651 (1949); **76,** 790 (1949).
63. Feynman, R. P.: *Phys. Rev.*, **76,** 749, 769 (1949).
64. Chamberlain, O., G. Pettengill, E. Segrè, and C. Wiegand: *Phys. Rev.*, **93,** 1424 (1954).

APPENDIX I

SOME USEFUL CONSTANTS AND CONVERSION FACTORS†

$$a_B = \hbar^2/m_e e^2 = 5.2917 \times 10^{-9} \text{ cm}$$
$$c = 2.99793 \times 10^{10} \text{ cm/sec}$$
$$e = 4.8029 \times 10^{-10} \text{ esu} = 1.6021 \times 10^{-20} \text{ emu}$$
$$h = 6.6252 \times 10^{-27} \text{ erg-sec}$$
$$\hbar = \frac{h}{2\pi} = 1.0544 \times 10^{-27} \text{ erg-sec}$$
$$m_e = 9.1085 \times 10^{-28} \text{ g} = 0.54878 \text{ mMU} = 0.51098 \text{ Mev}$$
$$m_n = 1.6747 \times 10^{-24} \text{ g} = 1.008982 \text{ MU} = 939.526 \text{ Mev}$$
$$m_p = 1.6724 \times 10^{-24} \text{ g} = 1.007593 \text{ MU} = 938.232 \text{ Mev}$$
$$N_A = 6.0247 \times 10^{23} \text{ MU/g}$$
$$R_\infty = \frac{2\pi^2 e^4 m_e}{ch^3} = 109{,}737 \text{ cm}^{-1}$$
$$\alpha = \frac{e^2}{\hbar c} = 7.2973 \times 10^{-3}$$
$$\alpha^{-1} = 137.038$$
$$\mu_B = \frac{e\hbar}{2m_e c} = 0.92732 \times 10^{-20} \text{ erg-gauss}^{-1}$$
$$\mu_N = \frac{e\hbar}{2m_p c} = 0.50504 \times 10^{-23} \text{ erg-gauss}^{-1}$$
$$\frac{\hbar}{m_e c} = 3.8615 \times 10^{-11} \text{ cm}$$
$$\frac{\hbar}{m_p c} = 2.1031 \times 10^{-14} \text{ cm}$$
$$\frac{\hbar^2}{2mb^2} = 22.451 \text{ mMU} = 20.906 \text{ Mev (for } m = 1 \text{ MU and } b = 10^{-13} \text{ cm)}$$
$$k = \left(\frac{2mT}{\hbar^2}\right)^{\frac{1}{2}} = 2.187 \times 10^{12} \text{ cm}^{-1} \text{ (for } m = 1 \text{ MU and } T = 1 \text{ Mev)}$$
$$\lambda\!\!\!^{-} = \left(\frac{\hbar^2}{2mT}\right)^{\frac{1}{2}} = 0.4572 \times 10^{-12} \text{ cm (for } m = 1 \text{ MU and } T = 1 \text{ Mev)}$$
$$1 \text{ mMU} = 0.93116 \text{ Mev} = 1.4918 \times 10^{-6} \text{ erg}$$
$$1 \text{ Mev} = 1.07392 \text{ mMU} = 1.6021 \times 10^{-6} \text{ erg}$$
$$1 \text{ erg} = 0.67034 \times 10^{6} \text{ mMU} = 0.62419 \times 10^{6} \text{ Mev}$$

† The data are from J. W. M. DuMond and E. R. Cohen, *Revs. Mod. Phys.*, **25**, 691 (1952).

APPENDIX II

BETA-STABLE NUCLIDES: THEIR MASS DECREMENTS (IN mMU) AND MASS DIFFERENCES BETWEEN ADJACENT ISOBARS (IN mMU)

In the two columns of the table below headed "Mass differences," successive values to the right of the dividing rule represent $Z + 1$, $Z + 2, \ldots$, and successive values moving to the left from the rule represent $Z - 1, Z - 2, \ldots$.

The value for $Z + 1$ gives $M({}_{Z+1}X^A) - M({}_ZX^A)$. The value for $Z + 2$ gives $M({}_{Z+2}X^A) - M({}_{Z+1}X^A)$. The value for $Z - 1$ gives $M({}_{Z-1}X^A) - M({}_ZX^A)$, etc. Accordingly, to obtain the mass decrement of an unstable isobar, add the appropriate differences to the mass decrement of the stable isobar, *e.g.*,

$$\Delta({}_{17}\mathrm{Cl}^{39}) = -23.94 + 0.61 + 3.5 = -19.8 \text{ mMU}$$

EC means that only electron capture is observed; this usually indicates that the mass difference is less than $2m_e \approx 1.1$mMU, the threshold for positron decay. For the most part these mass differences were converted from the data given in the table of isotopes by Hollander, Perlman, and Seaborg (Ref. 5, Chap. 6); however some more recent data have been included. The symbol l denotes mass decrements obtained from nuclear-reactions data by Li *et al.* The symbols o, n, and d denote mass-spectrographic values obtained from the laboratories of Ogata, Nier, and Duckworth respectively. The discrepancies between Li's and Ogata's mass decrements have not yet been resolved; hence both are given. The symbol s denotes mass decrements computed by Seaborg, Glass, and Thompson from alpha and beta decay energies, and the assumed values $\Delta(\mathrm{Pb}^{208}) = 41.00$, $B_n(\mathrm{Pb}^{207}) = 6.73$ Mev, $B_n(\mathrm{Pb}^{208}) = 7.38$ Mev, and $B_n(\mathrm{Pb}^{209}) = 3.87$ Mev.

For a detailed list of references see the end of the table.

The October, 1954, issue of *Reviews of Modern Physics* contains several excellent compilations of nuclear data that should prove useful to the reader. A number of the mass differences listed in the following table have been taken from R. W. King's Table of Total Beta Disintegration Energies contained in that issue.

A	Z	Symbol	Δ		Mass differences	
					. . . , Z − 2, Z − 1	Z + 1, Z + 2, . . .
1	1	H	8.145[o]	8.142[l]		
2	1	H	14.741[o]	14.735[l]		
3	2	He	....	16.977[l]	0.020	
4	2	He	3.879[o]	3.873[l]		
6	3	Li	....	17.021[l]	3.76	
7	3	Li	....	18.223[l]		0.928
9	4	Be	....	15.043[l]		
10	5	B	16.110[o]	16.114[l]	0.60	4.25
11	5	B	12.811[o]	12.789[l]		2.1
12	6	C	3.844[o]	3.804[l]	14.42	18.9
13	6	C	7.505[o]	7.473[l]		2.43
14	7	N	7.550[o]	7.515[l]	0.166	5.55
15	7	N	4.902[o]	4.863[l]	9.4	2.90
16	8	O	0.000	0.000	11.1	
17	8	O	....	4.533[l]	9.3	2.94
18	8	O	4.883[o]	4.857[l]	5.5	1.79, 4.5
19	9	F	4.444[o]	4.456[l]	4.8	3.44
20	10	Ne	−1.228[o]	−1.223[l]	7.56	
21	10	Ne	....	0.504[l]		3.83
22	10	Ne	−1.618[o]	−1.642[l]		3.05
23	11	Na	....	−2.945[l]	4.52	4.33
24	12	Mg	....	−7.372[l]	5.94	
25	12	Mg	....	−6.255[l]	4.0	
26	12	Mg	....	−9.198[l]		4.1
27	13	Al	−9.891[o]	−9.929[l]	2.84	4.85
28	14	Si	−14.175[o]	−14.233[l]	1.94, 4.99	12.5
29	14	Si	−14.295[o]	−14.350[l]	4.1	5.33
30	14	Si	−16.693[o]	−16.763[l]		4.57
31	15	P	−16.382[o]	−16.450[l]	1.58	5.5
32	16	S	−17.726[o]	−17.817[l]	0.11, 1.828	11.2
33	16	S	−18.059[o]	−18.119[l]	0.29	5.8
34	16	S	−21.291[o]		5.5	6.0
35	17	Cl	−19.94[o]		0.179	5.8
36	16	S	....			
	18	A	−20.97[n]		0.767	
37	17	Cl	−22.32[o]		4.6	0.876, 6.0
38	18	A	−25.09[n]		5.17	6.01
39	19	K	−23.94[n]		3.5, 0.61	7.6
40	18	A	−24.85[o]			1.57
	20	Ca	−24.65[n]		1.43	14.8
41	19	K	−25.10[n]		2.7	*EC*, 6.42
42	20	Ca	−27.84[n]		3.9	
43	20	Ca	−27.49[n]		1.98	2.6
44	20	Ca	−30.76[n]		5.3	3.91
45	21	Sc	−29.90[n]		0.273	2.19
46	20	Ca	....			
	22	Ti	−32.99[n]		2.55	8

A	Z	Symbol	Δ	Mass differences	
				. . . , $Z-2, Z-1$	$Z+1, Z+2,$ . . .
47	22	Ti	-33.28^n	1.92, 0.75	3.14
48	20	Ca	-32.21^n		
	22	Ti	-36.82^n	4.34	4.35, *EC*
49	22	Ti	-36.41^n	2.68, 1.9	0.67, 2.7
50	22	Ti	-39.26^n		2.54
	24	Cr	-37.96^n	1.27	>7.9
51	23	V	-39.47^n	2.4	0.34, 3.6
52	24	Cr	-42.92^n	4.5	5.0, 2.1
53	24	Cr	-42.28^n	0.6	. . . , 3.8
54	24	Cr	-43.7^n		*EC*
	26	Fe	-42.95^n	1.1	>9.0
55	25	Mn	-44.19^n	3.1	0.23, 3.71
56	26	Fe	-47.28^n	3.90	4.9, >1.9
57	26	Fe	-46.41^n		1.5, 3.48
58	26	Fe	-48.0^n		2.5
	28	Ni	-46.55^n		
59	27	Co	-48.7^n	1.68	1.15, >9.1
60	28	Ni	-50.98^n	3.02	6.65
61	28	Ni	-50.93^n	1.5	2.39
62	28	Ni	-53.18^n	3.9	4.25, 1.80
63	29	Cu	-50.74^n	0.068	3.63
64	28	Ni	-52.42^n		1.80
	30	Zn	-50.41^n	0.61	$\gtrsim 6.4$
65	29	Cu	-51.65^n	2.26	1.44, 3.4
66	30	Zn	-52.78^n	2.82	5.54
67	30	Zn	-51.84^n	0.61	1, 4.8
68	30	Zn	-53.13^n	$\gtrsim 3.2$	3.11
69	31	Ga	-52.22^n	0.97	3.61
70	30	Zn	-52.21^n		
	32	Ge	-53.63^n	1.77	
71	31	Ga	-52.49^n	2.2	0.26, 2.0
72	32	Ge	-55.39^n	>1.7, 4.3	4.68, *EC*
73	32	Ge	-53.30^n	1.6	*EC*, 2.90
74	32	Ge	-55.33^n		2.74
	34	Se	-53.80^n	1.46	*EC*
75	33	As	-54.29^n	1.22	*EC*, 2.92
76	32	Ge	-54.41^n		1.82
	34	Se	-56.43^n	3.18	4.9
77	34	Se	-55.41^n	2.64, 0.75	1.5, 2.9
78	34	Se	-57.68^n	4.4	3.6
	36	Kr	-54.86^n		
79	35	Br	-56.34^n	2.2, 0.17	1.7
80	34	Se	-57.95^n		2.0
	36	Kr	-58.06^n	2.1	
81	35	Br	-57.68^n	1.48	*EC*, 2.36
82	34	Se	-57.15^n		

A	Z	Symbol	Δ	Mass differences	
				. . . , $Z-2$, $Z-1$	$Z+1$, $Z+2$, . . .
	36	Kr	−60.32[n]	0.499	4.48
83	36	Kr	−59.41[n]	1.6, 1.0	0.9, 2.33
84	36	Kr	−61.69[n]	5.03	2.8
	38	Sr	−59.89[n]		3.2
85	37	Rb	−60.80[n]	2.7, 0.746	*EC*
86	36	Kr	−61.72[n]		
	38	Sr	−63.16[n]	1.9	4.5, *EC*
87	38	Sr	−63.23[n]	8.6, 3.9, 0.29	2.3, 3.3
88	38	Sr	−65.92[n]	3.0, 5.69	3.97, *EC*
89	39	Y	−65.79[n]	4.3, 4.8, 1.57	3.05
90	40	Zr	−66.89[n]	3.4, 6.1, 0.6, 2.34	4.8, *EC*
91	40	Zr	−65.6[n]	3.9, 3.2, 2.86, 1.651	1.2, 4.3
92	40	Zr	−66.0[n]	2.07, 3.9	1.0
	42	Mo	−64.6[d]		6.9
93	41	Cb	−64.60[n]	3.3, 0.068	*EC*, 3.3
94	40	Zr	−64.4[n]	5.8	
	42	Mo	−65.6[d]	2.22	4.62, *EC*
95	42	Mo	. . . .	1.17, 0.98	1.5, 2.2
96	40	Zr	−60.5[d]		
	42	Mo	−64.1[n]	3.39	>2.9
	44	Ru	−61.4[d]		
97	42	Mo	−63.4[d]	2.86, 2.07	*EC*, *EC*
98	42	Mo	−64.1[d]		
	44	Ru	. . . .		5.4
99	44	Ru	. . . .	1.47, 0.31	1.9
100	42	Mo	−61.4[d]		
	44	Ru	. . . .	3.0	3.92, *EC*
101	44	Ru	. . . .	2.2, 1.6	*EC*, 3.5
102	44	Ru	−63.9[d]		2.34
	46	Pd	−62.50[n]	1.2	2.2
103	45	Rh	−62.3[n]	0.81	0.6
104	44	Ru	−62.5[d]		
	46	Pd	−63.44[n]	2.8	4.0, 2.1
105	46	Pd	−61.39[n]	2.16, 0.612	*EC*, 2.92
106	46	Pd	−63.18[n]	0.042, 3.79	3.2
	48	Cd	−60.16[n]		
107	47	Ag	−61.3[n]	∼4, 1.3, 0.04	1.54, ∼3.3
108	46	Pd	−61.98[n]		1.9
	48	Cd	−61.38[n]	1.91	
109	47	Ag	−60.6[n]	1.13	0.17, 2.2
110	46	Pd	−60.34[n]		
	48	Cd	−61.42[n]	3.11	4.22
111	48	Cd	−60.22[n]	2.3, 1.12	*EC*, 2.7
112	48	Cd	−61.12[n]	0.2, 4.5	3.0
	50	Sn	−59.3[n]	0.72	2.99
113	48	Cd	−59.39[n]		

A	Z	Symbol	Δ	Mass differences	
				$\ldots, Z-2, Z-1$	$Z+1, Z+2, \ldots$
	49	In	−59.55[n]	2.3, <0.6	0.46
114	48	Cd	−60.03[n]		2.22
	50	Sn	−60.6[n]	2.13	
115	50	Sn	−59.8[n]	3, 1.56, 0.5	
116	48	Cd	−57.98[n]		
	50	Sn	−60.72[n]	3.17	5.07
117	50	Sn	−59.47[n]	3.2, 1.59	*EC*
118	50	Sn	−60.21[n]	4.3	*EC*, *EC*
119	50	Sn	−59.78[n]	2.9	*EC*, *EC*
120	50	Sn	−59.40[n]		2.9
	52	Te	−57.11[n]		5.4
121	51	Sb	−57.6[n]	0.41	*EC*, 2.4
122	50	Sn	−57.50[n]		
	52	Te	−58.06[n]	2.08	4.2
123	51	Sb	−57.0[n]	~1.5	
	52	Te	−56.3[n]		0.171
124	50	Sn	−55.08[n]		
	52	Te	−57.20[n]	3.11	3.46
	54	Xe	−54.20[n]	4.1	
125	52	Te	−55.4[n]	~2.6, 0.82	0.14, 0.49, 33
126	52	Te	−55.82[n]	1.1	2.41
	54	Xe	−55.24[n]	1.36	
127	53	I	−54.71[n]	1.3, 0.8	*EC*, 2.4
128	52	Te	−53.49[n]		*EC*
	54	Xe	−55.53[n]	2.1	4.3, *EC*
129	54	Xe	−53.98[n]	2.2, ~0.18	*EC*
130	52	Te	−51.46[n]		
	54	Xe	−54.98[n]	3.44	3.21, *EC*
	56	Ba	....	0.48	
131	54	Xe	−53.26[n]	2.4, 1.044	0.38, 2.8
132	54	Xe	−53.82[n]	0.24, 3.10	*EC*
	56	Ba	....		4.8
133	55	Cs	....	3.2, 3.0, 0.458	*EC*, 2.4, *EC*, 2.5
134	54	Xe	−51.96[n]	3.7	
	56	Ba	....	2.203	4.0, *EC*, *EC*
135	56	Ba	....	2.6, 1.24, 0.22	*EC*, 1.98
136	54	Xe	−49.54[n]	7.0	
	56	Ba	....	2.37	≥3, 3.33
	58	Ce	....		
137	56	Ba	....	0.72, 4.3, 1.3	*EC*, *EC*
138	56	Ba	....	5.20	*EC*
	58	Ce	....	1.07	4.0, 2.60, 3.60
139	57	La	....	2.5	*EC*, *EC*, 2.2, *EC*, 4.45
140	58	Ce	−47.8[d]	3.0, 4.15	3.49, *EC*
141	59	Pr	−47.7[d]	3.0, 2.61, 0.62	1.8, 3.9, 4.10, *EC*
142	58	Ce	−47.2[d]	2.7	

A	Z	Symbol	Δ	Mass differences	
				$\ldots, Z-2, Z-1$	$Z+1, Z+2, \ldots$
	60	Nd	....	2.39	
143	60	Nd	....	1.489, 1.00	*EC*
144	60	Nd	−40.9[d]	0.326, 3.2	*EC*
	62	Sm	−43.3[d]		3.65
145	60	Nd	....		2.04, *EC*, *EC*
146	60	Nd	−38.9[d]	1, 4.47	*EC*
147	62	Sm	....	0.98, 0.242	>0.223
148	60	Nd	−35.8[d]		
	62	Sm	−38.4[d]	2.7	*EC*
149	62	Sm	....	1.6, 1.13	*EC*, *EC*
150	60	Nd	−30.7[d]		
	62	Sm	−36.8[d]	≥4.7	
151	63	Eu	....	2.07, 1.2, 0.08	*EC*, *EC*
152	62	Sm	32.3[d]		
	64	Gd	....	2.38	*EC*
153	63	Eu	....	0.857	*EC*, *EC*
154	62	Sm	−28.8[d]		*EC*, 3.9
	64	Gd	−30.6[d]	2.0	4.0
155	64	Gd	....	2.4, 0.26	*EC*
156	64	Gd	−28.5[d]	1, 2.6	2.5, *EC*
	66	Dy	....		
157	64	Gd	....	1.8	*EC*, >0.349
158	64	Gd	−26.4[d]	2.8	
	66	Dy	....		
159	65	Tb	....	1.2	*EC*
160	64	Gd	−21.5[d]		
	66	Dy	−24.8[d]	1.95, 0.967	2.5, *EC*
161	66	Dy	....	2.0, 0.5	*EC*
162	66	Dy	−22.1[d]		*EC*
	68	Er	....	0.9	*EC*
163	66	Dy	....		
164	66	Dy	−18.6[d]		
	68	Er	−17.3[d]	1.0	
165	67	Ho	−17.8[d]	1.46	*EC*
166	68	Er	....	0.4, 1.98	3.33, *EC*, *EC*
167	68	Er	....		*EC*
168	68	Er	−15.1[d]		*EC*
	70	Yb	....		
169	69	Tm	....	0.35	*EC*
170	68	Er	− 9.3[d]		
	70	Yb	....	1.042	*EC*, 3.6
171	70	Yb	....	1.6, 0.11	*EC*, *EC*
172	70	Yb	....		*EC*, 2.4, *EC*
173	70	Yb	....		*EC*, *EC*
174	70	Yb	....		*EC*
	72	Hf	....	0.64	
175	71	Lu	....	0.54	*EC*

A	Z	Sym-bol	Δ	Mass differences	
				$\ldots, Z-2, Z-1$	$Z+1, Z+2, \ldots$
176	70	Yb	....		
	72	Hf	-6.6^d	1.3	*EC*, *EC*, 3.3
177	72	Hf	....	1.56, 0.53	*EC*, *EC*
178	72	Hf	-5.9^d		2.2, *EC*
179	72	Hf	....		*EC*, *EC*
180	72	Hf	3.1^d		*EC*
	74	W	....	0.76	*EC*
181	73	Ta	....	1.10	*EC*
182	74	W	4.2^d	1.86	*EC*, *EC*
183	74	W	6.7^n	0.70	*EC*, *EC*
184	74	W	7.6^d	1.5	*EC*
	76	Os	....	1.1	*EC*
185	75	Re	....	1.83, 0.46	*EC*
186	74	W	15.0^d		*EC*
	76	Os	....	1.15	*EC*
187	76	Os	....	1.43, 0.043	3.44, *EC*
188	76	Os	13.9^d	2.26	3.22, *EC*
189	76	Os	....	0.2	
190	76	Os	17.4^d		*EC*, 2.0
	78	Pt	....		*EC*, 2.90
191	77	Ir	....	0.336	*EC*, *EC*, *EC*
192	76	Os	22.7^d		*EC*, *EC*
	78	Pt	26.2^d	1.70	. . . , 3.16, 2.36
193	77	Ir	....	1.26	*EC*, *EC*, *EC*
194	78	Pt	24.2^n	2.4	3.01, *EC*
195	78	Pt	26.6^d	2.3	*EC*, *EC*, *EC*
196	78	Pt	27.0^n	>1.1	*EC*
	80	Hg	....	0.08, 0.83	
197	79	Au	....	1.77, 0.81	*EC*, *EC*
198	78	Pt	28.4^d	4.7	*EC*
	80	Hg	....	3.9, 1.48	*EC*, *EC*
199	80	Hg	....	1.9, 0.49	*EC*, *EC*
200	80	Hg	....	2.5	*EC*, *EC*
201	80	Hg	....	1.5	*EC*, *EC*
202	80	Hg	....		*EC*, *EC*
203	81	Tl	34.50^s	1.9, 0.523	*EC*, *EC*
204	80	Hg	....		*EC*, *EC*
	82	Pb	35.76^s	0.83	*EC*
205	81	Tl	37.53^s	1.8	*EC*, *EC*
206	82	Pb	38.20^s	1.62	5.17, *EC*
207	82	Pb	39.95^s	1.55	2.68, *EC*
208	82	Pb	41.00^s	5.36	*EC*, *EC*
	84	Po	45.22^s		*EC*, *EC*
209	83	Bi	45.14^s	4.21, 0.69	0.08, *EC*
210	84	Po	47.86^s	5.79, 0.07, 1.26	5.43, *EC*
211	84	Po	51.96^s	1.49, 0.66	0.96, *EC*

A	Z	Symbol	Δ	Mass differences . . . , Z − 2, Z − 1	Mass differences Z + 1, Z + 2, . . .
212	84	Po	54.47[s]	0.62, 2.42	1.71
	86	Rn	55.94[s]	.24	*EC*
213	84	Po	58.82[s]	1.49	.07
214	84	Po	61.46[s]	1.09, 3.40	1.14
215	85	At	65.23[s]	2.16, 0.81	0.0
216	84	Po	68.78[s]		0.50
	86	Rn	67.10[s]	2.18	
217	86	Rn	71.16[s]	1.41, 0.70	0.68
218	86	Rn	73.12[s]	0.35, 2.87	1.94
219	87	Fr	77.09[s]	1.56, 0.28	0.77
220	86	Rn	79.51[s]		0.96
	88	Ra	79.10[s]	1.36	
221	88	Ra	82.37[s]	1.00, 0.26	1.58
222	86	Rn	86.26[s]		0.04
	88	Ra	84.17[s]	2.19	2.43
223	88	Ra	87.54[s]	1.27	0.69
224	88	Ra	89.59[s]		1.47
	90	Th	90.77[s]	0.31	
225	89	Ac	92.83[s]	0.33	0.59, 2.31
226	88	Ra	95.35[s]		0.67
	90	Th	94.98[s]	1.05	2.86
227	90	Th	98.00[s]	1.40, 0.09	1.16, 2.46
228	90	Th	99.39[s]	0.04, 2.34	2.20, 0.32
229	90	Th	102.52[s]	1.96, 1.14	0.40, 1.39
230	90	Th	104.33[s]	1.22, 2.89	1.42
	92	U	105.28[s]	0.47	
231	91	Pa	107.46[s]	0.35	0.37, 2.06
232	90	Th	110.01[s]		0.48
	92	U	109.07[s]	1.42	2.90, 1.03
233	92	U	111.67[s]	1.33, 0.57	1.17
234	92	U	113.41[s]	0.50, 2.18	1.99, 0.52
235	92	U	116.68[s]	1.90, 1.50	0.18, 1.22
236	92	U	118.80[s]		0.98
	94	Pu	119.22[s]	0.56	
237	93	Np	121.43[s]	0.55	0.25, 1.59
238	92	U	124.54[s]		0.10
	94	Pu	123.28[s]	1.36	2.43, 1.20
239	94	Pu	126.18[s]	1.37, 0.77	0.84, 1.93
240	94	Pu	128.31[s]	0.38, 2.32	1.57, 0.06
241	95	Am	131.35[s]	1.54, 0.02	0.95
242	94	Pu	133.75[s]		.70
	96	Cm	133.82[s]	.63	
243	95	Am	136.65[s]		0.0
	96	Cm	136.65[s]	0.0	1.57
244	96	Cm	138.50[s]	1.61	2.44, 0.80
245	96	Am	141.38[s]		0.75

A	Z	Symbol	Δ	Mass differences	
				. . . , $Z-2, Z-1$	$Z+1, Z+2, \ldots$
246	98	Cf	145.06[s]		1.51
247	99	. .	150.11[s]		
248	98	Cf	149.20[s]		
249	98	Cf	151.80[s]	0.06	
250	98	Cf	153.95[s]	2.04	
251	98	Cf	157.25		
252	98	Cf	159.88[s]		
253	99	. .	162.96[s]	.25	
254	100	. .	165.70[s]		
255	100	. .	168.86[s]		

REFERENCE CODE

[l] Li, C. W., W. Whaling, W. A. Fowler, and C. C. Lauritsen: *Phys. Rev.*, **83**, 512 (1951).
Li, C. W.: *Phys. Rev.*, **88**, 1038 (1952).

[o] Ogata, K., and M. Mutsuda: *Phys. Rev.*, **89**, 27 (1953).

[n] Collins, T. L., A. O. Nier, and W. H. Johnson: *Phys. Rev.*, **84**, 717 (1951).
Collins, T. L., A. O. Nier, and W. H. Johnson: *Phys. Rev.*, **86**, 408 (1952).
Johnson, W. H., Jr.: *Phys. Rev.* **87**, 166 (1952).
Johnson, W. H., Jr.: *Phys. Rev.*, **88**, 1213 (1952).
Halsted, R. E.: *Phys. Rev.*, **88**, 666 (1952).
Collins, T. L., W. H. Johnson, Jr., and A. O. Nier: *Phys. Rev.*, **94**, 398 (1954).

[d] Duckworth, H. E., K. S. Woodcock and R. S. Preston: *Phys. Rev.* **78**, 479 (1950).
Duckworth, H. E., H. A. Johnson, R. S. Preston, and K. S. Woodcock: *Phys. Rev.*, **78**, 386 (1950).
Duckworth, H. E., R. S. Preston, and K. S. Woodcock: *Phys. Rev.*, **79**, 188 (1950).
Duckworth, H. E., and R. S. Preston: *Phys. Rev.*, **82**, 468 (1951).
Duckworth, H. E., C. L. Kegley, J. M. Olson, and G. S. Stanford: *Phys. Rev.*, **83**, 1114 (1951).
Stanford, G. S., H. E. Duckworth, B. G. Hogg, and J. S. Geiger: *Phys. Rev.*, **85**, 1039 (1952).
Geiger, J. S., B. G. Hogg, H. E. Duckworth, and J. W. Dewdney: *Phys. Rev.*, **89**, 621 (1953).
Hogg, B. G., and H. E. Duckworth: *Can. J. Phys.*, **30**, 637 (1952).
Hogg, B. G., and H. E. Duckworth: *Can. J. Phys.*, **31**, 942 (1953).

[s] Seaborg, G. T., R. A. Glass, and S. G. Thompson: *J. Inorg. and Nuclear Chem.* (from prepublication copy kindly furnished by Dr. R. A. Glass).

INDEX

Absorption, gamma-ray, 236–242, 468
Absorption coefficient, 238
Activity, 194–196
Alpha decay, 177, 187–194, 408–411
  angular momentum in, 416
  anomalies, 415–417
  energetics of, 187–190
  energy fine structure in, 193, 417
  excited nuclei in, 193, 194
  formation prohibition, 416
  Geiger-Nuttall law, 192, 409
  long-range particles, 193
  Q values for, 189
  systematics of, 190, 255
Alpha-disintegration energy, 190
Alpha nuclei, 360
Alpha-particle model, 358–361
  excited states, 360
Analyzers (*see* Electrostatic analyzers; Magnetic analyzers)
Angular frequency, 12
Angular momentum, 18, 19, 321, 372–377, 439
  in alpha decay, 416
  in beta decay, 425–427
  in gamma decay, 402
  orbital, 8
    nuclear, 377
  quasi-quantum mechanical methods, 352
  in scattering, 447, 448
  statistical weight and, 447
Anticoincidences, 146
Atomic energy levels, for hydrogen, 9
  for modified coulomb field, 21
  separation of substates, 21
  structure of, fine, 27–29
      gross, 25
      hyperfine, 39
  x-ray, 29–32
Atomic orbitals, 20
Atomic weights, chemical, 36
  physical, 36
Atoms, configurations of, 22
  energy levels of, 22, 25
  multiply ionized, 84, 85, 207
  structure of, 6, 7

Auger electrons, 181
Average nuclear energy, 55
Axial focusing, 74

Barn, 222
Barrier penetration, 192
Bessel functions, 339, 437
Beta decay, 177, 180
  allowed transitions in, 424
  angular momentum in, 425–427
  comparative half-life, 424
  continuous distribution in, 179
  double, 178
  elementary theory of, 418–425
  energetics of, 178
  excited nuclei in, 186, 187
  fifth-power law, 423
  forbidden transitions in, 425–427
  ft product, 424
  Kurie plot, 421, 422
  lifetime of, 422–425
  Q values for, 180
  Sargent diagram, 185
  statistical factor for, 420
Beta-ray spectroscopes, 104, 105
Beta stability, 183
  semiempirical line of, 187
  trends of, 183–186
Beta systematics, 257-261
Betatron, 68–70
  focusing in, 73–75
Binding energy, 55
Bohr atom, 8–10
Bombardment processes, 205–208
Box potential, one-dimensional, 14, 322, 323
  three-dimensional, 324, 325, 361
Branching, 197, 198
Breit-Wigner formula, 454
Bremsstrahlung, 165, 430
  inner, 183, 430

Central field (*see* Central forces)
Central forces, 325–327
  angular distributions for, 17

Central forces, coulomb potential, 322
effective, 331
exponential function, 322
Gaussian function, 322
Hooke's-law potential, 322
Morse function, 322
Φ equation, 327, 328
Θ equation, 328–330
Yukawa function, 322
Centrifugal barrier, 409
Centrifugal force, 331, 409, 438
Cerenkov detectors, 138
Chain rule, 354, 375, 378
Charge character (*see* Isobaric spin)
Charge density, 283
nonuniformity of, 293
Charge-independent hypothesis, 489
Charge symmetry, 474
Charged theory, 494–496
Cloud chamber, 154–156
Cloud ion chamber, 156
Cloudy crystal ball model, 467
Cockcroft-Walton circuit, 59
Coherent-scattering length, 486
Coincidence, circuit for, 144, 145
delayed, 145
resolving time, 126
Collective model, 383–385
coupled oscillations in, 387
excited states, 387, 388
Compound nucleus, 206, 449–454
Compressibility, 293
Compton effect, 237, 241
Conversion, internal, 178, 179, 406, 407
Conversion factors, 57, 519
Coordinate system, center-of-mass, 211, 228, 346
laboratory, 211
relative, 346
transformations between, 234–236
Correspondence principle, 397
Coulomb barrier, 190–192, 212, 234, 453
transparency of, 414, 453
Coulomb energy, 38, 283, 284, 365
Coulomb potential, 19, 322
Coulomb radius constant, 290–292
Counters, 124–127
Cross sections, capture, 230
classical, 234
definition of, 221–223
differential (*see* Differential cross section)
geometrical, 445
integrated, 230
low-velocity limit, 442
neutron (*see* Neutron cross section)
Cross sections, partial, 223
photocapture, 469
reaction, resonance in, 225, 454, 455, 459–460
S-wave, 441
theoretical, 230
total, 222, 223, 230
Crystal detectors, 137–139
Cyclotron, 65

D(γ,n)H reactions, 486, 487
Deadtime, 130
de Broglie waves, 10
Decay (*see* Alpha decay; Beta decay; Radioactive decay)
Decay constants, partial, 197
Decaying states, 349
Degeneracy, 20
Delayed neutrons, 297
Density of nuclear matter, 39, 271
Detectors, 124–127
Deuteron, central-force assumption, 477
magnetic moment, 497
quadrupole moment of, 57, 498–502
radius of, 478
Differential cross section, 227–230, 436, 438, 503
classical, 231
cosine law, 236
for gamma-ray absorption, 239–242
for neutron-proton scattering, 503
for proton-proton scattering, 503
Dipole moment, 48
Dispersion relation, 13
Double beta decay, 178
Dynamics, relativistic, 1–5

Einstein-Bohr frequency relation, 396
Elastic scattering, 205, 231–234
potential, 433–437, 448, 449
resonance in, 433, 434, 454
Electric excitation of nuclei, 221
Electric quadrupole moment (*see* Quadrupole moment)
Electron capture, 427–431
(*See also* *K* capture)
Electron exchange, 28
Electronic instruments, 139–150
Electronic stopping power, 164
Electrostatic analyzers, 93
cylindrical, 94–96, 103
spherical, 96, 104
Electrostatic generator, 60
Empirical *Q* values, 252

Energy, activation, fission, 297–305
  binding, 55
    of neutrons, 57
    particle, 57, 210
  coulomb, 38, 283, 284, 365
  excitation, 215, 298
  magnetic, 40, 378
  nuclear, 55, 270
  pairing (*see* Pairing energy)
  parabolic, 247, 259, 286, 289
  of reactions, 208
  surface, 282, 283
  symmetry, 284–285, 366
Energy eigenvalues, 14, 334, 345
Energy levels, 217, 274–279
  atomic (*see* Atomic energy levels)
  of charged particles, 159–162
  of complex nuclei, 357
  of spherical box, 337–339
  of spherical well, 339–342
Energy loss of electrons, 168–171
Energy width, 349, 450
  integrated, 453, 463
  partial, 310, 451
  reduced, 451
Equivalent nucleons, 374
Exchange force, 363, 365, 492–494
  Bartlett, 493
  Heisenberg, 493
  Majorana, 368, 493
  Serber, 504
Exchange operators, 492–494
Excitation energy, 215, 298
Exclusion principle, 20
  generalized, 273, 347, 491

Fission, 207, 281, 294–297
  activation energy, 297–305
    critical, 301
  asymmetrical, 308, 309
  borderline condition, 301
  neutron-induced, 307
  prompt neutrons from, 296
  Q value of, 295
  saddle point in, 303
  spontaneous, 198–203, 297
  sustained processes, 313–315
  tripartition, 308, 309
Fissionability, 305–307
Flip-flop circuit, 141
Focusing, axial, 74
  in betatron, 73–75
  geometric, 73
  phase, 78
  radial, 74

g factors, 28, 39, 41, 378
Gamma, 2
Gamma decay, angular momentum in, 402
  energetics of, 178
  excited nuclei in, 186, 187
Gamma-decay theory, classical, 391
  experimental confirmation, 407
  quantum generalization, 396–398
  selection rules in, 401–406
Gamma-ray absorption, 236–242, 468
Gamma-ray spectrometers, 105, 106
Gathering power, 92
Geiger counter, plateau, 131
  quenching, 130
Geiger-Müller region, 129
Generator, impulse, 60
Geometric focusing, 73
Green's function, 508
Gyromagnetic ratio (*g* factors), 28, 39, 41, 378

H(n,γ)D reaction, 486, 487
Hamiltonian, 321, 506
Harmonic oscillator, 7
  three-dimensional 322, 343
Hydrogenic system, 8, 19, 335–337

Impact parameter, 162, 230, 439
Impulse generator, 60
Incompressibility, 271, 293, 474
Independent-particle model, 20, 347, 369, 370, 400, 471
  magnetic moments, 377–383
  spin-orbit interaction, 28
Infinite spherical well, 341
  (*See also* Spherical box)
Inner *Bremsstrahlung*, 183, 430
Internal conversion, 178, 179, 406, 407
Ion sources, 80–86
Ionization chambers, 127–132
Ionization potentials, 26
Isobaric doublets, 247
Isobaric sections, 245, 246
Isobaric spin, 273, 489, 493
Isobars, 54
Isodiaspheres, 54
Isomeric states, 401
Isomerism, 178, 407
Isotopes, 35, 54
Isotopic spin, 273, 491
  (*See also* Isobaric spin)

K capture, 177, 189, 181, 429
  X-ray levels in, 182

K-conversion coefficients, 407
K/L ratios, 407

Landé formulas, 353, 378
Laplace's equation, 508
Laplacian operator, 318
Larmor frequency, 42, 43
Legendre polynomials, 330
Level spacing, 451
Linear accelerator, 62
  for electrons, 64
  for protons, 63
Liquid-drop model, 281, 356–358, 400
  difficulties with, 292–294
  rotational states, 357
Luminosity, 92

Magic numbers, 261–264, 369
Magnetic analyzers, 98–103
  double-focusing, 100
  flat, 97
  helical, 101, 102
  180° type, 98
  shaped fields, 100, 101
  254° type, 100
  wedge-shaped, 99
Magnetic energy, 40, 378
Magnetic field at nucleus, 40
Magnetic induction, 6
Magnetic moment, 39, 40, 377–383
  of deuteron, 496–498
  Schmidt limits, 379
Many-body problems, 346–348
Mass decrement, 54
  of beta stable nuclides, 244, 519–528
  valley, 286
Mass defect, true, 55
  (*See also* Mass decrement)
Mass-energy equation, 1
Mass spectroscopes, 108–115
  low-resolution instruments, 110–112
  precision instruments, 112–115
Mass surface, 244-249, 285–287
  empirical, 249–253
  semiempirical, 285–287
Mass unit, 35
Matrix element, 397–401
Matrix mechanics, 397
Matter waves, 10, 319
Meson production, 207
Meson theory, 509–515
  coupling to nucleons, 511
  fine-structure constant, 513
  invariance requirements in, 505
  mesic potential, 509
Meson theory, nuclear forces from, 515
  tensoral character, 510
  theoretical difficulties, 512–515
Microwave spectroscopy, 115–118
Mirror nuclei, 288, 424
Molecular spectra, 44
Momentum, 1–3
  angular (*see* Angular momentum)
Monochromatic wave, 12
Monopole moment, 48
Motion of charged particles, 5
Mu mesonic atoms, 38
Multiply ionized atoms, 84, 85, 207

Neutron cross section, capture, 310
  energy dependence, 224
  for fission, 307, 309–312
  for radiative capture, 312
  for reactions, 221–227
  regularities in, 225
  resonant processes, 456–459
  surface, 226, 229
  thermal, 313
  total, 224–226
Neutron-proton interaction, neutral theory, 494–496
  scattering by, 476, 479, 503
  spin dependence of, 481–483
  spin-independent central force, 476–481
  zero-range approximation, 478
Neutron-proton scattering, by bound protons, 479, 483–486
  by free protons, 486
  shape-independent analysis, 480
Neutron spectrometry, 107, 108
Neutrons, absorption of, 224
  activation by, 157
  binding energy, 57
  detection of, 156–159
  excess, 54
  sources of, 86–88
Noncentral interactions, 416
Nonfissionable material, 314
Normalization condition, 320, 327
Nuclear characteristics, 270–274
Nuclear configurations, 374
Nuclear emulsions, 150–154
  particle identification, 152
Nuclear energy, 55
  saturation of, 270
Nuclear forces, charge-symmetry, 273
  range of, 272
    effective, 480
  saturation, 474, 494
  short-range repulsions, 272, 504

Nuclear forces, strength of, 272, 474
Nuclear induction, 121
Nuclear magneton, 39
Nuclear orbitals, 374
  angular momenta of, 377
  filling order of, 373
Nuclear paramagnetism, 120
Nuclear radii, 38
Nuclear reactions, 214
  continuum theory of, 464
  excited states in, 215–221
  reciprocity theorem, 460–462
  statistical theory of, 462–467
  (*See also* Cross sections; Reactions)
Nuclear reactor, 87, 313, 315
Nuclear resonance, 454
Nuclear spin, 39
Nuclear tendencies, 270–274
Nucleon, 54, 273
Nucleon-nucleon collisions, at high energies, 502–505
  at low and moderate energies, 474–476
Nucleon-nucleon interaction, phenomenological, 490

Orbital angular momentum, 8
Oscillator number, 344

Packing fraction, 55, 56
Pair production, 106, 237
Pairing energy, 249, 260, 265, 376, 474
  anomalies, 264, 265
Pairing tendencies, 273, 366, 374
Parabolic energy, 247, 259, 286, 289
Parity, 402–405
  selection rules for, 405, 424–427
Partial waves, 437–445
  physical interpretation, 439–440
Particle binding energy, 57, 210
  Q values for, 254–256
Particle motion, 11
Penetrability factor, 414, 452
Perturbation methods, 351–352
  time-dependent, 350, 418
Phase focusing, 78
Phase shifts (*see* Partial waves)
Photoelectric effect, 8, 237
Photographic emulsions, 150
Photomultiplier, 134
Photoneutron production, 469
Photons, 8
Photoprotons, 469, 470, 475
Photoreactions, 467–471
  integrated cross section, 470
Polar coordinates, spherical, 326
Preamplifier, 141
Precessional motions, 42, 43, 353
Probability distributions, 15
Probability per unit time for escape, 411
Propagation constant, 12, 433, 518
Proportional counters, 127, 132
Proton-electron model, 52
Proton-neutron model, 52
Proton-proton scattering, 236, 476, 488–489, 492
Pulse amplifier, 139, 141
Pulse height, discriminator, 147
  multichannel analyzer, 149, 150
  single-channel analyzer, 148
  spectrum, 146

Q values, 208–211
  for alpha decay, 189
  for β^- decay, 180
  for β^+ decay, 181
  empirical, 252
  and particle binding energies, 254–256
  semiempirical, 293
Quadrupole moment, 45, 50, 51, 500
  and collective model, 383–385
  of deuteron, 497–502
  distortions associated with, 51
  and shell structure, 384
Quantization, 14
  angular momentum, 18, 19
  nuclear energies, 274
Quantum numbers, 15, 18, 19
Quantum theory, early developments, 7–10

Radial distribution functions, 15
Radial focusing, 74
Radial wave equation, 330–335
Radial wave functions, 334
  nodes in, 336
Radiation, by electric dipole, 398
  by electric multipoles, 398
  by magnetic multipoles, 398
  by moving charges, 391–396
Radio-frequency spectroscopy, 118–121
Radioactive decay, average lifetime, 176, 401
  chains of, 196–203
  disintegration constant, 176
  half-life, 176
  law of, 175, 176
  probability for, 310
  transformations in, 176–178
Ramsauer-Townsend effect, 443

Range, of charged nuclear particles, 159–162
of electrons, 168–171
extrapolated, 160
mean, 160
Reactions, chains of, 210
energetics of, 211–215
energy of, 208
nuclear (*see* Nuclear reactions)
proton groups from, 215
threshold energy, 208
yield curve, 218
Recovery time, 130
Reflection coefficient, 465
Relativistic dynamics, 1–5
Resolution, 91
Resolution time, 125
Resonance, in elastic scattering, 433, 434, 454
in reaction cross section, 225, 454, 455, 459–460
Rest mass, 1, 4
Rutherford scattering, 37, 232–234, 445–447
Rydberg constant, 10

Saturation, of nuclear densities, 271, 368
of nuclear energies, 270
of nuclear forces, 474, 494
Scale-of-2 circuit, 141–143
Scalers, 125
Scattering, 37, 234
angular momenta in, 447, 448
by coulomb field, 37, 232–234, 445–447
elastic (*see* Elastic scattering)
of elastic spheres, 231, 232
Fermi length, 480
by impenetrable sphere, 444
proton-proton, 236, 476, 488–489, 492
by spherical barrier, 443–445
by spherical well, 440–443
Schroedinger operator, 320
Schroedinger wave equation, 506
relativistic, 507
time-dependent, 506
time-independent, 319
Scintillation counters, 133, 158
Scintillation spectrometers, 137
Semiempirical functions, 287–290
Semiempirical mass surface, 285–287
Separation of variables, 324, 326, 327, 346, 347
Shell structure, in excited states, 385–388
in nuclear masses, 265–270
Shell structure, in quadrupole moments, 384
(*See also* Independent-particle model; Magic numbers)
Spallation, 207
Spark detectors, 137–139
Spectrometry, neutron, 107, 108
Spectroscopy, microwave, 115–118
radio-frequency, 118–121
Spherical box, 322
energy levels of, 337–339
Spherical polar coordinates, 326
Spherical well, 322, 339–342
energy levels of, 339–342
infinite, 341
scattering by, 440–443
(*See also* Central forces; Scattering)
Spin exchange operator, 493
Spin-orbit coupling, 474
Square well (*see* Spherical well)
Stacked foils, 227
Stopping of charged particles, semiclassical theory of, 162–168
Stopping power, 161
electronic, 164
"Straggling," 160
Surface energy, 282, 283
Surface tension, 358
Sustained fission process, 314
Symmetric theory, 494–496
Symmetry energy, 284–285, 366
Synchrocyclotron, 66
Synchrotron, 70
for electrons, 72
proton, 73

Tensor force, 498–502
Tensor-force operator, 499
Time-dependent wave equation, 348–351
Transition probability, electric, 402
magnetic, 402
per unit time, 311, 350, 449
Transmission coefficient, 465
Transuranic elements, 198
production of, 207
Trigger circuit, 147
Tunneling (barrier penetration), 192
Two-body problem, 346–348

Uniform model, 361–369
kinetic energy, 362
potential energy, 363
Uncertainty principle, 52, 350

Van de Graaff accelerator, 60
Voltage multipliers, 59

Wave equations, 317–320, 505–509
  amplitude, 319
  approximate solution of, 411–415
  Dirac, 507
  for electromagnetic fields, 318
  for heat, 318
  for matter waves, 319
  Maxwell's, 507
  for membrane, 318
  Schroedinger (*see* Schroedinger wave equation)
  solutions of, 323–348, 434–447
  for sound, 318
  for string, 318
  time-dependent, 348–351
Wave functions, 11, 35–57
Wave functions, for energy states, 320
    damping factor, 451
  for standing waves, 13
Wave mechanics, 10, 317–354
Wave motion, 11
Wave-particle nature, 10
Weiszäcker mass surface (semiempirical mass surface), 285–287
Wigner uniform model, 361–369

X-ray levels, 29-31
  in K capture, 182
  Moseley-Sommerfeld diagram, 31
X-ray spectra, 29
  critical absorption wavelengths, 30